S0-AUS-018

Logics and Models of Concurrent Systems

NATO ASI Series

Advanced Science Institutes Series

A series presenting the results of activities sponsored by the NATO Science Committee, which aims at the dissemination of advanced scientific and technological knowledge, with a view to strengthening links between scientific communities.

The Series is published by an international board of publishers in conjunction with the NATO Scientific Affairs Division

A Life Sciences **B Physics**	Plenum Publishing Corporation London and New York
C Mathematical and Physical Sciences	D. Reidel Publishing Company Dordrecht, Boston and Lancaster
D Behavioural and Social Sciences **E Applied Sciences**	Martinus Nijhoff Publishers Boston, The Hague, Dordrecht and Lancaster
F Computer and Systems Sciences **G Ecological Sciences**	Springer-Verlag Berlin Heidelberg New York Tokyo

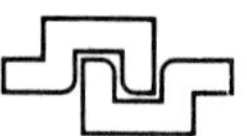

Series F: Computer and Systems Sciences Vol. 13

Logics and Models of Concurrent Systems

Edited by

Krzysztof R. Apt

L.I.T.P., Université Paris 7, 2, Place Jussieu
75251 Paris, France

Springer-Verlag Berlin Heidelberg New York Tokyo
Published in cooperation with NATO Scientific Affairs Division

Proceedings of the NATO Advanced Study Institute on Logics and Models of Concurrent Systems held at La Colle-sur-Loup, France, 8–19 October 1984

ISBN 3-540-15181-8 Springer-Verlag Berlin Heidelberg New York Tokyo
ISBN 0-387-15181-8 Springer-Verlag New York Heidelberg Berlin Tokyo

Library of Congress Cataloging in Publication Data.
NATO Advanced Study Institute on Logics and Models of Concurrent Systems (1984: La Colle-sur-Loupé, France) Logics and models of concurrent systems. (NATO ASI series. Series F, Computer and system sciences; vol. 13) "Proceedings of the NATO Advanced Study Institute on Logics and Models of concurrent Systems held at La Colle-sur-Loupé, France, 8–19 October 1984"—T.p. verso. 1. Parallel processing (Electronic computers)—Congresses. 2. Electronic data processing—Distributed processing—Congresses. I. Apt. Krzysztof R., 1949-. II. Title. III. Series: NATO ASI series. Series F, Computer and system sciences; no. 13. QA76.5.N16 1984 001.64 85-8092
ISBN 0-387-15181-8 (U.S.)

Printing: Beltz Offsetdruck, Hemsbach; Bookbinding: J. Schäffer OHG, Grünstadt
2145/3140-543210

Dear Reader,

You took this book in your hands because you are interested in concurrency. I hope that it will not disappoint you. It constitutes proceedings of the Advanced Course "Logics and models for verification and specification of concurrent systems" which took place in La Colle-sur-Loup, close to Nice, in France from 8 to 19 October 1984.

Some of the authors including the undersigned (see also page 244), sacrificed their vacation or part of it to meet the deadlines. Others kindly agreed to write a paper for this book even though they felt - contrary to our opinion - that the subject was already adequately treated in the literature (see e.g., page 72).

The outcome is a volume containing 17 articles presenting an overview of the current research in the area of verification and specification of concurrent systems. It contains excellent contributions both in the form of survey papers and articles opening new directions. This book will enable you to become familiar with the current research in temporal logic, syntax directed verification methods, CCS, Theoretical CSP and other new topics.

It is a great honour for me to be the editor of this book. Once again I would like to thank all the contributors for their effort and their cooperative spirit.

Krzysztof R. Apt

CONTENTS

Temporal logic

E. M. Clarke, M. C. Browne, E. A. Emerson, A. P. Sistla,
Using temporal logic for automatic verification of finite state systems 3

L. Fariñas-del-Cerro,
Resolution modal logics 27

B. Hailpern,
Tools for verifying network protocols 57

L. Lamport,
An axiomatic semantics of concurrent programming languages 77

A. Pnueli,
In transition from global to modular temporal reasoning about programs 123

Syntax directed verification methods

K. R. Apt,
Correctness proofs of distributed termination algorithms 147

N. Francez, B. Hailpern, G. Taubenfeld,
Script: A communication abstraction mechanism and its verification 169

W. P. de Roever,
The cooperation test: a syntax-directed verification method 213

Around CCS, Theoretical CSP and distributed systems

G. Boudol,
Notes on algebraic calculi of processes 261

S. Brookes, A. W. Roscoe,
Deadlock analysis in networks of Communicating Processes 305

K. M. Chandy, J. Misra,
A paradigm for detecting quiescent properties in distributed computations 325

Ph. Darondeau,
About fair asynchrony 343

S. Graf, J. Sifakis,
A logic for the specification and proof of controllable processes of CCS 369

E.-R. Olderog,
Specification-oriented programming in TCSP 397

Miscellaneous

D. Gabbay,
Theoretical foundations for non-monotonic reasoning in expert systems 439

J. Halpern, Y. Moses,
Towards a theory of knowledge and ignorance: preliminary report . 459

D. Harel, A. Pnueli,
On the development of reactive systems 477

TEMPORAL LOGIC

Using Temporal Logic for Automatic Verification of Finite State Systems

E. M. Clarke
Carnegie Mellon University

M. C. Browne
Carnegie Mellon University

E. A. Emerson
University of Texas, Austin

A. P. Sistla
University of Massachusetts, Amherst

1. Introduction.

Temporal logic has been extensively investigated for proving properties of programs--particularly for programs that involve nondeterminism or concurrency ([9], [11], [12]). However, most of the verification techniques developed so far involve manual construction of proofs, a task that may require a good deal of ingenuity and is usually quite tedious. In a series of papers ([1], [5], [6], [10]) we have argued that proof construction is unnecessary in the case of finite state systems and can be replaced by a model theoretic approach which will mechanically determine if the system meets a specification expressed in a propositional temporal logic. In this paper we survey that work and give a detailed example of how our approach might be used in verifying a finite state hardware controller.

The basic idea behind our approach is quite simple. The state-transition graph of a finite state system can be viewed as a finite Kripke structure, and an efficient algorithm can be given to determine whether a structure is a model of a particular formula - i.e., to determine if the program meets its specification. The algorithm, which we call a *model checker*, is similar to the global flow analysis algorithms used in compiler optimization and has complexity linear in both the size of the structure and the size of the specification. When the number of states is not excessive (i.e. not more than a few thousand) we believe that our technique may provide a powerful debugging tool.

Since our specification language is a branching-time temporal logic, it follows from ([7], [8]) that our logic cannot, in general, express correctness of fair execution sequences. The alternative of using a linear time logic is ruled out because any model checker for such a logic must have high

---

This research was supported by NSF Grants MCS-815553 and MCS-8302878.

NATO ASI Series, Vol. F13
Logics and Models of Concurrent Systems
Edited by K. R. Apt

complexity ([15]). We overcome this problem by moving fairness requirements into the semantics of our logic. Specifically, we change the definition of our basic modalities so that only fair paths are considered. Our previous model checking algorithm is modified to handle this extended logic without changing its complexity.

An obvious application for our method is in verifying complicated finite state systems that will ultimately be implemented as sequential circuits. Although this has been important problem for a long time, lack of any formal and efficient method of verification has prevented the creation of practical design aids. Since all the known techniques of simulation and prototype testing are time-consuming and not very reliable, there is an acute need for such tools. We illustrate our approach to this problem by verifying the correctness of a moderately tricky traffic controller expressed in a high-level state machine description language with a Pascal-like syntax (called SML). The output of the SML compiler can also be used to generate a PLA, PAL, or ROM--thus, permitting state machines that have been verified by our techniques to be implemented as circuits.

Most prior research on verifying finite state systems has involved some type of state reachability analysis. For example, in [16] and [18] reachability techniques are described for detection of system deadlocks, unspecified message receptions, and non-executable process interactions. An obvious advantage that our approach has over such methods is flexibility; our use of temporal logic provides a uniform notation for expressing a wide variety of correctness properties. Furthermore, it is unnecessary to formulate all of the specifications as reachability assertions since the model checker can handle both safety and liveness properties with equal facility.

Perhaps the research that is most closely related to our own is that of Quielle and Sifakis ([13], [14]), who have independently developed a system which will automatically check that a finite state CSP program satisfies a specification in temporal logic. The logical system that is used in [13], is not as expressive as our logic, however, and no attempt is made to handle fairness properties. Although fairness is discussed in [14], the approach that is used is much different from the one that we have adopted. Special temporal operators are introduced for asserting that a property must hold on fair paths, but neither a complexity analysis nor an efficient model checking algorithm is given for the extended logic.

Our paper is organized as follows: Section 2 contains the syntax and semantics of our logic. In Section 3 fixpoint characterizations are given for the various temporal operators. The fixpoint characterization are used in Section 4 to develop the basic model checking algorithm. An extension of the algorithm which only considers *fair computations* is discussed in section 5. In section 6 we outline how a model can be extracted from a program in a high-level state machine description language with a Pascal-like syntax and illustrate its use with examples. The paper concludes in section 7 with a discussion of directions for future research including the possibility of making our approach hierarchical.

2. The Specification Language.

Our specification language is a propositional, branching-time temporal logic called *Computation Tree Logic* (CTL) and is similar to the logical systems described in [3], [5], and [7]. The formal syntax for CTL is given below. AP is the underlying set of *atomic propositions*.

1. Every atomic proposition $p \in AP$ is a CTL formula.

2. If f_1 and f_2 are CTL formulas, then so are $\neg f_1$, $f_1 \wedge f_2$, AXf_1, EXf_1, $A[f_1 \, U \, f_2]$, and $E[f_1 \, U \, f_2]$.

The symbols $\wedge$ and $\neg$ have their usual meanings. X is the *nexttime* operator; the formula AXf_1 (EXf_1) intuitively means that f_1 holds in every (in some) immediate successor of the current program state. U is the *until* operator; the formula $A[f_1Uf_2]$ ($E[f_1Uf_2]$) intuitively means that for every computation path (for some computation path), there exists an initial prefix of the path such that f_2 holds at the last state of the prefix and f_1 holds at all other states along the prefix.

We define the semantics of CTL formulas with respect to a labeled state-transition graph (or *Kripke structure*). Formally, a *CTL structure* is a triple $M = (S, R, P)$ where

1. S is a finite set of states.

2. R is a binary relation on S ($R \subseteq S \times S$) which gives the possible transitions between states and must be total, i.e. $\forall x \in S \exists y \in S \, [(x,y) \in R]$.

3. $P : S \rightarrow 2^{AP}$ assigns to each state the set of atomic propositions true in that state.

A *path* is an infinite sequence of states $(s_0, s_1, s_2, \ldots)$ such that $\forall i \, [(s_i, s_{i+1}) \in R]$. For any structure $M = (S,R,P)$ and state $s_0 \in S$, there is an *infinite computation tree* with root labeled s_0 such that $s \rightarrow t$ is an arc in the tree iff $(s,t) \in R$. Figure 2-1 shows a CTL structure and the associated computation tree rooted at s_0.

We use the standard notation to indicate truth in a structure: $M, s_0 \models f$ means that formula f holds at state s_0 in structure M. When the structure M is understood, we simply write $s_0 \models f$. The relation $\models$ is defined inductively as follows:

$s_0 \models p$ iff $p \in P(s_0)$.

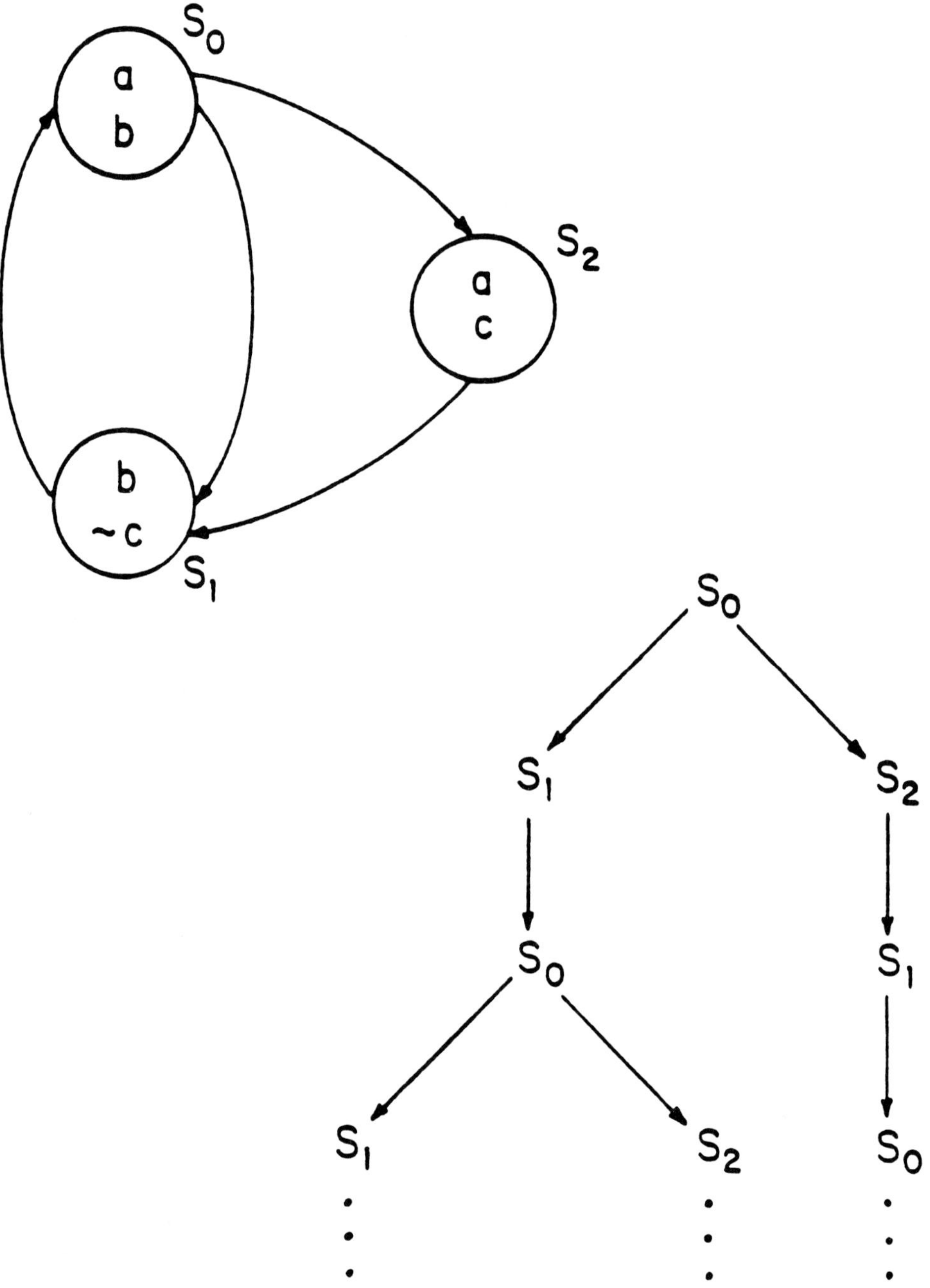

Figure 2-1: A CTL structure and its computation tree

$s_0 \models \neg f$ iff not($s_0 \models f$).

$s_0 \models f_1 \wedge f_2$ iff $s_0 \models f_1$ and $s_0 \models f_2$.

$s_0 \models AXf_1$ iff for all states t such that $(s_0,t) \in R$, $t \models f_1$.

$s_0 \models EXf_1$ iff for some state t such that $(s_0,t) \in R$, $t \models f_1$.

$s_0 \models A[f_1 \, U \, f_2]$ iff for all paths $(s_0, s_1, \ldots)$, $\exists i[i \geq 0 \wedge s_i \models f_2 \wedge \forall j[0 \leq j < i \rightarrow s_j \models f_1]]$.

$s_0 \models E[f_1 \, U \, f_2]$ iff for some path $(s_0, s_1, \ldots)$, $\exists i[i \geq 0 \wedge s_i \models f_2 \wedge \forall j[0 \leq j < i \rightarrow s_j \models f_1]]$.

We will also use the following abbreviations in writing CTL formulas:

$f_1 \vee f_2 \equiv \neg(\neg f_1 \wedge \neg f_2)$, $f_1 \rightarrow f_2 \equiv \neg f_1 \vee f_2$, and $f_1 \leftrightarrow f_2 \equiv (f_1 \rightarrow f_2) \wedge (f_2 \rightarrow f_1)$ for logical disjunction, implication, and equivalence, respectively.

AF(f) $\equiv$ A[True U f] intuitively means that f holds in the future along every path from s_0, i.e., f is *inevitable*.

EF(f) $\equiv$ E[True U f] means that there is some path from s_0 that leads to a state at which f holds, i.e., f *potentially* holds.

AG(f) $\equiv$ ¬EF(¬ f) means that f holds at every state on every path from s_0, i.e., f holds *globally*.

EG(f) $\equiv$ ¬AF(¬f) means that there is some path from s_0 on which f holds at every state.

3. Fixpoint Characterizations

Each of the modal operators such as AU, EG, EF, etc., may be characterized as an extremal fixpoint of an appropriate monotonic functional. Let M = (S,R,P) be an arbitrary structure. We use PRED(S) to denote the lattice of total predicates over S where each predicate is identified with the set of states that make it true and the ordering is set inclusion. Thus, each formula f is associated with an element of PRED(S), namely {s:M,s | = f}. Let τ : PRED(S) $\rightarrow$ PRED(S) be given; then

1. τ is *monotonic* provided that $P \subseteq Q$ implies $\tau[P] \subseteq \tau[Q]$;

2. τ is $\cup$-*continuous* provided that $P_1 \subseteq P_2 \subseteq \ldots$ implies $\tau[\cup_i P_i] = \cup_i \tau[P_i]$;

3. τ is $\cap$-*continuous* provided that $P_1 \supseteq P_2 \supseteq \ldots$ implies $\tau[\cap_i P_i] = \cap_i \tau[P_i]$.

A monotonic functional τ on PRED(S) always has both a least fixpoint, **lfp**Z.τ[Z], and a greatest fixpoint, **gfp**Z.τ[Z] (see Tarski [17]): **lfp**Z.τ[Z] = $\cap\{Z:\tau[Z] = Z\}$ whenever τ is monotonic, and **lfp**Z.τ[Z] = $\cup_i \tau^i$[False] whenever τ is also $\cup$-continuous; **gfp**Z.τ[Z] = $\cup\{Z:\tau[Z] = Z\}$ whenever τ is monotonic, and **gfp**Z.τ[Z] = $\cap_i \tau^i$[True] whenever τ is also $\cap$-continuous.

The modal operators have the following fixpoint characterizations:

$$A[f_1Uf_2] = \mathbf{lfp}Z.f_2 \vee (f_1 \wedge AXZ)$$

$$E[f_1Uf_2] = \mathbf{lfp}Z.f_2 \vee (f_1 \wedge EXZ)$$

$$AFf_1 = \mathbf{lfp}Z.f_1 \vee AXZ$$

$$EFf_1 = \mathbf{lfp}Z.f_1 \vee EXZ$$

$$AGf_1 = \mathbf{gfp}Z.f_1 \wedge AXZ$$

$$EGf_1 = \mathbf{gfp}Z.f_1 \wedge EXZ$$

If there is an upper bound on the branching degree of each node in computation tree corresponding to relation R and initial state s_0, then each of the functionals used in the fixpoint characterizations above is $\cup$-continuous and $\cap$-continuous as well as monotonic. This will, of course, be the case for all relations considered in this paper. We show that the fixpoint characterization for EF is correct:

Lemma 1: EFf_1 is the least fixpoint of the functional $\tau[Z] = f_1 \vee EXZ$.

Proof. We first show that EFf_1 is a fixpoint of $\tau[Z]$: Suppose $s_0 \models EFf_1$. Then by definition of $\models$, there is a path $(s_0,s_1,s_2,\ldots)$ in M such that for some k, $s_k \models f_1$. If $k = 0$, $s_0 \models f_1$. Otherwise $s_1 \models EFf_1$ and $s_0 \models EXEFf_1$. Thus, $EFf_1 \subseteq f_1 \vee EXEFf_1$. Similarly, if $s_0 \models f_1 \vee EXEFf_1$, then $s_0 \models f_1$ or $s_0 \models EXEFf_1$. In either case, $s_0 \models EFf_1$ and $f_1 \vee EXEFf_1 \subseteq EFf_1$. Thus $EFf_1 = f_1 \vee EXEFf_1$.

To see that EFf_1 is the least fixpoint of $\tau[Z]$, it suffices to show that $EFf_1 = \cup_{i\geq 0}\tau^i[\text{False}]$. It follows by a straightforward induction on i that $s_0 \in \tau^i[\text{False}]$ iff there is a finite path $(s_0,s_1,\ldots,s_i)$ in M and a $j \leq i$ for which $s_j \models f_1$. □

4. Model Checker

Assume that we wish to determine whether formula f is true in the finite structure $M = (S,R,P)$. Let $sub^+(f_0)$ denote the set subformulas of f_0 with main connective other than $\neg$. We label each state $s \in S$ with the set of positive/negative formulas f in $sub^+(f_0)$ so that $f \in label(s)$ iff $M, s \models f$ and $\neg f \in label(s)$ iff $M, s \models f$.

The algorithm makes $n + 1$ passes where $n = length(f_0)$. On pass i, every state $s \in S$ is labelled with f or $\neg f$ for each formula $f \in sub^+(f_0)$ of length i. Information gathered in earlier passes about formulas of length less than i is used to perform the labelling. For example, if $f = f_1 \wedge f_2$, then f should be placed in the set for s precisely when f_1 and f_2 are already present in the set for s. For modalities such as $A[f_1Uf_2]$ information from the successor states of s (as well as from s itself) is used. Since $A[f_1Uf_2] = f_2 \vee (f_1 \wedge AXA[f_1Uf_2])$, $A[f_1Uf_2]$ should be placed in the set for s when f_2 is already in the set for s or when f_1 is in the set for s and $A[f_1Uf_2]$ is in the set of each immediate successor state of s.

Satisfaction of $A[f_1Uf_2]$ may be seen to "radiate" outward from states where it holds immediately by virtue of f_2 holding. Let

$$A[f_1Uf_2])^0 = f_2,$$

$$(A[f_1Uf_2])^{k+1} = f_1 \wedge AX(A[f_1Uf_2])^k.$$

It can be shown that $M,s \models (A[f_1Uf_2])^k$ iff $M,s \models A[f_1Uf_2]$ and along every path starting at s, f_2 holds by the kth state following s. Thus, states where $(A[f_1Uf_2])^0$ holds are found first, then states where $(A[f_1Uf_2])^1$ holds, etc. If $A[f_1Uf_2]$ holds, $A[f_1Uf_2])^{card(s)}$ must hold since all loop-free paths in M are of length $\leq$ card(S). Thus, if after card(S) steps of radiating outward $A[f_1Uf_2]$ has still not been found to hold at state s, then put $\neg A[f_1Uf_2]$ in the set for s.

The algorithm for pass i is given in Figure 4-1. Figure 4-2 - 4-6 give snapshots of the algorithm in operation on the structure shown for the formula AFb $\wedge$ EFa (which abbreviates AFb $\wedge$~AF~a).

The algorithm presented above runs in time $O(length(f) \cdot (card(S) + card(R))^2$. In [6] we describe a more efficient model checking algorithm that is linear in the size of the CTL structure. This algorithm is also fairly simple, since it is based on a depth-first-search of the CTL structure.

Theorem 2: There is an algorithm for determining whether a CTL formula f is true in state s of the structure $M = (S, R, P)$ which runs in time $O(length(f) \cdot (card(S) + card(R)))$. □

The only remaining feature of the verifier that we need to discuss is the counterexample feature. When the model checker determines that a formula is false, it will attempt to find a path in the graph which demonstrates that the negation of the formula is true. For instance, if the formula has the form AG(f), our system will produce a path to a state in which $\neg$f holds. This feature is quite useful for debugging purposes.

The verifier has been operational since January, 1982. It is written in C and runs on a VAX 11/780 under Unix. Several programs are available for generating state machines for analysis by the model checker. One will be described in section 6. Another generates state machines from a switch level

```
for every state s∈S do
   for every f∈sub⁺(f₀) of length i do
      if f = A[f₁Uf₂] and f₂∈set(s) or
         f = E[f₁Uf₂] and f₂∈set(s) or
         f = EXf₁ and ∃t[(s,t)∈R and f₁∈set(t)] or
         f = f₁∧f₂ and f₁∈set(s) and f₂∈set(s)
      then add f to set(s) end if
   end for
end for;
A:for j = 1 to card(s) do
   for every state s∈S do
      for every f∈sub⁺(f₀) of length i do
         if f = A[f₁Uf₂] and f₁∈set(s) and ∀t[(s,t)∈R → f∈set(t)] or
            f = E[f₁Uf₂] and f₁∈set(s) and ∃t[(s,t)∈R ∧ f∈set(t)]
         then add f to set(s) end if
      end for
   B:end for
end for;
for every state s∈S do
   for every f∈sub⁺(f₀) of length i do
      if f ∉ set(s) then add ¬f to set(s) end if
   end for
C:end for
```

Figure 4-1: Pass i of Model Checking Algorithm

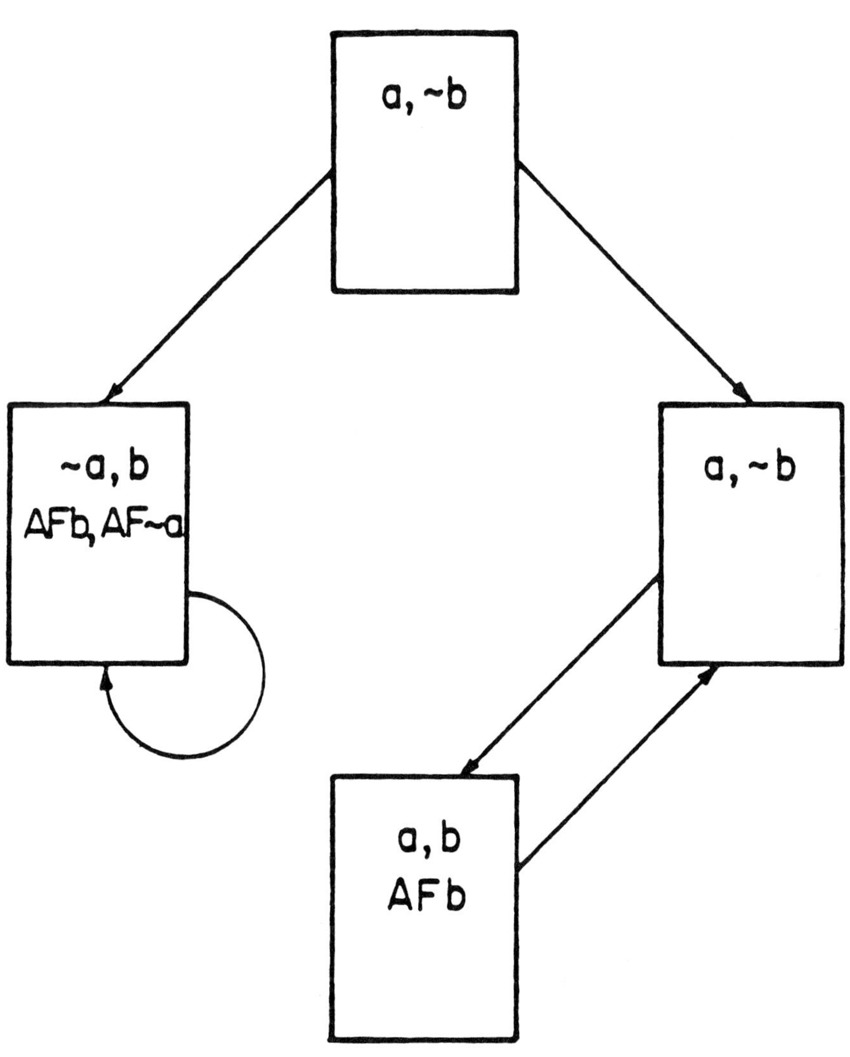

Figure 4-2: First time at label A in Pass 1

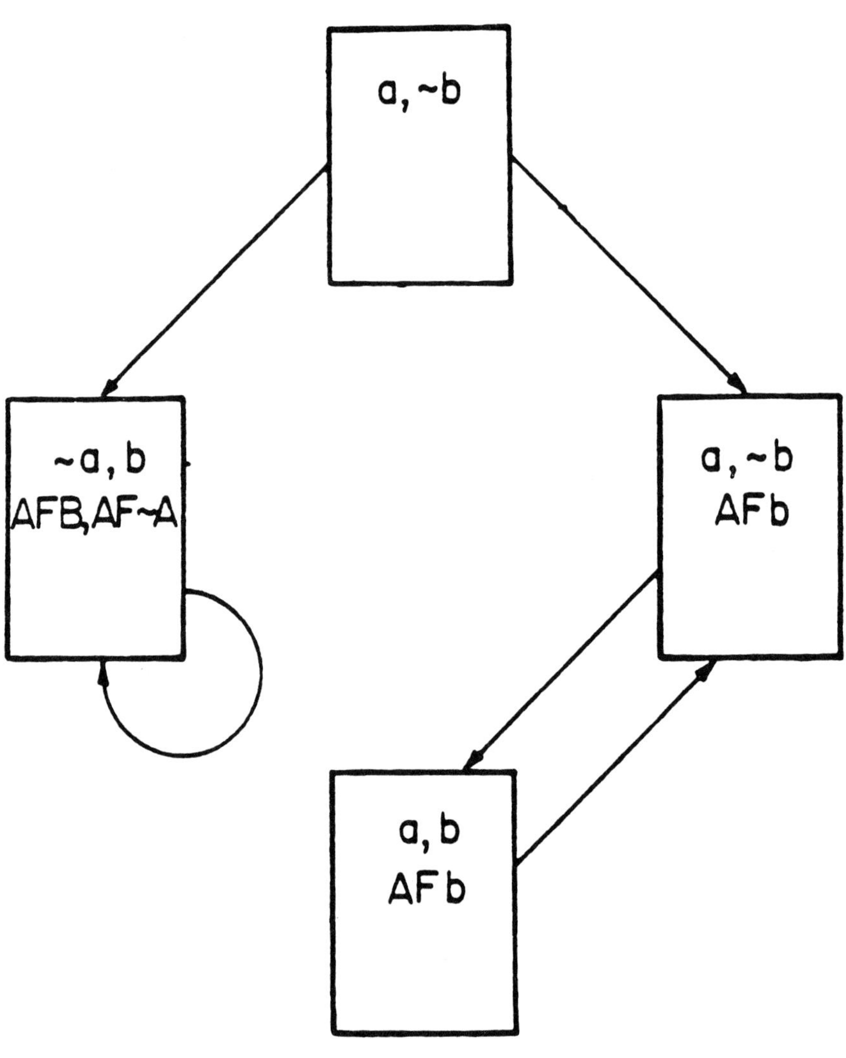

Figure 4-3: First time at label B in Pass 1

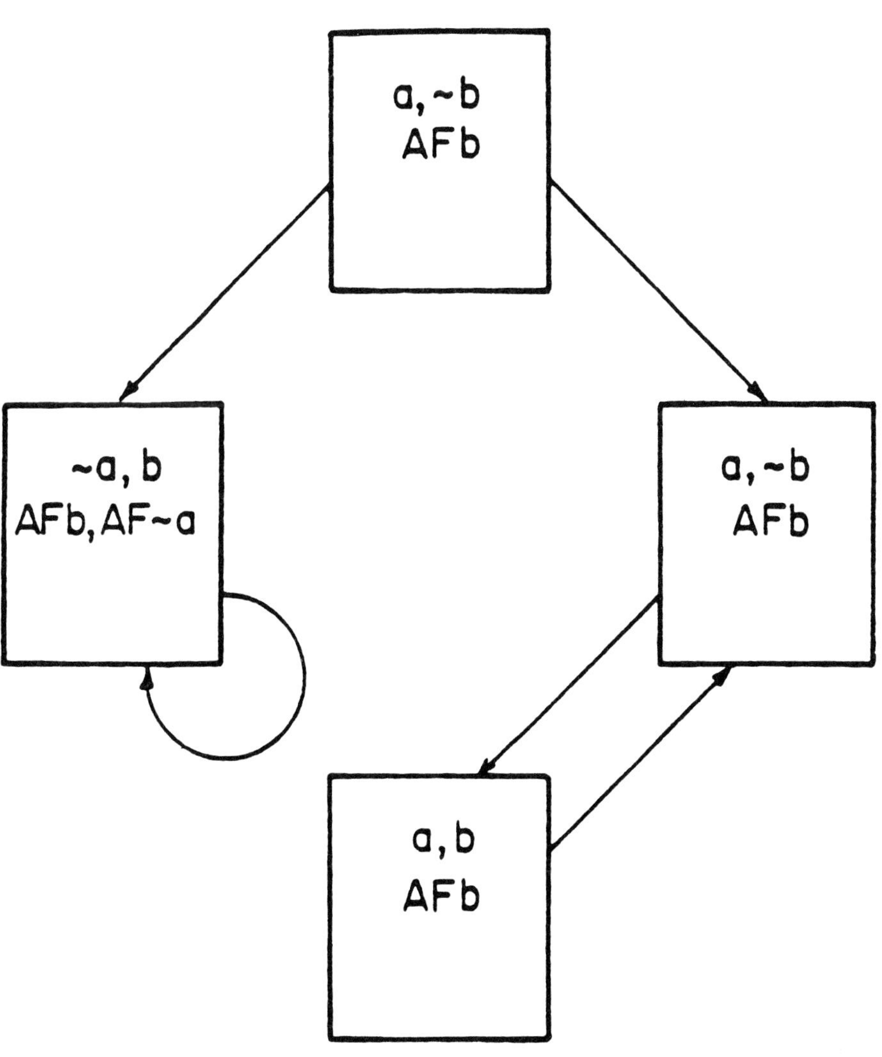

Figure 4-4: Second time at label B in Pass 1

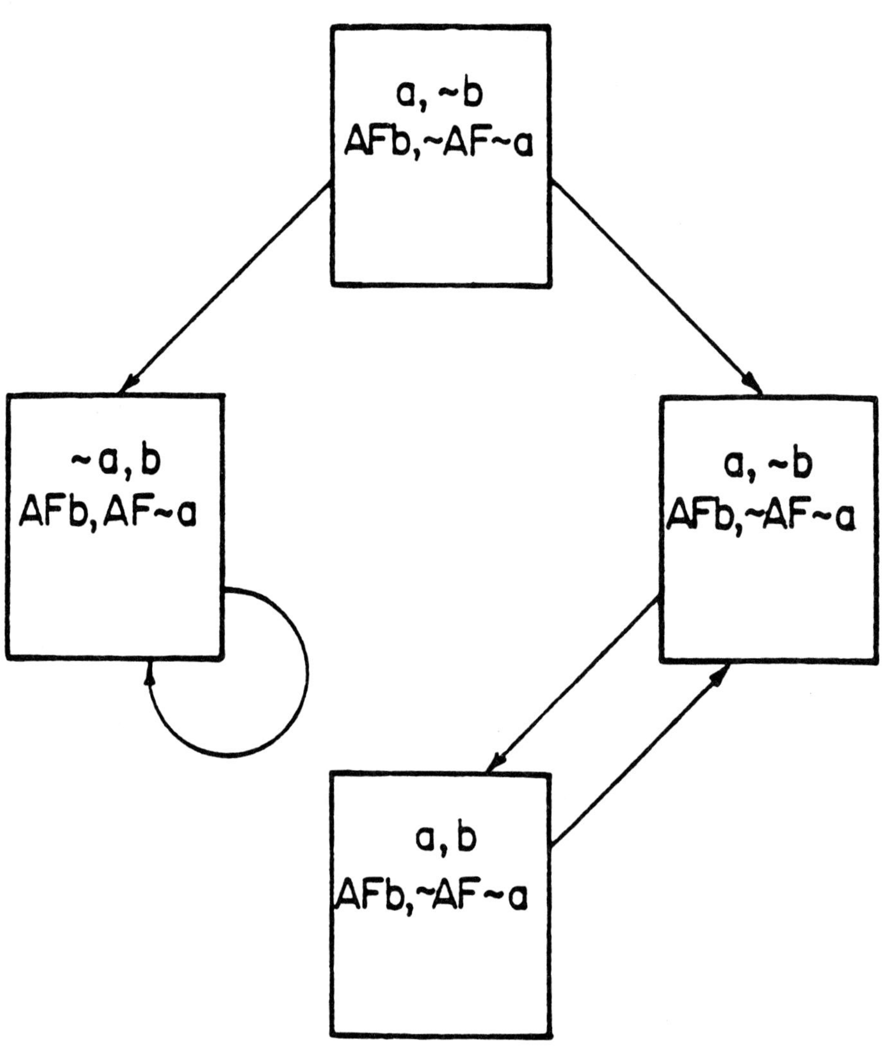

Figure 4-5: First time at label C in Pass 1

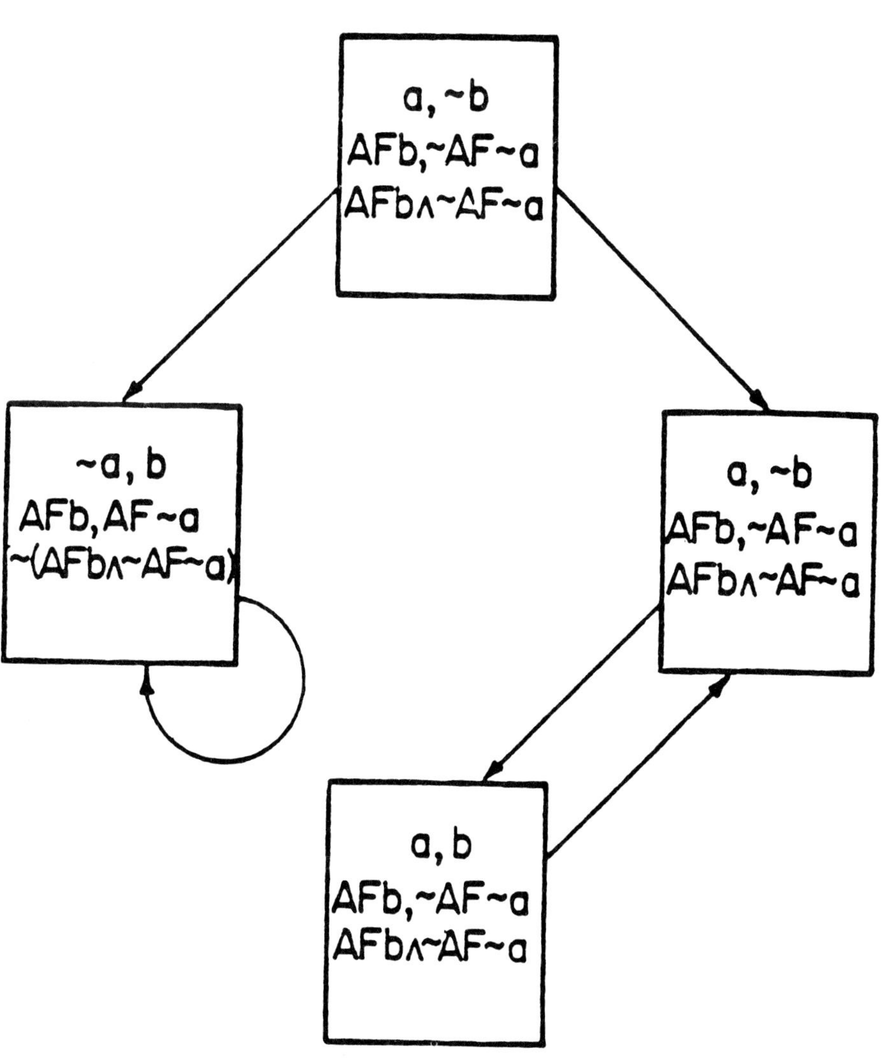

Figure 4-6: At termination

circuit description by using a unit-delay simulator to discover the transition relation of the corresponding CTL structure. The third is a compiler for a finite state subset of the CSP programming language.

5. Introducing Fairness into CTL

Occasionally, we are only interested in the correctness of *fair execution sequences*. For example, we may wish to consider only execution sequences in which each process is executed infinitely often. Unfortunately, this type of property cannot be expressed directly in CTL ([7], [8]). The alternative of using a linear time logic is ruled out because any model checker for such a logic must have high complexity. In [15] we prove that the following problem is NP-complete for linear temporal logic with the F and G operators and PSPACE-complete for linear temporal logic with the U operator or with the F and X operators:

> Given a structure M = (S,R,P), a state $s_0 \in S$ and a formula f, is there a path p in M starting from s_0 such that $p, s_0 \models f$?

In order to handle such properties we must modify the semantics of CTL slightly. Initially, the model checker will prompt the user for a series of *fairness constraints*. Each constraint can be an arbitrary formula of the logic. A path is said to be *fair* with respect to a set of fairness constraints if each constraint holds infinitely often along the path. More formally, a structure is a 4-tuple (S, R, P, F) where S, R, P have the same meaning as in section 2, and F is a collection of predicates on S i.e. $F \subseteq 2^S$. A path p is F-*fair* iff the following condition holds: *for each G ∈ F, there are infinitely many states on p which satisfy predicate g.* The definition in section 2 of truth in a CTL structure is now modified so that the path quantifiers in CTL formulas are restricted to F-fair paths. Examples of fairness constraints can be found in section 6. In [6] we show that handling fairness in this manner does not change the linear time complexity of the model checker. We will not discuss in this paper the specific modifications that must be made in the basic model checking algorithm; however, the key observation is contained in the following lemma.

Lemma 3: Given any finite structure M = (S, R, P), collection F = $\{G_1 \ldots G_k\}$ of subsets of S, and state $s_0 \in S$ the following two conditions are equivalent:

1. There exists an F- fair path in M starting at s_0.
2. There exists a strongly connected component C of (the graph of) M such that
   a. there is a finite path from s_0 to a state $t \in C$, and
   b. for each G_i, there is a state $t_i \in C \cap G_i$.

Proof:

(1) => (2): Suppose the F-fair path $s_0, s_1, s_2, \ldots$ exists in M. Then for each G_i there is a state $t_i \in G_i$ for which there exist infinitely many s_j that are equal to t_i. So for each pair t_i, t_j there is a path (which is some finite segment of the original path) from t_i to t_j. It follows that all the t_i lie in the same strongly connected component C of M. Certainly, there is a path from s_0 to some node $t \in C$ (take $t = t_1$). Moreover, by the choice of the t_i, each $t_i \in C \cap G_i$. Thus, C is the desired strongly connected component of (2).

(2) => (1): Suppose the strongly connected component C exists in M. Then finite paths of the following forms are also present in M: $(s_0, \ldots, t_1)$, $(t_1, \ldots, t_2)$, $\ldots$, $(t_{k-1}, \ldots, t_k)$, and $(t_k, \ldots, t_1)$. We then concatenate these finite paths to get a path: $s_0, \ldots, t_1, \ldots, t_2, \ldots, t_k, \ldots, t_1, \ldots, t_2, \ldots, t_k, \ldots, t_1, \ldots, t_2, \ldots, t_k, \ldots$ This path starts at s_0, and for each i there are infinitely many occurrences of $t_i \in G_i$ along it. Thus, this path is F-fair. □

6. Using the Model Checker to Verify a Finite State Hardware Controller

In order to assist with the design and verification of finite state machines, we have designed a language named SML (state machine language). In addition to being useful for verification, SML also provides a succinct notation for describing complicated finite state machines. A program written in SML is compiled into a finite state machine, which can then be verified using the model checker or implemented in hardware. At CMU, we have implemented an SML compiler that runs on a VAX 11/780. We also have access to design tools that can implement a finite state machine produced by the compiler as either a ROM, a PLA, or a PAL.

6.1. The Description Language and its Semantics

An SML program represents a synchronous circuit that implements a Moore machine. At a clock transition, the program examines its input signals and changes its internal state and output signals accordingly. Since we are dealing with digital circuits where wires are either high or low, the major data type is *boolean*. Each boolean variable may be declared to be either an *input* changed only by the external world but visible to the program, an *output* changed only by the program but visible to the external world, or an *internal* changed and seen only by the program. The hardware implementation of boolean variables may also be declared to be either active high or active low. The use of mixed logic in SML is permitted. Internal integer variables are also provided.

SML programs are similar in appearance to many imperative programming languages. SML statements include **if**, **while**, and **loop/exit**. A **cobegin** is provided to allow several statements to execute concurrently in lockstep. There is also a simple macro facility.

The semantics of SML programs is different from most programming languages, since we are not only interested in what a statement does, but how much time it takes to do it. In this respect, SML was influenced by the semantics of ESTEREL [2]. The complete semantics for SML will not be given here but will appear in a forthcoming paper [4]. A *program state* is an ordered pair, $\langle S, \sigma \rangle$, consisting of a statement S and a function σ that gives values to all of the identifiers. The semantics consist of a set of *rewrite rules* that describe how a program state is transformed into new program state. Each rewrite rule also specifies whether it takes a clock cycle to make the transformation or not. For example, two typical rewrite rules are:

$$\langle \textbf{raise}\ (I);\ S, \sigma \rangle \xrightarrow{1} \langle S, \sigma' \rangle \quad \text{where } \sigma' = \sigma[I \mapsto \mathit{true}]$$

$$\frac{E = \mathit{false}}{\langle \textbf{if}\ E\ \textbf{then}\ S_1\ \textbf{endif};\ S_2, \sigma \rangle \xrightarrow{0} \langle S_2, \sigma \rangle}$$

The first rule states that a **raise** statement followed by an arbitrary statement S can be rewritten in one clock cycle to statement S while simultaneously changing σ so that $\sigma'(I) = \mathit{true}$. The second rule states that an **if** statement followed by an arbitrary statement S_2 can be rewritten in no time to statement S_2 if the condition is false.

Given any program state, we can repeatedly apply the rewrite rules to find a new state that can be reached in one clock cycle. This new state is a successor of the original state in the finite state machine. So starting from the initial program state (which consists of the entire program and a function which assigns 0 to all integers and *false* to all booleans), we can repeatedly find successor states until we have built the entire finite state machine.

6.2. Example: A Traffic Controller

The best way to illustrate the use of SML is by an example. We will use SML to design a traffic controller that is stationed at the intersection of a two-way highway going north and south and a one-way road going east. For the sake of simplicity, no turns are permitted. At the north, south, and east of this intersection, there is a sensor that goes high for at least one clock cycle when a car arrives. When the intersection is clear of cross traffic, the controller should raise a signal indicating that the car is permitted to cross the intersection. Once the car has crossed, the sensor that indicated the arrival of the car will go low.

Let the names of the sensors be *N* (north), *S* (south), and *E* (east). Furthermore, let *N-Go*, *S-Go*, and *E-Go* be the names of the output signals for each end of the intersection.

Now that the problem is defined, we can express the correctness conditions of the controller in CTL.

$$\mathbf{AG}\ \neg(E\text{-}Go \wedge (N\text{-}Go \vee S\text{-}Go))$$

This formula is a safety property that is true if the controller does not permit collisions to occur. There are also several interesting liveness properties:

$$\mathbf{AG}\ (\neg N\text{-}Go \wedge N \rightarrow \mathbf{AF}\ N\text{-}Go)$$
$$\mathbf{AG}\ (\neg S\text{-}Go \wedge S \rightarrow \mathbf{AF}\ S\text{-}Go)$$
$$\mathbf{AG}\ (\neg E\text{-}Go \wedge E \rightarrow \mathbf{AF}\ E\text{-}Go)$$

These formulas state that every request to enter the intersection is eventually answered, so the controller is starvation-free. If all three of these formulas are true, the controller is deadlock-free as well.

$$\mathbf{EF}\ (N\text{-}Go \wedge S\text{-}Go)$$

Since we want to maximize the amount of traffic, this formula insures that the controller allows north and south traffic to cross the intersection simultaneously.

In addition to specifying the desired behavior of the controller, we must also specify the behavior of the cars. In particular, we don't want a car to enter the intersection and stay there forever. Since the model checker allows the specification of fairness constraints that must be true infinitely often, we must rephrase this condition to be that the cars must be out of the intersection infinitely often. Since a car from the north is in the intersection if *N-Go* is true, and it stays there while *N* is true, the fairness constraint for cars from the north is $\neg(N\text{-}Go \wedge N)$. There are similar constraints for traffic from the south and east.

6.3. An implementation of the Traffic Controller in SML

One approach to this problem is to provide two locks: `NS-Lock`, which is true when north-south traffic is in the intersection, and `EW-Lock`, which is true when east-west traffic is in the intersection. Traffic from one direction is forbidden to enter the intersection if the lock in the other direction is true. Figure 6-1 shows a program that uses this idea. The numbers at the beginning of each line were added for easy reference and are not part of the language.

A few comments are necessary to explain the operation of this program.

Line 5: In addition to declaring the two locks, `N-Req`, `S-Req`, and `E-Req` are also declared to be internal. `N-Req` will go high when a car arrives at the intersection from the north and go low when the car has crossed the intersection. `S-Req` and `E-Req` are similar.

Lines 7-9: `Wait` is a macro definition that delays until its parameter becomes true.

```
1       program intersect;
2
3       input N, S, E;
4       output N-Go, S-Go, E-Go;
5       internal NS-Lock, EW-Lock, N-Req, S-Req, E-Req;
6
7           procedure wait (expr)
8               while !(expr) do nop endwhile
9           endproc
10
11          cobegin
12              loop if !N-Req & N then raise (N-Req) endif endloop
13          ||
14              loop if !S-Req & S then raise (S-Req) endif endloop
15          ||
16              loop if !E-Req & E then raise (E-Req) endif endloop
17          ||
18              loop
19                  if N-Req then
20                      raise (NS-Lock);
21                      wait (!EW-Lock);
22                      raise (N-Go);
23                      wait (!N);
24                      cobegin
25                          if !S-Go & !S-Req | S-Go & !S then lower (NS-Lock) endif
26                      ||
27                          lower (N-Go) || lower (N-Req)
28                      end;
29                      wait (!E-Req)
30                  endif
31              endloop
32          ||
33              loop
34                  if S-Req then
35                      if !NS-Lock & !N-Req then raise (NS-Lock) else delay 1 endif;
36                      wait (!EW-Lock);
37                      raise (S-Go);
38                      wait (!S);
39                      cobegin
40                          if !N-Go & !N-Req then lower (NS-Lock) endif
41                      ||
42                          lower (S-Go) || lower (S-Req)
43                      end;
44                      wait (!E-Req)
45                  endif
46              endloop
47          ||
48              loop
49                  if E-Req then
50                      wait (!NS-Lock);
51                      cobegin raise (EW-Lock) || raise (E-Go) end;
52                      wait (!E);
53                      cobegin lower (EW-Lock) || lower (E-Go) || lower (E-Req) end
54                  endif
55              endloop
56          end
57      endprog
```

Figure 6-1: A First Attempt at Writing a Traffic Controller in SML

Line 12: If a car is not at the north end of the intersection (`!N-Req`), and the sensor at the north goes high (`N`), there is now a car at the north end of the intersection, so assert `N-Req`.

Lines 14 and 16: These statements do the same as line 12 for cars from the south and east.

Lines 18-31: This statement controls traffic from the north. The procedure is to lock the intersection (line 20), wait until the cross traffic releases the intersection (line 21), and then go (line 22). After the car has crossed (line 23), release the intersection if there is no south traffic about to enter the intersection (`!S-Go & !S-Req`) or if there is south traffic simultaneously leaving the intersection (S-Go & !S) (line 25). Do not accept another request from the north until any east traffic finishes crossing (line 29).

Lines 33-46: This statement controls traffic from the south. The algorithm is the same as for north traffic, except that north traffic changes NS-Lock if both north traffic and south traffic want to change it simultaneously. On line 35, south traffic sets NS-Lock only if north traffic isn't about to enter the intersection and set it. On line 40, north traffic will release NS-Lock if it is leaving the intersection simultaneously, so it is not necessary to test (N-Go & !N).

Lines 48-55: This statement controls traffic from the east. Once there is no north-south traffic (line 50), the intersection is locked and the car is allowed to go (line 51). After the car leaves (line 52), the intersection is released.

This program was compiled into a 72 state machine in approximately 10 seconds of CPU time on a VAX. However, the transitions of this state machine are dependent on the state of the input. In order to remove this dependency, each state had to be replaced with 8 states, one for each possible combination of inputs. An additional 35 seconds of CPU time was required to convert this state machine into a 576 state machine that the model checker can handle. We have already developed a new model checker algorithm that circumvents this problem and we hope to implement it in the near future.

6.4. Verifying the Traffic Controller with the Model Checker

Figure 6-2 shows a transcript of the model checker running on the program in figure 6-1. The numbers in parentheses are the total user cpu time and "system time", in 1/60ths of a second. As the transcript shows, the program allows simultaneous north and south traffic and is collision-free, but it is not deadlock-free. The model checker provides a counter example that can be used to diagnose the problem. In state 390, cars from the north and the south are in the intersection, and there is a car waiting from the east. Furthermore, the car from the north is leaving the intersection (N is false), so the controller will not allow another car from the north to cross until the car from the east has crossed. In state 417, another car arrives from the north, so N-Req is raised in state 432. In state 432, the car from the south leaves the intersection (S is false). But since N-Req is high, the controller does not lower NS-Lock in state 523! So state 523 is a deadlock, where the car from the east is waiting for the north-south traffic to unlock the intersection, and the north-south traffic is waiting for the car from the east to cross the intersection.

As the counter example illustrates, the problem with the program in figure 6-1 is that a car from the south will not lower NS-Lock when it leaves the intersection if N-Req is high, since it expects a car from the north to enter the intersection. However, the car from the north might be waiting for a car

```
% /bin/time emc -c inter1.emc
              CTL MODEL CHECKER (C version 2.5)

Taking input from inter1.emc...
Fairness constraint: ~(N-Go & N).
Fairness constraint: ~(S-Go & S).
Fairness constraint: ~(E-Go & E).
Fairness constraint: .

time:  (1284 141)

|= EF (N-Go & S-Go).
The equation is TRUE.


time:  (1305 149)

|= AG ~(E-Go & (N-Go | S-Go)).
The equation is TRUE.


time:  (1326 158)

|= AG (N & ~N-Go -> AF N-Go).
The equation is FALSE.

EF ~(N & ~N-Go -> AF N-Go)
        is true in state 1 because of the path:
State 1:  XCMP1 E S N
State 16:  E-Req S-Req N-Req XCMP2
State 104:  E-Req S-Req N-Req E-Go EW-Lock NS-Lock XCMP57
State 484:  E S-Req N-Req NS-Lock XCMP32
State 390:  S E-Req S-Req N-Req NS-Lock S-Go N-Go XCMP30
State 417:  E S N E-Req S-Req NS-Lock S-Go XCMP19

N & ~N-Go -> AF N-Go
        is false in state 417 if:
        1) ~(N & ~N-Go)
                is false in state 417, AND
        2) AF N-Go
                is false in state 417.

~(N & ~N-Go)
        is false in state 417 because the following propositions are true:
N ~N-Go

AF N-Go
        is false in state 417 because
EG ~N-Go
        is true in state 417.
An example of such a path is:
State 417:  E S N E-Req S-Req NS-Lock S-Go XCMP19
State 432:  E-Req S-Req N-Req NS-Lock S-Go XCMP17
State 523:  E N E-Req N-Req NS-Lock XCMP69
State 523:  E N E-Req N-Req NS-Lock XCMP69
        ...


time:  (1428 184)

|= .
End of Session.
     1:59.0 real         23.8 user          3.2 sys
%
```

Figure 6-2: Verifying the First Traffic Controller Program

from the east to cross (line 29), so it will not enter, and a deadlock will result. A simple solution is to replace the `wait` at line 29 with a loop that will lower `NS-Lock` if south traffic leaves the intersection while east and north traffic is waiting. The `wait` at line 44 must also be replaced by a similar loop. The result of these changes is the program shown in figure 6-3. This program compiles into 69 states (552 states for the model checker). The correctness of this program is shown by the transcript in figure 6-4.

```
program intersect;

input N, S, E;
output N-Go, S-Go, E-Go;
internal NS-Lock, E-Lock, N-Req, S-Req, E-Req;

    procedure wait (expr)
        while !(expr) do nop endwhile
    endproc

    cobegin
        loop if !N-Req & N then raise (N-Req) endif endloop
    ||
        loop if !S-Req & S then raise (S-Req) endif endloop
    ||
        loop if !E-Req & E then raise (E-Req) endif endloop
    ||
        loop
            if N-Req then
                raise (NS-Lock);
                wait (!E-Lock);
                raise (N-Go);
                wait (!N);
                cobegin
                    if S-Go & !S | !S-Go & !S-Req then lower (NS-Lock) endif
                ||
                    lower (N-Go) || lower (N-Req)
                end;
                while E-Req do
                    if S-Go & !S & N-Req then lower (NS-Lock) endif
                endwhile
            endif
        endloop
    ||
        loop
            if S-Req then
                if !NS-Lock & !N-Req then raise (NS-Lock) else delay 1 endif;
                wait (!E-Lock);
                raise (S-Go);
                wait (!S);
                cobegin
                    if !N-Go & !N-Req then lower (NS-Lock) endif
                ||
                    lower (S-Go) || lower (S-Req)
                end;
                while E-Req do
                    if N-Go & !N & S-Req then lower (NS-Lock) endif
                endwhile
            endif
        endloop
    ||
        loop
            if E-Req then
                wait (!NS-Lock);
                cobegin raise (E-Lock) || raise (E-Go) end;
                wait (!E);
                cobegin lower (E-Lock) || lower (E-Go) || lower (E-Req) end
            endif
        endloop
    end
endprog
```

Figure 6-3: The Corrected Traffic Controller Program

7. Conclusion

Although finite state systems occur in a variety of contexts and correctness is frequently an issue, we believe our verification technique may prove to be most useful in analyzing the correctness of sequential circuits. We believe, in fact, that this approach is already practical for small- and medium-size circuits. The example in section 6 shows how the model checker can be used in conjunction with a high level language for describing PLA's and ROM's, and in [10] we show how state-transition graphs can be extracted for analysis from a switch level circuit specification.

```
% /bin/time emc -c inter2.emc
              CTL MODEL CHECKER (C version 2.5)

Taking input from inter2.emc...
Fairness constraint: ~(N-Go & N).
Fairness constraint: ~(S-Go & S).
Fairness constraint: ~(E-Go & E).
Fairness constraint: .

time:  (1371 365)

|= AG ~(E-Go & (N-Go | S-Go)).
The equation is TRUE.


time:  (1391 371)

|= AG (N & ~N-Go -> AF N-Go).
The equation is TRUE.


time:  (1465 377)

|= AG (S & ~S-Go -> AF S-Go).
The equation is TRUE.


time:  (1543 383)

|= AG (E & ~E-Go -> AF E-Go).
The equation is TRUE.


time:  (1609 391)

|= .
End of Session.
     4:51.0 real        26.8 user          6.7 sys
%
```

Figure 6-4: Verifying the Corrected Traffic Controller Program

However, more research is needed to make our method practical for large circuits. Circuit designers cope with the complexity of large circuits by designing them hierarchically. It seems reasonable that large circuits could be verified hierarchically by verifying small subcircuits in detail, then using simplified models of them as components in larger circuits. This process can be automated to some extent. If one uses a subset of CTL, small circuits can be simplified by "hiding" or restricting the visibility of some of their internal nodes (more precisely by making it illegal to use the nodes in CTL formulas and merging groups of states that become indistinguishable into single states). We refer the reader to [10] for a more detailed discussion of how model checking might be made hierarchical.

Perhaps the most difficult remaining problem involves determining how to handle replication of components in circuits. Consider, for example, the circuit for a queue. In this case the circuit actually represents a family of circuits in which each member has a different number of cells for storing queue elements. There are many other families of circuits designed in this way--systolic arrays in particular. It seems possible to verify entire families of such circuits at one time by using some type of induction rule in addition to the model checker. This, however, is a topic for future research.

References

1. M. Browne, E. Clarke, D. Dill, B. Mishra. Automatic Verification of Sequential Circuits. Unpublished Manuscript.

2. G. Berry and L. Cosserat. The ESTEREL Synchronous Programming Language and its Mathematical Semantics. Ecole Nationalo Superieune des Mines de Paris (ENSMP), Centre de Mathematiques Appliquees, 1984.

3. M. Ben-Ari, Z. Manna, A. Pneuli. "The Logic of Nextime". *Eighth ACM Symposium on Principles of Programming Languages, Williamsburg, VA* (January 1981), 164-176.

4. M.C. Browne and E.M. Clarke. Unpublished Manuscript.

5. E.M. Clarke, E.A. Emerson. "Synthesis of Synchronization Skeletons for Branching Time Temporal Logic". Proceedings of the Workshop on Logic of Programs,Yorktown-Heights, NY, Lecture Notes in Computer Science #131, 1981.

6. E.M. Clarke, E.A. Emerson, A.P. Sistla. "Automatic Verification of Finite-State Concurrent Systems using Temporal Logic Specifications: A Practical Approach". , Tenth ACM Symposium on Principles of Programming Languages, Austin,Texas, 1983.

7. E.A. Emerson, E.M. Clarke. "Characterizing Properties of Parallel Programs as Fixpoints". Proceedings of the Seventh International Colloquium on Automata, Languages and Programming, Lecture Notes in Computer Science #85, 1981.

8. E.A. Emerson, J.Y. Halpern. ""Sometimes" and "Not Never" Revisited: On Branching versus Linear Time". POPL 83.

9. B.T. Hailpern, S. Owicki. "Verifying Network Protocols Using Temporal Logic". 192, Computer System Laboratory, Stanford University, June, 1980.

10. E.M. Clarke and B Mishra. "Automatic verification of Asynchronous Circuits". , Proceedings of Logics of Programs (ed. E. Clarke and D. Kozen), Springer Lecture Notes in Computer Science 164, Pittsburgh. Pa., 1983.

11. Z. Manna, A. Pneuli. "Verification of Concurrent Programs: The Temporal Framework". *The Correctness Problem in Computer Science (R.S. Boyer and J.S. Moore, eds.), International Lecture Series in Computer Science* (1981).

12. S. Owicki, L. Lamport. "Proving Liveness Properties of Concurrent Programs". *Stanford University Technical Report* (1980).

13. J.P. Quielle, J. Sifakis. "Specification and Verification of Concurrent Systems in CESAR". Proceedings of the Fifth International Symposium in Programming, 1981.

14. J.P. Quielle, J. Sifakis. "Fairness and Related Properties in Transition Systems". *IMAG* , 292 (March 1982).

15. A.P. Sistla, E.M. Clarke. "Complexity of Propositional Temporal Logic". , Proc. 14th Annual ACM Symposium on Theory of Computing, San Francisco, 1982.

16. D.P. Sidhu. "Rules for Synthesizing Correct Communication Protocols". PNL Preprint, to appear in SIGCOMM.

17. Tarski, A. "A Lattice-Theoretical Fixpoint Theorem and Its Application". *Pacific J. Math. 5* (1955), 285-309.

18. P. Zafiropulo, C. West, H. Rudin, D. Cowan, D. Brand. "Towards Analyzing and Synthesizing Protocols". *IEEE Transactions on Communications COM-28*, 4 (April 1980), 651-671.

RESOLUTION MODAL LOGICS

Luis Fariñas-del-Cerro
Langages et Systèmes Informatiques
Université Paul Sabatier
118, route de Narbonne
F - 31062 Toulouse Cedex

ABSTRACT

In this paper we describe a general way to define a resolution method in the framework of non classical logics.

1. INTRODUCTION

What does **resolution** means in the case of Modal Logics ? This question looks natural if we consider the fruitfulness of the resolution principle from both the theoretical and the practical point of view. The aim of this paper is to give some answers to this question.

We bear in mind the following resolution principle: **For any two clauses C_1 and C_2, if there is a literal L_1 in C_1 that is complementary to a literal L_2 in C_2, then delete L_1 and L_2 from C_1 and C_2 respectively, and construct the disjunction of the remaining clauses.**

We consider now literals governed by the modal operators [] (necessary) or <> (possible), and the definition: $[]A =_{def} \sim <> \sim A$, (by A we note a formula). Consider the two clauses $[]p \vee C_1$ and $<> \sim p \vee C_2$ (where p is a propositional variable) ; we have that $<> \sim p$ is equivalent to $\sim []p$. This suggests the following modal resolution rule:

$$\frac{[]p \vee C_1 \qquad <> \sim p \vee C_2}{C_1 \vee C_2}$$

The upper formulas of the rule will be called **premises.**

NATO ASI Series, Vol. F13
Logics and Models of Concurrent Systems
Edited by K. R. Apt

In the same way we consider the clauses []p v C_1 and [](~p v q) v C_2 and the axiom [](A v B) → <> A v []B then we can state a resolution rule such as:

$$\frac{[]p \vee C_1 \qquad [](\sim p \vee q) \vee C_2}{[]q \vee C_1 \vee C_2}$$

However if we consider the system with axioms [](A v B) → <>A v []B and []A → <> A, and the clauses <> p v C_1 and <> ~p v C_2. Then we can't have the rule:

$$\frac{<>p \vee C_1 \qquad <>\sim p \vee C_2}{C_1 \vee C_2}$$

As the relationship between <> p and []p in this system is given by []p → <> p and not the converse, the rule is not justified.

Everything suggests that the definition of resolution modal rules is linked to the relationship between the modal operators. We find the same idea in methods like the ones developped by Carnap [CR] and Lemmon [LE] and in the truth-tables methods of Anderson [AR] and Bayart [BA]. However it appears only explicitly as a basis to define resolution methods in Shimura [SM], Orlowska [OE] and Fariñas [FC1].

This kind of decision methods may be called syntactical, since semantics is not explicity mentioned.

A first step for defining resolution decision methods is to define the notion of a normal form. It is necessary because the elements of the normal form are a set of expressions that is closed under resolution rules. In other words, if we consider a conjunctive normal form ($F = \bigwedge_{i=1}^{m} C_i$, where each C_i is a clause) and R as a rule with n arguments, then:

$$R(C_1, \ldots, C_n) = C$$

if R is defined for $C_1, \ldots, C_n$, and we note that C must be a clause. The formulation of R, as seen above, is subordinated to the characterization of elementary inconsistency i.e. inconsistencies between disjuncts of the clauses.

In what follows we will see precisely what this means. To this end we consider a particular modal system, the system T of Feys-von Wright, from which examples will be taken.

The paper will be organised as follow: in section 2, we describe the system T (syntax and semantics), in section 3, we define a particular normal form for T, which is the same for every normal modal logic with only monadic modal operators. In section 4, we deal with the problem of modal resolution ; we will define what **resolvent clause** means in modal logic and then the resolution rule will be defined as in classical logic. The completeness theorem will be presented in section 5. In section 6, a refinement of the resolution rule will be given as well as the completeness theorem. Finally, in section 7 some applications of modal resolution will be sketched.

2. THE SYSTEM T

The modal formulas of the system T of Feys and von Wright are the expressions of the form (A & B), (A v B), (A → B), ~ A,[]A, or <> A where A and B are modal formulas. We introduce the constant symbol $\bot$ to be read "the false". The system T is a set of formulas obtained from the axiom schemas and rules:

1. A →(A → B)
2. (A → (B → C)) → ((A → B) → (A → C))
3. ((A →$\bot$)→$\bot$) → A
4. [](A → B) → ([]A → []B)
5. []A → A

R1. Modus ponens $\dfrac{A,\ A \rightarrow B}{B}$

R2. Necessitation $\dfrac{A}{[\,]A}$

We define the notions of proof and theorem in the usual way. A proof of a formula A from a set S of formulas is a finite sequence of formulas each of which is either an axiom or an element of set S or a formula obtainable from earlier formulas by a rule of inference. A formula A is derivable from a set S(S ⊢ A) iff it has a proof from set S. A formula A is a theorem of T(⊢ A) iff it is only derivable from the axioms. A set S of formulas is consistent if no formula of the form A & ~A is derivable from S.

The meaning of formulas is defined using the notion of a model. For us a model is a triple:

M = <G, R, m>

where G is a non-empty set of states. R is a reflexive relation on set G, and m is a meaning function that assigns to each propositional variable p a subset m(p) of G.

Given a model M we say that a formula A is satisfied by a state K in model M(M, K sat A) iff the following conditions are satisfied:

M, K sat p iff K ε m(p) where p is a propositional variable
M, K sat A iff not M, K sat A
M, K sat A v B iff M, K sat A or M, K sat B
M, K sat A & B iff M, K sat A and M, K sat B
M; K sat A → B iff M, K sat (~ A v B)
M, K sat A ↔ B iff M, K sat (A → B) & (B → A)
M, K sat []A iff all K' ε G if (K,K') ε R then M,K'sat A
M, K sat <> A iff there is a K' ε G and such (K,K') ε R and M, K' sat A.

Given a model M, to each formula A of the language we assign a set of states called the extension of A in model M (ext_M A):

$ext_M A = \{K \in G : M, K \text{ sat } A\}$

We admit the usual notions of truth and validity of formulas. A formula A is true in a model M ($\models_M A$) iff $ext_M\ A = G$. A formula A is valid in T($\models$A) iff A is true in every model for T. A formula A is a semantical consequence of a set S of formulas (S$\models$A) iff for any model M the formula A is true in M whenever all formulas in S are true in M. A formula A is satisfiable iff M, K sat A for some model M and state K. A set S of formulas is satisfied in a model M by a state K (M, K sat S) iff M, K sat A for all A ε S. A set S is satisfiable iff M, K sat S for some model M and state K.

3. CONJUNCTIVE NORMAL FORM (C.N.F.)

Let F be a formula, we shall say that F is in C.N.F. if it is of the form:

$$F = C_1 \ \&\ldots\&\ C_m$$

where m > 1 and each C_i (clause) is a disjunction (perhaps with only one disjunct) of the general form:

$$C_i = L_i \ \mathrm{v}\ldots\mathrm{v}\ L_{n_1} \ \mathrm{v}\ [\,]D_1 \ \mathrm{v}\ldots\mathrm{v}\ [\,]D_{n_2} \ \mathrm{v}\ <>A_1 \ \mathrm{v}\ldots\mathrm{v}<>A_{n_3}$$

where each L_i is a literal ; each D_i is a disjunction that possesses the general form of the clauses, and each A_i is a conjunction, where each conjunct possesses the general form of the clauses. Each disjunct in C_i will be called element.

We note by E(E') that E' is a subformula of E.

Examples:

The following formulas are in conjunctive normal forms:

- [](p v q v <>(r & t))
- <>((p v q) & t) & ~p
- ~p v p v [](r v s) v <>((p v []r) & e)
- ~p v []([]p v (<>(q & []r))) v <>([](<>([]q v <>t) & r) v []t) & p)

The **degree** d(A) of a formula A is defined in the following way:

- if A is a literal, d(A) = 0
- if d(A) = n and d(B) = m, d(AΔB) = max(m,n) provided that Δ is & or v.
- if d(A) = n, d(~ A) = n
- if d(A) = A, d(Δ A) = n+1 where Δ = [] or <>.

3.1. There is an effective procedure for constructing, for any given formula F in T, an equivalent formula F' in conjunctive normal form.

The proof is obtained by induction on the degree of the formula F.

The following example is given to illustrate this effective procedure. Take F as the formula [](p & <>(q v [](r & t)) & (p → [](q & <>t)). We obtain the conjunctive normal form by the following transformations:

1. []p & []<>(q v ([]r & []t)) & (p → [](q & <> t))
   using the fact that [](A & B) ↔ []A & []B

2. []p & [] <>((q v []r) & (q v []t)) & (p → ([](q & <>t)))
   using propositional methods

3. []p & [] <>((q v []r) & (q v []t) & (~p v [](q & <>t))
   using propositional methods

4. []p & []<>((q v []r) & (q v []t) & (~p v ([]q & []<>t))
   using the fact that [](A & B) ↔ []A & []B

In the same way we have:

5. []p & [] <> ((q v []r) & (q v []t)) & (~p v []q) & (~p v []<>t)

4. MODAL RESOLUTION

The aim of classical resolution is to delete two inconsistent literals from two given clauses, i.e. consider the clauses $p \vee C_1$ and $\sim p \vee C_2$. Then:

$$\frac{p \vee C_1 \qquad \sim p \vee C_2}{\emptyset \vee C_1 \vee C_2}$$

where $\emptyset$ denotes the empty symbol. The intuitive justification of this rule is that the set $\{p, \sim p\}$ is inconsistent and no proper subset of it is inconsistent.

By analogy the aim of modal resolution will be to delete two (or more) elements at each step of a resolution proof [OE][FC1][SM].

Therefore from a family of set INC of elements (disjunct of clauses) where each set of the family is inconsistent and no proper subset of it is inconsistent, a set of resolution rules (one for each set of the family) is defined.

For example consider the three clauses:

$[](p \vee q) \vee C_1$

$<>\sim p \vee C_2$

$[]\sim q \vee C_3$

Then the rule:

$$\frac{[](p \vee q) \vee C_1 \qquad <>\sim p \vee C_2 \qquad []\sim q \vee C_3}{C_1 \vee C_2 \vee C_3} \qquad (*)$$

is a resolution rule for the system T, because the set $[](p \vee q), <>\sim p, []\ q$ is inconsistent in T.

Since $[](A \vee B) \not\rightarrow []A \vee []B$ in T, it is easy to see that for each formula of the form $[](A \vee B \vee \ldots)$ we must define a new family in INC. This leads us to stress the following two problems.

1° The characterization of the set INC can be so complex as to give a decision method for the system T

2° The number of premisses in the resolution rules is variable.

Therefore this kind of method will be interesting for the subset of formulas [OE][FC1][FC2][FC3][FC8] or for the systems where INC is simple [OE][SM].

In order to solve these problems we will consider a new method which we think is closer to the idea of classical resolution principle [RJ]. Since the set INC will be reduced to the classical one (INC = {~p, p}). In this way we will give a set of operation, whose purpose is to find this classical inconsistency.

Before going on we return to an example. Consider again the set of clauses:

[](p v q)

<> ~p

[] ~ q

The set of these three clauses is inconsistent. Now we consider the two clauses [](p v q) and <> ~ p. Since []A & <> B → <>(A & B), it is possible to deduce in an informal way that the set {[](p v q), <> ~ p} is satisfiable, because there is a state, where the set {p v q, ~q} is satisfiable. Then from [](p v q) and <> ~p we can obtain <>q and the two clauses <> q and [] ~ q are inconsistent. From this we can deduce that the set INC can be simplified by breaking down the rule (*) into two new rules. Now we explain this more precisely. To this end we define a set of operations and properties.

Let C_1 and C_2 be two clauses. We define the operations:

$\Sigma(C_1,C_2)$ and $\Gamma(C_1)$, and the properties: (C_1,C_2) is resolvable (i.e. C_1 and C_2 are resolvable) and (C_1) is resolvable, recursively as follows:

Classical operations

a) $\Sigma(p, \sim p) = \emptyset$

And $(p, \sim p)$ is **resolvable.** p will be called a **resolved literal.**

b) $\Sigma((D_1 \vee D_2),F) = \Sigma(D_1,F) \vee D_2$

And if (D_1,F) is resolvable, then $((D_1 \vee D_2),F)$ is resolvable.

c) $\Sigma(D_1 \,\&\, F_1 \,\&\, D_2 \,\&\, F_2) = \Sigma(D_1,D_2) \,\&\, F_1 \,\&\, F_2$

And if (D_1,D_2) is resolvable, then $(D_1 \,\&\, F_1 \,\&\, D_2 \,\&\, F_2)$ is resolvable.

Modal operations

a) $\Sigma([\,]E, \Delta F) = \Delta\ \Sigma(E,F)$ provided that Δ is $[\,]$, or $<>$

And if (E,F) is resolvable, then $([\,]E, \Delta F)$ is resolvable.

b) $\Sigma([\,]E,F) = \Sigma(E,F)$

And if (E,F) is resolvable, then $([\,]E,F)$ is resolvable.

c) $\Gamma(E(\diamond (D \,\&\, D' \,\&\, F)) = E(<>(\Sigma(D,D') \,\&\, F))$

And if (D,D') is resolvable, then $(E(<>((D \,\&\, D') \,\&\, F))$ is resolvable.

4.1. If C_1 and C_2 are unit clauses (clauses with only one disjunct) and C_1 and C_2 are resolvable (or C_1 is resolvable), then a clause is called **resolvent** of C_1 and $C_2(C_1)$ if it is the result of substituting:

$\emptyset$ for every occurrence of $(\emptyset \,\&\, E)$

E for every occurrence of $(\emptyset \vee E)$

$\emptyset$ for every occurrence of $\Delta\ \emptyset$, where Δ is $[\,]$, or $<>$

in $\Sigma(C_1,C_2)(\Gamma(C_1))$, as many times as necessary.

We note by $R(C_1,C_2)$ (or $R(C_1)$) a resolvent of C_1 and $C_2(C_1)$ and by $Rp(C_1,C_2)(Rp(C_1))$ a resolvent of (C_1,C_2) with p as resolved literal.

4.2. Let C_1 v C and C_2 v C' be two clauses. The resolution rules:

1) $$\frac{C_1 \vee C \qquad C_2 \vee C'}{R(C_1,C_2) \vee C \vee C'}$$

is applied if C_1 and C_2 are resolvable.

And the rule:

2) $$\frac{C_1 \vee C}{R(C_1) \vee C}$$

is applied if C_1 is resolvable.

4.3. Let E(D v D v F) be a clause. The following rule will then be applied

3) $$\frac{E(D \vee D \vee F)}{E(D \vee F)}$$

4.4. Let S be a set a clause. A **deduction** of C from S is a finite sequence $C_1,\ldots,C_n$ such that:

C_n is C, and

C_i $(1 \leqslant i \leqslant n)$ is :

a clause of S, or
a clause obtained from C_j, $j < i$ using the inference rules 2) or 3) or a clause obtained from C_j and C_k, $j,k < i$, using the inference rule 1).

4.5. A deduction of the empty clause is called a **refutation.**

We give an elementary example to illustrate the method. Given the two unit clauses []p and <>(~p v q), a set of operations and properties corresponding to this set will be:

1. Σ([]p,<>(p v q)) = <>Σ(p,~ p v q).
   And if (p, ~p v q) is resolvable, then
   ([]p,<>(~p v q)) is resolvable.

2) Σ(p, ~p v q) = Σ(p, ~p) v q
   And if (p, ~ p) is resolvable then (p, ~ p v q) is resolvable.

3) Σ(p, ~p) = Ø
   And (p, ~ p) is resolvable. Therefore (p, ~ p v q) and ([]p,<>(~p v q) are resolvable and the inference rule 1) can be applied as follows:

   []p   <>(~p v q)
   ____
   <>q

   because <>q is the result of substituting q for (Ø v q) in <>(Ø v q).

Therefore in classical logic only one operation, Σ(p,~p), is sufficient to apply the resolution rule, while in modal logic more than one operation can be needed to do it.

Intuitively we say that if a set of clauses is inconsistent, then there is a state which is classically inconsistent. And the aim of the operations is to find such a state.

We return again to the example. Given the three clauses [](p v q), <>~p and []~q we obtain the following refutation:

[](p v q)   <>~p
____

using that:
Σ([](p v q), <>p) = <> (p v q, ~ p)
And Σ(p v q , ~p) = Ø v q

<>q   []~q
____
Ø

using that:
Σ(<>q,[]~q) = <>Σ(q,~q)
And Σ(q, ~q) = Ø

5. COMPLETENESS

5.1. A set of clauses S is unsatisfiable iff S is refutable.

To prove this theorem the following three lemmas are necessary.

5.2. The set $S = \{L_1,\ldots,L_{n_1},[]A_1,\ldots,[]A_{n_2},<>P_1,\ldots,<>P_{n_3}\}$ of unit clauses is unsatisfiable iff either $\exists A_i$ $1\leqslant i\leqslant n_2$ for which the set $\{L_1,\ldots,L_{n_1},[]A_1,\ldots,[]A_{i-1},A_i,[]A_{i+1},\ldots,[]A_{n_2}, <>P_1,\ldots,<>P_{n_3}\}$ is unsatisfiable or $\exists P_i$ $1\leqslant i\leqslant n_3$ for which $S_i = \{A_1\ldots,A_{n_3},P_i\}$ is unsatisfiable.

Proof.

a) suppose that $\{L_1,\ldots,L_{n_1},[]A_1,\ldots,[]A_{i-1},A_i,[]A_{i+1},\ldots, []A_{n_2},<>P_1,\ldots,<>P_{n_3}\}$ $1\leqslant i\leqslant n_2$ and $S_i = \{A_1,\ldots,A_{n_2},P_i\}$ $1\leqslant i\leqslant n_3$ are satisfiable. Then we can construct a model M satisfying S, from models M_i of S_i and a maximal consistent extension O of $\{L_1,\ldots,L_{n_1},A_1,\ldots,A_{n_2},<>P_1,\ldots,<>P_{n_3}\}$ that is different from the states of M^i. M is obtained by union of the M^i and O where the accessibility relation has been extended by a set of pairs (O,O^i) and (O,O) where O^i is a state in M_i such that: M_i,O^i sat S_i. Therefore it is easy to see that S is satisfiable in M.

b) The converse statement is obtained using the fact that $[](A \rightarrow B) \rightarrow ([]A \rightarrow []B)$, and that $[]A \rightarrow A$, the necessitation rule and propositional reasoning.

Then suppose $\{A_1,\ldots,A_{n_2},P_i\}$ is unsatisfiable then the following formulas are theorems:

1. $-\ \sim A_1 \vee\ldots\vee A_{n_2} \vee \sim P_i$
2. $-\ [](A_1 \& \ldots \& A_{n_2} \rightarrow \sim P_i)$
3. $-\ [](A_1 \& \ldots \& A_{n_2}) \rightarrow []\sim P_i$
4. $-\ \sim[]A_1 \vee\ldots\vee \sim[]A_{n_2} \vee \sim <>P_i$

And then $[]A_1$ &...& $[]A_{n_2}$ & $<>P_i$ is unsatisfiable.

The proof for the other case is analogous.

On the light of this lemma the modal operations in the resolution can be interpreted as the tool which prevents us to use formulas belonging to the sets S_i, S_j, if $i \neq j$ $ij = 0, \ldots, n_3$ to obtain inconsistency for set S.

For example for any formula $<>P_i$ $1 \leqslant n \leqslant n_3$ in S we obtain a set $S_i = \{A_1, \ldots, A_{n_2}, P_i\}$; from the modal operations point of view, this means that we can't define a rule as $\Sigma(<>P_i, <>P_j)$ And since the A_j, $j = 1, \ldots, n_2$ appears in S_i, the rule $\Sigma([]A_j, <>P_i)$ must be defined.

5.3. Given the two sets of unit clauses $S = \{L_i, \ldots, L_{n_1}, []A_1, \ldots, []A_{n_2}, <>(C_1$ &...& $C_{n_3}), \ldots, <>P_{n_4}\}$ and $S' = \{A_1, \ldots, A_{n_2}, C_1, \ldots, C_{n_3}\}$. If R is a refutation of S' then R can be transformed into a refutation of S.

Remark: to transform a refutation of S' into a refutation of S, it is sometimes necessary to modify the order in the application of rules in the refutation of S. We give the following two examples:

Example 1. Consider the set of clauses S = $\{[](p \vee q), [](\sim p \vee q), <>\sim q\}$. And S' = $\{p \vee q, \sim p \vee q, \sim q\}$. The refutation of S':

$$\frac{\dfrac{p \vee q \quad \sim q}{p} \qquad \dfrac{p \vee q \quad \sim q}{p}}{\emptyset}$$

must be reorganized in

```
p v q    ~p v q
---------------
         q          ~q
         -------------
               Ø
```

Because it is only in this way that we can obtain directly a refutation of S:

```
[](p v q)    []( ~p v q)
------------------------
          []q          <> ~q
          ------------------
                  Ø
```

Example 2. Consider the set of clauses S = {[](p v q), [](~p v t), <>(~q & ~t)}. And S' = {p v q,~p v t,~q,~t}. The refutation of S':

```
p v q     ~q        ~p v t     ~t
------------        -------------
     p                   ~ p
---------------------------------
              Ø
```

must be reorganized in

```
             ~p v t     ~t
             -------------
p v q               ~p
--------------------------
             q        ~q
             -----------
                  Ø
```

Because if is only in this way that we can obtain directely a refutation of S:

```
                [](~p v t)      <>(~q & ~t)
                ---------------------------
[](p v q)          <>(~q & ~p)
------------------------------
     <>(q & ~q)
     ----------
          Ø
```

And in consequence the proof of this lemma must proceed by induction on the number of inferences which use two formulas that belong to a conjunct governed by a <> .

Then an inference in a refutation R of S' with two premises D and D' is called **critical** iff some C_i (in the element $<>(C_1 \& \ldots \& C_{n_3})$ of S) are used to derive D and D'.

The proof of the lemma is obtained by induction on the number c(R) of critical inferences in R.

1. Suppose c(R) = 0. To obtain a refutation of S, every A_i is replaced by $[\,]A_i$, C_j by $<>(C_1 \& \ldots \& C_{n_3})$. And for every inference $\frac{B \quad B'}{B''}$ in R we have:

1.a. If B and B' have been replaced by []B and []B' respectively, then B" is replaced by []B"

1.b. If B and B' have been replaced by <> (B & F) and []B' (or []B and <>(B' & F)) respectively, then B" is replaced by <>(B" & F).

In other words the modal operation a) has been used.

2. Suppose c(R)>0 and I is the last critical inference in R.

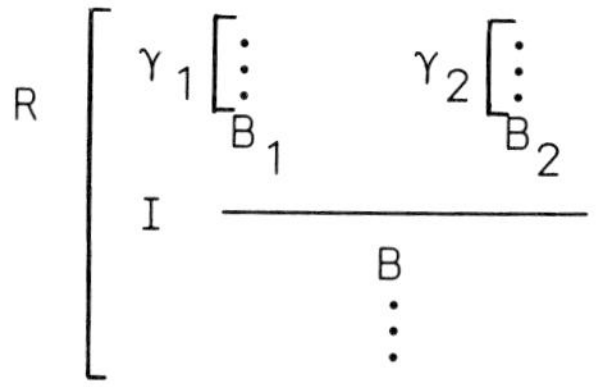

$$R \left[\begin{array}{c} \gamma_1 \left[\begin{array}{c} \vdots \\ B_1 \end{array} \right. \qquad \gamma_2 \left[\begin{array}{c} \vdots \\ B_2 \end{array} \right. \\ I \; \overline{\qquad\qquad\qquad} \\ B \\ \vdots \end{array} \right.$$

figure 1

Let $l(\gamma_i)$ be the number of inferences with two premises, between B_i and $C_1 \& \ldots \& C_{n_3}$ in γ_i. Now the proof is obtained by induction on $l(R) = l(\gamma_1) + l(\gamma_2)$.

2.1. If $l(R) = 0$. Then there is a deduction of B as in Fig.1. where each inference in γ_i has only one premise.

We consider the following two cases:

2.1.1. $i \neq j$, then a refutation of S will be:

$$
\begin{array}{c}
\vdots \\
\langle\rangle(C_i \;\&\; C_j \;\&\; F) \\
\vdots \\
\langle\rangle(B_i \;\&\; C_j \;\&\; F) \\
\vdots \\
\dfrac{\langle\rangle(B_1 \;\&\; B_2 \;\&\; F)}{\langle\rangle\,(B \;\&\; F)} \\
\vdots
\end{array}
$$

In other words the modal operation c) has been used.

2.1.2. $i = j$, then B can be deduced directly from C_i.

2.2. Suppose $l(R) = 1$. Then we can suppose that the refutation R is of the form:

$$
\dfrac{\dfrac{\begin{array}{cc}\vdots & \vdots \\ C_i & D\end{array}}{B_1 = Rp(C_i, D)} \qquad \begin{array}{c}\vdots \\ C_j\end{array}}{Rq(B_1, C_j) -}
\\
\vdots
$$

We consider the following two cases:

2.2.1. Suppose that q appears in C_i. Then the transformed deduction will be:

$$\dfrac{\dfrac{\begin{matrix}\vdots & \vdots \\ C_i & C_j\end{matrix}}{B_1 = Rq(C_i, C_j)} \qquad \begin{matrix}\vdots \\ D\end{matrix}}{Rp(B_1, D)}$$

Since $Rp(B_1,D)$ is identical to $Rp(B_1,C_j)$, we therefore obtain the result by induction hypothesis.

2.2.2. Suppose that q appears in D. The deduction is of the form:

$$\dfrac{\dfrac{\begin{matrix}\vdots & \vdots \\ C_i & D\end{matrix}}{B_1 = Rp(C_i, D)} \qquad \begin{matrix}\vdots \\ C_j\end{matrix}}{Rq(B_1, C_j)}$$

Then we have:

2.2.2.1. $i \neq j$. Then the transformed refutation of S will be:

$$\begin{matrix} \vdots \\ \dfrac{\dfrac{<>(C_i \;\&\; C_j \;\&\; F \qquad []D}{<>(Rp(C_i, D) \;\&\; C_j \;\&\; F)}}{<>(Rq(B_1 \;\&\; C_j) \;\&\; F)} \\ \vdots \end{matrix}$$

Therefore the modal operations a) and c) have been used.

2.2.2.2. The case where $i = j$ is trivial.

2.3. Suppose $l(R) = 2$ and the deduction is of the form:

$$\dfrac{\dfrac{\begin{matrix}\vdots & & \vdots\\ C_i & & D_1\end{matrix}}{B_1 = Rp(C_i, D_1)} \qquad \dfrac{\begin{matrix}\vdots & & \vdots\\ C_j & & D_2\end{matrix}}{B_2 = Rq(C_j, D_2)}}{\begin{matrix}Rr(B_1, B_2)\\ \vdots\end{matrix}}$$

Then we distinguish the following two cases:

2.3.1. Suppose that r appears in C_i and C_j then the transformed deduction will be:

$$\dfrac{\begin{matrix}\vdots\\ D_1\end{matrix} \qquad \dfrac{\begin{matrix}\vdots\\ C_i\end{matrix} \qquad \dfrac{\begin{matrix}\vdots & & \vdots\\ C_j & & D_2\end{matrix}}{B_2 = Rq(C_j, D_2)}}{B_3 = Rr(C_i, B_2)}}{Rp(D_1, B_3)}$$

And the proof is completed by the induction hypothesis.

2.3.2. Suppose that r appears in D_1 and D_2, then the transformed deduction will be:

$$\dfrac{\begin{matrix}\vdots\\ C_j\end{matrix} \qquad \dfrac{\begin{matrix}\vdots\\ C_i\end{matrix} \qquad \dfrac{\begin{matrix}\vdots & & \vdots\\ D_1 & & D_2\end{matrix}}{Rr(D_1, D_2) = B_4}}{Rp(C_i, B_4) = B_5}}{\begin{matrix}Rq(C_j, B_5)\\ \vdots\end{matrix}}$$

For the case where $l(\gamma_i) = 0$, for $i = 1$ or 2, the proof is obtained as in the case where $l(\gamma_1) > 2$ under-mentioned.

2.4. Suppose $l(R) > 2$ and the deduction of the form:

$$
\begin{array}{ll}
I_1 & \dfrac{\dfrac{\begin{matrix}\vdots & \vdots \\ C_i & D_1\end{matrix}}{D_2' = Rp_1(C_i, D_1)} \qquad \begin{matrix}\vdots \\ D_2\end{matrix}}{\vdots} \\
I_2 & \\
I_n & \dfrac{D_n' = Rp_{n-1}(D_{n-1}', D_{n-1}) \qquad \begin{matrix}\vdots \\ D_n\end{matrix}}{B_1 = Rp_n(D_n', D_n)} \qquad \begin{matrix}\vdots \\ C_j \\ \vdots \\ B_2\end{matrix} \\
I_{n+1} & \dfrac{\qquad\qquad\qquad\qquad}{\begin{matrix} B \\ \vdots \end{matrix}}
\end{array}
$$

We distinguish the following cases:

2.4.1. If p_2 appears in D_1. Then we exchange I_1 and I_2. And the proof is obtained by the induction hypothesis.

2.4.2. If p_2 appears in C_i. The proof then is obtained by induction on $l(\gamma_1)$.

2.4.2.1. If $l(\gamma_1) = 1$. Then the deduction

$$
\dfrac{\dfrac{\begin{matrix}\vdots & \vdots \\ C_i & D_1\end{matrix}}{D_2'} \qquad \begin{matrix}\vdots \\ D_2\end{matrix}}{Rp_2(D_2', D_2)}
\quad \text{is transformed into} \quad
\dfrac{\dfrac{\begin{matrix}\vdots & \vdots \\ C_i & D_2\end{matrix}}{D' = Rp_2(C_i, D_2)} \qquad \begin{matrix}\vdots \\ D_1\end{matrix}}{Rp_1(D', D_1)}
$$

Because p_2 appears in C_i.

2.4.2.2. If $l(\gamma_1) > 1$. Then there are the two subcases:

2.4.2.2.1. p_{n+1} appears in D_n'. Then the transformed deduction will be:

$$
\begin{array}{lll}
\vdots & \vdots & \\
C_i & D_1 & \vdots \\
\hline
D'_2 & C_j & \\
\vdots & \vdots & \\
D'_n & B_2 & \vdots \\
\hline
Rp_{n+1}(D'_n, B_2) & & D_n \\
\hline
 & B &
\end{array}
$$

And the proof of the lemma is obtained by induction hypothesis.

2.4.2.2.2. p_{n+1} appears in D_n. Then the transformed deduction will be:

$$
\begin{array}{llll}
\vdots & \vdots & & \\
C_i & D_1 & & \\
\hline
D'_2 & & C_j & \\
\vdots & & \vdots & \vdots \\
 & & B_2 & D_n \\
\hline
D'_n & & Rp_{n+1}(B_2, D_n) & \\
\hline
 & & B &
\end{array}
$$

And then we use the induction hypothesis of case 2.4.2.

And by consequence the lemma 5.4. has been proved.

5.4. Given the two sets of unit clauses $S = \{L_1, \ldots, L_{n_1}, []A_1, \ldots, []A_{n_2}, <> P_1, \ldots, <> P_{n_3}\}$ and $S' = \{L_1, \ldots, L_{n_1}, []A_1, \ldots, []A_{i-1}, A_i, []A_{i+1}, \ldots, []A_{n_2}, <>P_1, \ldots, <>P_{n_3}\}$, if R is a refutation of S' then R can be transformed into a refutation of S.

To obtain a refutation of S, from R, A_i is replaced by $[]A_i$.

And for every inference $\frac{B, A_i}{B'}$ in R we have either $\frac{B, []A_i}{[]B'}$ if B is of the form []B' or $\frac{B, []A_i}{B'}$ otherwise. In other words the modal operation a) or b) has been used.

Proof of theorem 5.1.

The proof of the theorem 5.1. is obtained by induction on $d'(S) = \sum_{i=1}^{n} d(C_i)$, where $C_i \in S$, and $d(C_i)$ is the degree of C_i.

If $d'(S) = 0$ then the theorem is proved by propositional methods [CHL].

Assume that the theorem holds when $0<d'(S)<n$. To complete the induction we consider $d'(S) = n+1$. The proof is obtained by induction on the number of v governing the disjuncts of the clauses in S (noted by $\nu(S)$).

If $\nu(S) = 0$, then using lemma 5.2., the induction hypothesis and lemmas 5.3. and 5.4. the result will be established. The induction step is proved as usual [CHL]. Let $C = E_1 \vee C_1$ be a clause in S. Construct separately refutations R_2 from $(S - \{C\}) \cup E_1)$ and R_1 from $(S - \{C\}) \cup C_1$ respectively.

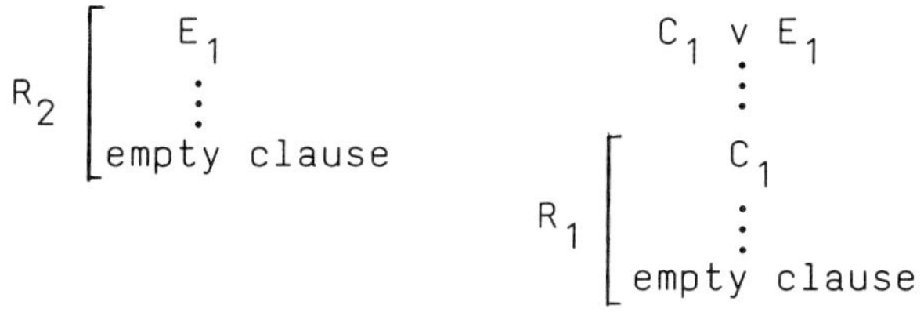

R_2 [E_1 ⋮ empty clause

$C_1 \vee E_1$ ⋮ R_1 [C_1 ⋮ empty clause

and put R_2 on the top of R_1 after adding C_1 to all clauses in R_2 (figure 2).

This kind of method can be extended easily to other modal logics. In this way a completeness theorem has been obtained for the propositional calculus K [FC4], S4 [FC6], S5 [FC5], for linear temporal logic of programs [CF2] and for a mutual belief logic [FS]. M. Cialdea [CM1] obtained the same result for a modal translation of the propositional intuitionistic calculus.

It is easy to see that for the set of prenex formulas of the first order modal calculus the method can be extended [FC1],[FC6],[FC7],[CF1] ; on the contrary when we consider the complete first order calculus some new problems arise, since permutation of quantifiers and modal operators don't hold, for example: $\exists x\ []p(x) \not\leftrightarrow []\ \exists xp(x)$. To solve this kind of problems it is necessary to dintinguish the skolem constant introduced by $\exists x$ in $\exists x\ []p(x)$ from the one, that is introduced by $\exists x$ in $[]\ \exists x\ xp(x)$ that can be different in each state [CM2].

6. DEDUCTION IN NORMAL FORM

By analogy with classical logic we can easily define a refinement of modal resolution i.e. normal form of deduction. We will present an extension of linear resolution to the modal operators. The definitions are essentially the same as for classical resolution. But each time a subformula of the modal formula is resolved, a **resolved** expression [CHL] is generated.

In what follows we suppose that clauses are ordered clauses; in other words the logical operators & and v are treated as non-commutative. We also have a mechanism for recording the information about resolved clauses. In this way the expression in a clause can by enclosed by $\boxed{}$. $\boxed{E}$ means that the expression E has been resolved.

Then we call a **sequence** an ordered clause with possible resolved expressions.

6.1. First formula of a sequence

Let S be a sequence. We call first formula of S the subformula of S defined recursively as follows:

- S is a first formula
- If F is a first subformula of S, and F is of the form $F_1 \vee F_2 \vee \ldots \vee F_n$, then F_1 is a first subformula
- If F is a first subformula of S and F is the form $F_1 \& F_2 \& \ldots \& F_n$, then each F_i is a first subformula
- If F is a first subformula of S and F is of the form $[]F_1$ or $<>F_1$, then F_1 is a first subformula.

6.2. Linear operations

Let C_1 and C_2 be two sequences. We define the operations

. $\Sigma(C_1,C_2)$
. $\Gamma(C_1)$

And the properties

. (C_1,C_2) is resolvable
. (C_1) is resolvable

recursively as follows:

- classical operations

Since the disjuncted clauses can possess the disjunction and conjunction symbols, it is necessary to introduce operations to manipulate these symbols by opposition to classical linear resolution where rules only in relation to the v operator are necessary.

. $\Sigma(A_1 \& \ldots \& A_n, A) = \Sigma(A_i, A) \& A_1 \& \ldots \& A_n$

And if (A_i,A) is resolvable, then $(A_1 \& \ldots A_n, A)$ is resolvable.

. $\Sigma(A, A_1 \& \ldots \& A_n) = \Sigma(A, A_i) \& A_1 \& \ldots \& A_n$

And if (A, A_i) is resolvable, then $(A, A_1 \& \ldots \& A_n)$ is resolvable

. $\Sigma(A_1 \vee \ldots \vee A_n, A) = \Sigma(A_1, A) \vee A_2 \vee \ldots \vee A_n$

And if (A_1, A) is resolvable then $(A_1 \vee \ldots \vee A_n)$ is resolvable

. $\Sigma(A, A_1 \vee \ldots \vee A_n) = A_1 \vee \ldots \vee A_{i-1} \vee \Sigma(A, A_i) \vee A_{i+1} \vee \ldots \vee A_n \vee \boxed{A}$

And if (A, A_i) is resolvable then $(A, A_1 \vee \ldots \vee A_n)$ is resolvable.

In this operation we express the fact that the expression A has been resolved, if (A, A_i) is resolvable.

. $\Sigma(p, \sim p) = \emptyset$

And $(p, \sim p)$ is resolvable in p.

- Reduction operations

. $\Gamma(E(\boxed{A} \vee A_1)) = E(A_1)$

. $\Gamma(E(A_1 \vee \ldots \vee \boxed{A_i} \vee \ldots \vee A_n)) = E(\Sigma(A_1, A_i) \vee A_2 \vee \ldots \vee \boxed{A_i} \vee \ldots \vee A_n)$

And if (A_1, A_i) is resolvable then $E(A_1 \vee \ldots \vee A_n)$ is resolvable.

. $\Gamma(E(A_1 \vee A_2 \vee A_1 \vee A_3)) = E(A_2 \vee A_1 \vee A_3)$

- Modal operations

. $\Sigma([\,]E, \Delta F) = \Sigma(E, F)$ provided that Δ is [], or <>.

And if (E,F) is resolvable, then $([\,]E, \Delta F)$ is resolvable

. $\Sigma([\,]E, F) = \Sigma(E, F)$

And if (E,F) is resolvable, then ([]E,F) is resolvable.

. $\Gamma(E(<>(A_1 \ \&\ldots\&\ A_n) = E(<>(\Sigma(A_i,A_j) \ \&\ A_1 \ \&\ldots\&\ A_n)))$

And if (A_i,A_j) is resolvable, then $(E(<>\ (A_1 \ \&\ldots\&\ A_n))$ is resolvable.

- Simplifications

. $\Gamma(E(A_1 \ \&\ \emptyset \ \&\ A) = \Gamma(E(\emptyset))$

. $\Gamma(E(A_1 \vee \emptyset \vee A) = E(A_1 \vee A)$

. $\Gamma(E\,\Delta(\emptyset)) = \Gamma(E(\emptyset))$ provided that $\Delta = [\,]$ or <> .

6.3. Let C_1 and C_2 be two sequences and p a first literal of C_1. If $(C_1,C_2)(C_1)$ is resolvable in p, then a remaining sequence obtained from $\Sigma(C_1,C_2)(\Gamma(C_1))$ after simplification and reduction will be called a **resolvent**.

6.4. Let S be a set of ordered clauses. A **linear deduction** from S of C_n, with a top ordered sequence C in S is a sequence $C_0,\ldots,C_n$ such that each C_i $(1 \leqslant i \leqslant n)$ is a resolvent either of C_{i-1}, or C_{i-1} against an ordered clause of S.

We give a modal version of a usual example for propositional calculus. Let us give the inconsistent set of clauses:

[](p v q)
[](~p v q)
[](p v ~q)
<>(~p v ~q)

Its refutation will be :

```
[](p v q)        [](~p v q)
------------------------------
[](q v p v q) v [](p v q)
------------------------------
[](p v q) v [](p v q)
------------------------------
[]q v [](p v q)        [](p v ~q)
------------------------------
[](p v q) v [](p v q) v [](q)      <>(~p v ~q)
------------------------------
<> (~q v q v p) v [](p v q) v []q v [](p v q)
------------------------------
<>p v [](p v q) v []q v [](p v q)
------------------------------
                Ø
```

where we have considered only the main steps in the proof.

6.5. Completeness

Let S be a set of ground sequences, and C a sequence in S. If S is unsatisfiable and S - {C} is satisfiable, then there is a linear refutation from S with top sequence C.

Proof. The proof proceeds by induction on the degree of S, using a reasoning similar to the one used in the case of modal resolution given in 5.

7. APPLICATIONS AND IMPLEMENTATIONS

Several implementations of this method have been done. For propositional S5, O. Galion [GO] has implemented a linear refinement in Pascal on a APPLE II. Rychlik [RP] and Kochut [KR] made a program which is a linear refinement, for a prenex subset of formulas of quantificational S5. It has been applied in an expert system in medecine. In [LE] and [FL] an implementation of linear refinement for the prenex formulas of linear temporal logic of programs has been done. It has been realized in Prolog on DEC LSI-11-23 and on DPS8. These programs have been used to prove properties of programs [CF2]. In the same way P. Combe and V. Leford [CL] devised a program for a subset of linear temporal formulas and used it for proving properties of network protocols.

One of the more important problems of these realisations is the difficulty for manipulating realistic sets of data. To solve this problem J. Henry [HJ] has implemented the modal resolution on a subset of prenex temporal formulas, that we will call Horn modal clauses, clauses with at most one of its propositional variables which is not negated. The programs have been realized in Prolog on a DPS8, and control facilities of Prolog can be used.

8. ACKNOWLEDGEMENTS

I wish to thank G. Minc and A. Raggio for their stimulating correspondance and encouragement, and E. Audureau, P. Enjalbert, D. Laurier and S. Soulhi for their comments.

9. BIBLIOGRAPHY

[AR] ANDERSON, R., Improved decision procedures for Lewis's calculus S4 and von Wright's calculus. J.S.L., Vol. 19, 3, (1953), pp. 101-214.

[BA] BAYART A., On truth-tables for M, B, S4 and S5. Logique et Analyse, Sept. 1970, pp. 335-375.

[CR] CARNAP, R., Modalities and quantification. J.S.L., vol.11, 2, (1946), pp. 33-64.

[CF1] CAVALLI, A.,R., FARIÑAS DEL CERRO, L., Specification and verification of networks protocols using temporal logic. Proceedings of the Sixième Colloque International sur la programmation, Springer-Verlag, LNCS n° 167, (1984).

[CF2] CAVALLI, A.R., FARIÑAS DEL CERRO, L., A decision method for linear temporal logic. Proceedings of the Seventh International Conference on Automata Deduction, Springer-Verlag, LNCS n° 170, (1984).

[CHL] CHANG, C., LEE, R., Symbolical logic and mechanical theorem proving. Academic Press, New-York, (1973).

[CM1] CIALDEA, M., Une méthode de résolution pour la logique intuitionniste propositionnelle. Rapport LSI, Université Paul Sabatier, Toulouse, (1983).

[CM2] CIALDEA, M., Ph.d. Thesis Université Toulouse III, in preparation.

[CL] COMBES, P., LEFORT, V., GENTIANE : un outil de preuve de cohérence de formules en logique temporelle. Note technique, CNET IPAA ILLC.

[FC1] FARIÑAS DEL CERRO, L., Déduction automatique et logique modale. Thèse d'Etat, Université de Paris VII, 1981.

[FC2] FARIÑAS DEL CERRO, L., Prolegomena for programming in modal logic. 6th European Meeting on Cybernetics and Systems Research, Vienne, Avril 1982, North-Holland, (1982).

[FC3] FARIÑAS DEL CERRO, L., Logique modale et processus communicants. Colloque AFCET "Les mathématiques de l'Informatique", Paris, (1982).

[FC4] FARIÑAS DEL CERRO, L., A simple deduction method for modal logic. Information Processing Letters, Vol. 14, n°2, (1982).

[FC5] FARIÑAS DEL CERRO, L., A deduction method for modal logic. Europeaan IA Conference, 11-14 July 1982, Orsay.

[FC6] FARIÑAS DEL CERRO, L., Les modalités de la correction totale. RAIRO Informatique Théorique, Vol. 16, n°4, (1982), pp. 349-363.

[FC7] FARIÑAS DEL CERRO, L., Temporal reasoning and termination of programs. Proceedings IJCAI 1983.

[FC8] FARIÑAS DEL CERRO, L., Un principe de résolution en logique modale. RAIRO Informatique Théorique, Vol. 18, n° 2, (1984).

[FL] FARIÑAS DEL CERRO, L., LAUTH, E., Raisonnement temporel : une méthode de déduction. Rapport LSI, Université Paul Sabatier, Toulouse, Novembre 1982.

[FS] FARIÑAS DEL CERRO, L., SOULHI, S., Mutual belief logic for processing definite reference. Proceedings of International Workshop on Natural Language Understanding and Logic Programming, Rennes, 18-20 Septembre 1984, North-Holland.

[GO] GALLION, O., Implémentation d'un démonstrateur de théorèmes. Rapport LSI, Université Paul Sabatier, Toulouse, Novembre 1981.

[HJ] HENRY, J., Implémentation d'un démonstrateur pour des clauses d'Horn en logique modale. Rapport LSI, Université Paul Sabatier, en préparation.

[KR] KOCHUT, E., RYCHLINK, P., Applications of modal logic in information systems, in Bolc, L., (ed.), Translating natural language into logical form, Springer, Symbolic Computation serie, to appear.

[LE] LAUTH, E., Une méthode de résolution linéaire ordonnées pour la logique temporelle linéaire. Rapport LSI-ENSEEITH, Université Paul Sabatier, Toulouse, (1983).

[LE] LEMMON, E., An introduction to modal logic. Amer. Philo. Generaly Monograph, (1977).

[SM] SHIMURA, M., Resolution in a new modal logic. Proceedings IJCAI 79, pp. 809-814.

[OE] ORLOWSKA, E., Resolution systems and their applications I & II. Fundamenta Informaticae, Vol. III, n°2, (1980), pp. 235-267 & 333-362.

[RJ] ROBINSON, J., A machine oriented logic based on the resolution principle. J. ACM, 12, (1965), pp. 23-41.

[RP] RYCHLINK, P., The use of modal default reasoning in information system. To appears in The Int. Journal of Man-Machine Studies.

Tools for Verifying Network Protocols

Brent Hailpern

IBM Thomas J. Watson Research Center
Yorktown Heights, New York 10598

Abstract: Recently, many papers have used temporal logic to verify network protocols [7, 16, 17, 23, 33, 35]. This paper serves as an introduction to the use of linear temporal logic and modular verification techniques for specifying and verifying network protocols.

Programs that implement computer communication protocols can exhibit extremely complicated behavior, because they must cope with asynchronous computing agents and the possibility of failures in the agents and in the communication medium. Surveys of the literature of protocol verification can be found in [3, 4, 8, 14, 32, 39]. Most approaches to verifying network protocols have been based upon reachability arguments for finite-state models of the protocols. This technique has the advantage of being easily automated. It encounters difficulties, however, as the state space of the protocol becomes large. Bochmann and Sunshine [3] present some techniques for reducing the state space: partial verification (not proving all aspects correct), combining or ignoring certain states, using assertions to classify states, and focusing search (not checking all paths). Recent work by Gouda [11] has extended finite-state techniques to proving correct data transfer.

In contrast, the approach described here models a protocol as a parallel program, and correctness proofs follow the Floyd-Hoare [9, 18] style of program verification. Logical assertions attached to the program abstract information from the representation of the state and allow reasoning about classes of states. This avoids the combinatorial explosion.

NATO ASI Series, Vol. F13
Logics and Models of Concurrent Systems
Edited by K. R. Apt

In this approach the network protocol system is modeled by a set of interacting modules that represent logical units of the system, such as the communication medium, transmitter, and receiver. Each module is specified (and verified) independently. The specification (and verification) of the system is implied by the conjunction of the specifications of the component modules. We will discuss tools for describing such modules: temporal logic, auxiliary variables (histories), and robust assertions. We will give some examples of assertions for some simple protocols, and will describe techniques used to prove protocols correct.

Modules

Reasoning about programs is much easier if the programs are composed of modules that can be understood independently. Modularity is a central part of many programming languages [24, 25, 37, 38, 40, 41], and has been exploited in specification and verification [10, 12, 15, 23, 34].

We view a concurrent program as a set of modules that interact through procedure calls. Systems based on message passing [10, 20] can be modelled using this technique by treating the communication medium as a module [16]. Modules may be either simple or compound. Simple modules consist of sequential code. Examples include processes, monitors [5, 19], ADA tasks [40], and distributed processes [6]; the last two combine process activity with monitor-like procedures. A compound module is simply a set of modules that we choose to treat as an entity; its components may be either simple or compound.

A module specification consists of three components: an invariant, a commitment, and a set of service specifications. The invariant describes the *visible* states of the module; these are the states that can exist when the module is about to interact with other modules. An invariant is a *safety* specification, because it guarantees that certain *bad* states never occur. The dual of safety is *liveness.* Liveness properties guarantee that certain *good* states will occur. For sequential programs, termination is usually the only liveness property of interest. However, many concurrent programs are intended to run forever; their liveness requirements typically take the form of a guarantee that some service is eventually provided. Liveness specifications, which are expressed using temporal logic, are given by the module commitment. Finally, the service specifications describe the safety and liveness properties of any procedures that the module makes available to its environment.

Temporal Logic and Liveness Properties

In this section we present a brief introduction to temporal logic. For more details on the theory of temporal logic and the use of temporal logic in program verification see [13, 22, 29, 30, 31].

Temporal logic provides operators for reasoning about the future, where the future is a program computation (a sequence of states that could arise during program execution). Informally, the first state in a computation represents the present; subsequent states represent the future. The temporal logic we are using has two operators $\Box$ (henceforth) and $\Diamond$ (eventually). The formula $\Box$ P (henceforth P) means "P is true for all states in the computation." The formula $\Diamond$ P is interpreted as "there is some state in the computation in which P is true." When we say that a temporal formula is true for a program, we mean that it is true for all computations of that program. Note that the present is considered to be part of the future in this temporal logic.

Temporal operators are particularly useful for stating liveness properties. For example, program termination, can be expressed by

$$\text{at P} \rightarrow \Diamond\ \text{after P},$$

where "at P" and "after P" are assertions that are true of states in which control is at the beginning or end of program P, respectively.

Combinations of the two temporal operators are also useful. The formula $\Box\,\Diamond$ P ("infinitely often P") implies that that are an infinite number of future states for which P is true. This combination is useful for stating recurring properties of a program, for example,

$$\Box \Diamond \text{(the buffer is not full).}$$

The formula $\Diamond \Box$ P ("almost always P") states that there is some point in the future at which P becomes true and remains true thereafter. An example of this combination is to state that deadlock is inevitable:

$$\Diamond \Box \text{(all processes are waiting).}$$

There are two temporal assertions about histories that prove useful in reasoning about liveness. The first is an assertion that the size of a given history will grow without bound. It is abbreviated as u(X), where

$$u(X) = \forall n(\Diamond(| X | > n)),$$

The second assertion states that a particular value occurs an unbounded number of times in the history. Letting c(X,m) be the number of occurrences of message m in history X, we have

$$uc(X,m) = \forall n(\Diamond(c(X,m) > n)).$$

Our basic liveness assumption concerning the execution of program statements is that they do not block:

$$\text{at s} \rightarrow \Diamond \text{ after s},$$

where s is any primitive statement that does not affect shared variables.

Auxiliary Variables

Auxiliary variables are used in specifications and proofs; they do not affect the results produced by a module. They are included in the code for convenience in reasoning about the program, but they do not have to be implemented.

One class of auxiliary variables that is useful for reasoning about parallel programs is the class of history variables. A history is an unbounded sequence that records the interactions between modules. History variables have frequently been used in reasoning about concurrent systems [10, 13, 16, 21, 27, 28]. The initial value of a history variable is the null sequence, and the only operation allowed is appending a new value.

We now introduce some notation for dealing with history variables. Suppose X and Y are history variables. We write

$$X \leq Y$$

to denote that X is a *prefix* (initial subsequence) of Y. This means that

$$| X | \leq | Y |$$

and the two sequences are identical in their first $| X |$ elements, where $| X |$ denotes the length of history X. If history X has elements a, b, c, d then we can write

$$X = < a \ b \ c \ d >$$

If $| X | = n$, then we may also write

$$X = < x_i >_{i=1}^{n}.$$

We denote concatenation of sequences by juxtaposition, that is,

$$X = < ab > < cd > = < abcd > .$$

We often speak about sequences of repeated messages. We use the superscripts * and + as defined for regular expressions:

$$X \in < x^* > \equiv \exists k \geq 0 (X = < x^k >)$$

$$X \in < x^+ > \equiv \exists k \geq 1 (X = < x^k >),$$

where $< x^k >$ denotes the message x repeated k times. These notations can also be combined. For example

$$X \in < x_i^+ >_{i=1}^{n}$$

means that X is a sequence that starts with one or more instances of x_1 , followed by one or more instances of x_2 , and so on, ending with one or more instances of x_n .

Another class of auxiliary variables, called private variables, are useful when dealing with inter-module procedure calls. It is convenient to specify the properties of these procedures in terms of variables that are local to both the called and calling modules. A variable x declared as private [27] in a module M will have one instance for each module that calls M, and the instance corresponding to caller C can be modified only when C calls M. Thus the private variable can be treated as if local in proofs of both M and C. Module M refers to C's version of x as x[C]; C refers to its version as x[*].

Module Specifications and Verification

We have already mentioned that module specifications contain an invariant, a commitment, and service specifications for each procedure. The service specifications express safety properties of the procedure by pre- and post-conditions, which have their usual partial-correctness interpretation. There is also a live-condition that describes liveness properties of the procedure; typically it gives conditions under which the procedure must terminate.

Ideally, the proof that a module meets its specifications should be independent of the code of other modules in the system. To achieve this, we require the assertions used in the specifications and proof of module m to be *robust* for m, meaning that no action of any other module can make the assertion false. One way of ensuring that an assertion is robust is to prove that it is invariant over every statement in the other modules of the system [26]. This approach does not meet our goals for modularity: we want assertions that can be determined to be robust without examining the code of other modules. We indicate below two kinds of assertions that satisfy this requirement. Our verification methodology depends on specifications being robust in modules where they appear, but it does not depend on the way robustness is established.

The simplest way of guaranteeing that a specification is robust for module m is to restrict it to variables that are local to m. With this approach, the invariant and commitment of a module must use only variables local to that module. The pre- and post-conditions of a service specification are a more complicated case. They must be robust for both the module being specified and the module that calls the procedure, because they will appear in proofs of both modules. For this reason, the pre- and post-conditions are restricted to variables that are local to both the calling and the called module: in effect, to procedure parameters and private variables of the called module. This makes private variables an important part of our approach.

An assertion can also be guaranteed robust for module m if it is *monotonic*, that is, once it becomes true it remains true forever. A monotonic predicate P is one that satisfies the temporal logic formula

$$P \rightarrow \Box P.$$

For example, a history variable can only be extended, never shrunk, so for any history variable h

$$\forall x(x \leq h \rightarrow \Box x \leq h).$$

Monotonic predicates are clearly robust for any module, because they can never be made false. More generally, an assertion is robust for m if it is monotonic with respect to any changes of variables not local to m. For example, if h is a non-local history variable and x is a local sequence, the assertion $x < h$ is robust for m, because it cannot be made false by changes to h. The robustness of this assertion can be deduced immediately from the monotonic growth of history variables. In our module specifications, we will sometimes explicitly mention other monotonic properties.

Now that we have indicated how modules are specified, let us consider their proof. For a simple module, the specifications are verified directly from the code, using proof rules for the language in which the module is written. We will not attempt to give such rules here; Howard has presented safety rules for monitors [21], while liveness rules have been discussed in [13, 29, 31]. Note that the proof of module A, which calls a procedure in module B, can use the service specifications of that procedure, without considering its code.

We require that the invariant of a simple module holds whenever the module is ready to interact with another module, either by accepting or by initiating a procedure call. At such times we will say that the module is *open*. Thus, a monitor is open when no process is executing within it, or when a process within it is ready to execute a call to a procedure in another module. Similarly, an ADA task is open when it is ready to call a procedure in another task or package, or when it is at a rendezvous point waiting for a call from another module. Requiring the invariant to hold when the module makes calls to another module is more strict than is often required; however, we will see that the result is a much more attractive interpretation of compound module invariants than would otherwise be possible. Verifying this extra requirement causes no difficulties.

For a compound module, the specifications are verified from the specifications of the components, without examining the code. The module invariant and commitment are verified by showing that they are implied by the conjunction of the component invariants and commitments. Procedures of the compound module may be procedures of some component, and in this case the service specifications of the component procedure can be carried over without change. Otherwise the service specifications are proved directly from the code.

There is an interesting point concerning the invariant of a compound module. Because it is implied by the conjunction of the component invariants, it must hold whenever all these invariants hold, that is, whenever all components of the compound module are open. Unfortunately, this may not convey much information, because it is likely that during execution of a system there will be few times when all of the modules are open. Fortunately, a much stronger interpretation of the compound module invariant is possible: at all times the variables in modules that *are* open have values that are consistent with the invariant.

Theorem: Suppose s is a state that can be reached during execution of a compound module M, and let x be a list of variables of components of M that are not open in s. Then, if the invariant of M is M.I, it is true in state s that $\exists x(M.I)$.

Proof sketch: Let c be a computation for M that ends in state s. We will not be too specific about how computations are expressed, but assume that a computation is a sequence of states together with the atomic actions that cause transitions between states. We will first derive a computation c' that ends in a state s' for which all modules are open, and all variables not in x have the same value as in s. We derive c' in a sequence of steps. Let $c_0 = c$, and derive c_{i+1} from c_i as follows. If all modules are open in the final state of c_i, let $c' = c_i$. If not, delete the last action in c_i from a module that is not open at the end of c_i; call this module n. Intuitively, this has the effect of *backing up* the computation by one step of n. The resulting sequence c_{i+1} is still a legitimate computation because the deleted action could affect only variables of n, and these variables are not accessible to subsequent actions of c_i. Also, any variables changed by the deleted action were in the set x, so all variables not in x have the same value in the last states of c_i and c_{i+1}.

The computation c' is thus obtained from c by backing up some modules to a point where all modules are open. In s', the final state of c', the compound invariant M.I must hold because all modules are open. Moreover, $\exists x(M.I)$ holds in state s because the values of all variables not in x are the same in s and s', and M.I holds in s'. **(End of proof sketch)**

Informally, the theorem above suggests that the module invariant is in some sense close to the visible behavior of the system it describes. More formally, this result allows us to make deductions about observable behavior of the system. In many cases we can derive useful information about the variables of a module based on the environment in which it is used. For example, suppose simple module A is part of compound module B, and that assertion P on the variables of A is implied by B's invariant. Then we can conclude that P is true whenever A is open, and not just when all modules of B are open. Note that it would be impossible to prove P's invariance directly from the code of A if it is only invariant in the environment of B.

Example: Bounded Buffer

As an example consider a bounded buffer. We assume that there are p producer processes and one consumer process; thus the buffer has a global input history, as well as private input histories for each producer. To be completely rigorous, we should have two output histories: a global one for the module and a private one for the consumer. An invariant would then state that the two histories are always equal. Because there is only one consumer process, we will treat the output history of the module as private to the consumer when appropriate.

```
Variables
    in: auxiliary history of item, initially null
    out: auxiliary history of item, initially null
    privIn: private auxiliary history of item,
            initially null
    empty: auxiliary boolean, initially true
    full: auxiliary boolean, initially false
Invariant
   out ≤ in  ∧  isMerge(in,privIn)  ∧  (empty  →  ¬ full)

Monotonic
    History variables are monotonic as described above.
```

Here isMerge is a predicate that is true if its first argument is some merge of the instances of its second argument. The first clause of the invariant states that the output history of the buffer is a prefix of the input history. The second clause states that "in" is composed of exactly those items that have been partitioned among the private histories privIn. The third clause asserts that empty and full are mutually exclusive conditions. The buffer has no liveness commitment that is independent of the procedures it provides to its environment. It provides two such procedures: put and get.

```
Operations


    put (i: item)
        pre:  true
        post: in[*] = in'[*] @ i
        live:
 ((at put ∧ □ ◇ ¬ full) ⇨ after put) ∧ (at put ⇨ ¬ empty)
    get (var i: item)
        pre:  true
        post: out = out' @ i
        live:
  ((at get ∧ ◇ ¬ empty) ⇨ after get) ∧ (at get ⇨ ¬ full)
```

We use @ as the history concatenation operator; ⇨ indicates temporal implication ("a ⇨ b" is defined as □ (a → ◇ b)). The primed auxiliary variables in the post-conditions represent the values those variables had before the operation had executed (thus, x' in a post-condition has the same value as x in the pre-condition). We also use the convention that private variables not mentioned by pre-/post-conditions of an operation are not changed by that operation.

The specification of the put procedure states that the operation can be called at any time. If put terminates then the private input history of the calling process has been increased by exactly the item passed to put; The operation will terminate if the buffer is repeatedly not full; "◇ ¬ full" is not enough to guarantee termination because another process could use up an empty space and leave this process blocked. Note that if only one process n can call put on a buffer, then "◇ ¬ full" does suffice, because the assertion "¬ full" is then robust with respect to n: no process other than n can cause "full" to become true. Furthermore, calling the put procedure guarantees that eventually the buffer will be empty (possibly at the time that put is called). The specification of the get procedure is similar.

Example: Unreliable Communication Medium

An ideal application for the tools listed above is to specify a module that does not exist, in that there is no code written for it. For example, an unreliable communication medium can be represented as a module [16]. Unlike the bounded buffer, the medium can lose, duplicate, and reorder messages. The specification will serve to describe exactly how unreliable the medium is.

Consider medium m, with input history A and output history B. The medium provides three services: send, receive, and exists. We will assume exactly one process calls "send" and exactly one process calls "receive" and "exists." More than one process can be managed using the private histories of the bounded buffer example. The send and receive procedure correspond to the get and put procedures of the buffer example. The exists procedure returns "true" if a message exists to be received and "false" otherwise.

The module invariant is weaker than that of the FIFO buffer. We require that the medium not create messages out of thin air,

$$m \in B \rightarrow m \in A.$$

In other words, nothing comes out that was not put in. The medium makes two commitments. The first defines the function of the exists function, that is, if an unbounded number of messages are sent to the medium, then the value of the exists function will be true infinitely often.

$$u(A) \rightarrow \Box\Diamond(\text{exists} = \text{true})$$

The second commitment constrains the medium to be honest with respect to a particular message. If a particular message is sent an unbounded number of times and and unbounded number of messages are received, then that particular message must be received eventually.

$$(\mathrm{uc}(A,m) \wedge \mathrm{u}(B)) \rightarrow \Diamond m \in B$$

Note that in the specification of the send operation, there is no bound on the medium: we assume that if too many messages are sent, the medium may lose them. The send and exists operations always terminate; the receive operation only terminates if a message exists to be received. We are assuming that "exists = true" is a robust assertion: no process, other than the unique receiver, can falsify it.

```
send (m: message)
     pre:   true
     post:  A = A′ @ <m>
     live:  at send ⇨ after send
receive (var m: message)
     pre:   true
     post:  B = B′ @ <m>
     live:  at receive ∧ ◊ exists=true  ⇨  after receive
exists
     pre:   true
     post:  true
     live:  at exists ⇨ after exists
```

The pre and post assertions of "exists" are both "true", which gives no safety information about the operation. In fact, "exists" is only used in reasoning about the liveness properties of the receive operation.

Global Constants

Network data-transfer protocols usually need to prove that their output is a prefix of their input (out $\leq$ in). The input and output, however, are probably not connected to the same module. In addition, intermediate stages of the network may not preserve transitive relations such as prefix ($\leq$) and equality ($=$), because order may not be preserved by unreliable media (the correct order may be reconstructed immediately before output). In order for a system assertion to be a conjunction of module assertions, we may have to distribute some common knowledge to the modules in the guise of auxiliary constants.

For example, we might say the system input is an unbounded sequence of values: $D \equiv d_1, d_2, \ldots$. The input module may then describe its input history "ih" as a prefix of D:

$$\exists n(ih = \langle d_i \rangle_{i=1}^{n}).$$

Similarly, if the identities and relative positions of the messages can be preserved throughout the system, the output should be able to conclude (given the appropriate hypothesis) that its output history "oh" is a prefix of D:

$$\exists m(oh = \langle d_i \rangle_{i=1}^{m}).$$

If when these invariants are composed, all hypotheses are fulfilled and we can show that $m \leq n$, then we can conclude that $oh \leq ih$. For more details see [16].

The global constant meets our criteria of a robust assertion: it cannot be made false by any module. As long as the constants are auxiliary, they cannot be used in any code, and hence the common knowledge need not exist in reality.

Creating Order Out of Chaos

Unreliable media present the problem of preserving the order of messages sent to the protocol system internally when that order may become confused. The protocols discussed in [16, 17] all use some form of sequence number attached to the messages sent on the unreliable media and some form of acknowledgment to coordinate which messages have been successfully received.

In Stenning's Data Transfer Protocol [36], the transmitter module sends a packet (n, m) to the receiver module along medium 1 (see Figure 1). Here m is the contents of the message and n is a potentially unbounded sequence number. The media are

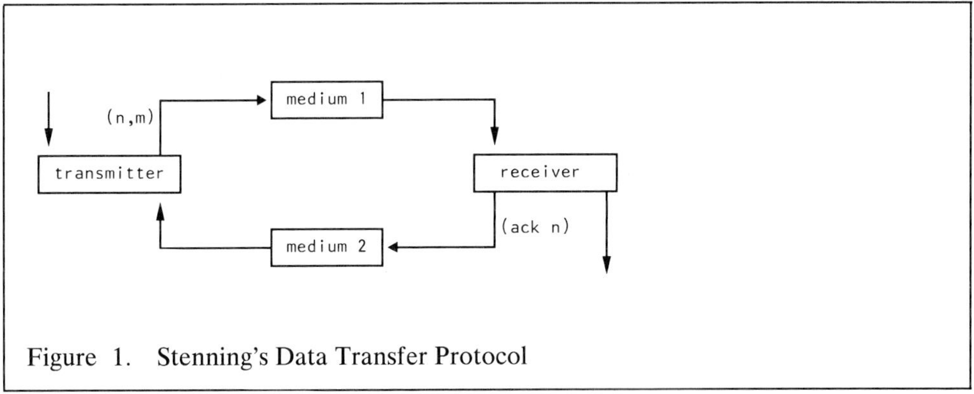

Figure 1. Stenning's Data Transfer Protocol

unreliable, as described above: messages can be lost, duplicated, or reordered. The receiver sends an acknowledgment, along medium 2, indicating the number of the highest sequence number received, such that all lower sequence numbers have been received.

The Alternating Bit Protocol [2] is similar to Stenning's protocol, in that sequence information is sent along one medium and an acknowledgment with sequence information is sent along a return medium. The difference is that the Alternating Bit uses only one bit of sequence information. The unreliable medium is not permitted to reorder messages, so the transmitter repeatedly sends the first message with sequence bit 1 until its detects an acknowledgment with sequence bit 1. The next message has sequence bit 0, then 1, then 0, and so on. The protocol is further complicated because the medium can corrupt messages, as well as, lose and duplicate them. The proof is similar to the proof of Stenning's protocol, except that the sequence number must be extracted from the history of sequence bits attached to the messages and acknowledgments. This is not a simple counting function, because the corrupted messages must be filtered out of the message histories.

Finally, Aho's protocol [1] describes a pair of communicating finite state machines. The protocols were invented to find the fewest number of states required to communicate over particular kinds of unreliable media. No sequence information is attached to the data, but by interpreting the pattern of messages sent, each module (and the proof of each module) can determine the sequence number of the current message. The system proof reduces to the proof of the Alternating Bit Protocol.

Conclusion

This paper gave a taste of some of the tools used to specify and verify network protocols. These tools included temporal logic, auxiliary variables, robust assertions, and modular proofs. No such introduction can discuss the meat of the techniques nor give the details of the protocols or proofs. Please consult the references to fill in the gaps and see some other tools and techniques.

Acknowledgments

More than just thanks are just due to Susan Owicki. She supervised my original research on verification of network protocols and contributed many fundamental concepts to our joint work. She is due the credit for the notion of a "robust assertion" and the one theorem presented in this paper. I would also like to thank Krzysztof Apt, who organized the INRIA/NATO course and convinced me that the world might tolerate yet another paper on verifying network protocols using temporal logic.

References

1] A. V. Aho, J. D. Ullman, and M. Yannakakis. Modeling communications protocols by automata. *Twentieth Annual Symposium on Foundations of Computer Science*, (San Juan, P.R.) pages 267-273, IEEE, October 1979.

2] K. A. Bartlett, R. A. Scantlebury, and P. T. Wilkinson. A note on reliable full-duplex transmissions over half-duplex links. *Communications of the ACM* **12** (5): 260-261, May 1969.

3] Gregor V. Bochmann and Carl A. Sunshine. Formal methods in communication protocol design. *IEEE Transactions on Communications* **COM-28** (4):624-631, April 1980.

4] Gregor V. Bochmann. A general transition model for protocols and communication services. *IEEE Transactions on Communications* **COM-28** (4):643-650, April 1980.

5] Per Brinch Hansen. *Operating System Principles.* Prentice-Hall, 1973.

6] Per Brinch Hansen. Distributed processes: A concurrent programming concept. *Communications of the ACM,* **21** (11): 934-941, November 1978.

7] E. M. Clarke, E. A. Emerson, and A. P. Sistla. Automatic verification of finite state concurrent systems using temporal logic specifications: A practical approach. *Tenth Annual ACM Symposium on Principles of Programming Languages*, (Austin) pages 117-126, January 1983.

8] Andre A. S. Danthine. Protocol representation with finite state models. In Paul E. Green, editor, *Computer Network Architectures and Protocols*, pages 579-606. Plenum Press, 1982.

9] Robert W. Floyd. Assigning meanings to programs. *Proceedings of Symposia in Applied Mathematics XIX*, pages 19-32, American Mathematical Society, 1967.

10] Donald I. Good and Richard M. Cohen. Principles of proving concurrent programs in Gypsy. *Sixth Annual ACM Symposium on Principles of Programming Languages*, (San Antonio) pages 42-52, January 1979.

11] Mohamed G. Gouda. On "A simple protocol whose proof isn't": The state machine approach. To appear in *IEEE Transactions on Communications*, April 1985.

12] John V. Guttag, Ellis Horwitz, and David Musser. Abstract data types and software validation. *Communications of the ACM,* **21** (12):1048-1064, January 1979.

13] Brent T. Hailpern. *Verifying Concurrent Processes Using Temporal Logic.* PhD thesis, Stanford University, 1980. *Lecture Notes in Computer Science*, volume 129. Springer Verlag, 1982.

14] Brent T. Hailpern. Specifying and verifying protocols represented as abstract programs. In Paul E. Green, editor, *Computer Network Architectures and Protocols*, pages 607-624. Plenum Press, 1982.

15] Brent Hailpern and Susan Owicki. Modular verification of concurrent programs. *Proceedings of the Ninth ACM Symposium on Principles of Programming Languages* (Albuquerque), pages 322-336, January 1982.

16] Brent Hailpern and Susan Owicki. Modular verification of computer communication protocols. *IEEE Transactions on Communications* **COM-31** (1):56-68, January 1983.

17] Brent Hailpern. A Simple Protocol Whose Proof Isn't. To be published in *IEEE Transactions on Communications*, April 1985.

18] C. A. R. Hoare. An axiomatic basis for computer programming. *Communications of the ACM* **12** (10):576+, May 1969.

19] C. A. R. Hoare. Monitors: An operating system structuring concept. *Communications of the ACM*, **17** (10): 549-557, October 1974.

20] C. A. R. Hoare. Communicating sequential processes. *Communications of the ACM* **21**(8): 666-677, August 1978.

21] John H. Howard. Proving monitors. *Communications of the ACM* **19** (5):273-279, May 1976.

22] Leslie Lamport. "Sometimes" is sometimes "not never": On the temporal logic of programs. *Seventh Annual ACM Symposium on Principles of Programming Languages*, (Las Vegas) pages 174-185, January 1980.

23] L. Lamport. Specifying concurrent program modules. *ACM Transactions on Programming Languages and Systems* **5**(2): 190-222, April 1983.

24] B. H. Liskov, R. A. Atkinson, T. Bloom, J. E. Schaffert, R. W. Scheifler, and A. Snyder. *CLU Reference Manual. Lecture Notes in Computer Science*, volume 114. Springer-Verlag, 1981.

25] James G. Mitchell, William Maybury, and Richard Sweet. Mesa language manual (version 5.0). Technical report CSL-79-3, Xerox Palo Alto Research Center, April 1979.

26] Susan S. Owicki and David Gries. Verifying properties of parallel programs: An axiomatic approach. *Communications of the ACM* **19** (5):279-285, May 1976.

27] Susan S. Owicki. Specifications and proofs for abstract data types in concurrent programs. In F. L. Bauer and M. Broy, editors, *Program Construction*, pages 174-197. Springer Verlag, 1979.

28] Susan S. Owicki. Specifications and verification of a network mail system. In F. L. Bauer and M. Broy, editors, *Program Construction*, pages 198-234. Springer Verlag, 1979.

29] Susan Owicki and Leslie Lamport. Proving liveness properties of concurrent programs. *ACM Transactions on Programming Languages and Systems* **4** (3):455-495, July 1982.

30] Amir Pnueli. The temporal logic of programs. *The Eighteenth Annual Symposium on Foundations of Computer Science*, (Providence) pages 46-57, IEEE, October 1977.

31] Amir Pnueli. The temporal semantics of concurrent programs. *Semantics of Concurrent Computation*, pages 1-20. Springer-Verlag, 1979.

32] Richard Schwartz and P. Michael Melliar-Smith. From state machines to temporal logic: Specification methods for protocol standards. *IEEE Transactions on Communications* **COM-30** (12):2486-2497, December 1982.

33] Richard L. Schwartz, P. M. Melliar-Smith, and Friedrich H. Vogt. An interval logic for higher-level temporal reasoning. *Second Annual ACM Symposium on Principles of Distributed Computing*, (Montreal) pages 173-186, August 1983.

34] Mary Shaw, William A. Wulf, and Ralph L. London. Abstraction and verification in Alphard: Defining and specifying iteration and generators. *Communications of the ACM,* **20** (8):553-564, August 1977.

35] Dennis E. Shasha, Amir Pnueli, and William Ewald. Temporal verification of carrier-sense local area network protocols. IBM Research Report RC 10132, Yorktown Heights, New York, August 1983.

36] N. V. Stenning. A data transfer protocol. *Computer Networks* **1** (2): 99-110, September 1976.

37] Robert E. Strom and Shaula Yemini. NIL: An integrated language and system for distributed programming. *SIGPLAN '83 Symposium on Programming Language Issues in Software Systems* (San Francisco), pages 73-82, August 1983.

38] Robert Strom and Shaula Yemini. The NIL distributed systems programming language: A status report. IBM Research Report RC 10864, Yorktown Heights, New York, December 1984.

39] Carl A Sunshine. Formal techniques for protocol specification and verification. *Computer* **12** (9):20-27, September 1979.

40] United States Department of Defense. *Reference Manual for the Ada Programming Language.* ACM-AdaTEC, July 1982.

41] N. Wirth. Modula: A language for modular multiprogramming. *Software Practice and Experience* **7**(1): 3-35, January-February 1977.

An Axiomatic Semantics of Concurrent Programming Languages

Leslie Lamport*

1 An Introduction to this Paper

A large body of research on the logic of concurrent programs may be characterized as the "axiomatic" school. Members of this school reason about safety properties ("something bad never happens") in terms of invariance, and liveness properties ("something good eventually does happen") using temporal logic.

While they are quite successful at proving properties of a given program, axiomatic methods have not provided a satisfactory semantics for concurrent programming languages. Axiomatic methods usually reason about the entire program, while a semantics should be compositional—deriving the meaning of a program from the meanings of its components. Even the Generalized Hoare Logic described in [4] and [9], which looks compositional, actually assumes a context of a complete program. The only attempt we know of at a truly compositional axiomatic semantics for concurrent programs that handles both safety and liveness properties is given in [14]. However, while it is axiomatic in a strict logical sense, that approach is not in the spirit of the axiomatic school because it essentially defines a new temporal logic operator for every programming-language construct.

In this paper, I present a new compositional, truly axiomatic semantics for concurrent programming languages. It is based upon temporal logic, but employs five fundamental ideas beyond those found in most temporal logic methods:

1. The addition of action predicates to describe "who" performs an action.
2. Defining an assertion to be true of a statement only if it is true of every program containing that statement.
3. The introduction of renaming operations that map an assertion about a statement S into an assertion about a larger statement containing S as a substatement.
4. Defining the relations between control points, described in [4] as state predicates, to be aliasing relations among variables.
5. Allowing "stuttering" actions, so an atomic operation is represented by a finite sequence of actions, only the last one having any effect.

*Work Supported in part by the National Science Foundation under grant number MCS-8104459 and by the Army Research Office under grant number DAAG29-83-K-0119.

NATO ASI Series, Vol. F13
Logics and Models of Concurrent Systems
Edited by K. R. Apt

The first idea was developed by Susan Owicki and myself in the late 1970's, and was published in [6]. (It was developed independently, in different contexts, by other researchers [1].) The second and third ideas were developed by me shortly afterwards. The second was also used in [6], though not featured prominently there. The third idea has never appeared in print, though I have talked about it in lectures starting in 1981. The fourth idea was discovered by Fred Schneider and myself in the spring of 1984 [10]. The fifth idea has been present in all of my work on temporal logic, starting with [5]. I was originally led to it by my philosophical objections to the "next time" operator; only later did I recognize its practical significance [8].

The first two ideas were used in [14], but they are not enough to permit a compositional semantics based upon a simple temporal logic. Combined with the third idea, they do permit a compositional semantics, but a semantics that I did not find satisfying. It seemed like a large, complicated structure had to be erected solely to reason about program control, making the enterprise of dubious merit. It was the fourth idea that gelled the method into a coherent form. The apparatus for handling program control was no longer an *ad hoc* "Kludge". Rather, it was the appropriate structure to deal with aliasing. Aliasing was not considered in other approaches, but it is a problem that must be dealt with in any realistic language, if only to handle procedure calls. The fifth idea is not needed for the semantics itself; in fact the semantics would be somewhat easier to understand had I abandoned it and employed the next-time operator favored in most other temporal logic approaches. However, allowing stuttering actions enables the semantics to address the practical issue of what it means for a compiler to be correct.

In this paper, I develop these five ideas, and show how they lead to a method for defining the semantics of concurrent programming languages. A complete semantics is given only for a simple language. However, the approach is "meta-compositional" in the sense that the meaning of each language construct is defined independently of the other constructs in the language. The semantics of a richer language can be given by defining the meanings of its additional constructs, without changing the meanings of the constructs from the simple language. (This is not the case in [14] where, for example, the axioms for the assignment statement would be invalid if an unfair **cobegin** were added to the language.) I will indicate the power of my method by informally describing how the meanings of some more complicated language constructs can be defined.

2 An Introduction to Semantics

2.1 What Are Semantics?

The syntax of a programming language defines the set of syntactically well-formed programs of that language. However, a program is more than just a string of characters; there should be a well-defined set of possible results of executing the program. The purpose of a semantics is to assign a mathematical *meaning* to each syntactically correct program that describes the effect of executing it.

I will regard a program Π to be a syntactic object, and denote by $\mathcal{M}[\![\Pi]\!]$ the mathematical object denoting its meaning. To define a formal semantics, one must specify the mapping $\Pi \rightarrow \mathcal{M}[\![\Pi]\!]$.

What is the purpose of a formal semantics? One purpose is to help us to understand the language. However, "understanding" is too vague to usefully characterize a formalism. I propose that a formal semantics should provide a formal basis for the following:

1. Deducing properties of a program written in the language.

2. Deciding if a compiler is correct, given a formal semantics for the target language into which the programs are compiled.

A semantics should provide a formal foundation, but not necessarily a practical method, for doing these things. A method for deducing properties of a program is called a *proof system*. A proof system is used to decide if a program works properly; a semantics is used to decide if a programming language is defined properly. One wants to reason about programs at a high level, hiding as much detail of the language as possible; a semantics should expose the language details. Although a semantics allows one, in principle, to verify properties of programs, its real purpose is to explain the language. A semantics should be used to verify the correctness of a proof system; it need not provide a practical method for reasoning about programs.

Programs can be very large and complicated. We want to reduce the problem of understanding a complex program to that of understanding its components. The meaning of a program should therefore be defined in terms of the meanings of its components. We must therefore define the meaning not just of an entire program, but of individual components—usually individual program statements. So, $\mathcal{M}[\![S]\!]$ must be defined for any program statement S, and it must be defined in terms of the substatements of S. For example, $\mathcal{M}[\![S_1; S_2]\!]$ should be defined in terms of $\mathcal{M}[\![S_1]\!]$ and $\mathcal{M}[\![S_2]\!]$. I will say that a semantics with this property is *compositional*.[1]

When defining a formal semantics, the first thing one has to decide is what kind of object $\mathcal{M}[\![S]\!]$ should be. The execution of a statement in a sequential program is usually considered to start in some input state and produce an output state, and $\mathcal{M}[\![S]\!]$ is defined to be a mathemtical object that describes the relation between the input and the output states. One way of doing this is to define $\mathcal{M}[\![S]\!]$ to be a set of ordered pairs of states.

Concurrent programs cannot be described with such a simple input/output semantics. Consider the following two program statements, where angle brackets denote indivisible atomic operations.

1. $\langle\, x := x + 1\,\rangle$

2. **begin** $\langle\, x := x + y\,\rangle$;
   $\langle\, x := x - y + 1\,\rangle$
   end

These statements both have the same relation between input and output states—they both increment the value of x by one. However, they are not equivalent when used as

[1]The terms *denotational*, *syntax-directed*, and *modular* have also been used to denote this property.

part of a concurrent program. Executing the first always has the effect of adding one to x, but executing the second can have a very different effect if the value of y is changed by some other process between the two assignments to x.

A semantics for a concurrent programming language must define the meaning of a statement in terms of its behavior. There are two fundamentally different approaches to doing this. The first approach is to define the meaning of a statement S in terms of the effects it produces that are "visible" outside S. For example, in a shared-variable language, the only visible effects of executing a statement are changes to shared variables. The alternative approach to defining the semantics of concurrent languages defines the meaning of a statement in terms of complete behaviors, which include all the effects of a statement's actions, whether externally visible or not. In most languages, these invisible effects include changes to the control state (the values of "program counters").

An approach that mentions only visible effects is very appealing, and it has been taken by a number of researchers [3,11]. For many years, I regarded it as the proper way to think about programs, and found it unnatural to reason about things like the control state that are internal to the program. However, years of experience reasoning about concurrent programs has led me to conclude that one should think about them in terms of the complete state, including externally invisible compents of the state. I will not attempt to justify this conclusion here, and will simply adopt the second approach, defining the meaning of a program in terms of complete behaviors that describe the internal as well as the externally-visible effects of program operations.

Having decided that the meaning of a program is its set of possible behaviors, we must decide what a behavior is. The simplest notion of a behavior is a sequence of states. Each action of the program transforms the state. Nondeterminism, leading to sets of behaviors, appears when there are several choices of a possibile next state from the same current state.

It is sometimes argued that a sequence of states cannot adequately model the execution of a concurrent program because it has no notion of concurrent activity, and that one should instead use a partially ordered set of actions. However, a partially ordered set contains exactly the same information as the set of all total orderings consistent with the partial order. Since the meaning of a statement is the *set* of behaviors, which includes all possible sequences that represent the real, partially ordered set of actions, nothing has been lost by considering sequences. The basic assumptions being made are that the execution of a program consists of discrete atomic actions, and the possible effect of an atomic action depends only upon the current state. It appears that any digital system can be accurately modeled in this way by making the atomic actions small enough and including enough information in the current state.

It turns out that to define the semantics of concurrent languages, one needs more information about a behavior than just the sequence of states; one must also know "who" performed the actions. For example, the natural definition of a fair **cobegin** states that in each infinite behavior, every nonterminating process performs infinitely many actions. Formalizing this definition requires the ability to decide which process performs each action. I will therefore define a behavior to be a sequence of the form:

$$s_0 \xrightarrow{\alpha_1} s_1 \xrightarrow{\alpha_2} \cdots$$

where the s_i are states and the α_i are actions. Fairness of a **cobegin** can be expressed by stating that for every process and every n: if there is no state s_i with $i > n$ in which the process has terminated, then infinitely many of the α_i are actions of that process. I will explain later exactly what states and actions are.

The semantics that I am aiming for is an axiomatic one, in which the meaning of a program is a set of axioms in a formal system. An important advantage of an axiomatic semantics is that it is very formal. A formal mathematical system is one in which reasoning can be reduced to a strict application of axioms and inference rules. Automated deduction systems can usually be applied only to a formal system. A semantics in which $\mathcal{M}[\![S]\!]$ is defined to be a set of sequences is really semi-formal, based upon the informal mathematical concepts of sets and sequences. Formalizing it requires formalizing these mathematical concepts. With an axiomatic semantics, this extra step is unnecessary; $\mathcal{M}[\![S]\!]$ is already a set of axioms in a formal system.

The problem with an axiomatic semantics is that one can understand the meaning of a formal logical system only by constructing a semantic model for it in terms of concepts that we already understand. Having constructed a semantics in which $\mathcal{M}[\![S]\!]$ is a set of axioms in some formal system is only half the job; we also have to define a semantics for the formal system in terms of well-understood mathematical concepts.

I will give a temporal logic semantics—one in which the axioms are temporal logic formulas. I will rely upon the usual semantic model of temporal logic, described later, to provide a basis for an intuitive understanding of the axioms.

2.2 Different Kinds of Semantics

2.2.1 Behavioral Semantics

An obvious method of defining a semantics for concurrent programs is to let the meaning of a statement be its set of possible behaviors, and to explicitly construct the behaviors in $\mathcal{M}[\![S]\!]$ from the behaviors of its components. For example, the set of behaviors $\mathcal{M}[\![S_1\,;\,S_2]\!]$ consists of all infinite behaviors in $\mathcal{M}[\![S_1]\!]$ together with all concatenations of finite behaviors in $\mathcal{M}[\![S_1]\!]$ with behaviors in $\mathcal{M}[\![S_2]\!]$. This can be expressed formally by:

$$\begin{aligned}\mathcal{M}[\![S_1\,;\,S_2]\!] \;=\; & \{\sigma \in \mathcal{M}[\![S_1]\!] : \sigma \text{ infinite}\} \\ & \cup\ \{\sigma\tau : \sigma \in \mathcal{M}[\![S_1]\!],\ \tau \in \mathcal{M}[\![S_2]\!],\ \text{and } \sigma \text{ finite}\}\end{aligned}$$

I will call such a semantics a *behavioral* semantics.

Behavioral semantics have their problems. While they work well for sequential programming constructs, they are less satisfactory for concurrent languages. The behaviors of

cobegin $S_1 \,\square\, S_2$ **coend**

are obtained by forming interleavings of behaviors from S_1 and S_2, and interleavings are rather awkward mathematically—especially for a fair **cobegin**, where only fair interleavings are allowed.

A more serious problem is raised by the language construct

assign processor to S

Intuitively, this statement causes the compiler to assign a physical (or virtual) processor to execute S. In terms of behaviors, it means that any behavior that reaches S must either subsequently reach the end of S or else include an infinite number of actions of S. In other words, a process cannot be "starved" while it is executing this statement. This is a perfectly reasonable—and compilable—statement. It can be used to construct a fair **cobegin** from an unfair one as follows:

unfair cobegin **assign processor to** S_1 $\square$
assign processor to S_2 **coend**

More complicated uses of the **assign processor** statement are also possible.

Considered completely by themselves, the statements S and

assign processor to S

have the same sets of behaviors, so it is not clear how one could apply to the **assign processor** statement the same approach used above to define $\mathcal{M}[\![S_1; S_2]\!]$.

2.2.2 Action Semantics

Instead of defining $\mathcal{M}[\![S]\!]$ to be the set of behaviors itself, one can define it to be something that can be used to construct the set of behaviors. Since a behavior is generated by a sequence of actions starting in some state, an obvious approach is to let $\mathcal{M}[\![S]\!]$ be the set of all possible actions together with the set of all possible starting states. I will call such a semantics an *action* semantics. Given an action semantics, one can define the behaviors of S to be the set of all behaviors that can be obtained from these actions starting from the specified starting states.

An action semantics is well-suited to expressing parallelism, since the set of possible actions of

cobegin $\pi_1 \square \pi_2$ **coend**

is just the union of the sets of possible actions of π_1 and π_2. Action semantics have long been favorites of theoretical computer scientists [15] because they lead to mathematically well-behaved formalisms. Unfortunately, these semantics are unsatisfactory because they cannot express fairness. Consider a coin-flipping program with two possible actions: toss a head and toss a tail. It can be viewed as the parallel composition of two processes: one that generates only heads and the other that generates only tails. An unfair coin flipper can generate any infinite sequence of heads and tails, while a fair one can generate only sequences containing infinite numbers of both heads and tails. Both the fair and the unfair coin flipper have the same set of actions (toss a head and toss a tail), so an action semantics cannot distinguish between the two.

2.2.3 Action-Axiom Semantics

The problem of fairness is solved by using an *action-axiom* semantics in which the meaning of a statement consists of a set of actions together with a set of temporal logic axioms that state conditions under which an action must eventually occur. For example, the fair coin flipper requires two axioms:

- At any time, a head must eventually occur.
- At any time, a tail must eventually occur.

The meaning of

assign processor to S

consists of the meaning of S plus the following additional axiom:

- If S is being executed—more precisely, if control is in S—then an action of S must eventually occur.

We are thus led to let $\mathcal{M}[\![S]\!]$ consist of a set of actions, a set of temporal logic axioms, and a set of starting states. But how do we specify the actions? Instead of introducing some new method for specifying actions, I will specify the actions as well as the fairness properties with temporal logic axioms. Starting states will be specified by ordinary, nontemporal axioms.

To give a compositional action semantics, we must define the axioms of $\mathcal{M}[\![S_1; S_2]\!]$ in terms of the axioms of $\mathcal{M}[\![S_1]\!]$ and $\mathcal{M}[\![S_2]\!]$; and, of course, we must also do the same for other language constructs besides the "$;$". We will see that there is a standard prescription for doing this.

The axioms in $\mathcal{M}[\![S]\!]$ define a set of behaviors for S—namely, the set of all behaviors satisfying the temporal logic axioms starting in states that satisfy the axioms for the starting state. Although this defines a set of behaviors for every statement, it is different from a semantics in which $\mathcal{M}[\![S]\!]$ is taken to be a set of behaviors because the meaning of S is obtained from the meaning of its components by "composing" axioms, not by composing behaviors.

2.3 Is This Fair?

It can be argued that the semantics of a programming language should be defined in terms of constructive operations rather than with axioms. One should give a procedure for constructing the set of behaviors of a program rather than a set of axioms to describe it.

While a purely constructive approach would be nice, it seems to be impossible to deal with fairness constructively. Even a behavioral semantics, which looks constructive, really includes axioms for fairness. A behavioral semantics defines the meaning of a fair **cobegin** in terms of fair interleaving. The definition of a fair interleaving of two behaviors goes something like this:

> Construct all interleavings and then throw away the ones that do not satisfy the fairness condition.

This is remarkably similar to the definition of the set of behaviors obtained from a set of actions and a set of constraints, which can be expressed as:

> Construct all behaviors generated by the set of actions and then throw away those that do not satisfy the constraints.

One might argue that fair interleaving is a simple, basic concept, and I have given a particularly jaundiced expression of it. However, there are many different fairness constraints one might want to define, each of which would require a different definition of fair interleaving. For example, consider two coin-flipping processes, one with the single action *head* and the other with two actions: *tail* and *coin lost*. The first process generates only the sequence of all heads, the second process generates either a sequence of all tails or a finite string of tails followed by a sequence of *coin lost* actions. The behaviors resulting from executing the two processes concurrently are defined to consist of all possible fair sequences of heads and tails plus all sequences consisting of a finite number of heads and tails followed by nothing but *coin lost* actions.

This is a perfectly reasonable example, which the reader may find more familiar if he replaces *coin lost* by *abort program*. A behavioral semantics for this way of combining processes would require a more complicated definition of fair interleaving, and a formal statement of this definition would look a lot like a temporal logic axiom. Fair interleaving is not a simple concept. One particular type of fair interleaving has been used so commonly that we tend to take it for granted and forget that we have never seen a constructive definition of it.

Fairness does not appear to be a constructive concept. One specifies fairness by adding axioms to exclude unfair behaviors rather than by explicitly constructing only the fair ones. Infinite objects, such as behaviors, are constructed as limits of finite approximations—a method often described as "denotational". This does not work with fairness because there exist sequences of fair behaviors whose limits are unfair—for example, let $\sigma_1, \sigma_2, \ldots$ be the sequence of coint-flipping behaviors in which all actions of σ_n are heads, except for every $2^n th$ action, which is a tail. Each σ_n is fair, but the limit as n goes to infinity is the behavior having only heads, which is unfair.

The topological approach of [2] solves this problem by considering only convergent sequences and defining a topology in which sequences like the above diverge. However, one might view this approach as:

> Construct all sequences obtainable from the actions and throw away those that do not converge.

This looks suspiciously like the more overtly axiomatic approach. The whole distinction between constructive and axiomatic methods is probably illusory, disappearing when methods are examined closely enough.

2.4 Programs and Implementations

2.4.1 Correctness of an Implementation

One question that a semantics of a programming language should answer is: What does it mean for a compiler to be correct? Given a program Π in the high-level language, the compiler transforms it into a program π in some lower-level language. Correctness of the compiler means that π is a correct implementation of Π, but what does that mean? To speak of correctness, we must have formal semantics for both the high-level and the low-level languages, so $\mathcal{M}[\![\Pi]\!]$ and $\mathcal{M}[\![\pi]\!]$ are defined. However, this is not enough to determine what it means for $\mathcal{M}[\![\pi]\!]$ to represent a correct implementation of $\mathcal{M}[\![\Pi]\!]$.

Consider the case of sequential programs, in which the semantics of a program is a relation on the set of program states, the pair (s, t) being in the relation $\mathcal{M}[\![\Pi]\!]$ if and only if it is possible for program Π to start in state s and terminate in state t. In this case, $\mathcal{M}[\![\Pi]\!]$ and $\mathcal{M}[\![\pi]\!]$ are relations on two different sets of states. The states of Π specify the values of program variables like x and y; the states of π might specify the values of machine registers like *memory location* 3124 or the *program counter*. Correct implementation means that there is a correspondence between the sets of states of Π and π such that, under this correspondence, every possible execution of π is a possible execution of Π.

More formally, to establish a correspondence between the semantics of the two sequential programs, we must define a mapping F from the states of π to the states of Π. For example, suppose the variable x in Π of type *integer* is implemented in π as a two-byte integer stored in bytes 3124 and 3125 of memory. If, in a state s of π, bytes 3124 and 3125 have the values 12 and 97, then the value of x in the state $F(s)$ of Π is $12 \times 256 + 97$. In general, correctness of the implementation means that for each pair (s, t) in $\mathcal{M}[\![\pi]\!]$, the pair $(F(s), F(t))$ must be in $\mathcal{M}[\![\Pi]\!]$.

What about concurrent programs? As we have seen, the meaning of a concurrent program must be expressed in terms of its behavior—either directly, with a behavioral semantics, or indirectly with axioms about its behavior. Let us therefore consider first a behavioral semantics, in which $\mathcal{M}[\![\Pi]\!]$ and $\mathcal{M}[\![\pi]\!]$ are sets of behaviors. Intuitively, π is a correct implementation of Π if every possible behavior of π represents a possible behavior of Π. We therefore need some way of interpreting behaviors of π as possible behaviors of Π—that is a mapping F such that for any behavior σ in $\mathcal{M}[\![\Pi]\!]$, $F(\sigma)$ is a sequence of states and actions of Π. We can then say that π is a correct implementation of Π if, for every σ in $\mathcal{M}[\![\pi]\!]$, $F(\sigma)$ is in $\mathcal{M}[\![\Pi]\!]$.

In defining this mapping F, we are faced by the problem that Π and π may have different grains of atomicity. An atomic operation of Π may be implemented by a sequence of 42 atomic operations of π. For example, the atomic operation

$$\langle\, x := x + 1 \,\rangle$$

of Π might be implemented in π by 42 machine-language operations. Moreover, interleaved among these 42 atomic operations of π might be other machine-language operations that belong to the implementation of an operation from a different process of Π. It would therefore seem that the mapping F must be quite complicated, taking sets of actions into single actions.

There is very simple solution to this problem—we require that to every action of π there correspond a single action of Π. The execution of a single atomic operation of Π might therefore be represented by 42 actions in a behavior in $\mathcal{M}[\![\Pi]\!]$. The first 41 of these actions will be "stuttering" actions that do not change the state of Π; the 42nd will do all the work. This makes it conceptually very easy to define the mapping F from behaviors of π to behaviors of Π. As in the sequential case, there must be a mapping F from states of π to states of Π. We also assume that F maps actions of π to actions of Π—for example, every machine-language instruction executed by π corresponds to the execution of some atomic operation of Π.[2] To extend F to a mapping on behaviors, if

---

[2]A single machine-language instruction could actually be used in the implementation of several atomic

σ is the behavior

$$s_0 \xrightarrow{\alpha_1} s_1 \xrightarrow{\alpha_2} \cdots$$

of π, we define $F(\sigma)$ to be the behavior

$$F(s_0) \xrightarrow{F(\alpha_1)} F(s_1) \xrightarrow{F(\alpha_2)} \cdots$$

The implementation is correct if, for every behavior σ of $\mathcal{M}[\![\pi]\!]$, $F(\sigma)$ is a behavior in $\mathcal{M}[\![\Pi]\!]$.

This seems nice in theory, but how can it be achieved in practice? The first 41 machine-language operations in the implementation of the atomic assignment must change the state in such a way that they these changes are invisible when viewed at the higher level. More precisely, the 41 intermediate states of the computation must all be mapped by F into the same state as the starting state. How is this possible?

A complete answer to this question is beyond the scope of this paper. The trick lies in the definition of F, which must "unscramble" the intermediate states in the appropriate way. I will not explain here how it is done. I will only mention that, while it sounds like magic, it in fact is a simple extension of the basic idea of invariance that underlies most concurrent program verification. An explanation and examples can be found in [6] and [8].

I won't consider the problem of compiler correctness. The purpose of this discussion is to point out that in order to permit a simple definition of correctness of an implementation, I cannot define a semantics in which the execution of an atomic program statement is always represented as a single atomic action. I must allow "stuttering" actions. In the action-axiom semantics, the specification of an action α must allow a finite series of null transitions $s \xrightarrow{\alpha} s$ as well as the final action $s \xrightarrow{\alpha} t$ that "does the work".

I have described correctness of an implementation in terms of a behavioral semantics, where $\mathcal{M}[\![\Pi]\!]$ is a set of behaviors. In an action-axiom semantics, the meaning $\mathcal{M}[\![\Pi]\!]$ of a program Π is a set of axioms that determines the set of possible behaviors. Section 5.7 explains how this concept of correctness is translated into a relation between the sets of axioms $\mathcal{M}[\![\Pi]\!]$ and $\mathcal{M}[\![\pi]\!]$. The only observation I will make here is that the axioms of $\mathcal{M}[\![\Pi]\!]$ must permit stuttering actions. More precisely, these axioms should not be able to distinguish stuttering; if an axiom is true for a behavior σ, then it should also be true for the behavior obtained from σ by adding stuttering actions. This will be guaranteed by using a temporal logic in which no formula can distinguish stuttering—a temporal logic with no "next-time" operator.

2.4.2 The Interface

The semantics of a program is traditionally defined by describing how it affects the values of variables. However, program variables are internal to the program; all that a

actions of Π—for example, if it were part of a subroutine called during the execution of several different statements of Π. The mapping F should therefore take state, action pairs into actions, so the action α_i of π is mapped into the action $F(s_{i-1}, \alpha_i)$ of Π. In other words, the state of π determines which atomic statement of Π is being executed by the execution of a machine-language statement.

user sees is what he types into the program and what the program types out to him. A semantics of a program should describe its input and output, not just how it affects internal objects like variables.

Given the machine-dependence of most input and output, an explicit semantics for input and output seems like a useless exercise. Instead, observe that input and output can be representend by variables. A terminal screen can be represented as a Boolean array, each element representing the presence or absence of light at one point on the screen. Keyboard input can be simulated through a variable whose value represents the sequence of characters that have been typed but not yet processed. I will use the term *interface variables* to describe variables that represent input and output.

In general, an interface variable describes the interaction between the program and its environment. They are *global* or *free* variables, in contrast to the *local* or *bound* variables that are declared in ordinary program declarations. For example, variables declared in a Pascal **var** declaration are local.

Let us again consider the mapping F, introduced above to define what it means for a lower-level program π to be correct implementation of a higher-level program Π. Recall that F describes how the variables of Π are implemented in terms of the "variables" of π—the machine registers, if π is a machine-language program. We really don't care how the local variables of Π are implemented, since they are not externally visible. The compiler is free to implement local variables any way it wishes.

The compiler does not have such freedom in its implementation of interface variables. The implementation of the interface variables must be defined *a priori* if the program is to interact with its environment in a useful way. For example, suppose that the terminal screen is represented by a Boolean array. The semantics of the program Π would provide no information about real output if the compiler could define the array elements to represent completely arbitrarily points on the screen—or to represent the values of arbitrary one-bit registers in the machine.

I have considered the implementation of the states of Π in terms of states of π, but what about the implementation of actions? Just as there are local and interface state functions, there are internal and external actions. Most actions in a program behavior are internal, being caused by program execution. However, some actions represent operations external to the program—for example, the actions that represent the entering of an input character. The semantics of Π does not distinguish this operation, which changes the value of the interface variable representing the input buffer, from program operations that change the value of variables—for example, the program operation that removes a character from the input buffer. The compiler is free to implement internal actions of Π by any internal actions of π. However, the external actions of Π must be implemented by fixed actions of π, which may be internal or external. For example, the sequence of actions of Π that add a character to the input buffer may be implemented by a sequence of actions external to π, representing external operations that put the character into an input register and actions of π that move the character from the input register into the memory registers that implement the input buffer. The compiler would be of little use if it could implement the operation of typing a character, defined in the semantics of Π simply as an operation that changes the variable representing the input buffer, as an internal operation of π that adds a randomly chosen character to the buffer.

Thus, the representation of local variables and internal actions of Π by F may be arbitrary, but the representation of interface variables and external actions must be fixed. The meaning $\mathcal{M}[\![\Pi]\!]$ of Π can be defined in a completely machine-independent fashion. The machine dependency, which exists for any real compiler, is contained in the details of how interface variables and external actions are to be implemented.

Thus far, I have been talking only about implementing a complete program Π. We should consider the problem of implementing a single statement S. In this case, all the global (undeclared) variables of S must be regarded as interface variables, and their implementations must be fixed *a priori*. For example, if statements S and T were to be implemented independently, their implementations could be combined to implement $S; T$ only if a variable x common to both were implemented as the same set of machine registers.

Of course, one is seldom interested in implementing a single statement of a program. These considerations would apply to a language that allows separate compilation of components such as subroutines. I will not consider the problem of separate compilation. My purpose in discussing implementation of individual statements is to point out that the concept of global and local variables occurs at all levels of a program. Variables global to a statement S may be local to a larger statement containing S.

3 The Programming Language

The goal of this paper is to explain how the semantics of any programming language can be defined, and not to give a complete semantics for aparticular language. However, to show how the formalism works, it is helpful to define rigorously the semantics of some language. I will therefore formally define the semantics of a simple language called L, and will indicate informally how the semantics of language primitives other than those in L can defined.

The language L contains an atomic assignment statement—one whose execution is an indivisible, atomic action. L has the usual sequential control structures: concatenation (;), **if** and **while** statements, plus a fair **cobegin**. The tests in **while** and **if** statements are also taken to be atomic. L has a **new** statement that declares a local variable, so

new x : **integer** **in** S **ni**

declares x to be a local variable of type **integer** whose scope consists of the statement S. The **new** statement has an optional **init** clause to specify the initial value, so

new x : **integer** **init** $2 * x$ **in** S **ni**

declares that the initial value of x in S is twice the value of the variable x whose scope includes the **new** statement. The assignment of the initial value to x is assumed to be an atomic action. The **new** statement also has an optional **alias** clause that is used to declare that the new variable is the alias for something else. For example,

new x : **integer** **alias** y **in** S **ni**

declares x to be an alias for y.

It may seem strange to introduce aliasing—a concept usually ignored in simple examples—in the language L. Aliasing is an important concept because it underlies the semantics of procedure calls. If *proc* is a procedure defined with single integer-valued a call-by-name parameter *param*, then the call *proc*(*arg*) can be simulated by the statement

new *param* : **integer** **alias** *arg* **in** S **ni**

where S is the body of *proc*. (Call by value and call by reference can be simulated with call by name through the use of auxiliary variables.)

For reasons that will be clear later, the concept of aliasing is central to our semantics, and we will need to understand a more general kind of aliasing than real programming languages usually allow. In particular, L will allow a variable to be aliased to an expression. To understand what that means, consider the declaration

new f : **real** **alias** $9 * c/5 + 32$ **in** S **ni**

In this case, we can think of f and c as representing a single temperature, where f is its value in degrees Farenheit and c is its value in degrees Celsius. The two assignment statements $f := 32$ and $c := 0$ have exactly the same effect; executing either one changes the value of f to 32 and the value of c to zero.

As another example, assume a type **gaussian** which represents a Gaussian integer—a number of the form $m + n\sqrt{-1}$, where m and n are integers. If x and y are variables of type **integer**, then

new z : **gaussian** **alias** $x + y * \sqrt{-1}$ **in** S **ni**

defines z to be a variable of type **gaussian** whose real part is aliased to x and whose imaginary part is aliased to y. Assigning a value to z in S also assigns values to x and y so that the relation

$$z = x + y * \sqrt{-1}$$

holds throughout the execution of S. Similarly, changing the value of x in S also changes the value of z.

In the examples of **alias** clauses given so far, assigning a value to any variable produces a well-defined result. However, this need not be the case. Inside the body S of the statement

new c : **integer** **alias** $a + b$ **in** S **ni**

assigning a value to a or b changes the value of c in the obvious way, but what is the result of assigning a value to c? I define an assignment to c to be a nondeterministic statement that can change the values of a and b in any way such that $a + b$ equals the new value of c.

However, I will assume that the aliasing relations are such that they can always be maintained by the proper choice of values. More precisely, a program is considered illegal if its execution would force the aliasing relations to be violated. For example, the statement

new b **: integer alias** $\sqrt{a}$ **in** S **ni**

is illegal if, at any time during its execution, the value of a is not a perfect square.

This approach to aliasing is similar to the one I will take for type constraints—namely, a program is illegal if its execution would force a type violation. For example, the statement

new b **: boolean init** $\neg c$ **in** ...

is illegal in any context in which c is not declared to be of type **boolean**.

While typing consistency is easy for a compiler to enforce in language L, the consistency of aliasing relations can be determined at compile time only if the kind of expression that can appear in an **alias** is restricted in some way. In fact, some restriction is obviously necessary if the compiler is to have any chance at compiling the code. Those restrictions are irrelevant to our semantics, so they are not discussed.

The basic syntax of L is given by the syntax diagrams in Figure 1. I will not bother to give a formal syntax for identifiers. The only types that I will use in L are **integer** and **boolean**. Expressions are assumed to be the usual ones constructed from variable names and the ordinary operations on integers and booleans—for example, an expression like

$$(x * y + z = 17) \supset (x > y \vee \neg b)$$

I will enclose **if** and **while** tests, assignment statements, and the **init** clause of a **new** statement in angle brackets to emphasize their atomicity.

In addition to the usual information, the syntax diagrams of Figure 1 also have labels attached to the nonterminal components. These labels are called ***primitive selectors***. A primitive selector identifies a component of a compound statement—for example, the primitive selector ***then*** identifies the "**then**-clause" of an **if** statement. The "..." label in the specifications of the **cobegin** indicates that the primitive selectors for the clauses of a **cobegin** are integers, and likewise for a list of statements.

In more formal terms, the primitive selectors label the edges in the parse tree of a statement or program.[3] A *selector* for a statement S is a sequence of primitive selectors that represents a path starting from the root in S's parse tree. A selector identifies a component of a program or statement. For example, the selector *else, body, 2* identifies the substatement $\langle\, x := x + 4 \,\rangle$ in the following statement:

```
if ⟨ x > 0 ⟩
  then ⟨ x := x + 1 ⟩
  else while ⟨ y > 0 ⟩
         do ⟨ y := y − 1 ⟩;
            ⟨ x := x + 4 ⟩
         od;
       ⟨ y := 17 ⟩
fi
```

[3]Trivial nodes that have only a single son are eliminated from the parse tree, which is why there is no primitive selector associated with the first box in the syntax diagram defining a statement.

program:

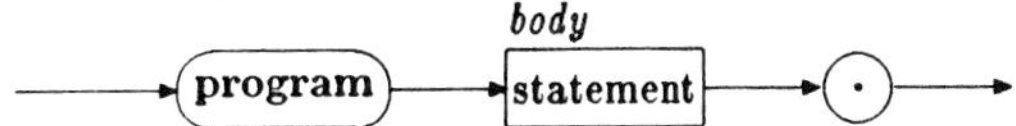

statement:

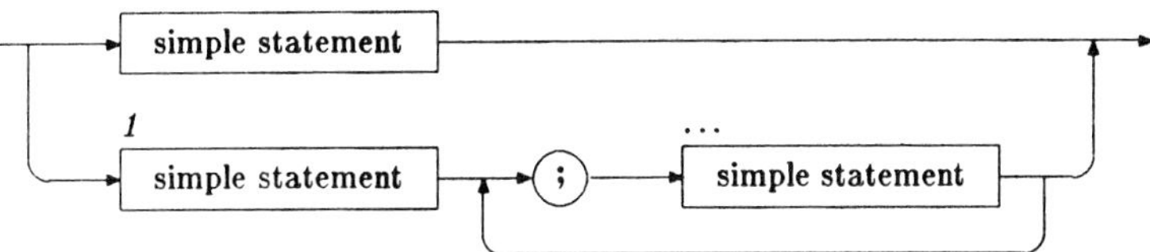

simple statement:

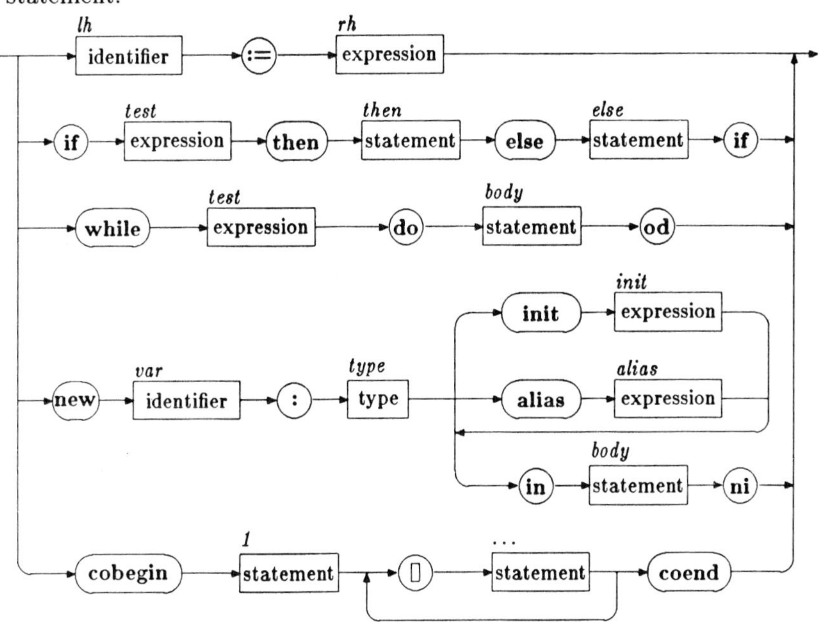

Figure 1: Basic syntax of language L.

More formally, given a program or statement S, a substatement of S consists of a pair S, γ, where γ is a selector for S. A substatement of S is, when viewed by itself, a statement. I will often write something like: "T is the substatement S, γ of S." This means that the substatement, when viewed alone, is the same as the statement T. However, T and S, γ are formally two different kinds of objects—one is a complete statement and the other is part of a statement.

The null selector selects the entire statement, so "S," denotes S viewed as a substatement of itself. Since "S," looks rather strange, I will simply write S to denote both the entire statement S and that statement viewed as a substatement of itself.

4 States and Actions

The meaning $\mathcal{M}[\![S]\!]$ of a statement S will be a set of temporal logic axioms defining the behaviors of S and a set of nontemporal axioms defining its set of initial states. To give a semantics for these axioms, I must define the the set $\mathcal{S}(S)$ of all possible states of S and the set $\mathcal{A}(S)$ of all possible actions of S. The initial-state axioms then define a set of states—namely, the set of all states in $\mathcal{S}(S)$ that satisfy those axioms; and the temporal axioms define a set of behaviors—namely, the set of all sequences

$$s_0 \xrightarrow{\alpha_1} s_1 \xrightarrow{\alpha_1} \cdots$$

with $s_i \in \mathcal{S}(S)$ and $\alpha_i \in \mathcal{A}(S)$ that satisfy those axioms.

Intuitively, the state of a statement at some time during its execution contains all the information needed to describe its possible behavior at future times. To define the set $\mathcal{S}(S)$, we must consider what information must be in the state of S.

4.1 Program Variables

The future behavior of a program certainly depends upon the current values of its variables, so a state must specify the values of all program variables. More precisely, a state in $\mathcal{S}(S)$ must include a mapping *val* from the set of variables of S to a set of values. For the simple language L, in which all variables are of type **integer** or **boolean**, the set of values consists of the set $Z \cup \{true, false\}$, where Z denotes the set of all integers.

Let S be the statement

cobegin $S_1 \,\square\, S_2$ **coend**

and suppose that S_1 and S_2 both contain **new** x statements. Each of these statements declares a different variable, but both variables have the same name x. Both of the variables named x may be defined at the same time, and may have different values. To facilitate the discussion, I will use the term *identifier* to denote the syntactic object constituting the name of a variable, and the term *variable* to denote the variable itself. Thus, S has two different variables having the same identifier x. This situation does not arise in a sequential program because, at any instant during its execution, there is at most one currently active variable for any identifier. However, it does arise in concurrent programs and must be considered.

To define *val*, we must define the value it assigns to each of the variables of S, which requires giving different names to different variables. Assigning unique names to variables is a nontrivial problem, since different variables may be represented in the program by the same identifier. It is solved with selectors. I let $x(S, \gamma)$ be the name of the variable with identifier x that is declared in a **new** statement whose selector in S is γ—in other words, where γ is the path in the parse tree of S leading to the **new** statement. A "global" variable with identifier x—that is, the variable denoted by an occurrence of the identifier x outside the scope of any **new** x statement—is given the name $x()$.

I consider $x()$ to be a variable of any statement S, even if the identifier x never appears in S. For example, suppose S is the statement:

$\langle\, y := y + 1 \,\rangle$;
new z **: in** $\langle\, z := y \,\rangle$ **ni**

Then the variables of S consist of the single "bound" variable $z(S, 2)$ plus the infinite set of "free" variables $x()$, $y()$, $z()$, …, only one of which actually appears in S. Even though the variable $x()$ does not appear in S, it may appear in other statements in the complete program. The correctness of a program containing

cobegin $S \;\square\; T$ **coend**

may depend upon the obvious fact that S does not change the value of $x()$. The value of $x()$ is included as part of S's state so we can say formally that S does not change that value.

To summarize, defining the set of states $\mathcal{S}(S)$ of S requires defining the set of variables of S. The variables of S consist of the following:

- For any **new** x statement of S with selector γ, the variable named "$x(S, \gamma)$".
- For any identifier x, the variable named "$x()$".

The mapping *val* assigns a value to each of these variables.

The names of variables come up quite often when talking about programs. If S is a hundred page program, then the name $x(S, \gamma)$ takes up one hundred pages. Writing even the simplest statements about S would therefore require quite a bit of paper. Such a practical consideration is as irrelevant for the semantics of a programming language as is the cost of tape for the theory of Turing-machine computability. However, it does pose a problem in writing examples, since a simple assertion about a five-line program might take one or two pages. The solution is, of course, to give names to statements and substatements. I will use the ordinary labeling convention to do this. For example, consider the program.

```
s: if ⟨ x > 0 ⟩
     then   ⟨ x := x + 1 ⟩
     else t: new y
               in ⟨ y := x ⟩;
                  ⟨ x := y + 2 ⟩
```

```
            ni;
            ⟨ z := 17 ⟩
fi
```

The variable y declared by the **new** y statement will be called simply $y(t \text{ of } s)$. However, you should remember that its complete formal name is:

$$y\left(\begin{array}{l}\mathbf{if}\langle x > 0 \rangle \\ \quad \mathbf{then} \ldots \\ \quad \mathbf{else} \ldots \\ \mathbf{fi}\end{array}, \; else, 1\right)$$

4.2 Control Variables

There is more to a state than the values of program variables. To determine the future behavior at some point during the execution of the statement

```
u: begin s: ⟨ x := x + 1 ⟩;
         t: ⟨ y := y + 1 ⟩
   end
```

we need to know whether control is at the beginning of statement s, at the beginning of statement t, or at the end of statment t. Since the state must determine the statement's possible future behavior, it must contain this control information.

I will describe this control information in terms of the boolean-valued *control* variables *at*, *in*, and *after*. For any substatement S, γ, there are control variables $at(S, \gamma)$, $in(S, \gamma)$, and $after(S, \gamma)$, where the values of these variables equal *true* when

$at(S, \gamma)$: control is at the beginning of substatement S, γ

$in(S, \gamma)$: control is at the beginning of or inside S, γ, but not at its exit point. Note that $at(S, \gamma) \supset in(S, \gamma)$ is always true.

$after(S, \gamma)$: control is at the exit point of S, γ—that is, at the point just after its execution is completed.

In addition to complete substatements, the *at*, *in*, and *after* variables are also defined for certain parts of statements that denote atomic operations—namely, the *test* of an **if** or **while** statement and the *init* clause of a **new** statement (if it has one). Also, the control variables $at(\Pi)$, $in(\Pi)$, and $after(\Pi)$ are defined for a complete program Π.

The statement u above thus has eight control variables: $at(u)$, $in(u)$, $after(u)$, $at(s \text{ of } u)$, $in(s \text{ of } u)$, $after(s \text{ of } u)$, $at(t \text{ of } u)$, $in(t \text{ of } u)$, and $after(t \text{ of } u)$. They are not all independent, however, since we have

$$\begin{aligned} at(u) &= at(s \text{ of } u) \\ after(u) &= after(t \text{ of } u) \\ in(u) &= in(s \text{ of } u) \wedge in(t \text{ of } u) \\ after(s \text{ of } u) &= at(t \text{ of } u) \end{aligned} \qquad (1)$$

These equations represent aliasing relations between the control variables. The study of these aliasing relations is deferred until later.

The mapping *val* that assigns values to variables must assign values to the control variables as well as the ordinary program variables. Of course, we must assume that *at*, *in*, and *after* are not identifiers, so they cannot be used for ordinary program variables.

Variables like *at*, *in*, and *after* are sometimes called "dummy" or "ghost" variables. This seems to imply that they are not as real as ordinary program variables. Indeed, I have found that many computer scientists regard their use as somewhat distasteful—perhaps even immoral. Control variables are every bit as real as ordinary program variables. They differ from program variables only in that the programmer does not explicitly write them. Every programmer knows that he can often simplify a program's control structure—that is, eliminate control variables—by adding program variables; and, conversely, he can eliminate program variables by using a more complex control structure—that is, by adding control variables. A compiler handles both kinds of variables in very much the same way; in the compiled version of a program, the values of program variables and control variables are both encoded in terms of the contents of memory registers and program-location counters.

I therefore prefer to use the term *implicit* variables for variables other than ordinary program variables. Some languages employ other implicit variables besides control variables. For example, a language that provides a buffered message-passing primitive will contain implicit variables whose values describe the set of messages in the queues.

Ordinary program variables may be free (undeclared), like $x()$, or bound (declared), like $x(S,\gamma)$. I have written all control variables as bound variables, but are they really bound? Remember that the free variables are interface variables and bound variables are internal ones. In order to use a compiled version of a statement S, one must know where its starting and ending control points are, but need know nothing of its internal control points. This suggests that $\mathit{at}(S)$, $\mathit{in}(S)$, and $\mathit{after}(S)$ are interface variables for statement S, while, for any non-null selector γ, $\mathit{at}(S,\gamma)$, $\mathit{in}(S,\gamma)$, and $\mathit{after}(S,\gamma)$ are internal variables. The control variables $\mathit{at}(S)$, $\mathit{in}(S)$, and $\mathit{after}(S)$ are best viewed as undeclared and might better be written as $\mathit{at}()$, $\mathit{in}()$, and $\mathit{after}()$. (They are not written that way both for historical reasons and because it would tend to be confusing.) These variables are implicitly declared, and aliased to other control variables, when S is written as part of a larger statement.

4.3 Are There Other State Components?

Does a mapping *val* from variable names of S values tell us everything we need to know about the current state of S in order to determine its future behavior? At first glance, it might seem that it doesn't. For example, what is the effect of executing

$$s\colon\ x := y + 1$$

when the value of y is 17? The answer depends upon the type of x. If x is of type **integer**, then the execution sets x to 18. However, if x is of type **boolean**, then executing s produces an error.

Moreover, suppose x is of type integer and $y = 17$, so executing s changes the value of x to 18. What does this execution do to the value of y? If y is not aliased to x, then its value is left unchanged. However, if s appears inside the statement

new y : **integer** **alias** x **in** ... **ni**

then the value of y is also changed to 18.

It would therefore seem that we should add types and aliasing information to the state. In fact, we needn't. The reason is that, in language L, types and aliasing relations are *static* properties; they do not change during execution of the program. Executing an action of L does not change the type of a variable or any aliasing relations. (We sometimes think of executing a **new** statement by first executing its declarations, but that makes no sense because declarations are not actions.)

In a more complex language, types and aliasing relations can be dynamic. For example, in Pascal, if x is a variable of type pointer, then the aliasing relation "$x\uparrow$ is aliased to y" is dynamic, since its truth is changed by assigning a new value to x. In these cases, it may be necessary to add types and aliasing information to the state. However, in most languages, aliasing relations among control variables will be static, and can be handled the same way as in language L.

4.4 Renaming

For any statement S, let $\mathcal{V}(S)$ denote the set of names of variables of S. A state *val* of $\mathcal{S}(S)$ is a mapping that assigns a value to each variable name in $\mathcal{V}(S)$. For a compositional semantics, we must be able to derive information about the states of S from information about the states of its component substatements. This requires the fundamental concept of a *renaming* mapping.

Let statement T be the substatement S, γ of S. Every variable of T is a variable of S, except that it may be known by a different name. I will define $\rho_{S,\gamma}$ to be the mapping on names such that if v is the name of a variable in T, then $\rho_{S,\gamma}(v)$ is the name of the corresponding variable in S. Hence,

$$\rho_{S,\gamma} : \mathcal{V}(T) \rightarrow \mathcal{V}(S)$$

The variable $x(T, \mu)$, which is the variable of T with identifier x that is declared in the **new** statement T, μ, is called by the name $x(S, \gamma, \mu)$ when it is regarded as a variable of S. Thus,

$$\rho_{S,\gamma}(x(T, \mu)) = x(S, \gamma, \mu)$$

A variable that has the name $x()$ as a variable in T is undeclared in T. If it is undeclared in S, then it has the same name as a variable of S, so $\rho_{S,\gamma}(x()) = x()$. However, if it is declared in the **new** x statement S, ν, so ν is a prefix of γ, then $\rho_{S,\gamma}(x()) = x(S, \nu)$.

The renaming mappings compose in the natural way. If T is the substatement S, γ of S, then for any substatement T, δ of T, we have

$$\rho_{S,\gamma,\delta} = \rho_{S,\gamma} \circ \rho_{T,\delta} \qquad (2)$$

By taking this equality to be a definition, we can formally define $\rho_{S,\gamma}$ for any selector γ by defining it for all primitive selectors. This formal definition should be obvious and is omitted.

Let T be the substatement S,γ of S. A state *val* of $\mathcal{S}(S)$ is a mapping from $\mathcal{V}(S)$ to values, and $\rho_{S,\gamma}$ is a mapping from $\mathcal{V}(T)$ to $\mathcal{V}(S)$. The composition $val \circ \rho_{S,\gamma}$ is therefore a mapping from from $\mathcal{V}(T)$ to values, which is a state in $\mathcal{S}(T)$. Thus, the mapping $\rho_{S,\gamma}$ induces a mapping

$$\rho^*_{S,\gamma} : \mathcal{S}(S) \rightarrow \mathcal{S}(T)$$

from states of S to states of T, defined by

$$\rho^*_{S,\gamma}(val) \stackrel{\text{def}}{=} val \circ \rho_{S,\gamma} \tag{3}$$

for any $val \in \mathcal{S}(S)$.[4]

It follows easily from (2) that the mappings $\rho^*_{S,\gamma}$ satisfy the following "adjoint" form of (2).

$$\rho^*_{S,\gamma,\delta} = \rho^*_{T,\delta} \circ \rho^*_{S,\gamma} \tag{4}$$

4.5 Actions

The states of S are defined using the set $\mathcal{V}(S)$ of variable names. The actions of S will be defined in terms of a set $\mathcal{A}(S)$ of atomic-action names of S.

The atomic actions of S are the components written in angle brackets. In the language L, there are just four kinds of atomic actions: assignment statements, **if** tests, **while** tests, and **init** clauses (of **new** statements). (I assume that the initial-value assignment of the **new** statement is performed as a single atomic action.) The set $\mathcal{A}(S)$ of atomic-action names of S consists of the set of all components S,γ of S such that γ is a selector for one of the following: an assignment statement, the *test* component of an **if** statement, the *test* component of a **while** statement, or the *init* component of a **new** statement. For reasons having to do with defining compiler correctness that are irrelevant to the remainder of this paper, if Π is a complete program, then $\mathcal{A}(\Pi)$ is defined to contain one additional action name: the name λ, which is the name of a null action.[5]

Since action names are just the names of substatements, the renaming mappings can be applied to them in the usual way. Thus, if T is the substatement S,γ of S, then

---

[4]The renaming mapping $\rho^*_{S,\gamma}$ has no connection with the mapping F discussed in Section 2.4.1 between the states of an implementation and the states of a higher-level program.

[5]The following example shows why the λ action is needed. Let S be the statement

$$x := x^2$$

of program Π, and consider the 42 steps in the machine-language implementation π of Π that execute statement S. As mentioned earlier, 41 of them will be stuttering actions that leave the value of x unchanged. Before the first 41 steps have been executed, π's state may no longer have the information needed to deduce the initial value of x. For example, after 20 steps, the state of π may show that x will wind up with the value 4, but may not show whether it started equal to 2 or -2. This means that the single nonstuttering action must be among the first 20 steps, and the remaining steps must be stuttering actions of the statement following S. If S is the last statement of Π, then these remaining steps are λ actions.

$$\rho_{S,\gamma} : \mathcal{A}(T) \rightarrow \mathcal{A}(S)$$

is defined in the obvious way—namely, $\rho_{S,\gamma}(T,\mu) = S,\gamma,\mu$.

4.6 States and Actions: A Formal Summary

For every statement S in the language L, I have defined the following:

- A set $\mathcal{V}(S)$ of variable names, consisting of:
  - all program-variable names of the form $x()$ for every identifier x and of the form $x(S,\gamma)$, where γ is the selector in S of a **new** x statement.
  - all control-variable names of the form $at(S,\gamma)$, $in(S,\gamma)$, and $after(S,\gamma)$, for all substatements S,γ of S.
- The set $\mathcal{S}(S)$ of states of S, which is defined defined to be the set of all mappings

  $$val : \mathcal{V}(S) \rightarrow Z \cup \{true, false\}$$

- The set $\mathcal{A}(S)$ of atomic-action names of S, defined to be the set of all components of the form S,γ where S,γ is a **while** or **if** test, an atomic assignment, or an **init** clause of a **new** statement.
- If T is the substatement S,γ of S, the renaming mappings

  $$\rho_{S,\gamma} : \mathcal{V}(T) \rightarrow \mathcal{V}(S)$$
  $$\rho^*_{S,\gamma} : \mathcal{S}(S) \rightarrow \mathcal{S}(T)\rho_{S,\gamma} : \mathcal{A}(T) \rightarrow \mathcal{A}(S)$$

  These renaming mappings satisfy (2) and (4).

5 Temporal Logic

In the action-axiom semantics, I use temporal logic to express the constraints describing when an action must eventually occur. Temporal logic, introduced into the study of concurrent programs by Pnueli [13], is now quite familiar. I will therefore only sketch the logic that I will need, and refer the reader to [5] and the appendix of [6] for more details.

5.1 Predicates

The building-blocks of our temporal logic are *predicates*. For any program statement S, I define a set of predicates. There are two kinds of predicates: state predicates and action predicates.

A state predicate of S is just an expression constructed from variable names in $\mathcal{V}(S)$, including control variable names. For example,

$$at(S,\gamma) \vee \neg b() \;\supset\; x(S,\mu) = y() + 1$$

I will also include as predicates such expressions as $v \in Z$, where v is a variable name and Z denotes the set of integers.

Since a state in $\mathcal{S}(S)$ assigns a value to all variable names in $\mathcal{V}(S)$, it assigns a value to a predicate. For any state s of $\mathcal{S}(S)$, I denote by $s \models P$ the value assigned to the state predicate P by the state s.

A predicate is normally a boolean-valued expression, but I have not restricted predicates in this way; $y() + 17$ is just as much a predicate as $\neg b()$. The reason is that there is no way of knowing whether an expression has a boolean value without knowing the types of all its variables, and the types of undeclared variables are not known. We must have rules for computing the value of $y() + 17$ even when the value of $y()$ is *true*. I will handle this problem by adding an additional *undefined* value, and define *true* + 17 to equal *undefined*.

The presence of an *undefined* value means that we must be careful when manipulating expressions, since the usual rules of arithmetic and logic don't hold. For example, $x + 1 > x$ does not equal *true* if x is a boolean. However, $x \in Z \supset (x + 1 > x)$ should always have the value *true*.

It is necessary to allow predicates to have *logical value variables* (not to be confused with program and control variables) and quantifiers. Thus,

$$\forall \eta : x() + \chi > y(S, \gamma) + \eta$$

is a predicate containing the free logical value variable χ, the bound logical value variable η, and the two program variables $x()$ and $y(S, \gamma)$ in $\mathcal{V}(S)$. For any predicate P and state s of $\mathcal{S}(S)$, $s \models P$ is a formula involving values and value variables.

An action predicate of S is an expression of the form $Act(S, \gamma)$, where S, γ is a substatement of S. The action predicate $Act(S, \gamma)$ defines a boolean-valued function on the set $\mathcal{A}(S)$ that has the value *true* on an action-name α if and only if α is the name of an atomic action of the substatement S, γ. I write $\alpha \models Act(S, \gamma)$ to denote the value of $Act(S, \gamma)$ on α. Remembering that atomic-action names are just components S, μ of S, we see that $S, \mu \models Act(S, \gamma)$ equals true if and only if $\mu = \gamma, \nu$ for some ν.

Let $\mathcal{PR}(S)$ denote the set of all state and action predicates of S. Since state predicates are built out of variable names and action predicates are all of the form $Act(S, \gamma)$, the renaming mappings induce mappings on predicates in the obvious way. If T is the substatement S, γ of S, then

$$\rho_{S,\gamma} : \mathcal{PR}(T) \rightarrow \mathcal{PR}(S)$$

These renaming mappings satisfy the expected relation (2). Moreover, if P is a tautology of $\mathcal{PR}(T)$, then $\rho_{S,\gamma}$ is a tautology of $\mathcal{PR}(S)$.

5.2 The Unary Temporal Operators

I will begin with the simpler form of temporal logic, using only unary temporal operators. The formulas of this logic are constructed from predicates, the usual logical operations, and the two unary temporal operators $\Diamond$ and $\Box$. More precisely, for any statement S, the set $\mathcal{TL}(S)$ of temporal logic formulas of S consists of all formulas constructed from $\mathcal{PR}(S)$ with the logical operators and the unary operators $\Diamond$ and $\Box$.

Just as predicates are true or false for states, temporal logic formulas are true or false for behaviors. Let $\mathcal{B}(S)$ denote the set of all finite and infinite sequences of the form

$$s_0 \xrightarrow{\alpha_1} s_1 \xrightarrow{\alpha_2} \cdots \tag{5}$$

where the s_i are states in $\mathcal{S}(S)$ and the α_i are atomic-action names in $\mathcal{A}(S)$. We give a semantics for temporal logic formulas by defining $\sigma \models A$ for any behavior σ in $\mathcal{B}(S)$ and any temporal logic formula A in $\mathcal{TL}(S)$.

If σ is the sequence (5), for any nonnegative integer n let σ^{+n} be the sequence

$$s_n \xrightarrow{\alpha_{n+1}} s_{n+1} \xrightarrow{\alpha_{n+2}} \cdots$$

unless σ is finite and n is less than the length m of σ, in which case σ^{+n} is defined to be the sequence consisting of the single state s_m. We define $\sigma \models A$ inductively as follows.

- If A is a state predicate, then $\sigma \models A \stackrel{\text{def}}{=} s_0 \models A$. (The value of a state predicate is its value in the starting state.)

- If A is an action predicate, then $\sigma \models A \stackrel{\text{def}}{=} \alpha_1 \models A$. (The value of an action predicate is its value for the first action.) However, if σ consists of the single state s_0 with no actions, then $\sigma \models A \stackrel{\text{def}}{=} \mathit{false}$.

- The logical connectives "distribute" in the obvious way. For example,

$$\sigma \models (A \vee B) \stackrel{\text{def}}{=} (\sigma \models A) \vee (\sigma \models B)$$

- The temporal operators are defined by

$$\begin{aligned} \sigma \models \Box A &\stackrel{\text{def}}{=} \forall n : \sigma^{+n} \models A \\ \sigma \models \Diamond A &\stackrel{\text{def}}{=} \exists n : \sigma^{+n} \models A \end{aligned}$$

Note that $\Diamond$ is the dual of $\Box$—that is, $\Box A \equiv \neg\Diamond\neg A$ for any A. The operator $\leadsto$ is defined by

$$A \leadsto B \stackrel{\text{def}}{=} \Box(A \supset \Diamond B)$$

Note also that $\Box\Diamond A$ has the intuitive meaning that A is true infinitely often.

5.3 The Binary Temporal Operators

While the unary temporal operator $\Box$, and the operators derivable from it, are quite natural and easy to understand, they are not sufficiently expressive. We need an additional binary temporal operator. There are many binary operators that are equivalent in the sense that one can be represented by another. My favorite one, introduced in [6], is the operator $\trianglelefteq$, whose semantics is defined as follows.

$$\sigma \models (A \trianglelefteq B) \stackrel{\text{def}}{=} \forall n : (\forall m \leq n : \sigma^{+m} \models A) \supset \sigma^{+n} \models B$$

Intuitively, $A \trianglelefteq B$ means that B holds for at least as long as A does—that is, A holds for a length of time $\leq$ the length of time that B holds, so it represents a "temporal $\leq$".

I will extend the definition of $\mathcal{TL}(S)$ to include temporal formulas constructed with the operator $\trianglelefteq$ as well as $\Box$ and $\Diamond$. The unary operators can be defined in terms of $\trianglelefteq$; for example, $\Box A \equiv \mathit{true} \trianglelefteq A$. Thus, the single operator $\trianglelefteq$ is all we need.

The operator $\triangleleft$ is defined in terms of $\trianglelefteq$ by

$$A \triangleleft B \stackrel{\text{def}}{=} (A \vee \neg B) \trianglelefteq B$$

A little thought shows that

$$\sigma \models (A \triangleleft B) \stackrel{\text{def}}{=} \forall n : (\forall m < n : \sigma^{+m} \models A) \supset \sigma^{+n} \models B$$

so $A \triangleleft B$ means that A holds for a length of time $<$ the length of time that B holds. The operators $\triangleleft$ and $\trianglelefteq$ obey the same transitivity relations that $<$ and $\leq$ do. For example,

$$(A \trianglelefteq B) \wedge (B \triangleleft C) \ \supset \ (A \triangleleft C)$$

I will use $\trianglelefteq$ to define a new type of temporal formula that is useful for specifying actions. For any action name $\alpha \in \mathcal{A}(S)$ and any predicates P and Q, I define $\{P\}\langle\alpha\rangle\{Q\}$ to be the temporal logic formula that means that executing α starting in a state in which P is true can produce a state in which Q is true. (It is just the ordinary Hoare triple for the atomic action α, viewed as a temporal formula.) However, we must allow stuttering actions of α which do nothing, and hence leave P true. The formal definition is

$$\{P\}\langle\alpha\rangle\{Q\} \stackrel{\text{def}}{=} P \supset (\mathit{Act}(\alpha) \triangleleft P \vee Q)$$

Intuitively, $\sigma \models \{P\}\langle\alpha\rangle\{Q\}$ asserts that if, P is true in the initial state of σ and the first one or more actions of σ are α actions, then $P \vee Q$ remains true through the first state before the first action that is not an α action. If $Q \supset \neg\mathit{Act}(\alpha)$ holds, which is the only case in which this is formula will be used, then Q will be true only after the last of these initial α actions. Hence, it asserts that α can perform a series of stuttering actions leaving P true, and can also "finish" by making Q true.

The formula $\{P\}\langle\alpha\rangle\{Q\}$ is used to describe how an action can change the state. It is also necessary to state that an action does not change something. I therefore introduce the formula $e \stackrel{\alpha}{\not\to}$, which asserts that the action α does not change the value of the expression e. It is defined by

$$e \stackrel{\alpha}{\not\to} \stackrel{\text{def}}{=} \forall \eta : (e = \eta) \ \supset \ \mathit{Act}(\alpha) \triangleleft (e = \eta)$$

5.4 Renaming

Having already extended the renaming mappings to predicates, it is easy to extend them to temporal logic formulas constructed from predicates. For example, for any variable names v and w, we have

$$\rho_{S,\gamma}(\Box(v \vee \Diamond w)) \ = \ \Box(\rho_{S,\gamma}(v) \vee \Diamond\rho_{S,\gamma}(w))$$

Thus, if T is the substatement S, γ of S,

$$\rho_{S,\gamma} : \mathcal{TL}(T) \rightarrow \mathcal{TL}(S)$$

The renaming mappings do ***not*** induce any mappings on behaviors. This is because they map states and atomic-action names in opposite directions:

$$\rho^*_{S,\gamma} : \mathcal{S}(S) \rightarrow \mathcal{S}(T)$$
$$\rho_{S,\gamma} : \mathcal{A}(T) \rightarrow \mathcal{A}(S)$$

Since a behavior consists of an alternating sequence of states and action names, the renaming mappings do not work on behaviors. This may be the source of the difficulties encountered in trying to give a behavioral semantics—one in which $\mathcal{M}[\![S]\!]$ is a set of behaviors—to concurrent programming languages

5.5 Temporal Logic as Semantics

For each statement S of the programming language, I have defined a set $\mathcal{TL}(S)$ of temporal logic formulas, and a notion of semantic validity $\models$ for these formulas. In an action-axiom semantics, the meaning of S includes a set of temporal logic formulas that must be satisfied by the behaviors of S. This set of formulas is specified by giving axioms and inference rules, which means that we have a logical system and a notion of a provable formula. I will not discuss provability, and will restrict myself to validity.

I have defined $\sigma \models A$ for a behavior σ and a temporal logic formula A, but I have not defined the concept $\models A$—validity of a formula. For any formula $A \in \mathcal{TL}(S)$, one usually defines $\models A$ to equal ***true*** if and only if $\sigma \models A$ equals ***true*** for all behaviors σ in $\mathcal{B}(S)$.

The formulas A for which $\models A$ is true are those that are true for all sequences of states and actions from S, so their truth rests only on the properties of S's sets of states and actions, not on properties of S's dynamic behavior—for example, the formula $\Box(x() \in Z \supset (x^2 \geq x))$. A formula A is said to valid for all behaviors in some subset Σ of $\mathcal{B}(S)$, written $\models_\Sigma A$, if $\sigma \models A = \textbf{\textit{true}}$ for all $\sigma \in \Sigma$. The valid formulas for a program S are those that are valid for the set of all behaviors of S.

Note that $\models_\Sigma$ *false* is true if and only if Σ is the empty set. The semantics I give can produce contradictory sets of axioms for a program—axioms from which one can deduce the formula *false*. This is not an inconsistency in the system; rather it is an indication that there are no legal behaviors of the program, so the program is illegal. This will be the case, for example, if a program assigns a boolean value to a variable of type **integer**.

I consider the notion $\models_\Sigma$ of semantic validity only for sets Σ having the property that for any $\sigma \in \Sigma$ and any $n \geq 0$: $\sigma^{+n} \in \Sigma$. Intuitively, this means that the temporal logic does not assume any preferred starting state. Formally, this means that the truth of $\models A$ implies the truth of $\models \Box A$—a rule of inference known to logicians as the *Necessitation Rule*. This rule implies that whenever we give a predicate P as a temporal-logic axiom, we are really asserting that $\Box P$ is true.

The validity of the Necessitation Rule means that it is impossible to write a temporal logic formula which asserts that the program is executed only in certain starting states. Thus, one should define the semantics $\mathcal{M}[\![S]\!]$ of S to consist of both a set of temporal logic axioms that constrain the allowed behaviors of S and a set of nontemporal axioms—that is, predicates—that constrain the starting state. The semantic meaning $\mathcal{M}[\![S]\!]$ defines the set of behaviors of S to be the set of all behaviors σ such that:

- $\sigma \models A$ for every temporal axiom $A \in \mathcal{M}[\![S]\!]$, and
- $s_0 \models A$ for every nontemporal axiom $A \in \mathcal{M}[\![S]\!]$, where s_0 is the starting state of σ.

However, as I will show, it is not necessary to specify any initial states for a substatement S of a program. The only initial-state specification that must be added is that a complete program starts at its entry point.

5.6 There Won't Be a Next Time

An important "feature" of the temporal logic I am using is that there is no "next time" operator. There is no way in this logic to express the concept of the next state in the behavior. In fact, no formula in the logic can distinguish between two behaviors that differ only in the addition of "stuttering" actions—that is, where an action $s \xrightarrow{\alpha} t$ in the behavior is replaced by the finite sequence of actions

$$s \xrightarrow{\alpha} s \xrightarrow{\alpha} \cdots \xrightarrow{\alpha} s \xrightarrow{\alpha} t$$

It is the inability to distinguish stuttering that makes it easy to talk about a lower-level program implementing a higher-level one.

5.7 Implementation Mappings

I can now continue the discussion, begun in Section 2.4, of what it means for a lower-level program to correctly implement a higher-level one. Let Π be the higher-level program and π be its lower-level implementation. From the point of view of behaviors, we saw that there should be mappings F from the states and actions of π to the states and actions of Π so that if σ is the behavior

$$s_0 \xrightarrow{\alpha_1} s_1 \xrightarrow{\alpha_2} \cdots$$

of π, then $F(\sigma)$, which is defined to be

$$F(s_0) \xrightarrow{F(\alpha_1)} F(s_1) \xrightarrow{F(\alpha_2)} \cdots$$

is a behavior of Π.

How are the mappings F defined? In action-axiom semantics, one never mentions states, just state predicates—mappings from the state into a set of Booleans. A state is determined by the values of all state predicates. To define a mapping $F : \mathcal{S}(\pi) \rightarrow \mathcal{S}(\Pi)$, one defines a mapping F^* that maps state predicates of Π into state predicates of π. Intuitively, F^* defines the state predicates of Π in terms of the state predicates of π. For example, $F^*(x(\Pi, \gamma) > 0)$ is the state predicate of π that "implements" the state predicate $x(\Pi, \gamma) > 0$ of Π; in other words, it is the translation of the high-level statement that the value of the variable $x(\Pi, \gamma)$ is positive into a lower-level statement involving the values of memory registers, program counters, etc. Defining the mapping F^* requires describing how the variables (both program and control variables) of Π are implemented by the "variables" (machine registers) of π. The mappings F and F^* are related by

$$s \models F^*(P) \equiv F(s) \models P$$

for any state s in $\mathcal{S}(\pi)$ and state predicate P in $\mathcal{PR}(\Pi)$.

In a similar way, F^* is defined to map action predicates of Π into action predicates of π, so $F^* : \mathcal{PR}(\Pi) \rightarrow \mathcal{PR}(\pi)$. Finding the mapping F^* is the heart of the proof that π correctly implements Π. The discussion in Section 2.4 of the dual mapping F applies equally well to F^*, and I will not discuss further how F^* is actually constructed.

Since temporal logic formulas are constructed from predicates and temporal operators, there is an obvious extension of F^* to a mapping from $\mathcal{TL}(\Pi)$ to $\mathcal{TL}(\pi)$. For example,

$$F^*(in(\Pi, \rho) \lhd x(\Pi, \gamma) > 0) \quad = \quad F^*(in(\Pi, \rho)) \lhd F^*(x(\Pi, \gamma) > 0)$$

It follows from these definitions that for any behavior σ of π and any formula A in $\mathcal{TL}(\Pi)$:

$$\sigma \models F^*(A) \equiv F(\sigma) \models A$$

In terms of behaviors, π correctly implements Π if, for every possible behavior σ of π, $F(\sigma)$ is a possible behavior of Π. For simplicity, let us ignore the initial-state specification, so the meaning $\mathcal{M}[\![\Pi]\!]$ of Π in an action-axiom semantics is a set of temporal logic axioms, and $F(\sigma)$ is a possible behavior of Π if and only if $F(\sigma) \models A$ is true for all $A \in \mathcal{M}[\![\Pi]\!]$. But $F(\sigma) \models A$ is true if and only if $\sigma \models F^*(A)$ is, so π correctly implements Π if and only if $\sigma \models F^*(A)$ is true for all $A \in \mathcal{M}[\![\Pi]\!]$ and all behaviors σ of π. The behaviors of π consist of the sequences satisfying all the axioms of $\mathcal{M}[\![\pi]\!]$. It follows from this that π correctly implements Π if, for every axiom A in $\mathcal{M}[\![\Pi]\!]$, $F^*(A)$ is implied by the axioms in $\mathcal{M}[\![\pi]\!]$. Thus, proving correctness of the implementation involves deducing, from the axioms for π, the truth of $F^*(A)$—the translation of A into an assertion about π—for every axiom A in $\mathcal{M}[\![\Pi]\!]$.

As explained in Section 2.4, a compiler is free to implement local variables and internal actions in any fashion, but interface (global) variables and external actions have a fixed implementation. The mapping F^* is defined on state predicates by defining $F^*(v)$ in terms of the variables of π, for every variable v of Π. The definition of $F^*(v)$ is arbitrary for a local variable v, but is fixed for an interface variable. To prove the correctness of an implementation, we are allowed to define $F^*(v)$ any way we like if v is a local variable, but must use the predetermined definition if v is an interface variable. Similar comments apply to actions.

I find it helpful to think of the semantics $\mathcal{M}[\![\Pi]\!]$ of Π as the specification of a lower-level implementation. When viewed this way, there is an implicit existential quantification over the names of all local variables and internal actions. More precisely, the specification consists of the conjunction of all the axioms in $\mathcal{M}[\![\Pi]\!]$, with existential quantification over these variable and action names. The names of interface variables and external actions represent fixed, externally defined objects.

6 The Semantics of Language L

With these preliminaries out of the way, I can now give the semantics of language L. This is done by defining the meaning $\mathcal{M}[\![S]\!]$ of S, where S is any statement or complete program. I define $\mathcal{M}[\![S]\!]$ to consist of a set of temporal logic axioms that specify the set of behaviors of S. As discussed below, for a complete program Π, I will also need one nontemporal axiom—that is, a predicate—to specify the starting state.

The basic idea behind achieving a compositional semantics is the requirement that any axiom asserted about a statement T must be valid for any statement containing T as a substatement. Of course, an axiom about T must be renamed to become an axiom about a statement containing T. The formal statement of this idea is:

> *Composition Principle*: If T is substatement S, γ of S, then for any formula A: if $A \in \mathcal{M}[\![T]\!]$ then $\rho_{S,\gamma} A \in \mathcal{M}[\![S, \gamma]\!]$.

6.1 Syntactic Predicates

I observed in Section 4.3 that there is information we need in order to define $\mathcal{M}[\![S]\!]$ that is not in the state of S—namely, type and aliasing information. This information is not in the state because it is determined syntactically and does not change during execution of S. Unfortunately, it may be determined not by the syntax of S, but by the syntax of the complete program containing S. For example, the aliasing relations defined by a **new** statement are not known when defining $\mathcal{M}[\![S]\!]$ for a statement S in its body.

For our simple language L, typing information can be handled by ordinary axioms; the fact that a variable v is of type integer is expressed by the requirement that the value of v always be an integer. Aliasing relations can also be expressed by similar requirements—for example the aliasing relation defined by

> **new** z **: gausian alias** $x + y\sqrt{-1}$ **in** ...

is expressed by requiring that the value of $z(S)$ always equals the value of $x() + y()\sqrt{-1}$. However, the fact that $z(S)$ is *not* aliased to the variable $a()$ cannot be expressed in this way.

The absence of aliasing relations is expressed with a new relation $\perp$, where $v \perp w$ means intuitively that assigning a value to the variable named v does not change the value of the variable named w, and vice-versa. An ordinary state predicate such as $v = w$, which asserts that the values of v and w are equal, is true or false for a particular state. However, the truth of the expression $v \perp w$ depends only upon the syntactic structure of the program; it is true for one state of S if and only if it is true for all states of S.

An expression like $v \perp w$, whose value is a boolean that depends only on the program syntax, is called a *syntactic predicate*. Unfortunately, if v and w are undeclared variables of S, then the value of $v \perp w$ depends upon the syntax of the program that contains S, and its value is not determined when we are defining $\mathcal{M}[\![S]\!]$. Thus, a syntactic predicate either has a definite boolean value, or else has an undetermined value.

I will allow syntactic predicates to appear in a temporal logic formula of $\mathcal{TL}(S)$ anywhere that an ordinary state predicate can. However, there is no reason to write $\Diamond(v \perp w)$, since if $v \perp w$ is ever true, then it is always true for every state of S. Formally, a syntactic predicate in a temporal logic formula of $\mathcal{TL}(S)$ is viewed as a boolean constant if its value is determined by S, and as a logical variable if its value is undetermined.

Formally, a syntactic predicate appearing in an axiom of $\mathcal{M}[\![S]\!]$ is a constant if its value is determined by S, and it is a logical variable if its value is not determined. Thus, writing the syntactic predicate $x(S,\gamma) \perp y(S,\mu)$ is simply an "abbreviation" for either *true* or *false*, since the aliasing relations of variables declared in S are determined. On the other hand, a syntactic predicate such as $x() \perp y()$ represents a logical variable, since aliasing relations between undeclared variables are undetermined. Because there is an implicit universal quantification over all free logical variables in an axiom, an axiom containing a syntactic predicate is asserted to be true whatever value is assigned to it.

We can apply renaming mappings to syntactic predicates in the obvious way. Thus, if P is a syntactic predicate for T, and T is the substatement S,γ of S, then $\rho_{S,\gamma}(P)$ is a syntactic predicate for S. When the predicate P occurs in an axiom A of $\mathcal{M}[\![T]\!]$, the expression $\rho_{S,\gamma}(P)$ occurs in $\rho_{S,\gamma}(A)$, which, by the Composition Principle, is an axiom of $\mathcal{M}[\![S]\!]$. A little thought reveals that, to ensure the validity of the Composition Principle, we want the following property to hold:

> *Syntactic Composition Property*: For any syntactic predicate P: if the value of P is defined for T, then the value of $\rho_{S,\gamma}(P)$ is also defined for S and equals the value of P.

The use of syntactic predicates is not really necessary. I could include the information that they express in the state. Had I done so, a syntactic predicate having an undetermined value would become a component of the state, and $\mathcal{S}(S)$ would include states having all possible values of that predicate. A syntactic predicate whose value is determined in a statement S could be represented either as a state component constrained to have only one possible value, or as a constant.

6.1.1 Aliasing

The absence of aliasing will be expressed by the relation $\perp$ between variable names in $\mathcal{V}(S)$. This will be done axiomatically by defining a logical system for deriving $\perp$ relations To do this, I must first introduce a relation $\prec$, where $v \prec \{w_1,\ldots,w_n\}$ means that the variable name v is not directly aliased to any variable names other than $w_1,\ldots,w_n$. It is convenient to extend this relation to a relation between sets of variable names, where $\{v_1,\ldots,v_m\} \prec \{w_1,\ldots,w_n\}$ means that each of the variable names v_i is not directly aliased to any variable names other than the w_j. We then have the obvious inference rule:

> For any sets $V, W \in \mathcal{V}(S)$: if $V' \subseteq V$, $W \subseteq W'$, and $V \prec W$, then $V' \prec W'$.

The relation $\perp$ on $\mathcal{V}(S)$ is defined so that $v \perp w$ means that neither v nor w is aliased, directly or indirectly, to the other. In other words, it means that $v \neq w$ and there do not exist both a chain of $\prec$ relations from v and a chain of $\prec$ relations from w that lead to a common variable name. This leads to the following rules for deriving $\perp$ relations.

- If $v \prec \emptyset$, $w \prec \emptyset$, and $v \neq w$, then $v \perp w$.
- If $v \perp w$ then $w \perp v$.
- If $v \prec \{w_1, \ldots, w_n\}$, $w_1 \perp w$, ... , $w_n \perp w$, and $v \neq w$, then $v \perp w$.

I extend $\perp$ to a relation on finite sets by letting $\{v_1, \ldots, v_n\} \perp \{w_1, \ldots, w_n\}$ denote $\forall i, j : v_i \perp w_j$.

Having given general rules for reasoning about $\prec$, I must define the relation for variables names in $\mathcal{S}(S)$ for an arbitrary statement S. The value of a syntactic predicate $V \prec W$ or $V \perp W$ will be undetermined if V and W both contain the names of undeclared variables of S. To define the values of the ones that are determined, I will take the Syntactic Composition Property as an axiom, and give a recursive definition based upon the structure of S.

The first observation is that a program variable cannot be aliased to a control variable, and vice-versa. I therefore require that $v \perp w$ equal ***true*** whenever v is a program variable and w is a control variable.

Since the only dependency relations on program variables are introduced by the **alias** clauses of **new** statements, all dependency relations among program variables are obtained from the Syntactic Composition Property and the following axiom:

> If S is the statement **new** x ... **alias** exp ... and y_1, ..., y_n are all the variable names in exp, then $x(S) \prec \{y_1(), \ldots, y_n()\}$.

I must now define the dependency relations on control variable names. I will do this by assuming the Syntactic Composition Property and defining the relations introduced by each language construct. There are a number of aliasing relations that are similar to the ones introduced by an **alias** clause, except that the aliasing relations for the control variables are implicit in the program structure rather stated explicitly in a **new** statement. To define the $\prec$ relations, I will write down these aliasing equations, where the control variable comprising the left-hand side of an equation is considered to depend upon each of the variables on the right-hand side. There is one set of equations for each programming language construct.

Besides these aliasing equalities, some other aliasing relations are given as boolean expressions—that is, asserting that the boolean expressions are true. No dependency relations are implied by these expressions, but they are listed here for future reference.

There is only one axiom that explicitly defines $\perp$ relations; it is given for the **cobegin** statement.

assignment $in(S) = at(S)$
$\neg(at(S) \wedge after(S))$

if

$$\begin{aligned}
in(S, test) &= at(S, test) \\
after(S, test) &= at(S, then) \lor at(S, else) \\
at(S) &= at(S, test) \\
in(S) &= in(S, test) \lor in(S, then) \lor in(S, else) \\
after(S) &= after(S, then) \lor after(S, else)
\end{aligned}$$

$$\neg(at(S, test) \land (in(S, then) \lor in(S, else) \lor after(S)))$$

$$\neg(in(S, then) \land in(S, else))$$

while

$$\begin{aligned}
at(S) &= at(S, test) \\
in(S, test) &= at(S, test) \\
after(S, test) &= at(S, body) \lor after(S) \\
after(S, body) &= at(S, test) \\
in(S) &= at(S, test) \lor in(S, body)
\end{aligned}$$

$$\neg(at(S, test) \land (after(S) \lor in(S, body)))$$

new There are two cases. If there is no **init** clause, then:

$$\begin{aligned}
at(S) &= at(S, body) \\
after(S) &= after(S, body) \\
in(S) &= in(S, body)
\end{aligned}$$

If there is an **init** clause, then:

$$\begin{aligned}
at(S) &= at(S, init) \\
in(S, init) &= at(S, init) \\
after(S, init) &= at(S, body) \\
in(S) &= in(S, init) \lor in(S, body) \\
after(S) &= after(S, body)
\end{aligned}$$

$$\neg(at(S, init) \land in(S, body))$$

cobegin If there are n clauses in the **cobegin**, then

$$\begin{aligned}
at(S) &= at(S, 1) \land \ldots \land at(S, n) \\
after(S) &= after(S, 1) \land \ldots \land after(S, n) \\
in(S) &= in(S, 1) \land \ldots \land in(S, n) \\
\{in(S, i), after(S, i)\} &\perp \{in(S, j), after(S, j)\} \text{ for } i \neq j
\end{aligned}$$

sequence If S is $S_1; \ldots S_n$, then for all $i = 1, \ldots, n$:

$$\begin{aligned}
after(S, i-1) &= at(S, i) \text{ if } i > 0 \\
in(S) &= in(S, i)
\end{aligned}$$

$$\neg(in(S, i) \land in(S, j)) \text{ for } i \neq j$$

program If S is the complete program, then

$$\begin{aligned}
at(S) &= at(S, body) \\
in(S) &= in(S, body) \\
after(S) &= after(S, body)
\end{aligned}$$

A close study of these aliasing relations reveals that we can prove a relation such as $in(S,\gamma) \perp at(S,\mu)$ if and only if the substatements S,γ and S,μ lie in different clauses of a **cobegin**.

The $\perp$ relations among program variables and the aliasing and $\perp$ relations among control variables are regarded as axioms in a separate system for reasoning about syntactic expressions. However, they play the same function as axioms of $\mathcal{M}[\![S]\!]$. For example, if S,γ is an assignment statement, then the aliasing relation $\neg(at(S,\gamma) \wedge after(S,\gamma))$ allows us to deduce $\Diamond(\neg at(S,\gamma))$ from $\Diamond after(S,\gamma)$.

6.1.2 Syntactic Typing Relations

Because the type structure of our language L is so simple, no explicit reference to types need appear in its semantics. However, this is not the case for a language in which the action of an assignment statement is affected by the types of its left- and right-hand sides—for example, if coercion was performed. We would also have to introduce explicit reference to types if a type mismatch in an assignment statement produced a run-time error or an indeterminate result, or if it halted the process executing the assignment.

Explicit reference to types is done by introducing predicates such as $type(x) =$ **integer**. If the types of variables are determined syntactically by the program text, then these predicates would be syntactic predicates. Otherwise, they would have to be ordinary state predicates, and the state would have to include components that determine their values.

6.1.3 Reasoning About Syntactic Expressions

Although a syntactic predicate like $v \perp w$ resembles an ordinary state predicate like $v = 7$, it is logically quite different. The variable name "v" denotes the value of the variable in the expression $v = 7$, while it denotes the name itself in $v \perp w$. For example, from the expressions $v = 7$ and $w = v$ we can deduce $w = 7$. However, from the syntactic expression $u \perp v$ and the ordinary expression $w = v$ we cannot in general deduce $u \perp w$; just because the *values* of two variables happen to be equal in some state does not imply that the variables have the same aliasing relations. We can only make that conclusion if $w = v$ is a syntactic equality of names, rather than an expression denoting equality of values.

By introducing syntactic predicates as a class of entities separate from ordinary state predicates, with their own logical system for reasoning about them, I have circumvented the need to distinguish between the use of a variable name as a name and as a value. In a syntactic predicate, a variable name represents itself. In a state predicate, it represents the value of the variable. Using two different logical systems avoids confusion. One cannot make invalid deductions, like deducing a $\perp$ relation from the equality of the values of v and w, because inferences about $\perp$ can be made only in the logic for reasoning about syntactic predicates, whereas equality of values can be expressed only with state predicates, and one reasons about them with a separate logic.

For languages in which types and aliasing relations are dynamic properties, so they must be reflected in the state, we cannot use this trick for separating the two different uses of variable names. We must then write $value(v)$ rather than the variable name v

to denote the value of v. Equality of values is denoted by the predicate $value(w) = value(v)$, and $w = v$ denotes equality of names.

6.1.4 Logical Name Variables

Just as I introduced logical value variables in state predicates, I will also introduce *logical name variables* for syntactic predicates. A logical value variable is a logical variable with an implicit range in the set of values that a variable may have. Similarly, a logical name variable is a logical variable with an implicit range in the set of names that a variable may have. I will use the letter ν to denote a logical name variable.

The use of logical name variables has an important implication with respect to renaming. Consider an axiom of the form $\forall \nu : A(\nu)$. Viewed as a formula in $\mathcal{TL}(S)$, it is equivalent to an infinite conjunction of the form $A(v_1) \wedge A(v_2) \wedge \cdots$, where the v_i are all the names in $\mathcal{V}(S)$. However, the two formulas behave differently under a renaming mapping ρ. In particular, $\rho(\forall \nu : A(\nu))$ equals $\forall \nu : \rho(A(\nu))$, so the renamed formula includes a quantification over variable names not present in $\rho(A(v_1) \wedge \cdots)$.

6.2 Starting States

One might expect that the meaning $\mathcal{M}[\![S]\!]$ of a statement S should include a set of axioms that determine the set of starting states. However, consider what the initial value of a program variable should be. The user has no way of specifying it, since an **init** clause of a **new** statement is interpreted as an executable action that replaces the initial value with the specified one. One might want to specify that the initial value of a variable v of type **integer** should be an integer. However, $\mathcal{M}[\![S]\!]$ will contain an axiom asserting that this is true for every state during the execution of S, so it is therefore true of the initial state. Similarly, the axioms in $\mathcal{M}[\![S]\!]$ will assert that the aliasing relations specified by **new** statements are true throughout the execution, so they are also constrained to hold in the initial state.

What about the initial values of control variables? Surely we should require that a statement S should start in a state in which $at(S)$ is true. However, this would be a mistake because it would violate the Composition Principle, since $\rho_{T;S,2}(at(S))$ should not be true of the starting state of the sequence of statements $T; S$, and our whole approach is based upon the Composition Principle.

Remember that the only reason for specifying the starting state is to be able to obtain from our semantics a set of behaviors. However, we are really interested only in the set of behaviors of a complete program, not of its substatements. There is no reason to constrain the starting states of substatements; we need only constrain the starting state of a complete program, which we do by simply assuming that $at(\Pi)$ is true of the initial state of a complete program Π. We can do this without violating the Composition Principle because a complete program cannot be part of any larger statement.

6.3 Behavior Axioms

I now define the set $\mathcal{M}[\![S]\!]$ of behavioral axioms for any statement and complete program S. This will, of course, be done compositionally, giving a set axioms for each language construct. Remember that in addition to the axioms given explicitly below, $\mathcal{M}[\![S]\!]$ also contains all the axioms implied by the Composition Principle.

I will include in $\mathcal{M}[\![S]\!]$ axioms to assert that the appropriate aliasing relations hold throughout the execution of S. For control variables, those aliasing relations were already described in Section 6.1.1. Rather than write them over again, I will simply assume that the aliasing relations described there appear as axioms in $\mathcal{M}[\![S]\!]$ for the appropriate construct describing S. For example, the list of axioms for the assignment given below are assumed implicitly to include the axioms $in(S) = at(S)$ and $\neg at(S) \wedge after(S)$ from Section 6.1.1. (However, the $\perp$ relations given for the **cobegin**, being syntactic predicates, are not axioms in $\mathcal{M}[\![S]\!]$.)

In addition to the aliasing relations for control variables, we should also assert their types. Therefore, we implicitly add the axiom $v \in \{true, false\}$ to $\mathcal{M}[\![S]\!]$ for every control variable v in $\mathcal{V}(S)$.

There are also axioms relating the action predicate $Act(S)$ to the action predicates of its components. For example, the axioms for a **while** statement S would include the following:

- $Act(S) \equiv Act(S, test) \vee Act(S, body)$
- $\neg(Act(S, test) \wedge Act(S, body))$

The first asserts that the only actions of S are the *test* action and the actions of its body; the second asserts that the *test* action is not an action of the body. These and similar axioms are assumed for all the constructs and are not included. Note that these axioms are given only for compound statements; there is no such axiom for the assignment statement.

In the following description of the axioms, formal axioms are followed by their informal explanations. For any programming-language expression *exp*, I let *exp*() denote the expression obtained by replacing every identifier y in *exp* by the variable name $y()$.

6.3.1 Assignment

If S is the statement $\langle x := exp \rangle$, then $\mathcal{M}[\![S]\!]$ contains the following axioms:

1. $Act(S) \supset at(S)$
   The atomic statement S can be executed only when control is at S.

2. $\forall \eta : \{at(S) \wedge exp() = \eta\}\langle S\rangle\{after(S) \wedge x() = \eta\}$
   Executing S sets the value of x to *exp* and changes control from $at(S)$ to $after(S)$.

3. $\forall \nu : \{x(), at(S), after(S)\} \perp \nu \supset \nu \overset{S}{\not\to}$
   (Note that ν is a logical name variable.) The statement S does not modify any variable not aliased to x, $at(S)$, or $after(S)$.

4. $\Box\Diamond Act(S) \supset \Diamond\neg at(S)$
   There cannot be infinitely many actions of S while control remains forever at S. (The reader may find this easier to understand if he replaces the implication by a disjunction.) In other words, there can be only finitely many stuttering actions of S before the assignment is executed.

An understanding of these axioms for assignment is crucial to an appreciation of how action-axiom semantics works, so some further discussion of them is in order. The four axioms are indeed action axioms, since they describe the behavior of the assignment action S. The four axioms assert the following:

1. When the action *may* occur.

2. What changes to the state components executing the action *may* perform.

3. What state components the action may not change.

4. When the action *must* change the state.

Every atomic program action is described by four similar axioms.

Note that axioms 1-3 assert safety properties, while axiom 4 states a liveness property. From the axioms for the other statements, it will follow that in language L, if $at(S)$ ever becomes true, it can be made false only by executing action S. Axiom 2 asserts that $at(S)$ can then become false only when $after(S)$ becomes true and the assignment of exp to x occurs. In a richer language, executing another statement might make $at(S)$ become false—for example, by aborting the process containing statement S. However, Axioms 1-4 would still be valid.

Observe that Axiom 2 determines the value of x immediately after execution of S. However, it asserts nothing about x's value after the execution of any other action.

For language L, Axiom 4 implies that if $at(S)$ is true then eventually it will become false (thereby making $after(S)$ true). However, this depends upon the fact that that L does not have any form of unfair **cobegin**. The axiom is valid for more general languages that do have these features.

It is instructive to consider what these axioms imply in case statement S appears inside declarations that produce a type mismatch—say in which x is of type **integer** and exp of type **boolean**. The axioms for those declarations will imply that the value of x is always an integer and the value of exp is always a boolean. It then follows from Axiom 2 that executing an S action can never make $at(S)$ false, since doing so would require setting the value of x to a boolean, contradicting the axioms for the declarations. However, I have already observed that, for language L, $at(S)$ must eventually become false. Thus, the set of axioms for the incorrect program—the one producing a type mismatch in statement S—are contradictory, implying that only the empty set of behaviors satisfy them. However, in a richer language, if S were contained inside an unfair **cobegin**, then the axioms might not be contradictory, and might be satisfied by a behavior in which a process remained stalled forever with $at(S)$ true. In this case, the type mismatch would force that process to "die", allowing other processes to proceed.

6.3.2 The if Statement

If S is the statement **if** $\langle exp \rangle$ **then** ... , then the following axioms are in $\mathcal{M}[\![S]\!]$. They are the standard four action axioms—in this case, for the *test* action. Note their similarity to the corresponding axioms for the assignment statement.

1. $Act(S, test) \supset at(S, test)$
   The test can be executed only when control resides at it.

2. $\{at(S, test)\}\langle S, test\rangle\{[at(S, then) \wedge exp()] \vee [at(S, else) \wedge \neg exp()]\}$
   Control remains at the beginning of the test until it either reaches the entry point of the **then** clause with *exp* true, or else it reaches the entry point of the **else** clause with *exp* false.

3. $\forall \nu : \{at(S, test), after(S, test)\} \perp \nu \supset \nu \overset{S,test}{\not\leftarrow}$
   The test does not modify any variable it shouldn't. (Again, ν is a logical name variable.)

4. $\Box\Diamond Act(S, test) \supset \Diamond\neg at(S, test)$
   There can be only finitely many stuttering actions of the test before it is really executed. This is the only liveness axiom for the **if** statement.

6.3.3 The while Statement

The axioms for the statement **while** $\langle exp \rangle$ **do** ... are analogous to the ones for the **if** statement, and are given without comment.

1. $Act(S, test) \supset at(S, test)$

2. $\{at(S, test)\}\langle S, test\rangle\{(at(S, body) \wedge exp()) \vee (after(S) \wedge \neg exp())\}$

3. $\forall \nu : \{at(S, test), after(S, test)\} \perp \nu \supset \nu \overset{S,test}{\not\leftarrow}$

4. $\Box\Diamond Act(S, test) \supset \Diamond\neg at(S, test)$

6.3.4 The new Statement

The **new** statement is a declaration. If it has no **init** clause, then it performs no new action. The axioms describing this statement therefore do not follow the pattern for action axioms followed by the preceding statements. Instead, they assert relations that hold throughout the execution.

If S is the statement

new x **:** *type* **in** ...

then the following axiom is in $\mathcal{M}[\![S]\!]$, where we identify **integer** with the set Z and **boolean** with the set $\{true, false\}$.

1. $x(S) \in type$
   The value of x is always consistent with the type declaration.

If S is the statement

new x : *type* **alias** *exp* **in** ...

then $\mathcal{M}[\![S]\!]$ contains the above axiom plus the following:

2. $x(S) = exp()$
   The aliasing relation always holds.

If S is the statement

new x : *type* **init** *exp* **in** ...

then the following axioms hold. The first is, of course, the same as for the other versions of the **new** statement. The last four are the action axioms for the initial-assignment action, following the standard pattern. They are almost identical to the corresponding axioms for the assignment statement, the only difference (in axiom 3 below) indicating that the **init** clause performs an assignment to the variable $x(S)$ declared in the **new** statement rather than to the undeclared variable $x()$.

1. $x(S) \in type$

2. $Act(S, init) \supset at(S, init)$

3. $\forall \eta : \{at(S, init) \wedge exp() = \eta\}\langle S\rangle\{after(S, init) \wedge x(S) = \eta\}$

4. $\forall \nu : \{x(S), at(S), after(S)\} \perp \nu \supset \nu \overset{S,init}{\not\rightarrow}$

5. $\square\Diamond Act(S, init) \supset \Diamond\neg at(S, init)$

6.3.5 The cobegin Statement

If S is the statement

cobegin $S_1 \,\square \ldots \square\, S_n$ **coend**

then the following axiom is in $\mathcal{M}[\![S]\!]$.

1. $\forall i$ s.t. $1 \leq i \leq n : (\square\Diamond Act(S)) \supset (\square\Diamond Act(S, i))$
   If S performs infinitely many actions, then each process of S performs infinitely many actions. In other words, if S is never starved, then no subprocess of S is starved. This is the fairness axiom.

6.3.6 Sequences of Statements

No new axioms are needed for the sequence of statements $S_1; \ldots ; S_n$. All necessary properties are obtained from the aliasing relations among its control variables, the relations among its action predicates, and the Composition Principle.

6.3.7 A Complete Program

If Π is a complete program, then the only additional axiom in $\mathcal{M}[\Pi]$ is:

1. $in(\Pi) \supset Act(\Pi, body)$
   The complete program never stops executing until it reaches the end, whereupon $in(\Pi)$ becomes false.

This axiom asserts the absence of any external actions while control is in progam Π, reflecting the absence of any explicit input or output in language L.

7 Other Language Features

While I have given a formal semantics only for the simple language L, action-axiom semantics can be used to describe a wider variety of concurrent programming language constructs than any other method I know of. In this section, I will consider a few interesting constructs. In doing so, I will not bother to give the usual axioms that describe the relations among control variables and among action predicates.

7.1 Constructs That Constrain Their Environment

Most language constructs constrain the behavior of their components. For example, an **if** statement determines when its **then** and **else** clauses can be executed. The following three language constructs constrain the behavior of a larger program containing them. They are therefore impossible to specify in a compositional, purely behavioral semantics. It is the Composition Principle that makes them expressible with action-axiom semantics.

7.1.1 The assign processor Command

As described above, the statement

assign processor to ...

directs the compiler to guarantee that the body of the statement gets its share of computing cycles, so it is not starved. This is expressed by the axiom:

$$in(S) \supset \Diamond Act(S)$$

7.1.2 Atomic Actions

One might want to introduce "angle brackets" as a language construct, so $\langle S \rangle$ denotes that S is to be executed as an indivisible atomic action. This is done by requiring that no other actions are interleaved with the executions of S, expressed formally by:

$$Act(\langle S \rangle) \supset in(\langle S \rangle) \trianglelefteq Act(\langle S \rangle)$$

7.1.3 Write Protection

Imagine a situation in which one wants the variable x to be modified only in a particular statement, but to be accessible elsewhere. This might be expessed by the following statement S:

encapsulate x **in** S'

The semantics of this statement are described formally by:

$$\forall \eta : x() = \eta \supset (\neg Act(S)) \lhd (x() = \eta)$$

which asserts that the value of x remains unchanged while any action not in S is executed.

7.2 Synchronization and Communication

The bread and butter of concurrent programming language constructs are the synchronization and interprocess communication mechanisms. I will discuss only two.

7.2.1 Semaphores

The usual semaphore P and V operations are variants of the atomic assignment statement: $P(s)$ looking much like the assignment $\langle s := s - 1 \rangle$ and $V(s)$ looking like $\langle s := s + 1 \rangle$. There are two basic differences. First of all, the $P(s)$ operation may be performed only when s is positive. One way of expressing this is to change the first axiom of the assignment statement to:

$$Act(P(s)) \supset (at(P(s)) \wedge s > 0)$$

However, this would require changing other axioms, since deadlock is represented by the absence of any possible actions, and the axiom given above for the complete program asserts that this is impossible.

The other way of handling this is to allow only stuttering actions of $P(s)$ to occur when $s \leq 0$. This is achieved by replacing the second axiom of the assignment statement with the following:

$$\forall \eta : \{at(P(s)) \wedge (x() = \eta)\} \langle P(s) \rangle \{after(P(s)) \wedge (x() = \eta - 1 \geq 0)\}$$

The second change that must be made to the assignment axioms is in the liveness condition. We can no longer require that an infinite number of actions of $P(s)$ cause the operation to be completed, since they might all occur when s has the value zero. Several liveness axioms have been proposed for the semaphore. Probably the most common are weak liveness, expressed by

$$(\Box(s > 0) \wedge \Box\Diamond Act(P(s))) \supset \Box\neg at(P(s))$$

and strong liveness, expressed by

$$(\Box\Diamond(s > 0) \wedge \Box\Diamond Act(P(s))) \supset \Box\neg at(P(s))$$

(They are discussed in [12].) In both these cases, the $V(s)$ operation is just an ordinary atomic assignment.

More complicated versions of the semaphore impose a specific queueing discipline, like first-come-first-served, on the execution of competing $P(s)$ operations. They may require adding a queue of waiting processes to the state, plus predicates to describe the state of the queue.

7.2.2 CSP-Like Communication Primitives

The easiest way to model the CSP "!" and "?" operations is in terms of channels. We include the operations $\langle\, x?\xi \,\rangle$ and $\langle\, exp!\xi \,\rangle$ for any variable x and expression *exp*. They denote CSP-like synchronous communication over a channel named ξ. We modify the **cobegin** statement by adding a clause of the form **channels** $\xi_1, \ldots, \xi_m$, which declares the channel names ξ_i.

As explained in [9], we consider communication actions to be actions of the channel, so $Act(S)$ is identically *false* if S is a ! or ? operation. A channel ξ has a separate atomic action for every pair of statements $\langle\, x?\xi \,\rangle$, $\langle\, exp!\xi \,\rangle$ contained in different clauses of the **cobegin** in which ξ is declared. This atomic action is axiomatized much like the assignment statement $\langle\, x := exp \,\rangle$, except that its execution changes the values of the four control variables $at(x?\xi)$, $after(x?\xi)$, $at(exp!\xi)$, and $after(exp!\xi)$.

To do this formally, we must extend our variable-naming convention in the obvious way to channel variables and add new syntactic predicates $S, \gamma \in !\, v$ and $S, \gamma \in ?\, v$ to assert that the substatement S, γ is a ! or ? operation of the channel named v. The safety axiom for the declaration of channel ξ will be something like:

$$\begin{array}{l} \forall \gamma, \mu, i, j \text{ s.t. } i \neq j : \; S, i, \gamma \in !\,\xi(S) \wedge S, j, \mu \in ?\,\xi(S) \supset \\ \quad \forall \eta : \{ at(S, i\gamma) \wedge at(S, j, \gamma) \wedge \rho_{S,i,\gamma}(S, i, \gamma, left()) = \eta \} \\ \qquad \langle\, \xi(S) \,\rangle \, \{ after(S, i\gamma) \wedge after(S, j, \gamma) \wedge \rho_{S,j,\mu}(S, j, \mu, left()) = \eta \} \end{array}$$

Note that $\rho_{S,i,\gamma}(S, i, \gamma, left())$ is the *exp* of $exp!\xi$, with all component variables appropriately renamed, and similarly for $\rho_{S,j,\mu}(S, j, \mu, left())$.

It is straightforward to extend this approach to guarded communication commands such as $\langle\, exp \rightarrow x?\xi \,\rangle$, which means that the communication action may be carried out only if *exp* has the value *true*. The new safety axiom is obtained from the above in much the same way that the safety axiom for the $P(s)$ semaphore operation is obtained from the corresponding axiom for the assignment statement—the guards here playing the part of the enabling condition $s > 0$ for the $P(s)$ operation.

There are several different choices of liveness properties that one can require of these channels. They are all basically simple to express with temporal logic formulas. However, their formal statement requires some careful manipulation of syntactic predicates, which I won't bother doing.

The safety properties of CSP-like communication primitives are expressed more easily with a formal semantics based only upon externally observable actions, such as [11]. When shared variables are not allowed, such a semantics can define the meaning of a process as the set of possible communications it can engage in. However, this kind of semantics does not seem capable of handling liveness properties easily.

7.3 Procedures

Although language L does not have procedures, its **new** statement contains the basic mechanism needed for procedure calls. A call of a nonrecursive procedure can be simulated by replacing the procedure call by **new** statements plus the body of the procedure. For example, let *proc* be a procedure with a declaration

procedure *proc*(a : **integer**, **var** b : **boolean**) *body*

in which its first argument is call by value and its second is call by name. The call $proc(x + y, z)$ can be translated to

new a **init** $x + y$ **in** **new** b **alias** z
in *body* **ni** **ni**

To handle call by reference parameters, one needs to introduce pointer variables into the language. Of course, aliasing and procedure calls become more interesting when pointers and arrays are introduced, but a discussion of the problems raised by pointers and arrays is beyond the scope of this paper.

While this method of handling procedure calls works only for nonrecursive procedures, the basic idea applies to recursive ones as well. Replacing a procedure call by the body of the procedure produces an infinite program text for recursive procedures; but nowhere have I made use of the assumption that the program text is finite. Of course, the compositional method of recursively defining $\mathcal{M}[\![S]\!]$ no longer terminates with a finite set of axioms. However, the definition can be viewed as an algorithm for enumerating an infinite collection of axioms.

Thus, adding recursion means that $\mathcal{M}[\![S]\!]$ consists of an infinite set of axioms. It is in this case that the distinction between a semantics and a proof system becomes evident. An infinite set of axioms is unsatisfactory as a proof system, because ordinary logic provides no way of deducing a conclusion whose correctness is based upon an infinite set of assumptions. Such deductions are required to prove nontrivial properties of recursive programs. Thus, I have not provided a proof system for programs with recursive procedures.

On the other hand, a semantics is concerned with validity, not proof. The meaning of a program Π is the set of behaviors that satisfy the axioms in $\mathcal{M}[\![\Pi]\!]$, and this is well-defined even for an infinite set of axioms. The problem of proof systems is discussed in the conclusion.

7.4 More General Types and Aliasing

Let us now consider a language in which a type mismatch does not produce an illegal program, but generates "incorrect" behavior. As mentioned earlier, this requires adding predicates of the form $type(x) = \ldots$, which are syntactic predicates if types can be determined syntactically and state predicates if types are dynamic.

First, suppose that a type mismatch in the assignment $x := exp$ causes x to be set nondeterministically to any value in its range. This is easily represented by changing axiom 2 of the assignment to the following, where $type\_valid(x, \eta)$ is true if and only if the type of x permits it to be assigned the value η.

$$\forall \eta : \{at(S) \wedge exp() = \eta\} \langle S \rangle \\ \{after(S) \wedge (x() = \eta \vee \neg type\_valid(x(), \eta))\}$$

Next, suppose that a type mismatch causes the assignment to "hang up", effectively deadlocking the process. This requires that axiom 4 be changed so it does not demand termination in this case. There are several different liveness requirements one could make in this case, since the value of the expression *exp* could change. One reasonable possibility is the following:

$$\Box\Diamond(Act(S) \wedge type\_valid(x(), exp())) \supset \Diamond\neg at(S)$$

Allowing a more general form of aliasing, such as the one defined in [10], presents a similar problem if one requires that an assignment which would violate an aliasing constraint cause the process to hang up. One approach to this is to put the aliasing constraints in the state, just as I did with type constraints. The new state components would correspond to the "location" values often used to handle aliasing.

7.5 Nonatomic Operations

Every construct that I have mentioned specifies the atomic actions. For example, I have defined the semantics only of an atomic assignment statement. It is easy to give the semantics of an assignment statement with smaller atomic operations. For example, an assignment

$$\langle x \rangle := \langle exp \rangle$$

in which the evaluation of *exp* and the changing of x are distinct atomic operations can be represented by

$$\langle t := exp \rangle;\ \langle x := t \rangle$$

where t is an implicit variable. A similar translation is possible when the evaluation of the right-hand side is broken into smaller atomic operations; it is described in [4].

The situation changes when no atomicity is specified. For example, consider an assignment statement $x := y + 1$ that has the expected effect only if x and y are not modified by any other operation during the course of its execution. If any such modification does take place, then x may be set to any value consistent with its type. We can think of this assignment as a compound statement for which we know nothing about its internal structure except its partial correctness property (when executed alone) and the fact that it always terminates (unless the process executing it is starved).

Handling such nonatomic operations requires a new class of state predicate—the "generalized dynamic logic" predicates $[S]P$ introduced in [7]. The second assignment axiom for an atomic assignment is replaced by the following one for a nonatomic assignment $x := exp$:

$$\forall \eta : \{in(S) \wedge [S](x() = \eta)\} \langle S \rangle \{after(S) \wedge x() = \eta\}$$

Note that the rules for reasoning about these generalized dynamic logic predicates imply that

$$at(S) \supset ([S](x() = \eta) \equiv (exp = \eta))$$

The liveness axiom for a nonatomic assignment is simply

$$\Box\Diamond Act(S) \supset \Diamond\neg in(S)$$

8 Conclusion

I have given an axiomatic semantics for a simple concurrent programming language L, and have indicated how the same method can be applied to more complicated language constructs. Most of this paper has been devoted to developing the fundamental ideas upon which the method is based. The axioms themselves are reasonably simple—simple enough so I feel that they do provide an understanding of the language constructs. For example, the difference between a weakly fair and a strongly fair semaphore is described quite concisely and precisely by their respective axioms.

A programming language semantics provides a logical basis for a proof system for reasoning about programs in the language. One can talk about the soundness and completeness of the proof system in terms of the semantics. Note that it makes no sense to talk about soundness and completeness of the semantics. Indeed, the semantics $\mathcal{M}[\![S]\!]$ of a program can include contradictory axioms; this simply means that there are no valid behaviors for S, so there is something wrong with the program, not with the semantics.

The obvious task now is to investigate existing proof systems in terms of this semantics. Unfortunately, such an undertaking is beyond the scope of this paper. However, some brief remarks are in order. The Generalized Hoare Logic (GHL) presented in [4] and [9] introduced *at*, *in*, and *after* as predicates rather than variables. The relation $||$ used in [4] is just the relation $\perp$.

The semantics of GHL formulas was not stated with sufficient precision in [4], since the relation between the statement S and its name, denoted $'S'$, was never made clear. A close examination of GHL reveals that there is an implicit complete program Π, and that if S is the substatement Π, γ of Π, then a formula written in terms of S should really be written in terms of Π, γ.

To verify the soundness of GHL, one must express the GHL formula $\{P\}\, S\, \{Q\}$ as a temporal logic formula. As explained in [9], it suffices to consider the case $P = Q$, for which the definition is simply:

$$\{P\}\, S\, \{P\} \stackrel{\text{def}}{=} \{P\}\langle\Pi, \gamma\rangle\{P\}$$

where S is the substatement Π, γ of the implied complete program Π. The soundness of the general rules for reasoning about GHL formulas follows easily from their interpretation as temporal logic formulas. The soundness of the axioms and rules given in [4] for each language construct can be deduced from the axioms for the corresponding construct given here in Section 6.3, together with the Composition Principle.

As described in [9], other logical systems for proving safety properties of concurrent programs can be described in terms of GHL, so the soundness of GHL can be used to prove the soundness of the other systems. GHL is manifestly not a complete system for reasoning about concurrent programs, since it does not address questions of liveness.

It is not clear how to use our semantics to prove completeness of GHL for the class of properties it can express.

A method for proving liveness properties of programs is given in [12]. It considers a simple language that is essentially the same as language L except without the **new** statement. The method explicitly assumes a complete program Π, and is based upon temporal logic plus the following single axiom:

Atomic Action Axiom: For any atomic action Π, γ of Π:

$$at(\Pi, \gamma) \supset \Diamond after(\Pi, \gamma)$$

To prove the soundness of this axiom, we must show that

$$\Box(in(\Pi, \gamma) \supset \Diamond Act(\Pi, \gamma))$$

holds for every substatement and atomic action Π, γ of Π. This is intuitively clear, since the language contains only fair **cobegin** statements, and is derivable from our axioms by induction on the size of Π. The above Atomic Action Axiom then follows easily from our liveness axiom for complete programs, the liveness axioms for the individual statements, plus the Composition Principle. The additional axioms given in [12] for weakly and strongly fair semaphore operations can similarly be derived from the ones I gave earlier.

Acknowledgements

I wish to thank Fred Schneider and Willem-Paul de Roever for their detailed comments on an earlier draft of this paper.

References

[1] Karl M. Abrahamson. *Decidability and Expressiveness of Logics of Processes.* Ph. D. Thesis, issued as Technical Report No. 80-08-01, Department of Computer Science, University of Washington. (August 1980).

[2] Denotational Semantics of Concurrency. J. W. de Bakker and J. C. Zucker. *Fourteenth ACM Symposium on the Theory of Computing*, San Francisco, (May, 1982), 153-158.

[3] Z. C. Chen and C. A. R. Hoare. Partial Correctness of Communicating Sequential Processes. *Proceedings of the Second IEEE International Conference on Distributed Computer Systems*, (1981) 1-12.

[4] L. Lamport. The "Hoare Logic" of Concurrent Programs. *Acta Informatica 14* (1980), 21-37.

[5] L. Lamport. "Sometime" Is Sometimes "Not Never". *Proceedings of the Seventh Annual ACM Conference on the Principles of Programming Languages*, (January 1980) 174-185.

[6] L. Lamport. Specifying Concurrent Program Modules. *ACM Transactions on Prog. Logic and Sys. 5*, 2 (April 1983) 190-222.

[7] L. Lamport. Reasoning About Nonatomic Operations. *Proceedings of the Tenth Annual ACM Conference on the Principles of Programming Languages*, (January 1983) 28-37.

[8] L. Lamport. What Good Is Temporal Logic? *Information Processing 83*, R. E. Mason (ed.), Elsevier Science Publishers, North Holland (1983), 657-668.

[9] L. Lamport and F. B. Schneider. The Hoare Logic of CSP and All That. *ACM Transactions on Prog. Logic and Sys. 6*, 2 (April 1984) 281-296.

[10] L. Lamport and F. B. Schneider. Constraints: A Uniform Approach to Aliasing and Typing. To appear in *Proceedings of the Twelfth Annual ACM Conference on the Principles of Programming Languages*, (January 1985).

[11] R. Milner. *A Calculus of Communicating Systems.* Lecture Notes in Computer Science, Number 92. Springer-Verlag, Berlin (1980).

[12] S. S. Owicki and L. Lamport. Proving Liveness Properties of Concurrent Programs. *ACM Trans. on Prog. Lang. and Systems 4*, 3 (1982), 455-495.

[13] A. Pnueli. The Temporal Logic of Programs. *Proceedings of the 18th IEEE Symposium on the Foundations of Computer Science* (1977), Providence Rhode Island.

[14] H. Barringer, R. Kuiper. and A. Pnueli. Now You May Compose Temporal Logic Specifications. *Sixteenth ACM Symposium on the Theory of Computing*, (May, 1984).

[15] J. Sifakis. A Unified Approach for Studying the Properties of Transition Systems. *Theoretical Computer Science 18* (1982), 227-258.

In Transition From Global to Modular Temporal Reasoning about Programs

Amir Pnueli

Department of Applied Mathematics
The Weizmann Institute of Science
Rehovot 76100, Israel

The role of Temporal Logic as a feasible approach to the specification and verification of concurrent systems is now widely accepted. A companion paper in this volume ([HP]) defines more precisely the area of applicability of Temporal Logic as that of ***reactive*** systems.

One of the serious criticisms directed against the Temporal Logic approach as represented in [MP1], [MP2] and [OL] is its inherent ***globality***. By this we mean that we can only verify a complete program, and that the methodology does not provide rules for deducing properties of the complete program from properties of its constituents. Since systematic development can be viewed as the inverse of the verification process, the same complaint may be expressed by saying that given a specification for a reactive system, the methodology does not provide guidelines for deriving specifications for the modules into which the system may be decomposed.

Aware of this criticism, several recent efforts have been made to develop a compositional temporal logic approach to reactive systems verification. Representative of such efforts are the works reported in [BK], [L2], [BKP1] and [BKP2].

The Algol 60 report ([Na]) introduced a three way partition of the definition of a programming language. Borrowed from the field of linguistics, this partition considers in turn the ***syntax***, the ***semantics*** and the ***pragmatics*** of a given language. The syntax defines the set of legal sentences that are admissible in the language. The semantics defines the meaning of each legal sentence. The pragmatics attempts to indicate how these sentences should be constructed and combined to achieve certain goals. In teacing a new programming language, we usually find that students have little difficulties with the syntax and semantics, but most of the course concentrates on instilling a proper grasp of the pragmatics. We may loosely describe pragmatics as the ***style*** or recommended ***mode*** of using the language.

This three ways partition is most appropriate also for the definition of a

NATO ASI Series, Vol. F13
Logics and Models of Concurrent Systems
Edited by K. R. Apt

verification (or development) system. If we take the Temporal Logic proof system as an example, then its syntax and semantics are the subjects that belong to the realm of logic. The pragmatics of this system should tell us how the logical tools should be used in order to specify and verify (develop) reactive systems. In particular, in addition to giving us formal rules, it should also outline a recommended ***style*** of applying these formal rules in the most advantageous and natural way.

The work reported in [BKP1] presents an adequate account of the syntax and semantics of a compositional temporal logic system for the modular verification of concurrent systems. However, it provides very little pragmatic insight about the recommended style of verifying programs in this sytem. The current paper attempts to remedy this deficiency by comparing the pragmatics of the global temporal logic approach to that of the modular (compositional) approach. This is mainly done by means of an example, but even based on this simple example, some general conclusions may be drawn.

Before presenting the evidence for those conclusions, let us speculate first what type of differences can we expect between the global and modular styles of temporal verification beyond the obvious syntactic differences. The current situation in temporal verification, that of transition from globality to modularity, is very reminiscent of a similar transition in sequential verification between Floyd's and Hoare's systems in the early 70's. If we look beyond the obvious syntactic advantages and gained insight provided by Hoare's ingenious notation, we find that there is almost one to one pragmatic mappings between proofs in the two systems. In both systems the difficult and creative task is the identification of the invariant and convergence functions (***variants*** according to Gries). Once, these have been properly identified, and their mutual consistency (verification conditions) established, it is easy and almost a mechanical task to construct either a Floyd or a Hoare style proof. In fact, it is not always clear which of the systems is intended in a given context. For example, the important ***proof outline*** concept introduced by Owicki and Gries is a purely Floydish notion, even though it is embedded in a Hoare-like framework. More comments about this pragmatic mappings and its implications in concurrent verification appear in [LS].

In view of this precedent we should not be surprised that, at first glance, the modular style of temporal verification may appear radically different from the global style and offer exciting new insights. However, a deeper examination may reveal that underneath both styles lie the same basic safety and liveness properties (the concurrent extensions of the sequential invariants and variants). The modular style would, of course, present these common properties in a cleaner and more encapsulated form, an important advantage that we should not underrate.

The Global Style of Temporal Verification

We refer the reader to [MP1], [MP2], [MP3] for the syntax and semantics of the temporal language, the description of the shared variables model and the interpretation of temporal formulas over computations of a given program.

To repeat some of the definitions, we consider concurrent programs that have the general form:

$$P : \bar{y} := g(\bar{x}) \; ; \; [P_1 \| \cdots \| P_m].$$

Here $\bar{y} := g(\bar{x})$ is an initializing statement, assigning to the shared working variables $\bar{y}$ initial values that may depend on the input $\bar{x}$. This statement is followed by the concurrent execution of the m processes $P_1, \ldots, P_m$. Each process, P_i, is a sequential program that we may represent by a transition diagram. We may identify ℓ_0^i as the initial location for each process P_i. A state of the program is a tuple $< \ell^1, \ldots, \ell^m; \eta_1, \ldots, \eta_n >$ where ℓ^i, $i = 1, \ldots, m$ is the current location of the process P_i and η_j, $j = 1, \ldots, n$ is the current value of the shared variable y_j. We assume that the atomic steps of each of the processes are well defined and they provide a relation, denoted by $s \xrightarrow{P_i} s'$ holding between two program states s and s' such that s' is obtainable by a single atomic step of P_i applied to s. In this case we say that s' is a *P_i-successor* of s.

An ***initialized*** $(\bar{\xi})$ ***computation*** of P (corresponding to the input $\bar{x} = \bar{\xi}$) is an ***infinite*** labelled sequence of states:

$$\sigma : s_0 \xrightarrow{P_{i_0}} s_1 \xrightarrow{P_{i_1}} s_2 \rightarrow \cdots$$

such that:

(i) $s_0 =< \bar{\ell}_0 \, ; g(\bar{\eta}) >$ i.e. the first state corresponds to the situation just after the initializing statement.

(ii) For each transition $s_k \xrightarrow{P_{i_k}} s_{k+1} \in \sigma$, s_{k+1} is obtainable from s_k by an atomic step of P_{i_k}.

(iii) For each $j = 1, \ldots, m$, σ contains infinitely many P_j steps (weak fairness).

A $(\bar{\xi})$ ***computation*** of P is any suffix of an initialized $(\bar{\xi})$ computation. A state is $(\bar{\xi})$ ***accessible*** if it appears in a $(\bar{\xi})$ computation.

A ***state formula*** φ is any first order formula built over the input variables $\bar{x}$, the working variables $\bar{y}$ and a set of basic propositions of the form $at\,\ell_j^i$ for ℓ_j^i a location within P_i. Given a state $s =< \ell^1, \ldots, \ell^m; \bar{\eta} >$ in a $\bar{\xi}$ computation, a state formula φ is interpreted over s by taking $\bar{x} = \bar{\xi}$, $\bar{y} = \bar{\eta}$ and $at\ell_j^i$ being true iff $\ell^i = \ell_j^i$. If φ evaluates to true over s, we say that s is a ***φ-state***.

Temporal formulas are built over state formulas, using the temporal operator $\bigcirc$(*next*), $\Box$ (*always*), $\Diamond$ (*eventually*), U (*until* – strong version) and $\mathcal{U}$ (*unless* – the weak version of until) and the usual boolean operators.

For state formulas φ and ψ and a process P_i, we say that P_i ***leads from*** φ to ψ, denoted by $\varphi \overset{P_i}{\rightsquigarrow} \psi$, if every P_i-successor of an accessible φ-state is a ψ-state. That is, every s' such that $s \overset{P_i}{\rightsquigarrow} s'$ for some s which is accessible and satisfies φ, must satisfy ψ. If $\varphi \overset{P_i}{\rightsquigarrow} \psi$ for every $i = 1, \ldots, m$, we say that the ***program*** P leads from φ to ψ and denote it by $\varphi \overset{P}{\rightsquigarrow} \psi$. Statements such as $\varphi \overset{P_i}{\rightsquigarrow} \psi$ are usually proved by considering all the possible transitions (atomic steps) in P_i, and checking the verification conditions associated with them. Further details about the establishment of these low level statements is provided in [MP3]. A more structured approach to their establishment is presented in [G]. In some sense the $\overset{P_i}{\rightsquigarrow}$ relation is the only semantics of the program P that the global proof system requires.

We will illustrate the proof methodology on an example program presented in Fig. 1. This program, due to G. Peterson [Pe], is an algorithm for solving the mutual exclusion problem. Each of the two processes P_1 and P_2 has an ***idling section***, represented by ℓ_0, m_0 respectively, from which it ***may*** exit in order to enter a ***critical section***, represented by ℓ_3 and m_3 respectively. The algorithm guarantees that only one of the processes is in its critical section at any instant, and that whenever a process wishes to enter its critical section it will eventually succeed.

The set of properties that one may want to prove about reactive systems is partitioned into two classes, the class of ***safety*** properties and the class of liveness properties.

Safety Properties

A temporal property φ is classified as safety property if for every infinite computation σ, φ holds on σ iff it holds on ***every*** finite prefix of σ. The simpler safety properties can be expressed by formulas of the form $\Box\psi$, $\varphi \rightarrow \Box\psi$, $\varphi \mathcal{U} \psi$. Some of the important safety properties of reactive systems are: partial correctness, fault absence, mutual exclusion, deadlock absence, invariance, etc.

A basic proof rule for properties of the form $\Box\psi$ is the following:

Let θ denote the state formula characterizing the initial state immediately after execution of the initializing statement but before any of the concurrent steps is taken:

$$\theta : [\bar{y} = g(\bar{x})] \wedge at\, \ell_0^1 \wedge \cdots \wedge at\, \ell_0^m.$$

Then, the invariance rule is:

$$\left.\begin{array}{l}\theta \rightarrow \psi \\ \psi \overset{P}{\rightsquigarrow} \psi\end{array}\right\} \Rightarrow \Box\psi.$$

That is, if ψ can be shown to hold initially, and is preserved by each atomic step of P, then it is an invariant of the program.

We illustrate this rule by deriving several invariants for our example program, culminating in an invariant that guarantees mutual exclusion. Observe first that $\theta : (y_1 = y_2 = t = F) \wedge at\, \ell_0 \wedge at\, m_0$.

We start by proving $\Box\varphi_1$ where $\varphi_1 : y_1 \equiv at\ell_{1..3}$. The statement $at\, \ell_{1..3}$ is an abbreviation for $at\, \ell_1 \vee at\, \ell_2 \vee at\, \ell_3$. To show that φ_1 holds initially we observe that initially $y_1 = F$ and $at\, \ell_{1..3} = F$ since $at\, \ell_0 = T$. To show that $\varphi_1 \overset{P}{\rightsquigarrow} \varphi_1$, i.e. that φ_1 is preserved under each atomic step of P, we have to consider all the atomic steps of P. It is clear that no steps of P_2 affect either y_1 or $at\, \ell_{1..3}$. We consider therefore the following steps of P_1:

$\ell_0 \rightarrow \ell_1$: makes $y_1 = at\, \ell_{1..3} = T$.

$\ell_0 \rightarrow \ell_0$, $\ell_1 \rightarrow \ell_2$, $\ell_2 \rightarrow \ell_2$, $\ell_2 \rightarrow \ell_3$: leave φ_1 invariant.

$\ell_3 \rightarrow \ell_0$: makes $y_1 = at\, \ell_{1..3} = F$.

We thus conclude that $\Box\varphi_1$ is valid. In a similar way we establish:

$$\Box\psi_1 \quad \text{where} \quad \psi_1 : y_2 \equiv at\, m_{1..3}.$$

Consider next $\Box\varphi_2$ where $\varphi_2 : at\, \ell_3 \wedge at\, m_2 \rightarrow t$. Initially $at\, \ell_3 \wedge at\, m_2 = F$ and so is t. The only steps that may endanger the truth of φ_2, called potentially falsifying transitions, are the following:

$\ell_1 \rightarrow \ell_2$: makes $at\, \ell_3 = F$.

$\ell_2 \rightarrow \ell_3$ while $at\, m_2$: This is possible only when $\sim y_2 \vee t$ holds. By $at\, m_2$ and ψ_1, $y_2 = T$, hence $t = T$.

$m_1 \rightarrow m_2$: makes $t = T$.

We conclude $\Box\varphi_2$, i.e. $\Box(at\, \ell_3 \wedge at\, m_2 \rightarrow t)$. In a similar way we establish:

$$\Box\psi_2 \quad \text{where} \quad \psi_2 : at\, m_3 \wedge at\, \ell_2 \rightarrow \sim t.$$

Finally, we consider $\Box\varphi$ where $\varphi : at\, \ell_3 \wedge at\, m_3 \rightarrow F$. Initially $at\, \ell_3 \wedge at\, m_3 = F$. The only falsifying transitions are:

$\ell_2 \rightarrow \ell_3$ while $at\, m_3$: By ψ_2, $t = F$. By $at\, m_3$ and ψ_1, $y_2 = T$. Hence this transition is impossible.

$m_2 \rightarrow m_3$ while $at\, \ell_3$: Similarly impossible.

We conclude $\Box(at\,\ell_3 \wedge at\,m_3 \rightarrow F)$ which is equivalent to $\Box\sim(at\,\ell_3 \wedge at\,m_3)$, proving mutual exclusion.

There are several general observations concerning the style of proving safety properties, that can be based even on this small but nontrivial example.

The first is a general principle that advocates that invariance properties should be proved by using only the invariance rule presented above, plus some auxiliary invariants such as φ_1, φ_2, ψ_1 and ψ_2. This recommendation can be made provided we can show that it is adequate for establishing all invariance properties. The adequacy or completeness of the invariance rule, is indeed proved in [MP4]. This adequacy is strongly dependent on our ability to refer to the program locations in an unrestricted way, as is illustrated for example in φ_2.

The fact that some additional references are needed in order to have a complete proof principle for safety properties, was already established in [OG]. The claim made there was that ***auxiliary variables*** are essential for the completeness of the proof principle.

That is, in order to prove the validity of a formula of the form $\Box\varphi$, we may need references to variables that do not explicitly appear in φ or in the program. The auxiliary variables that were selected there were ***history variables*** recording sequences of events or values that the regular program variables assumed throughout the computation.

Our recommendation implies that the only auxiliary references required are the program locations, and they obviate the need for history variables.

Another approach that our recommendation outrules is that of ***backwards analysis***. Such arguments often appear in informal proofs of concurrent algorithms, and run as follows:

To show that a state in which $at\,\ell_3 \wedge at\,m_3$ holds is impossible, assume that it did hold. Then in a previous state we must have had either $at\,\ell_2 \wedge at\,m_3$ or $at\,\ell_3 \wedge at\,m_2$. These could have existed only if in some previous instant another situation could be identified, etc. Thus, we construct a tree of all possible past histories and show that each branch in this tree leads to a contradiction. To properly formalize such arguments we need to add ***past operators*** to our temporal language. This addition has been independently suggested by several workers ([KVR], [BK]) who realized that many safety properties assume simpler forms using the past oeprators. On the other hand it was established in [GPSS] that any mixed formula, using both past and future operators, is equivalent (when interpreted over computations) to a pure future formula. Thus, there was a natural reluctance not to add to the language operators that could always be translated away.

Thus the methodological recommendation that we associate with global proofs of safety properties can be formulated as:

Always prove invariances by the invariance rule. You ***may*** use location variables and as many auxiliary invariants as are necessary. Do ***not*** use history variables, backward analysis or past operators since they are not necessary.

This stylistic recommendation, which seems quite appropriate for global verification, should be reexamined when we consider modular verification.

Liveness Properties

A partial characterization of liveness properties is the following: the temporal property φ is a liveness property if for every infinite computation σ, φ holds on σ iff it holds on ***infinitely many*** finite prefixes of σ. Simple examples of liveness properties are expressed by formulas of the form, $\Diamond\psi$, $\varphi \to \Diamond\psi$, $\varphi U \psi$, $\Box\Diamond\psi$, $\Diamond\Box\psi$, etc.

Liveness properties are usually proved by showing that if we are currently at the end of a computation segment that does not satisfy φ, then eventually the computation will extend to a segment that does satisfy φ. Thus, φ will hold on infinitely many prefixes.

The basic liveness rule strongly depends on the type of fairness assumed. For the weak fairness we assumed it has the following form: Let φ and ψ be two state formulas and P_k one of the processes:

$$\left.\begin{array}{l} \varphi \overset{P}{\hookrightarrow} (\varphi \vee \psi) \\ \varphi \overset{P_k}{\hookrightarrow} \psi \end{array}\right\} \Rightarrow \left\{\begin{array}{l} \varphi \to \varphi U \psi, \text{ or} \\ \varphi \to \Diamond\psi \end{array}\right.$$

This basic rule is adequate for liveness properties that need one ***helpful*** step for their achievements. The more general case is handled by combining the basic rule with some induction principle. In the finite state case the combined rule appears as follows: Let $\varphi_0, \varphi_1, \ldots, \varphi_n$ be state formulas, and $h_1, \ldots, h_n$ identification of ***helpful*** processes, one for each state formula φ_i, $i = 1, \ldots, n$.

$$\left.\begin{array}{l} \text{For every } i = 1, \ldots, n: \\ \varphi_i \overset{P}{\hookrightarrow} \bigvee_{j \le i} \varphi_j \\ \varphi_i \overset{P_{h_i}}{\hookrightarrow} \bigvee_{j < i} \varphi_j \end{array}\right\} \Rightarrow \left(\bigvee_{j \le n} \varphi_j\right) \to \Diamond\varphi_0.$$

The main liveness property that should be proved for our example program is that of ***accessibility***. This guarantees that whenever a process wishes to enter its critical section it will eventually succeed. For P_1 this requirement is expressed by:

$$at\,\ell_1 \to \Diamond at\,\ell_3.$$

This is provable by taking in the proof rule above:

$$
\begin{array}{ll}
\varphi_0 : at\,\ell_3 & \\
\varphi_1 : at\,\ell_2 \wedge at\,m_2 \wedge t \quad , & h_1 = 1 \\
\varphi_2 : at\,\ell_2 \wedge at\,m_1 \wedge \sim t, & h_2 = 2 \\
\varphi_3 : at\,\ell_2 \wedge at\,m_0 \wedge \sim t, & h_3 = 1 \\
\varphi_4 : at\,\ell_2 \wedge at\,m_3 \wedge \sim t, & h_4 = 2 \\
\varphi_5 : at\,\ell_2 \wedge at\,m_2 \wedge \sim t, & h_5 = 2 \\
\varphi_6 : at\,\ell_1 \quad , & h_6 = 1
\end{array}
$$

The premises of the rule for $i = 1, \ldots, 6$ are easy to check. In checking them we may freely use the invariants φ_1, ψ_1 previously derived.

Such a proof can be nicely displayed in a proof diagram as shown in Fig. 2. In spite of the linear appearance of this diagram, it helps to view it as a tree, or at least an acyclic graph, which represent an exploration of all possible developments starting in a state satisfying φ_6. It shows that:

1) Starting from a φ_6-state, P_1 will eventually lead to a state which satisfies φ_5, φ_4, φ_3 or φ_2.

2) Starting from a φ_5-state, P_2 will eventually lead to a φ_4-state.

3) Starting from a φ_4-state, P_2 will eventually lead to a φ_3-state.

4) Starting from a φ_3-state, P_1 will eventually lead to a φ_0-state, unless a previous action of P_2 leads to a φ_2-state first.

5) Starting from a φ_2-state, P_2 will eventually lead to a φ_1-state.

6) Starting from a φ_1-state, P_1 will eventually lead to a φ_0-state.

Thus, any future development eventually leads to a φ_0-state.

The view of liveness proofs of this form as acyclic graphs is also emphasized in [OL] where they are referred to as lattice diagrams.

The globality of such a proof is reflected in two features. First, all the assertions φ_0-φ_6 speak freely about the intimate details of *both* processes, such as the values of their location. Next, we observe that the history of progress from φ_6 to φ_0, skips freely between actions caused by P_1 and actions affected by P_2. Thus the exits out of φ_6, φ_3 and φ_1 are guaranteed by P_1, while the exits out of φ_5, φ_4 and φ_2 are guaranteed by P_2.

The Modular Approach

The modular or compositional approach to temporal reasoning about reactive systems, should of course provide rules for building up proofs of compound programs from proofs of their constituents. Obviously, each programming construct for building up compound statements, such as sequential composition, conditionals, white, etc. should be matched by a corresponding proof rule. It does not take long to realize that the most problematic construct in reactive systems is the parallel composition '$\|$'. We denote $[P]\psi$ the statement that the module P satisfies the temporal formula ψ. This means that every computation generated by the interaction of P with its environment satisfies ψ. A more precise definition of the notion of a computation generated by such an interaction will be given later. With this notation we may say that we are looking for a proof rule, corresponding to parallel composition that will have the following general form:

$$\left.\begin{array}{l}[P_1]\psi_1 \\ [P_2]\psi_2 \\ C(\psi_1,\psi_2,\psi)\end{array}\right\} \Rightarrow [P_1 \parallel P_2]\psi.$$

Namely, what temporal formulas ψ that are valid for the module $P_1 \parallel P_2$, can we deduce given that ψ_i is valid specification for P_i, $i = 1, 2$. The unknown element in this rule is the ***connection*** formula $C(\psi_1, \psi_2, \psi)$ which is a purely temporal formula (i.e. containing no $[P]\varphi$ constructs) that connect ψ to ψ_1 and ψ_2. For example it would be most satisfactory to have:

$$C(\psi_1,\psi_2,\psi) : \psi_1 \wedge \psi_2 \rightarrow \psi$$

or some elaboration of the simple conjunction.

Another constraint essential to the modular approach is the ***encapsulation principle***. For the particular case of parallel composition it means that ψ_1, ψ_2 and ψ may refer only to variables that are ***externally observable*** outside of P_1, P_2 and $P_1 \parallel P_2$. Technically, encapsulation explicitly appears in the rule corresponding to the programming constructs imposing encapsulation, such as blocks, variable or channel declarations, etc. However, since completeness of the global proof system strongly depended on the ability to refer to program locations, we have to realize that such references are obviously forbidden in any reasonable encapsulation scheme. And hence, whatever suggestions are made for a modular proof system cannot rely on references to program locations.

The Assume-Guarantee (AG) Paradigm

A most important observation (see [L2]) is that in modular specification the specification should include two parts. The fisrt part describes the desired behavior of the module P. The second part describes the behavior of the environment, under which the module is guaranteed to behave as specified in the first part.

In transformational systems (i.e. sequential programs), we may interpret the Hoare triplet $\{\varphi\}P\{\psi\}$ as providing precisely this two element specification. The ***post-condition*** ψ specifies the guarantee (***commitment***) that the module ψ makes to the environment: "when I terminate, I will produce a final state that satisfy ψ". The ***pre-condition*** φ specifies the ***assumption*** that is made about the environment: "P will be activated only on initial states satisfying φ". The nature of the contract between environment and module is such that if the environment violates the assumption, the module may behave arbitrarily.

It is intuitively appealing to generalize the Hoare triplet into a statement $< \varphi > P < \psi >$ that can be interpreted also for reactive systems. In such generalization φ and ψ are temporal formulas. The ***assumption*** φ constrains the behavior of the environment. The ***guarantee*** ψ specifies the behavior of the module P when ensured of φ. The meaning of the complete statement $< \varphi > P < \psi >$ is that in any execution such that the environment behaves according to φ, it is guaranteed that P behaves according to ψ. This generalization was essentially suggested and discussed in [FP].

An important element in being able to split a specification into an assumption and a guarantee, is the ability to distinguish actions and steps performed by the environment from those performed by the module. In [BKP1] and [BKP2], a special mechanism was introduced to achieve this distinction through edge labelling. Whether such mechanism is necessary depends to a large extent on the computational model. The determining criterion is whether when we observe an event such as a change of a value of a variable or a message being sent in the execution of $P_1 \parallel P_2$ say, we can always uniquely determine the identity of the process (P_1 or P_2) that generated the event. This cannot be done in the shared variables model or in a message based system such as CCS where channels do not uniquely belong to processes. Hence for such models an augmentation such as edge labelling is needed.

In this paper we study modular verification in a slightly simpler model, that of ***distributed*** shared variables system. In this model each shared variable is ***owned*** by a unique process which is the only one allowed to modify it.

The parallel composition rule that naturally associates with the AG triplet is:

$$\left.\begin{array}{l} < \varphi_1 > P_1 < \psi_1 > \\ < \varphi_2 > P_2 < \psi_2 > \\ \theta \wedge \psi_1 \rightarrow \varphi_2 \\ \theta \wedge \psi_2 \rightarrow \varphi_1 \end{array}\right\} \Rightarrow < \theta > P_1 \parallel P_2 < \psi_1 \wedge \psi_2 > .$$

In this rule φ_1, φ_2 and θ are environment assumptions made by P_1, P_2 and $P_1 \parallel P_2$ respectively. Similarly, ψ_1, ψ_2 and $\psi_1 \wedge \psi_2$ are the guarantees given by P_1, P_2 and $P_1 \parallel P_2$ respectively.

Unfortunately this rule is unsound for arbitrary temporal formulas. Let NIL be the empty program that does nothing, and ψ an arbitrary formula. Substituting in the rule above:

$$P_1 = P_2 = NIL, \quad \theta = true$$
$$\varphi_1 = \varphi_2 = \psi_1 = \psi_2 = \psi$$

we obtain that all the premises are trivially satisfied. Yet the conclusion $< true > NIL \parallel NIL < \psi >$ claims that the trivial program $NIL \parallel NIL = NIL$ satisfies every formula ψ unconditionally.

There are two ways to correct the rule so that it becomes sound. The first is to restrict the formulas φ, φ_i, ψ_i to safety properties and reinterpret the $< \varphi > P < \psi >$ triplet as stating the following:

For every ***finite*** computation:

$$s_0 \rightarrow s_1 \rightarrow \cdots \rightarrow s_k \rightarrow s_{k+1}$$

if $(s_0 \rightarrow \cdots \rightarrow s_k)$ satisfies φ and P executed the $s_k \rightarrow s_{k+1}$ step then $(s_0 \rightarrow \cdots \rightarrow s_{k+1})$ satisfies ψ. Note that some of the steps in $(s_0 \rightarrow \cdots \rightarrow s_k)$ may have been performed by the ***environment***.

A consequence of this definition is that any ***infinite*** computation that satisfies φ and in which P performed infinitely many steps, also satisfies ψ. This direction is the one taken in [MC] and for which soundness and completeness have been established in [RZ].

One explanation to the failure of the parallel rule in its original form is the lack of the appropriate induction structure. In restricting ourselves to safety properties the induction is provided by the computation itself. In the verification of functional languages this is known as ***computational*** or ***fixpoint*** induction. On the other hand when we want to establish liveness properties we must rely on an explicit inductive structures.

A version of the AG parallel rule that depends on explicit well founded induction is the following:

Let $\mathcal{A}$ be a well founded domain. Let $\varphi_1(\alpha)$, $\varphi_2(\alpha)$, $\psi_1(\alpha)$, $\psi_2(\alpha)$ be temporal formulas that depends ***monotonically*** on a parameter $\alpha \in \mathcal{A}$. The requirement of monotonicity means that for every $\alpha, \beta \in \mathcal{A}$:

$$(\alpha < \beta) \Rightarrow (\varphi(\beta) \rightarrow \varphi(\alpha)).$$

$$\left.\begin{array}{l} < \varphi_1(\alpha) > P_1 < \psi_1(\alpha) > \\ < \varphi_2(\alpha) > P_2 < \psi_2(\alpha) > \\ \theta \wedge [(\forall \beta < \alpha)\psi_1(\beta)] \rightarrow \varphi_2(\alpha) \\ \theta \wedge [(\forall \beta < \alpha)\psi_2(\beta)] \rightarrow \varphi_1(\alpha) \end{array}\right\} \Rightarrow < \theta > P_1 \parallel P_2 < \forall \alpha \psi_1(\alpha) \wedge \psi_2(\alpha) >$$

We will illustrate this rule on the following simple example:

$$P_1 : \begin{array}{l} x := T \\ when\ y\ do\ z := T \end{array} \qquad P_2 : when\ x\ do\ y := T.$$

Under the distributed variables model, P_1 is the only process that can modify x or z and P_2 is the only process that can modify y. In particular, the environment external to both cannot modify any of x, y or z.

We wish to prove the statement:

$$< T > P_1 \parallel P_2 < \Diamond z >$$

which states that when we run P_1 in parallel with P_2 we are guaranteed that z will eventually turn true. As the well founded domain we choose $\mathcal{A} = \{0, 1, 2\}$. Accordingly we take

$$\begin{array}{ll}
\theta = \varphi_1(0) = \varphi_2(0) = & T \\
\psi_1(0) = \varphi_2(1) = & \Diamond\Box x \\
\psi_2(0) = \varphi_1(1) = & T \\
\psi_1(1) = \varphi_2(2) = & \Diamond\Box x \\
\psi_2(1) = \varphi_1(2) = & \Diamond\Box y \\
\psi_1(2) = & \Diamond\Box x \wedge \Diamond\Box z \\
\psi_2(2) = & \Diamond\Box y
\end{array}$$

The logical premises are easy to check. The nonlogical premises are:

$$\begin{array}{lll}
\alpha = 0 & < T > P_1 < \Diamond\Box x > & < T > P_2 < T > \\
\alpha = 1 & < T > P_1 < \Diamond\Box x > & < \Diamond\Box x > P_2 < \Diamond\Box y > \\
\alpha = 2 & < \Diamond\Box y > P_1 < \Diamond\Box x \wedge \Diamond\Box z > & \\
 & < \Diamond\Box x > P_2 < \Diamond\Box y > . &
\end{array}$$

It is not difficult to see that they are valid statements. Consequently we may conclude:

$$< T > P_1 \parallel P_2 < \Diamond\Box x \wedge \Diamond\Box z \wedge \Diamond\Box y >$$

from which the result follows.

Unified Specifications

An alternative to the AG triplet is to have a single temporal specification that contains both the assumption and the guarantee in one formula. We use the notation $[P]\varphi$ inspired by the Dynamic Logic ***box*** construct, to mean that ***all open computations*** of P satisfy the specification of φ.

Intuitively, an ***open computation*** of P is a computation of P interleaved with arbitrary environment steps. An environment step may change the values of all the variables except for the variables owned by P or the control location in P. In this paper we restrict our consideration to nonterminating programs. Dealing with termination or sequential composition introduces extra complexity that we would like to avoid in this discussion. The parallel composition rule in this framework has the following simple form:

$$\left.\begin{array}{l}[P_1]\varphi_1 \\ [P_2]\varphi_2\end{array}\right\} \Rightarrow [P_1 \parallel P_2](\varphi_1 \wedge \varphi_2).$$

We illustrate the rule first on the simple example presented above. It is not difficult to see that the following are valid statements:

$$[P_1]\{\Diamond\Box x \wedge (\Diamond\Box y \rightarrow \Diamond\Box z)\}$$
$$[P_2]\{(\Diamond\Box x \rightarrow \Diamond\Box y)\}.$$

Taking the conjunction of the two specifications, we get by propositional reasoning:

$$[P_1 \parallel P_2]\{\Diamond\Box x \wedge \Diamond\Box y \wedge \Diamond\Box z\}.$$

It is obvious that even though we use unified specifications it is easy to identify in them conjunctions of AG pairs. For example, the specification of P_1 contains the two pairs $T \rightarrow \Diamond\Box x$ and $\Diamond\Box y \rightarrow \Diamond\Box z$, while the specification of P_2 contains the pair $\Diamond\Box x \rightarrow \Diamond\Box y$.

The basic idea underlying compositional and modular verification, and of course the converse process, that of program development, is to analyze first each module in isolation. The result of such analysis will be the specifications of each module, such as φ_1 and φ_2 above. Then, the properties of $P_1 \parallel P_2$ are deduced from the conjunction $\varphi_1 \wedge \varphi_2$. An important measure of success of a modular scheme is to what extent can we abstract away and hide internal details of P_1 and P_2 in φ_1 and φ_2 and yet be able to deduce all of the interesting properties of $P_1 \parallel P_2$. In particular we should not allow φ_1 (and φ_2) to mention variables which are not externally observable, by either P_2 or the environment external to both. For example, φ_1 should not mention the control locations of P_1, or any other private variables which are local to P_1. It should certainly, being a property of P_1, never mention any of the control locations of P_2.

We focus our attention on an example similar to the one we analyzed by the global approach. As a first step we transform it into a form acceptable in the distributed variables model. The problem in the original form is the variable t which is modified by both processes. To distribute it we split t into two variables t_1 and t_2. The original value of t is always represented by $t_1 \oplus t_2$ which is equivalent to $t_1 \not\equiv t_2$.

Under this splitting we obtain the distributed program represented in Fig. 3.

Safety Properties

The main safety property we would like to prove, and should be able to derive from $\varphi_1 \wedge \varphi_2$, is mutual exclusion. This means proving $\Box(\neg(at\, \ell_3 \wedge at\, m_3))$. We allowed a single exception to our rule of not being permitted to mention ℓ_3 or m_3 within φ_1 or φ_2. This is because otherwise we have no direct way of specifying mutual exclusion.

In order to proceed we must devise φ_1 and φ_2 that will connect the state of being at or outside of ℓ_3 (m_3 respectively) with the communications exchanged between the processes by means of the shared variables y_1 and t_1 (y_2 and t_2). A standard φ_1 that always exists and is in fact used in order to establish the completeness of the parallel rule, is the ***temporal semantics*** of P_1, $\hat{\varphi}_1$. This is a formula that specifies fully and precisely all the open computations that P_1 admits. If the temporal language is expressive enough, it is easy to derive such a formula. For example, if we allow quantification over propositions it is given by the following:

$$(\exists q_0, q_1, q_2, q_3)\Big\{q_0 \wedge \Box\Big[\bigwedge_{\substack{i \neq j \\ i,j \in \{0,\ldots,3\}}} (q_i \to \neg q_j) \wedge$$

$$\Big[\bigvee_{i=0}^{3}\big(q_i \wedge \bigcirc q_i \wedge \bigcirc(y_1, t_1) = (y_1, t_1)\big) \vee$$

$$[q_0 \wedge \bigcirc q_1 \wedge \bigcirc(y_1, t_1) = (T, t_1)] \vee [q_1 \wedge \bigcirc q_2 \wedge \bigcirc(y_1, t_1) = (y_1, t_2)] \vee$$
$$[q_2 \wedge (\neg y_2 \vee (t_1 \neq t_2)) \wedge \bigcirc q_3 \wedge \bigcirc(y_1, t_1) = (y_1, t_1)] \vee$$

$$[q_3 \wedge \bigcirc q_0 \wedge \bigcirc(y_1, t_1) = (F, t_1))\Big] \wedge$$

$$(\Diamond \neg q_1) \wedge (\Diamond \neg q_3) \wedge \neg \Box(q_2 \wedge [\neg y_2 \vee (t_1 \neq t_2)]) \wedge q_3 \equiv at\,\ell_3\Big\}.$$

It is clear that in this formula we are simulating the role of the $at\,\ell_i$ which we are forbidden to explicitly mention by the "abstract" propositions q_0-q_3. We feel that in using such a $\hat{\varphi}_1$ we cheat in the sense that we are formally adhering to the requirement of abstraction and modularity while in fact the same information is indirectly encoded and present. This transfers the burden of the proof of the requirement $[P_1 \parallel P_2](\Box\neg(at\,\ell_3 \wedge at\,m_3))$ to proving the implication $\hat{\varphi}_1 \wedge \hat{\varphi}_2 \to (\Box\neg(at\,\ell_3 \wedge at\,m_3))$, while no real abstraction has been made in proving $[P_1]\,\hat{\varphi}_1$ which is automatically valid.

In contrast with this situation, we would like to present next a specification φ_1 for P_1 which does not represent the full semantics of P_1 but only as much as is necessary in order to guarantee the mutual exclusion between P_1 and P_2.

We derive an inspiration for such specification from the invariants we have used in the global method. A crucial invariant used there was:

$$\Box[at\,\ell_3 \wedge at\,m_2 \to (t_1 \neq t_2)]$$

(translating t into $t_1 \neq t_2$).

Since when we examine P_1 we cannot mention $at\,m_2$ we have to replace this assertion by a statement that can be observed by P_1, and from which the fact that P_2 is currently at m_2 (or at m_3 in fact) can be deduced. A candidate for such a statement is the formula:

$$\theta_2 : [y_2 \wedge (t_2 = \ominus t_2)]\mathcal{S}[y_2 \wedge (t_2 = \ominus \neg t_1)].$$

In this formula we use two ***past*** operators, $\mathcal{S}$ – ***since***, and $\ominus$ – ***previous***.

The statement $t_2 = \oplus\neg t_1$ describes an instant in which the current value of t_2 equals the negation of the previous value of t_1 (i.e. the one that t has in the immediately preceding instant. Similarly $t_2 = \oplus t_2$ expresses the fact that the value of t_2 has been preserved over the last transition. The full θ_2 states that there was an instant in the past in which the operation $t_2 := \neg t_1$ has been performed and since then t_2 was not changed. It also requires that y_2 has been continuously true throughout this development. It is not difficult to intuitively see that if indeed P_2 is at m_2 then θ_2 fairly describes its recent history. Consider now the key invariant with $at\, m_2$ replaced by θ_2:

$$\Box\alpha_1 : \Box[at\,\ell_3 \wedge \theta_2 \rightarrow (t_1 \neq t_2)].$$

We verify that it holds over all executions of P_1. Initially $at\,\ell_3$ is false, hence $\alpha_1 = T$. Falsifying transitions are those that cause either $at\,\ell_3$ or θ_2 to become true or $t_1 \neq t_2$ to become false. Consider each of these cases.

The first case is that θ_2 turned from *false* to *true* in the last step. A formula pSq can *become* true only if q is currently true $\big(pSq \rightarrow q \vee \oplus\,(pSq)\big)$. Hence we know that $t_2 = \oplus\neg t_1$, since in the last step, P_1 was either at ℓ_2 or at ℓ_3 it could not have changed t_1 so we must have $t_2 = \neg t_1$ which establishes α_1.

Therefore we may assume that θ_2 was true also in the previous instant and consider the transition $\ell_2 \rightarrow \ell_3$ performed by P_1. Since θ_2 was true in the previous instant $y_2 = T$ and this transition is possible only if previously $t_1 \neq t_2$. By θ_2, t_2 has not changed, and obviously t_1 is not changed by the $\ell_2 \rightarrow \ell_3$ transition, hence $t_1 \neq t_2$ also presently.

The last case to be considered is that the transition falsified $t_1 \neq t_2$. Since after the transition P_1 is at ℓ_3, it could not be done by P_1. By θ_2 either t_2 is preserved or equals $\oplus\neg t_1$. In both cases we conclude that $t_2 \neq t_1$.

A second invariant establishes a similar connection between P_1 being at ℓ_2 or ℓ_3 and its recent history:

$$\Box\beta_1 : \Box[at\,\ell_{2,3} \rightarrow \theta_1]$$

where

$$\theta_1 : [y_1 \wedge (t_1 = \oplus t_1)]S[y_1 \wedge (t_1 = \oplus t_2)].$$

The two cases to be considered are:

$\ell_1 \rightarrow \ell_2$, but this establishes $y_1 \wedge (t_1 = \oplus t_2)$. The $y_1 = T$ part can be derived independently.

The only P_1 transitions that can falsify θ_1 are $\ell_3 \rightarrow \ell_0$ that makes $y_1 = F$ but also $at\,\ell_{2,3} = F$, and $\ell_1 \rightarrow \ell_2$ that may change t_1, which we have already considered.

The environment cannot falsify θ_1 if it has been previously true since it cannot modify t_1.

From α_1 and β_1 we deduce the following valid specification for P_1:

$$[P_1](\,\Box[at\,\ell_3 \wedge \theta_2 \rightarrow (t_1 \neq t_2)] \wedge \Box[at\,\ell_3 \rightarrow \theta_1]).$$

By completely symmetric arguments we can derive:

$$[P_2](\,\Box[at\,m_3 \wedge \theta_1 \rightarrow (t_2 = t_1)] \wedge \Box[at\,m_3 \rightarrow \theta_2]).$$

By taking the conjunction of these specifications and using propositional reasoning we can deduce:

$$[P_1 \parallel P_2](\,\Box[at\,\ell_3 \wedge at\,m_3 \rightarrow (t_1 \neq t_2) \wedge (t_2 = t_1)])$$

which establishes mutual exclusion.

We observe that establishing an invariant that contains a past formula is done in exactly the same way as for state invariants, i.e. by considering all possible transitions and showing that they all *lead* from θ to θ.

Liveness

For showing liveness, we must show that both $at\,\ell_1 \rightarrow \Diamond at\,\ell_3$ and $at\,m_1 \rightarrow \Diamond at\,m_3$ are valid for $P_1 \parallel P_2$. We apologize again for mentioning ℓ_1 and m_1 in public but this is the easiest way of expressing accessibility. Remember that in the global liveness proof we had to switch back and forth between P_1 and P_2 in order to establish the liveness property of P_1. Here the situation is remedied by formulating explicit Assume-Guarantee assumptions.

Thus, the specification we prove for P_1 is:

$$[P_1](A_2 \wedge (A_1 \rightarrow G_1))$$

where A_1, the assumption P_1 makes about P_2's behavior is:

$$\begin{aligned} A_1 : \; & \Box[(t_2 \neq t_1) \rightarrow P_r(t_2)\mathcal{U}(t_2 = t_2)] \wedge \\ & \Box[(t_2 = t_1) \rightarrow \Diamond\{\,\Box\neg y_2 \vee (t_2 \neq t_1)\}]. \end{aligned}$$

We use here the abbreviation $P_r(t_2) : t_2 = \bigcirc t_2$ to denote that the value of t_2 is *preserved* over the next step. Obviously in order to get from ℓ_1 to ℓ_3, P_1 can get to ℓ_2 independently of P_2's behavior. At ℓ_2, P_1 must be guaranteed of some cooperation from P_2. There are two cases to be considered. If currently $t_1 \neq t_2$ then A_1 ensures that t_2 will not be changed unless t_1 was changed first. Inspecting the program P_2 we see that this is a reasonable assumption to make since the only assignment that P_2 makes to t_2 is $t_2 := \neg t_1$. In this case, A_1 ensures that eventually P_1 will detect that $t_1 \neq t_2$ and proceed to ℓ_3. In the other case that currently $t_2 = t_1$, the assumption we can make about P_2 is more complicated. It states that either P_2 will get to m_0 and never venture out again, in which case $\Box\neg y_2$ is guaranteed. Or if it does depart from m_0 it must eventually perform $t_2 := \neg t_1$ which brings us back to the previous case.

It is also clear that if $\Box\neg y_2$ is eventually established, P_1's arrival at ℓ_3 is also guaranteed. Thus we have shown, somewhat informally, that $[P_1](A_1 \rightarrow G_1)$ is a valid statement, where $G_1 : at\,\ell_1 \rightarrow \Diamond at\,\ell_3$.

To assure P_2 of similar cooperation we must also prove $[P_1]A_2$, where A_2 is the assumption that P_2 may make about P_1.

$$\begin{aligned} A_2 : \; & \Box[(t_1 = t_2) \rightarrow P_r(t_1)\mathcal{U}(t_1 \neq t_2)] \wedge \\ & \Box[(t_1 \neq t_2) \rightarrow \Diamond\{\Box\neg y_1 \vee (t_1 = t_2)\}]. \end{aligned}$$

This can be verified in the following way. Since the only assignment P_1 makes to t_1 is $t_1 := t_2$, then if currently $t_1 = t_2$, P_1 can never change t_1's value unless t_2 changes first. In the $t_1 \neq t_2$ case, then regardless of P_1's current position, one of the following events must eventually happen:

Either P_1 gets stuck in ℓ_0, but then $\Box\neg y_1$ is established,
or P_1 gets stuck in ℓ_2, but then it must have found at least one instant in which $t_1 = t_2$
or P_1 eventually performs $t_1 := t_2$, making $t_1 = t_2$ true at least for that instant.

In a completely similar way we can establish:

$$[P_2]\big(A_1 \wedge (A_2 \rightarrow G_2)\big)$$

where $G_2 : at\,m_1 \rightarrow \Diamond at\,m_3$.

By using the parallel rule we easily conclude

$$[P_1 \parallel P_2](G_1 \wedge G_2)$$

which establishes liveness (accessibility) for both P_1 and P_2.

Conclusions and Discussion

Admittedly based on a single example, we may still summarize our experience by saying that there is an obvious advantage and a distinct style of reasoning associated with the compositional approach. While there is an obvious link with the global proof, the process of identifying the assumptions and guarantees that define the interface between parallel components, gives a much better insight into the structure of the proof, and why the algorithm works. Thus we strongly believe that the explicit formulation of assertions such as θ_2 that summarizes precisely which aspects of the behavior of P_2 are needed by P_1 in order to ensure mutual exclusion, improves our understanding of the algorithm. Similar comments apply to the A_1, A_2 assumptions made in the liveness proof.

However, there is a price to be paid. Being no longer allowed to mention location variables in the interface assertions, we must achieve the same expressive power using additional devices. Two suggestions can be made towards this goal.

The first is to use history variables in the style of [OG], [HO]). Having a sequence variable in which all the interesting events are recorded is adequate in order to replace the use of location variables and still provide full support for modular proofs. Similar structures sometimes referred to as *traces* have been suggested in communication based systems.

The alternative presented in this paper is to extend temporal logic by introducing past operators and use them in order to refer in a restricted way to the history.

Thus, as another conclusion of our comparative study of the global vs. the compositional approach, we suggest that some way of referring to the past is very helpful in any compositional approach.

Acknowledgement: I wish to thank Sarah Fliegelmann for her perfect typing of this manuscript and Y. Barbut for the drawings.

References

[BK] Barringer, H., Kuiper, R. — A Temporal Logic Specification Method Supporting Hierarchical Development, University of Manchester (November 1983).

[BKP1] Barringer, H., Kuiper, R., Pnueli, A. — Now You May Compose Temporal Logic Specifications, Proc. of the 16th ACM Symposium on Theory of Computing (1984) 51-63.

[BKP2] Barringer, H., Kuiper, R., Pnueli, A. — A Compositional Temporal Approach to a CSP-like Language, Proc. of IFIP Conference, The Role of Abstract Models in Information Processing.

[FP] Francez, N., Pnueli, A. — A Proof Method for Cyclic Programs, Acta Informatica 9 (1978) 133-157.

[GPSS] Gabbay, D., Pnueli, A., Shelah, S., Stavi, J. — On the Temporal Analysis of Fairness, Proc. of the 7th ACM Symposium on Principles of Programming Languages (1980) 163-173.

[G] Gerth, R. — Transition Logic, Proc. of the 16th ACM Symposium on Theory of Computing (1984) 39-50.

[HO] Hailpern, B., Owicki, S. — Modular Verification of Computer Communication Protocols, IEEE Trans. on Communications, COM-31, 1 (Jan. 1983) 56-68.

[HP] Harel, D., Pnueli, A. — On the Development of Reactive Systems, This issue.

[KVR] Koymans, R., Vytopil, J., De Roever, W.P. — Real Time Programming and Asynchronous Message Passing, 2nd ACM Symposium on Principles of Distributed Computing, Montreal (1983) 187-197.

[L1] Lamport, L. — What Good is Temporal Logic?, Proceedings IFIP (1983) 657-668.

[L2] Lamport, L. — Specifying Concurrent Program Modules, ACM TOPLAS, 5, 2 (1983) 190-222.

[LS] Lamport, L., Schneider, P. — The "Hoare Logic" of CSP and All That, ACM TOPLAS, 6, 2 (April 1984) 281-296.

[MC] Misra, J., Chandy, K.M. — Proofs of Networks of Processes, IEEE Transactions on Software Engin. SE-7, 4 (July 1981).

[MP1] Manna, Z., Pnueli, A. - Verification of Concurrent Programs: The Temporal Framework, in Correctness Problem in Computer Science, R.S. Boyer, J.S. Moare (eds.) Academic Press (1982) 215-273.

[MP2] Manna, Z., Pnueli, A. — Adequate Proof Principles for Invariance and Liveness Properties of Concurrent Programs, Science of Computer Programming, 4,3 (1984) 257-290.

[MP3] Manna, Z., Pnueli, A. — Verification of Concurrent Programs: A Temporal Proof System, Proc. 4th School on Advanced Programming, Amsterdam (June 1982) 163-255.

[MP4] Manna, Z., Pnueli, A. — How to Cook a Temporal Proof System for Your Pet Language, Proceeding of the Symposium of Principles of Programming Languages (1983).

[N] Naur, P. (Ed.) — Revised Report on the Algorithmic Language Algol 60, CACM, 6, 1 (1963) 1-17.

[OG] Owicki, S., Gries, D. — An Axiomatic Proof Technique for Parallel Programs, Acta Informatica 6 (1976) 319-340.

[OL] Owicki, S., Lamport, L. — Proving Liveness Properties of Concurrent Programs, ACM TOPLAS 4, 3 (July 1982) 455-495.

[Pe] Peterson, G.L. — Myths about the Mutual Exclusion Problem, Information Processing Letters 12, 3 (1981) 115-116.

[RZ] De Roever, W.P., Zwiers, J. — manuscript.

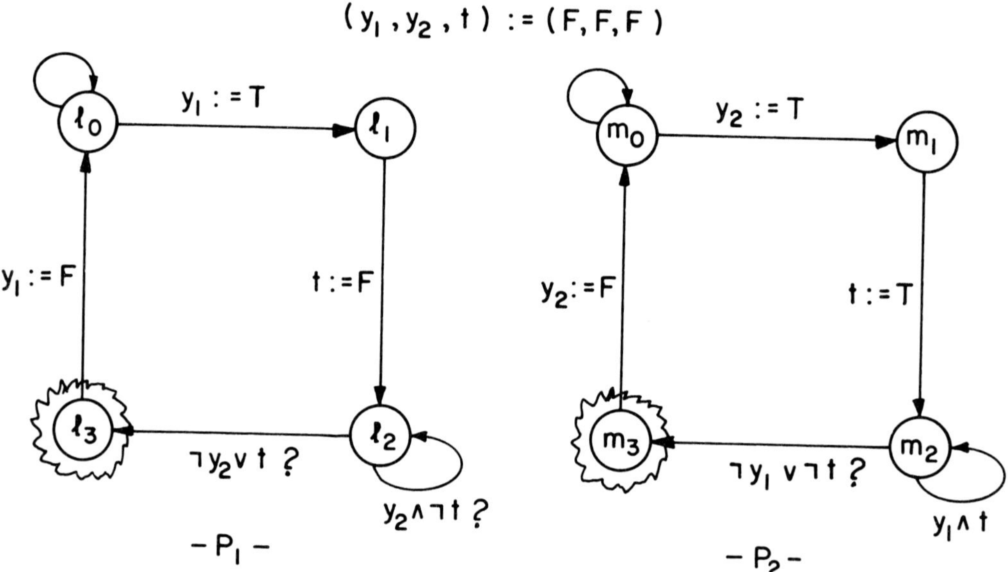

Fig. 1 – Mutual Exclusion Program.

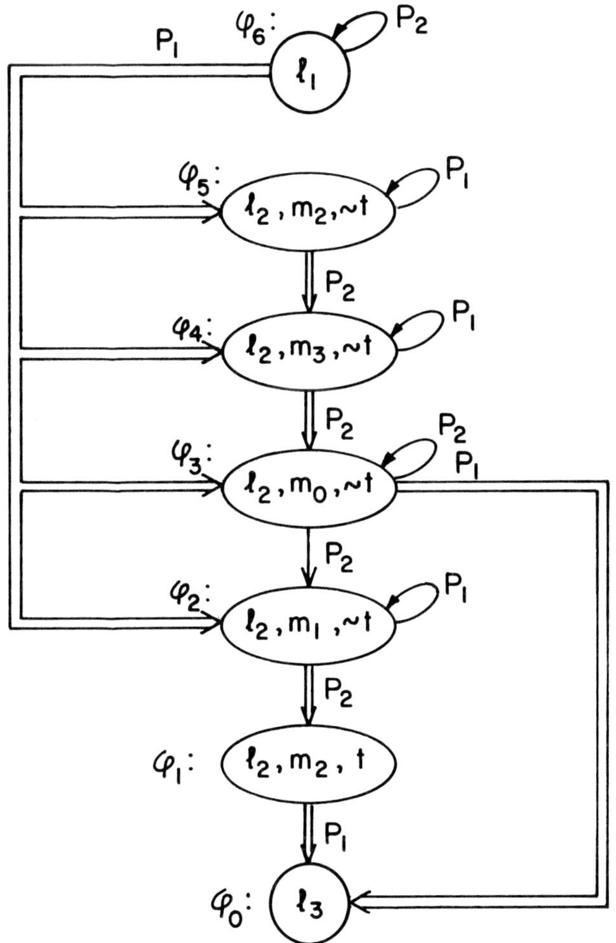

Fig. 2 – Proof Diagram for Liveness.

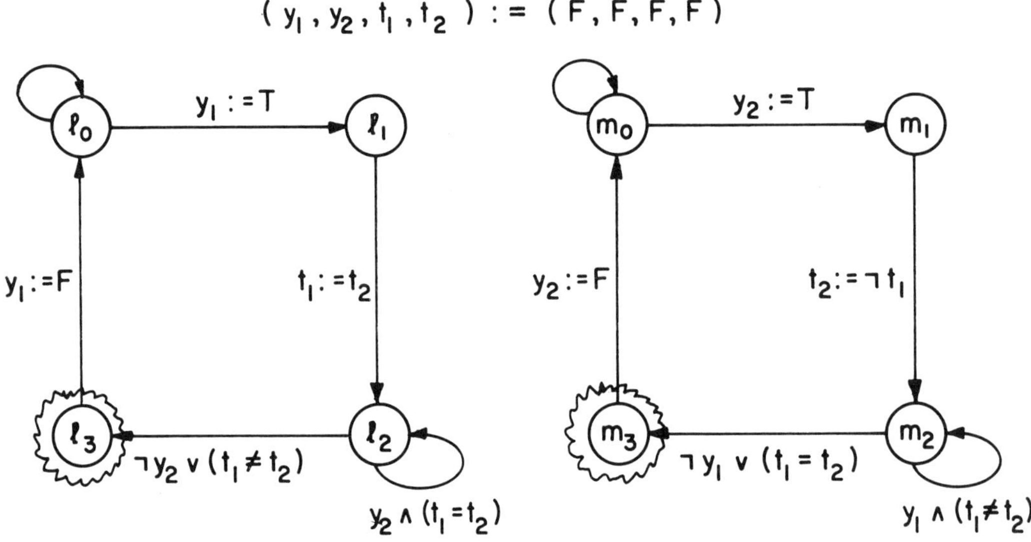

Fig. 3 – Distributed Exclusion Program.

SYNTAX DIRECTED VERIFICATION METHODS

CORRECTNESS PROOFS
OF
DISTRIBUTED TERMINATION ALGORITHMS

Krzysztof R. Apt
L.I.T.P, Université Paris 7
2, Place Jussieu, 75251 Paris, FRANCE

Abstract The problem of correctness of the solutions to the distributed termination problem of Francez [F] is addressed. Correctness criteria are formalized in the customary framework for program correctness. A very simple proof method is proposed and applied to show correctness of a solution to the problem.

1. INTRODUCTION

This paper deals with the distributed termination problem of Francez [F] which has received a great deal of attention in the literature. Several solutions to this problem or its variants have been proposed, however their correctness has been rarely discussed. In fact, it is usually even not explicitly stated what properties such a solution should satisfy.

A notable exception in this matter are papers of Dijkstra, Feijen and Van Gasteren [DFG] and Topor [T] in which solutions to the problem are systematically derived together with their correctness proofs. On the other hand they are presented in a simplistic abstract setting in which for example no distinction can be made between deadlock and termination. Also, as we shall see in the next section, not all desired properties of a solution are addressed there. Systematically derived solutions in the abstract setting of [DFG] are extremely helpful in understanding the final solutions presented in CSP. However, their presentation should not relieve us from providing rigorous correctness proofs of the latter ones - an issue we address in this paper.

Clearly, it would be preferable to derive the solutions in CSP *together* with their correctness proofs, perhaps by transforming accordingly the solutions provided first in the abstract setting. Unfortunately such techniques are not at present available.

This paper is organized as follows. In the next section we define the problem and propose the correctness criteria the solutions to the problem should satisfy. Then in section 3 we formalize these criteria in the usual framework for program correctness and in section 4 we propose a very simple proof method which allows to prove them. In section 5 we provide a simple solution to the problem and in the next section we give a detailed proof of its correctness. Finally, in section section 7 we assess the proposed proof method.

NATO ASI Series, Vol. F13
Logics and Models of Concurrent Systems
Edited by K. R. Apt

Throughout the paper we assume from the reader knowledge of Communicating Sequential Processes (CSP in short), as defined in Hoare [H], and some experience in the proofs of correctness of very simple loop free sequential programs.

2. DISTRIBUTED TERMINATION PROBLEM

Suppose that a CSP program

$$P \equiv [P_1 \,\|\cdots\|\, P_n],$$

where for every $1 \leqslant i \leqslant n$ $P_i :: INIT_i ; * [S_i]$ is given. We assume that each S_i is of the form $\underset{j \in \Gamma_i}{\Box} g_{i,j} \rightarrow S_{i,j}$ for a multiset Γ_i and

i) each $g_{i,j}$ contains an i/o command adressing P_j,
ii) none of the statements $INIT_i$, $S_{i,j}$ contains an i/o command.

We say then that P is in a *normal form*. Suppose moreover that with each P_i a *stability condition* B_i, a Boolean expression involving variables of P_i and possibly some auxiliary variables, is associated. By a *global stability condition* we mean a situation in which each process is at the main loop entry with its stability condition B_i true.

We now adopt the following two assumptions :

a) no communication can take place between a pair of processes whose stability conditions hold,

b) whenever deadlock takes place, the global stability condition is reached.

The *distributed termination problem* is the problem of transforming P into another program P' which eventually properly terminates whenever the global stability condition is reached.

This problem, due to Francez [F], has been extensively studied in the literature.

We say that the global stability condition is (not) reached in a computation of P' if it is (not) reached in the natural restriction of the computation to a computation of P. In turn, the global stability condition is reached (not reached) in a computation of P if it holds in a possible (no) global state of the computation. We consider here partially ordered computations in the sense of [L].

We now postulate four properties a solution P' to the distributed termination problem should satisfy (see Apt and Richier [AR]) :

1. Whenever P' properly terminates then the global stability condition is reached.
2. There is no deadlock.

3. If the global stability condition is reached then P' will eventually properly terminate.
4. If the global stability condition is not reached then infinitely often a statement from the original program P will be executed.

The last property excludes the situations in which the transformed parallel program endlessly executes the added control parts dealing with termination detection. We also postulate that the communication graph should not be altered.

In the abstract framework of [DFG] only the first property is proved. Second property is not meaningful as deadlock coincides there with termination. In turn, satisfaction of the third property is argued informally and the fourth one is not mentioned.

Solutions to the distributed termination problem are obtained by arranging some additional communications between the processes P_i. Most of them are programs $P' \equiv [P_1 \| \ldots \| P_n]$ in a normal form where for every i, $1 \leq i \leq n$

$$
\begin{array}{l}
P_i :: \text{INIT}_i ; \ldots, \\
\quad *[\underset{j \in \Gamma_i}{\square} \cdots ; g_{i,j} \rightarrow \ldots ; S_{i,j} \\
\quad\quad \square \text{ CONTROL PART}_i \\
\quad]
\end{array}
$$

where ... stand for some added Boolean conditions or statements not containing i/o commands, and CONTROL PART_i stands for a part of the loop dealing with additional communications. We assume that no variable of the original process $P_i :: \text{INIT}_i ; *[S_i]$ can be altered in CONTROL PART_i and that all i/o commands within CONTROL PART_i are of new types.

We now express the introduced four properties for the case of solutions of the above form using the customary terminology dealing with program correctness.

3. FORMALIZATION OF THE CORRECTNESS CRITERIA

Let p,q,I be assertions from an assertion language and let S be a CSP program. We say that {p} S {q} holds in the sense of *partial correctness* if all properly terminating computations of S starting in a state satisfying p terminate in a state satisfying q. We say that {p} S {q} holds in the sense of *weak total correctness* if it holds in the sense of partial correctness and moreover no computation of S starting in a state satisfying p fails or diverges. We say that S is *deadlock free relative to* p if in the computations of S starting in a state satisfying p no deadlock can arise. If $p \equiv$ true then we simply say that P is *deadlock free*.

Finally, we say that {p} S {q} holds in the sense of *total correctness* if it holds in the sense of weak total correctness and moreover S is deadlock free relative to p. Thus when {p} S {q} holds in the sense of total correctness then all computations of S starting in a state satisfying p properly terminate.

Also for CSP programs in a normal form we introduce the notion of a global invariant I. We say that I is a *global invariant of* P *relative to* p if in all computations of P starting in a state satisfying p, I holds whenever each process P_i is at the main loop entry. If p ≡ <u>true</u> then we simply say that I is a *global invariant of* P.

Now, property 1 simply means that

$$\{\underline{true}\}\ P'\ \{\bigwedge_{i=1}^{n} B_i\} \qquad (1)$$

holds in the sense of partial correctness.

Property 2 means that P' is deadlock free.

Property 3 cannot be expressed by refering directly to the program P'. Even though it refers to the termination of P' it is not equivalent to its (weak) total correctness because the starting point - the global stability condition - is not the initial one. It is a control point which can be reached in the course of a computation.

However, *in the case of* P' we can still express property 3 by refering to the weak total correctness of a program derived from P'. Consider the following program

CONTROL PART ≡
$[P_1 :: *[\text{CONTROL PART}_1] \| \ldots \| P_n :: *[\text{CONTROL PART}_n]]$.

We now claim that to establish property 3 it is sufficient to prove for an appropriately chosen global invariant I of P'

$$\{I \wedge \bigwedge_{i=1}^{n} B_i\}\ \text{CONTROL PART}\ \{\underline{true}\} \qquad (2)$$

in the sense of total correctness.

Indeed, suppose that in a computation of P' the global stability condition is reached. Then $I \wedge \bigwedge_{i=1}^{n} B_i$ holds where I is a global invariant of P'. By the assumption a) concerning the original program P no statement from P can be executed any more. Thus the part of P' that remains to be executed is equivalent to the program CONTROL PART. Now, on virtue of (2) property 3 holds.

Consider now property 4. As before we can express it only by refering to the program CONTROL PART. Clearly property 4 holds if

$$\{ I \wedge \neg \bigwedge_{i=1}^{n} B_i \} \text{ CONTROL PART } \{\underline{\text{true}}\} \qquad (3)$$

holds in the sense of weak total correctness. Indeed, (3) guarantees that in no computation of P' the control remains from a certain moment on indefinitely within the added control parts in case the global stability condition is not reached.

Assuming that property 2 is already established, to show property 3 it is sufficient to prove (2) in the sense of weak total corrctness. Now (2) and (3) can be combined into the formula

$$\{I\} \text{ CONTROL PART } \{\underline{\text{true}}\} \qquad (4)$$

in the sense of weak total correctness.

The idea of expressing an eventuality property of one program by a termination property of another program also appears in Grumberg et al. [GFMR] in one of the clauses of a rule for fair termination.

4.PROOF METHOD

We now present a simple proof method which will allow us to handle the properties discussed in the previous section. It can be applied to CSP programs being in a normal form. So assume that $P \equiv [P_1 \parallel \ldots \parallel P_n]$ is such a program.

Given a guard $g_{i,j}$ we denote by $b_{i,j}$ the conjunction of its Boolean parts. We say that guards $g_{i,j}$ and $g_{j,i}$ *match* if one contains an input command and the other an output command whose expressions are of the same type. The notation implies that these i/o commands address each other, i.e. they are within the texts of P_i and P_j, respectively and address P_j and P_i, respectively.

Given two matching guards $g_{i,j}$ and $g_{j,i}$ we denote by $Eff(g_{i,j}, g_{j,i})$ the effect of the communication between their i/o commands. It is the assignment whose left hand side is the input variable and the right hand side the output expression.

Finally, let

$$\text{TERMINATED} \equiv \bigwedge_{\substack{1 \leq i \leq n, \\ j \in \Gamma_i}} \neg b_{i,j}.$$

Observe that TERMINATED holds upon termination of P.

Consider now partial correctness. We propose the following proof rule:

RULE 1 : PARTIAL CORRECTNESS

$$\frac{\begin{array}{l}\{p\}\ INIT_1\ ;\ldots;\ INIT_n\ \{I\},\\ \{I \land b_{i,j} \land b_{j,i}\}\ Eff(g_{i,j}, g_{j,i})\ ;\ S_{i,j}\ ;\ S_{j,i}\ \{I\}\\ \text{for all } i,j \text{ s.t. } i \in \Gamma_j,\ j \in \Gamma_i \text{ and } g_{i,j}, g_{j,i} \text{ match}\end{array}}{\{p\}\ P\ \{I \land TERMINATED\}}$$

This rule has to be used in conjunction with the usual proof system for *partial* correctness of nondeterministic programs (see e.g. Apt [A1]) in order to be able to establish its premises. Informally, it can phrased as follows. If I is established upon execution of all the $INIT_i$ sections and is preserved by a joint execution of each pair of branches of the main loops with matching guards then I holds upon exit. If the premises of this rule hold then we can also deduce that I is a global invariant of P relative to p.

Consider now weak total correctness. We adopt the following proof rule:

RULE 2 : WEAK TOTAL CORRECTNESS

$$\frac{\begin{array}{l}\{p\}\ INIT_1\ ;\ldots;\ INIT_n\ \{I \land t \geq 0\},\\ \{I \land b_{i,j} \land b_{j,i} \land z=t \land t \geq 0\}\ Eff(g_{i,j},g_{j,i});S_{i,j};S_{j,i}\{I \land 0 \leq t < z\}\\ \text{for all } i,j \text{ s.t. } i \in \Gamma_j,\ j \in \Gamma_i \text{ and } g_{i,j}, g_{j,i} \text{ match}\end{array}}{\{p\}\ P\ \{I \land TERMINATED\}}$$

where z does not appear in P or t and t is an integer valued expression.

This rule has to be used in conjunction with the standard proof system for *total* correctness of nondeterministic programs (see e.g. Apt [A1]) in order to establish its premises. It is a usual modification of the rule concerning partial correctness.

Finally, consider deadlock freedom. Let

$$BLOCKED \equiv \land \{\neg b_{i,j} \lor \neg b_{j,i} : 1 \leq i,j \leq n,\ i \in \Gamma_j,\ j \in \Gamma_i,\ g_{i,j} \text{ and } g_{j,i} \text{ match}\}$$

Observe that in a given state of P the formula BLOCKED holds if and only if no communication between the processes is possible. We now propose the following proof rule

RULE 3 : DEADLOCK FREEDOM

$$\frac{\begin{array}{l}I \text{ is a global invariant of } P \text{ relative to } p,\\ I \land BLOCKED \rightarrow TERMINATED\end{array}}{P \text{ is deadlock free relative to } p}$$

The above rules will be used in conjunction with a rule of auxiliary variables.

Let A be a set of variables of a program S. A is called the set of *auxiliary variables* of S if

i) all variables from A appear in S only in assignments,
ii) no variable of S from outside of A depends on the variables from A . In other words there does not exist an assignment x:=t in S such that $x \notin A$ and t contains a variable from A.

Thus for example {z} is the only (nonempty) set of auxiliary variables of the program

$[P_1 :: z:=y \; ; \; P_2 ! \; x \; \| \; P_2 :: P_1 \; ? \; u \; ; \; u:=u+1]$

We now adopt the following proof rule first introduced by Owicki and Gries in [OG1, OG2].

RULE 4 : AUXILIARY VARIABLES

Let A be a set of auxiliary variables of a program S. Let S' be obtained from S by deleting all assignments to the variables in A. Then

$$\frac{\{p\} \; S \; \{q\}}{\{p\} \; S' \; \{q\}}$$

provided q has no free variable from A.
Also if S is deadlock free relative to p then so is S'.

We shall use this rule both in the proofs of partial and of (weak) total correctness. Also without mentioning we shall use in proofs the well-known consequence rule which allows to strengthen the preconditions and weaken postconditions of a program.

5. A SOLUTION

We now present a simple solution to the distributed termination problem. It is a combination of the solutions proposed by Francez, Rodeh and Sintzoff [FRS] and (in an abstract setting) Dijkstra, Feijen and Van Gasteren [DFG].

We assume that the graph consisting of all communication channels within P contains a Hamiltonian cycle. In the resulting ring the neighbours of P_i are P_{i-1} and P_{i+1} where counting is done within $\{1,\ldots,n\}$ clockwise.

We first present a solution in which the global stability condition is detected by one process, say P_1. It has the following form where the introduced variables s_i, $send_i$ and $moved_i$ do not appear in the original program P :

For i = 1

```
Pi :: sendi := true ;
      *[ □  gi,j → Si,j
        j∈Γi
         □ Bi ; sendi ; Pi+1! true → sendi := false
         □ Pi-1 ? si → [si → halt □ ¬ si → sendi := true]
      ]
```

and for i ≠ 1

```
Pi :: sendi:=false ; movedi:=false ;
      *[ □ gi,j → movedi:=true ; Si,j
        j∈Γi
         □ Pi-1? si → sendi:=true
         □ Bi ; sendi ; Pi+1! (si ∧ ¬ movedi) → sendi:=false ;
                                                movedi:=false
      ]
```

In this program we use the halt instruction with an obvious meaning. Informally, P_1 decides to send a *probe* true to its right hand side neighbour when its stability condition B_1 holds. A probe can be transmitted by a process P_i further to its right hand side neighbour when in turn its stability condition holds. Each process writes into the probe its current status being reflected by the variable moved. moved turns to true when a communication from the original program takes place and turns to false when the probe is sent to the right hand side neighbour. P_1 decides to stop its execution when a probe has made a full cycle remaining true. This will happen if all the moved variables are false at the moment of *receiving* the probe from the left hand side neighbour.

We now modify this program by arranging that P_1 sends a final termination wave through the ring once it detects the global stability condition. To this purpose we introduce in all P_i's two new Boolean variables $detected_i$ and $done_i$. The program has the following form :

For i = 1

```
Pi ::  sendi:=true ; donei:=false ; detectedi:=false ;
      * [ □ ¬ donei, gi,j → Si,j
          j∈Γi
           □ ¬ donei ; Bi ; sendi ; Pi+1!true → sendi:=false
           □ ¬ donei ; Pi-1 ? si →
                       [ si → detectedi:=true □ ¬ si → sendi:=true]
           □ detectedi ; Pi+1! end → detectedi:=false
           □ ¬ donei ; Pi-1? end → donei:=true
        ]
```

and for $i \neq 1$

```
Pᵢ ::  sendᵢ:=false ; movedᵢ:=false ; doneᵢ:=false ; detectedᵢ:=false ;
       * [ □ ¬ doneᵢ ; gᵢ,ⱼ → movedᵢ:=true ; Sᵢ,ⱼ
          j∈Γᵢ
           □ ¬ doneᵢ ; Pᵢ₋₁ ? sᵢ → sendᵢ:=true
           □ ¬ doneᵢ ; Bᵢ ; sendᵢ ; Pᵢ₊₁!(sᵢ ∧ ¬ movedᵢ) →
                                             sendᵢ:=false ;
                                             movedᵢ:=false
           □ ¬ doneᵢ ; Pᵢ₋₁ ? end → detectedᵢ:=true ; doneᵢ:=true
           □ detectedᵢ ; Pᵢ₊₁! end → detectedᵢ:=false
         ]
```

We assume that end is a signal of a new type not used in the original program. (Actually, to avoid confusion in the transmission of the probe we also have to assume that in the original program no messages are of type Boolean. If this is not the case then we can always replace the probe by a Boolean valued message of a new type).

6. CORRECTNESS PROOF

We now prove correctness of the solution given in the previous section using the proof method introduced in section 4. We do this by proving the formalized in section 3 versions of properties 1-4 from section 2.

Proof of property 1

We first modify the program given in the previous section by introducing in process P_1 auxiliary variables $received_1$ and $forward_1$. The variable $received_1$ is introduced in order to distinguish the situation when s_1 is initially true from the one when s_1 turns true after the communication with P_n. $forward_1$ is used to express the fact that P_1 sent the end signal to P_2. Note that this fact cannot be expressed by referring to the variable $detected_1$. This refined version of P_1 has the following form :

```
P₁ ::  send₁ := true; done₁:=false ; detected₁:=false ;
         received₁:=false ; forward₁:=false ;
       * [  □  ¬ done₁ ; g₁,ⱼ → S₁,ⱼ
           j∈Γ₁
            □ ¬ done₁ ; B₁ ; send₁ ; P₂! true → send₁:=false
            □ ¬ done₁ ; Pₙ?s₁ → received₁:=true ;
              [s₁ → detected₁:=true □ ¬ s₁ → send₁:=true]
            □ detected₁ ; P₂! end → forward₁:=true ;
                                    detected₁:=false
            □ ¬ done₁ ; Pₙ ? end → done₁:=true
         ]
```

Other processes remain unchanged. Call this modified program R. On virtue of rule 4 to establish property 1 it is sufficient to find a global invariant of R which upon its termination implies $\bigwedge_{i=1}^{n} B_i$.

We do this by establishing a sequence of successively stronger global invariants whose final element is the desired I. We call a program $Eff(g_{i,j}, g_{j,i})$; $S_{i,j}$; $S_{j,i}$ corresponding to a joint execution of two branches of the main loops with matching guards a *transition*. Here and elsewhere we occasionally identify the Boolean values false, true with 0 and 1, respectively. To avoid excessive use of brackets we assume that "$\rightarrow$" binds weaker than other connectives.

Let

$$I_1 \equiv \sum_{i=1}^{n} send_i \leq 1.$$

Then I_1 is clearly a global invariant of R : it is established by the initial assignments and is preserved by every transition as setting of a send variable to true is accompanied by setting of another true send variable to false.

Consider now

$$I_2 \equiv \forall i > 1\ [s_i \wedge send_i \rightarrow (\forall j(1 \leq j < i \rightarrow B_j) \vee \exists j \geq i\ moved_j]$$
$$\wedge\ [s_1 \wedge received_1 \rightarrow \forall j\ (1 \leq j \leq n \rightarrow B_j)].$$

We now claim that $I_1 \wedge I_2$ is a global invariant of R. First note that I_2 is established by the initial assignments in a trivial way.

Next, consider a transition corresponding to a communication from the original program P. Assume that initially $I_1 \wedge I_2$ and the Boolean conditions of the guards hold.

Consider now the first conjunct of I_2. If initially for no $i > 1$ $s_i \wedge send_i$ holds then this conjunct is preserved since the transition does not alter s_i or $send_i$. Suppose now that initially for some $i > 1$ $s_i \wedge send_i$ holds. If initially also $\exists j \geq i\ moved_j$ holds then this conjunct is preserved. If initially $\forall j\ (1 \leq j < i \rightarrow B_j)$ holds then by assumption a) from section 2 at least one of the processes involved in the transition has an index $\geq i$. The transition sets its moved variable to true which establishes $\exists\ j \geq i\ moved_j$.

The second conjunct of I_2 is obviously preserved - if initially $s_1 \wedge received_1$ does not hold then it does not hold at the end of the transition either. If initially $s_1 \wedge received_1$ holds then also $\forall j\ (1 \leq j < n \rightarrow B_j)$ initially holds so by assumption a) from section 2 the discussed transition cannot take place.

Consider now a transition corresponding to a sending of the probe from P_i to P_{i+1} $(1 \leq i \leq n)$. Suppose that at the end of the transition $s_k \wedge send_k$ for some $k\ (1 < k \leq n)$ holds. Due to the global invariant I_1 and the form of the transition $k = i+1$. Thus in the initial state $B_i \wedge s_i \wedge \neg moved_i \wedge send_i$ holds. Now, on virtue of I_2 initially

$$\forall j\ (1 \leq j < i \rightarrow B_j) \vee \exists j \geq i\ moved_j$$

holds. Thus initially

$$\forall j\ (1 \leq j < i+1 \rightarrow B_j) \vee \exists j \geq i+1\ moved_j$$

holds. This formula is not affected by the execution of the transition. Thus at the end of the transition the first conjunct of I_2 holds.

Suppose now that at the end of the transition $s_1 \wedge received_1$ holds. If initially $s_1 \wedge received_1$ holds then also $\forall j\ (1 \leq j \leq n \rightarrow B_j)$ initially holds. Suppose now that initially $s_1 \wedge received_1$ does not hold. Thus the transition consists of sending the probe from P_n to P_1. Then initially $B_n \wedge s_n \wedge \neg moved_n \wedge send_n$ holds so on virtue of I_2 initially $\forall j\ (1 \leq j \leq n \rightarrow B_j)$ holds, as well. But this formula is preserved by the execution of the transition. So at the end of the transition the second conjunct of I_2 holds.

The other transitions do not affect I_2. So $I_1 \wedge I_2$ is indeed a global invariant of R. Now, $I_1 \wedge I_2$ upon termination of R does not imply yet $\bigwedge_{i=1}^{n} B_i$. But it is now sufficient to show that upon termination of R $s_1 \wedge received_1$ holds.

Consider now

$$I_3 \equiv detected_1 \rightarrow s_1 \wedge received_1.$$

Then I_3 is clearly a global invariant of R. Next, let

$$I_4 \equiv forward_1 \rightarrow s_1 \wedge received_1$$

Then $I_3 \wedge I_4$ is a global invariant of R. Indeed, when $forward_1$ becomes true, initially $detected_1$ holds, so on virtue of I_3 $s_1 \wedge received_1$ initially holds. But $s_1 \wedge received_1$ is not affected by the execution of the transition in question.

Now we show that upon termination of R $forward_1$ hold. To this purpose consider

$$I_5 \equiv done_2 \rightarrow forward_1.$$

Clearly I_5 is a global invariant : $done_2$ and $forward_1$ become true in the same transition.

Let now

$$I \equiv \bigwedge_{i=1}^{5} I_i.$$

Then I is the desired global invariant : upon termination of R $done_2$ holds and $done_2 \wedge I$ implies $\bigwedge_{i=1}^{n} B_i$.

Proof of property 2

We now also modify processes P_i for $i \neq 1$, by introducing in it the auxiliary variable $forward_i$ for the same reasons as in P_1.

The refined versions of P_i $(i \neq 1)$ have the following form :

```
Pi :: sendi:==false ; movedi:=false ; donei:=false ;
       detectedi:=false ; forwardi:=false ;
      *[  □ ¬ donei ; gi,j → movedi:=true ; Si,j
         j∈Γi
          □ ¬ donei ; Pi-1 ? si → sendi:=true
          □ ¬ donei ; Bi ; sendi ; Pi+1!(si ∧ ¬ movedi) →
                                sendi:=false ;
                                movedi:=false
          □ ¬ donei ; Pi-1 ? end → detectedi:=true ;
                                   donei:=true
          □ detectedi ; Pi+1! end → forwardi:=true ;
                                    detectedi:=false
       ]
```

Call this refined version of the program S. We now prove that S is deadlock free. In the subsequent proofs it will be more convenient to consider second premise of rule 3 in the form $I \wedge \neg TERMINATED \rightarrow \neg BLOCKED$. Let for $i = 1,\ldots,n$

$$TERMINATED_i \equiv done_i \wedge \neg detected_i .$$

Note that if in a deadlock situation of S $TERMINATED_i$ holds then P_i has terminated. The following natural decomposition of $\neg TERMINATED$ allows us to carry out a case analysis.

$$\begin{aligned} \neg TERMINATED \equiv & \\ & [\neg TERMINATED_1 \wedge \forall i\,(i\neq 1 \rightarrow TERMINATED_i)] \\ & \vee \exists i\,(1 < i < n \wedge \neg TERMINATED_i \wedge TERMINATED_{i+1}) \\ & \vee \forall i\, \neg TERMINATED_i . \end{aligned}$$

Case 1 It corresponds to a deadlock situation in which P_1 did not terminate and all P_i for $i\neq 1$ have terminated.

Let

$$I_6 \equiv \neg detected_n \wedge done_n \rightarrow forward_n,$$
$$I_7 \equiv forward_n \rightarrow done_1.$$

It is straightforward to see that I_6 and I_7 are global invariants of S. Let now

$$I_8 \equiv done_2 \rightarrow forward_1,$$
$$I_9 \equiv detected_1 \rightarrow \sum_{i=1}^{n} send_i = 0,$$

$$I_{10} \equiv \text{forward}_1 \rightarrow \sum_{i=1}^{n} \text{send}_i = 0,$$

$$I_{11} \equiv \text{forward}_1 \rightarrow \neg\, \text{detected}_1.$$

Then I_8, I_9, $I_9 \wedge I_{10}$, $I_9 \wedge I_{10} \wedge I_{11}$ are all global invariants of S. To see this consider by way of example $I_9 \wedge I_{10} \wedge I_{11}$ under the assumption that $I_9 \wedge I_{10}$ is already shown to be a global invariant. It is obviously established by the initial assignments of S. The only transition which can falsify $I_9 \wedge I_{10} \wedge I_{11}$ in view of invariance of $I_9 \wedge I_{10}$ is the one involving recpetion of the probe by P_1. But then initially send_n holds so by I_{10} initially $\neg\, \text{forward}_1$ holds. The transition does not change the value of forward_1. So forward_1 remains false and I_{11} holds at the end of the transition.

Let now

$$J \equiv \bigwedge_{i=6}^{11} I_i.$$

J is a global invariant of S. Observe now that

$$J \wedge \text{TERMINATED}_n \rightarrow \text{done}_1$$

on the account of I_6 and I_7

and

$$J \wedge \text{TERMINATED}_2 \rightarrow \neg\, \text{detected}_1$$

on the account of I_8 and I_{11}.

Thus

$$J \wedge \text{TERMINATED}_2 \wedge \text{TERMINATED}_n \rightarrow \text{TERMINATED}_1,$$

i.e.

$$J \wedge [\neg\, \text{TERMINATED}_1 \wedge \forall i\ (i \neq 1 \rightarrow \text{TERMINATED}_i)]$$

is unsatisfiable.

Case 2 It corresponds to a deadlock situation in which for some i, $1 < i < n$, P_i did not terminate whereas P_{i+1} did terminate. Let some i, $1 < i < n$, be given.

Let

$$I_{12} \equiv \text{done}_{i+1} \rightarrow \text{forward}_i,$$
$$I_{13} \equiv \text{detected}_i \rightarrow \text{done}_i,$$
$$I_{14} \equiv \text{forward}_i \rightarrow \text{done}_i \wedge \neg\, \text{detected}_i.$$

It is straightforward to see that I_{12}, I_{13} and $I_{13} \wedge I_{14}$ are global invariants. Let

$$K \equiv I_{12} \wedge I_{13} \wedge I_{14}.$$

Then K is a global invariant and

$$K \wedge TERMINATED_{i+1} \rightarrow TERMINATED_i$$

on the account of I_{12} and I_{14}.

Thus

$$K \wedge \neg TERMINATED_i \wedge TERMINATED_i$$

is unsatisfiable.

In fact we showed that neither case 1 nor case 2 can arise.

<u>Case 3</u> It corresponds to a deadlock situation in which none of the processes has terminated.

Let

$$I_{15} \equiv done_1 \rightarrow forward_n.$$

I_{15} is a global invariant. Also I_{12} for all i s.t. $1 < i < n$ and $I_{13} \wedge I_{14}$ for all i s.t. $1 < i \leqslant n$ are global invariants.

Let

$$L \equiv I_{15} \wedge \bigwedge_{i=2}^{n-1} I_{12} \wedge \bigwedge_{i=2}^{n} (I_{13} \wedge I_{14}).$$

Then L is a global invariant and

$$L \wedge \exists i\ (i \neq 2 \wedge done_i) \rightarrow \exists i\ TERMINATED_i$$

on the account of I_{15}, $\bigwedge_{i=2}^{n-1} I_{12}$ and $\bigwedge_{i=2}^{n} I_{14}$.

Thus

$$L \wedge \forall i\ \neg TERMINATED_i \rightarrow \forall i\ (i \neq 2 \rightarrow \neg done_i). \qquad (5)$$

Hence

$$L \wedge \forall i\ \neg\ TERMINATED_i \wedge done_2 \rightarrow detected_2 \wedge \neg done_3 \rightarrow \neg BLOCKED.$$

It remains to consider the case when $\neg done_2$ holds. Let

$$I_{16} \equiv \sum_{i=0}^{n} send_i = 0 \rightarrow s_1 \wedge received_1,$$
$$I_{17} \equiv s_1 \wedge received_1 \wedge \neg detected_1 \rightarrow forward_1,$$
$$I_{18} \equiv forward_1 \rightarrow done_2.$$

Then I_{16}, I_{17} and I_{18} are global invariants.

Let BLOCKED (P) stand for the formula BLOCKED constructed for the original program P from section 2. Assumption b) of section 2 simply means that

$$\phi \equiv \text{BLOCKED}(P) \rightarrow \bigwedge_{i=1}^{n} B_i$$

is a global invariant of P. But by the form of S ϕ is also a global invariant of S as the added transitions do not alter the variables of P. Thus

$$M \equiv L \wedge I_{16} \wedge I_{17} \wedge I_{18} \wedge \phi$$

is a global invariant of S.

We now have

$M \wedge \forall i \neg \text{TERMINATED}_i \wedge \neg \text{done}_2 \wedge \text{BLOCKED} \rightarrow$ (by (5))
$M \wedge \forall i \neg \text{done}_i \wedge \text{BLOCKED} \rightarrow$ (by the form of S)
$M \wedge \forall i \neg \text{done}_i \wedge \text{BLOCKED} \wedge \text{BLOCKED}(P) \rightarrow$ (since ϕ is a part of M)
$M \wedge \forall i \neg \text{done}_i \wedge \text{BLOCKED} \wedge \bigwedge_{i=1}^{n} B_i \rightarrow$ (by the form of S)
$M \wedge \forall i \neg \text{done}_i \wedge \sum_{i=1}^{n} \text{send}_i = 0 \wedge \neg \text{detected}_1 \rightarrow$ (since I_{16}, I_{17} and I_{18} are parts of M)

$\forall i \neg \text{done}_i \wedge \text{done}_2$

which is a contradiction.

This simply means that

$M \wedge \forall i \neg \text{TERMINATED}_i \wedge \neg \text{done}_2 \rightarrow \neg \text{BLOCKED}$

which concludes the proof of case 3.

By rule 3 S is now deadlock free where $J \wedge K \wedge M$ is the desired global invariant. By rule 4 P' is deadlock free.

Proof of properties 3 and 4

We first modify the program CONTROL PART by introducing in process P_1 an auxiliary variable count_1 which is used to count the number of times process P_1 has received the probe. Other processes remain unchanged. Thus the processes have the following form :

Let

$$I_{20} \equiv count_1 = 2 \rightarrow \forall j\ (1 < j \rightarrow \neg moved_j)$$

Then $I_1 \wedge I_{19} \wedge I_{20}$ is a global invariant : when $count_1$ becomes 2 then initially due to I_{19} $\forall j\ (1 < j < i \rightarrow \neg moved_j)$ holds. At the end of the transition additionally $\neg moved_n$ holds. Moreover, no $moved_i$ variable is ever set to true.

Let

$$I_{21} \equiv \forall i > 1\ (count_1 = 2 \wedge send_i \rightarrow s_i).$$

Consider now $I_1 \wedge \bigwedge_{j=19}^{21} I_j$ and suppose that by an execution of a transition $send_i$ is set to true when $count_1 = 2$. If $i = 2$ then s_2 holds as s_2 is always set to true. So assume that $i > 2$. Then initially by I_{20} and I_{21} $s_{i-1} \wedge \neg moved_{i-1}$ holds. At the end of the transition $s_i = s_{i-1} \wedge \neg moved_{i-1}$ so s_i holds as desired.

Also when $count_1$ becomes 2 then for the same reasons as in the case of

I_{19} no $send_i$ for $i > 1$ can be true. This shows that $I_1 \wedge \bigwedge_{j=19}^{21} I_j$ is a global invariant.

Let now

$$I_{22} \equiv count_1 = 3 \rightarrow \sum_{i=1}^{n} send_i = 0$$

Then $I_1 \wedge \bigwedge_{j=19}^{22} I_j$ is a global invariant. Indeed, when at the end of a transition, $count_1$ becomes 3 then initially on the account of I_{19}, I_{20} and I_{21} $send_n \wedge \forall i < n\ \neg send_i \wedge s_n \wedge \neg moved_n$ holds. Thus at the end of the transition $s_1 \wedge detected_1 \wedge \forall i\ \neg send_i$ holds.

Also $\sum_{i=1}^{n} send_i = 0$ is preserved by every transition.

Finally, let

$$I_{23} \equiv count_1 \leq 3.$$

Then

$$N \equiv I_1 \wedge \bigwedge_{j=19}^{23} I_j$$

is a global invariant of T.

Indeed, when at the beginning of a transition $count_1$ is 3 then on the account of I_{22} no sending of the probe can take place thus $count_1$ cannot be incremented. We thus showed that $count_1$ is bounded.

We can now prove formula (4) from section 3. Indeed, consider premises of rule 2 for the program T. Choose for p I_1, for I the global invariant N of T and for t the expression

$$5\,n + 3 - [(n+1).count_1 + \sum_{i=1}^{n} done_i + holds(send)]$$

where holds (send) is the smallest j for which $send_j$ holds if it exists and 0 otherwise.

We already showed that N is a global invariant. It is thus sufficient to show that t is always non-negative and decremented by each transition. But for all $b_{i,j}$ and $b_{j,i}$ mentioned in the premises of rule 2

$$N \wedge b_{i,j} \wedge b_{j,i} \rightarrow t > 0,$$

so t is initially positive. Clearly t is decremented by every transition and

$$N \rightarrow t \geq 0$$

so t remains non-negative after every transition.

Thus by rule 2

{p} T {<u>true</u>}

holds in the sense of weak total correctness so by rule 4 formula (4) from section 3 holds.

This concludes the correctness proof.

7. ASSESSMENT OF THE PROOF METHOD

The proposed in section 4 proof method is so strikingly simple to state that it is perhaps useful to assess it and to compare it critically with other approaches to proving correctness of CSP programs. First of all we should explain why the introduced rules are sound.

Soundness of rules 1 and 2 has to do with the fact that the CSP programs considered in section 4 are equivalent to a certain type of nondeterministic programs. Namely consider a CSP program P of the form introduced in section 2. Let

$$T(P) \equiv INIT_1 ;\ldots; INIT_n ;$$
$$*[\ \underset{(i,j)\in\Gamma}{\Box}\ b_{i,j} \wedge b_{j,i} \rightarrow Eff(g_{i,j},g_{j,i}) ; S_{i,j} ; S_{j,i}] ;$$
$$[TERMINATED \rightarrow skip]$$

where $\Gamma = \{(i,j) : i \in \Gamma_j,\ j \in \Gamma_i,\ g_{i,j}$ and $g_{j,i}$ match$\}$.

Note that upon exit of the main loop of T(P) BLOCKED holds (which does not necessarily imply TERMINATED). It is easy to see that P and T(P) are equivalent in the sense of partial correctness semantics (i.e. when divergence, failures and deadlocks are not taken into account) and "almost" in the sense of weak total correctness semantics (i.e. when deadlocks are not taken into account) as deadlocks in P translate into failures at the end of execution of T(P). Now, both rules 1 and 2 exploit these equivalences.

Consider now rule 3. In a deadlock situation every process is either at the main loop entry or has terminated. Thus a global invariant holds in a deadlock situation. Moreover, the formula BLOCKED $\wedge \neg$ TERMINATED holds in a deadlock situation, as well. Thus the premises of rule 3 indeed ensure that no deadlock (relative to p) can arise.

Finally, as is well known, rule 4 is sound because auxiliary variables affect neither the control flow of the program (by requirement i)) or the values of the other variables (by requirement ii)).

It is worthwhile to point out that the rule of auxiliary variables is not needed in the correctness proofs. This follows from two facts. First, it is not needed in the context of nondeterministic programs as the theoretical completeness results show (see [A1]). And secondly, due to the equivalence between P and T(P) and the form of the rules, every correctness proof of T(P) can be rewritten as a correctness proof of P.

However, as we have seen in the previous section, this rule is very helpful in concrete correctness proofs.

It is true that the proposed proof method can be only applied to CSP programs in a normal form. On the other hand it is easy to prove that every CSP program (without nested parallelism) can be brought into this form (see Apt and Clermont [AC]). Thus in principle this proof method can be applied to prove correctness of arbitrary CSP programs. What is perhaps more important, many CSP programs exhibit a normal form.

Let us relate now our proof method to two other approaches to proving correctness of CSP programs - those of Apt, Francez and De Roever [AFR] and of Manna and Pnueli [MP].

When discussing the first approach it is more convenient to consider its simplified and more comprehensive presentation given in [A2]. Consider then a CSP program in the special form with all $INIT_i$ parts being empty. Let each branch of the main loop constitute a bracketed section. Given a bracketed section <S> associated with a branch that starts with a Boolean condition b within the text of process P_i, choose the assumption {b} <S> {<u>true</u>} for the proof of the {<u>true</u>} P_i {$TERMINATED_i$}. Then it is easy to see that

$$A_i \vdash_N \{\underline{true}\}\ P_i\ \{TERMINATED\}$$

where A_i stands for the set of chosen assumptions (and according to the notation of [A2] the subscript "N" indicates a provability in the sense of partial correctness). Now, the premises of rule 1 are equivalent to the set of conditions stating that the chosen sets of assumptions cooperate w.r.t. the global invariant I. The simple form of the premises is due to the fact that in their presentation use of the communication axiom, formation rule and arrow rule is combined.

This shows that (under the assumption that all $INIT_i$ parts are empty) proof rule 1 can be derived in the proof system considered in [A2]. This provides another, very indirect proof of its soundness.

Consider now proof rule 2. The main difference between this rule and the corresponding set of rules of [A2] is that termination is proved here in a global fashion - expression t can contain variables from various processes. To cast this reasoning into the framework of [A2] one needs to consider for each process P_i a modified version of t in which variables of other processes are replaced by auxiliary variables. Once this is done, premises of rule 2 can be reformulated appropriately and rule 2 can be derived.

Now, proof rule 3 is nothing else but a succint reformulation of the corresponding approach of [A2] where the bracketed sections are chosen as above.

The way the $INIT_i$ parts are handled is based on the observation that these program sections can be moved outside the scope of the parallel composition. In the terminology of Elrad and Francez [EF] $[INIT_1 \| \ldots \| INIT_n]$ is a communication closed layer of the original program.

In the approach of [AFR] and [A2] bracketed sections can be chosen in a different way thus shifting slightly the emphasis from global to more local reasoning (for example by reducing I_{11} to a local loop invariant). This cannot be done in the framework of the proposed here method.

Comparison with [MP] can be made in a much more succint way. In [MP] two type of transitions are considered in the case of CSP programs : local transitions and communication transitions. All proof rules refer to this set of transitions. When applied to CSP programs INV-rule becomes very similar to our rule 1. The main difference is that in our framework the only allowed transitions are those consisting of the joint execution of a pair of branches of the main loops with matching i/o guards. Such a choice of transitions does not make much sense in the framework of [MP] where programs are presented in a flowchart like form and thus have no structure. Appropriate combinations of IND and TRNS rules become from this point of view counterparts of rules 2 and 3.

From this discussion it becomes clear that the proof method presented in section 4 does not differ in essence from the approaches of [AFR] [A2] and [MP]. It simply exploits the particular form of CSP programs to which it is restricted.

Acknowledgements We would like to thank to L. Bougé, C. Delporte-Gallet, N. Francez and A. Pnueli for interesting and helpful discussions on the subject of this paper. Also we are grateful to Mrs A. Dupont for her speedy and efficient typing of the manuscript.

REFERENCES

[A1] APT, K.R., Ten years of Hoare's logic, a survey, part II, Theoretical Computer Science 28, pp. 83-109, 1984.

[A2] APT, K.R., Proving correctness of CSP programs, a tutorial, Tech. Report 84-24, LITP, Université Paris 7, 1984 (also to appear in the Proc. International Summer School "Control Flow and Data Flow : Concepts of Distributed Programming", Marktobedorf, 1984).

[AC] APT, K.R. and CLERMONT Ph., Two normal form theorems for CSP programs, in preparation.

[AFR] APT, K.R., FRANCEZ N. and DE ROEVER, W.P., A proof system for Communicating Sequential Processes, ACM TOPLAS 2 No 3, pp. 359-385, 1980.

[AR] APT, K.R. and RICHIER, J.L., Real time clocks versus virtual clocks, Tech. Report 84-34, LITP, Université Paris 7, 1984, (also to appear in the Proc. International Summer School "Control Flow and Data Flow : Concepts of Distributed Programming", Marktobedorf, 1984).

[DFG] DIJKSTRA, E.W., FEIJEN, W.H. and van GASTEREN, A.J.M., Derivation of a termination detection algorithm for distributed computations, Inform. Processing Letters 16, 5, pp. 217-219, 1983.

[EF] ELRAD, T.E. and FRANCEZ, N., Decomposition of distributed programs into communication closed layers, Science of Computer Programming 2, No 3, pp. 155-174, 1982.

[F] FRANCEZ, N., Distributed termination, ACM TOPLAS 2, No 1, pp. 42-55, 1980.

[FRS] FRANCEZ , N., RODEH, M. and SINTZOFF, M., Distributed termination with interval assertions, in : Proc. Int Colloq. Formalization of Programming Concepts, Peniscola, Spain, Lecture Notes in Comp. Science, vol. 107, 1981.

[GFMR] GRUMBERG, O., FRANCEZ N., MAKOWSKY J., and DE ROEVER W.P., A proof rule for fair termination of guarded commands, in : J.W. de Bakker and J.C. Van Vhet eds., Algorithmic languages, IFIP, North Holland, Amsterdam, pp. 399-416, 1981.

[H] HOARE, C.A.R., Communicating sequential processes, CACM 21, 8, pp. 666-677, 1978.

[L] LAMPORT, L., Time, clocks and the ordering of events in a distributed system, CACM 21, 7, pp. 558-565, 1978.

[MP] MANNA, Z. and PNUELI, A., How to cook a temporal proof system for your pet language, in : Proc. of the Symposium on Principles of Programming Languages, Austin, Texas, 1983.

[T] TOPOR, R.W., Termination detection for distributed computations, Inform. Processing Letters 18, 1, pp. 33-36, 1984.

Script: A Communication Abstraction Mechanism and its Verification

Nissim Francez
Department of Computer Science
The Technion, Haifa 32000, Israel

Brent Hailpern
IBM Thomas J. Watson Research Center
Yorktown Heights, New York 10598

Gadi Taubenfeld
Department of Computer Science
The Technion, Haifa 32000, Israel

Abstract:

In this paper, we introduce a new abstraction mechanism, called a *script*, which hides the low-level details that implement *patterns of communication.* A script localizes the communication between a set of *roles* (formal processes), to which actual processes *enroll* to participate in the action of the script. The paper discusses the addition of scripts to the languages CSP and Ada, and to a shared-variable language with monitors. Proof rules are presented for proving partial correctness and freedom from deadlock in concurrent programs using scripts.

CR Categories:

[D.1.3] programming techniques - concurrent programming.
[D.2.2] software engineering - tools and techniques.
[D.3.3] programming languages - language constructs.
[D.4.1] operating systems - process management
[F.3.1] logics and meaning of programs - specifying and verifying and reasoning about programs.
[F.3.3] logics and meaning of programs - studies in program constructs.

General Terms: communication primitives, abstraction mechanisms, concurrent programming, proof rules, correctness, deadlock.

Other Keywords: script, role, enrollment

[1] Earlier versions of parts of this paper were presented at the Second ACM Symposium on Principles of Distributed Computing, Montreal, August 1983 and at the FSE-TCS, Bangalore, India, December 1984. Nissim Francez was a WTVS at IBM Research (Yorktown) while on a sabbatical leave from the Technion, Haifa, Israel.

NATO ASI Series, Vol. F13
Logics and Models of Concurrent Systems
Edited by K. R. Apt

I. Introduction

Abstraction mechanisms have been widely recognized as useful programming tools and have been incorporated into modern programming languages [4, 11, 19, 20, 25, 27]. The main subjects of abstraction suggested so far are

- *control sequencing abstractions*, which hide sequences of elementary transfers of control, such as looping constructs, if statements, procedures, and exception handling statements,
- *data abstractions*, as manifested in abstract data types, which hide the concrete representation of abstract objects (for example, is a stack implemented by a linked list with pointers or by an array?), and
- *synchronization abstractions*, as manifested in monitors and the like, which hide details of low-level mechanisms for enforcing mutual exclusion.

Besides hiding low-level information, abstraction mechanisms also restrict the use of such information to patterns that are generally recognized as well structured. They also save programming effort by enabling a single description to be used many times.

Recently, another low-level mechanism has emerged as playing an important role as a programming tool, namely *inter-process communication*. Several modern programming languages [4, 11, 14, 19, 20, 25, 27] support multiprocessing and distributed processing in one way or another. Every such language has a construct to support inter-process communications; some of the constructs are slightly higher-level than others, but all can be considered low-level because they handle some primitive communication between two partners at a time.

The purpose of this paper is to introduce an abstraction mechanism, whose subject is *communications*. To our knowledge, no such abstraction has been proposed. Such a mechanism will

- allow the hiding of low-level details concerning sequencing of communications, choice of partners, and larger scale synchronization (involving more than just a pair of processes),
- restrict the patterns of communication, which are arbitrary in current languages, to well-structured patterns, and
- enable a single definition of frequently used patterns, for example various buffering regimes.

Even when such well-structured patterns are identified and added as primitive constructs (as happened in the case of looping), it is still useful to permit a user to define, in an application-oriented way, his own abstractions. A trend toward such well-designed patterns exists already, for example "idioms" [12].

In designing our communication abstraction mechanism, which we call a *script*, we adhered to the following design goals and restrictions.

- The abstraction will be designed in a context of a *fixed network*. Thus, we shall not deal in this paper with dynamic concurrency, where processes are dynamically generated, destroyed, or re-configured.
- The abstraction should be modular and the behavior of an instance of an abstraction should not depend on the context of use, except by a predefined interface mechanism. We chose "parameters passing" for our interface.
- The abstraction should be modularly verifiable [10, 18].
- The abstraction mechanism is biased toward models of disjoint processes (that is, no shared variables). Communication is achieved by some message passing actions or remote procedure calls.

We would like to emphasize that some techniques, with other goals, concerned with abstracting communication exist in the literature. For example, a general module interface hides the specific communication primitive being used from the user: procedure call (either local or remote), coroutine, message transfer, and so on [15, 23]. These techniques, however, are interested in encapsulating a *single* communication, while we are interested in encapsulating *patterns of communication* involving many primitive communication actions and many participants.

The rest of the paper is organized as follows. In Section II, we informally describe the structure of the suggested communication abstraction mechanism and we discuss several alternatives regarding possible semantics. Some example scripts are informally described. In Section III, we present the examples in a Pascal-like syntax. In Section IV, one of the example scripts, broadcast, is developed in three host languages: CSP, Ada[2], and a shared-memory language with monitors. Section V presents proof rules for partial correctness of programs using scripts. Section VI extends the proof system toward proving absence of deadlocks. Section VII concludes with some discussion of future work.

II. Scripts

In this section we introduce the *script*, the suggested mechanism to abstract from the internal details of the implementation of patterns of communication. Basically, a *script* is a parameterized program section, to which processes *enroll* in order to participate. The guiding idea behind the concept of enrollment is that the execution of the role (in a given script instance) is a logical continuation of the enrolling process, in the same way that a sequential subroutine is a continuation of the execution of its caller. If each process is allocated to a different processor, the role should be executed by the same processor on which the main body of the enrolling process is executed. Thus, no changes in the underlying communication network are needed to execute a script.

The Structure of a Script

A script consists of the following components:

- *roles* - these are formal process parameters, to which (actual) processes enroll. We shall discuss the enrollment below. We also permit *indexed families of roles* in analogy to such families of actual processes.
- *data parameters* - these are ordinary formal parameters (as in ordinary procedures); however, they are associated with the roles. Thus, each group of formal data parameters is bound at enrollment time to the corresponding actual parameters supplied by the enrolling process.
- *body* - this is a concurrent program section, where for each role there is a corresponding part of the body, a process. All the roles are considered to be concurrent. The body describes the details of sequences of basic communications among the various roles. Thus, the body specifies the scenario in which the roles take place.

As a typical example, we may consider a script implementing a scenario of (software) *broadcast*. In this scenario, there is a role of a *transmitter*, with which is associated a (value) data parameter, x, to be transmitted. There is also a group of *recipient* roles, with each is associated a (result) data parameter, which will be assigned the value of x after the appropriate communication. The externally observable behavior of the script is that the value of x is passed to all the recipients and assigned to their corresponding data parameters.

The body of the script could hide the various broadcast strategies:

- a star-like pattern where the transmitter communicates directly with each recipient, either in some pre-specified order, or non-deterministically.

[2] Ada is a registered trademark of the U.S. Department of Defense.

- a spanning tree, generating a wave of transmissions, where every role, on receiving x from its parent role, transmits it to every one of its descendant roles (again with different orderings).
- others; see [24, 26] for a discussion of various broadcast patterns and their relative merits.

Sections III and IV show how a broadcast script could be coded in our target languages.

One immediate question raised by considering the broadcast example is "how generic should a script be?". Should the type of x, in the broadcast script, be allowed to vary, or should a different script be needed to broadcast an integer, a stack, and so on? We shall not commit ourselves to a definite answer to these questions. Rather, we use the principle that a script is as generic as its host programming language allows. In a language that admits other forms of generic constructs, such as Ada, we could allow the script to contain the same.

Our second example is a replicated and distributed database *lock manager* script. Consider n nodes in a network, each of which can hold a copy of a database. At any one time k nodes hold copies. The membership of this set of *active* nodes may change, but it always has k members. Readers and writers attempt to interact with this database through a lock manager script. The roles in this script consist of the k lock managers, a reader (possibly an indexed family of readers), and/or a writer. This script can hide various read/write locking strategies:

- lock one node to read, all nodes to write.
- lock a majority of nodes to read or write.
- multiple granularity locking as described in [16].

The third example introduces a script that causes the rotation of data values around a ring of processes. The script hides the direction of rotation, the number of rotation steps, and the details of the rotation handling. We show in this example how different enrollment patterns to the same script achieve different effects.

Our next example is the remote server facility of the Accent operating system [22]. Accent is a communication-oriented operating system for a collection of processors connected by a network. The operating system attempts to make the location of resources in the system transparent to the user. All processes communicate through local ports, with network servers to perform the actual communication across the network. We will model this port communication facility.

Our final example is a *recursive* script implementing the winning strategy for the *Tower of Hanoi* game. This example also shows the use of *nested enrollments*, where an enrollment to one script occurs within the body of another script.

Script Enrollment

We next describe several possibilities for the semantics of enrollment of a process in an instance of a script.

Obviously, a process has to name the instance of the script in which it enrolls, and the name of the role it wishes to play. Furthermore, the process must supply actual data parameters for the formal parameters associated with that role. For the sake of verifiability, we assume that the data parameter passing modes are value, result, and value-result. The usual aliasing-preventing restrictions will be imposed.

We want to distinguish between two kinds of enrollment, based on the relationship between processes enrolling in the same (instance of a) script.

- *Partners-named enrollment* - A process not only names the role in which it enrolls, but also names the identities of (some or all of) the other processes it wants to communicate with in the script. Thus a process T may specify that it wishes to enroll in a broadcast script as a transmitter, while it wishes to see process P, Q, and R enroll as recipients in the same instance of the script. Similarly, process P might specify its enrollment in the broadcast script as a recipient with T as the transmitter. In such cases, the processes will jointly enroll in the script only when their enrollment specifications match, that is they all agree on the binding of processes to roles. It is also possible to have more elaborate naming conventions, for example by specifying that a given role should be fulfilled by either process A or process B.

The partners-named enrollment generalizes the naming conventions of the host language for primitive communications, as in CSP's **!** and **?** or Ada's entry call.

- *Partners-unnamed enrollment* - Sometimes, a process does not care about, or does not need to know, the identities of its communication partners. In such a case, it will specify only its own role during enrollment; no matching is then needed for joint enrollment.

  In the broadcast example, a process T may wish to broadcast x to any process interested in receiving the value.

  Another reason for unnamed enrollment is that the host language may permit unnamed primitive communications: for example the accept statement in Ada, which accepts an entry call from any potential caller. A similar extension of the CSP primitives is proposed in [6].

Note that a mixture of the two enrollment regimes is also possible, where only a partial naming is supplied. In the broadcast example, P may specify the transmitter T, but not care about the other recipients.

If more than one process tries to enroll in the same role of the same instance of a script (each matching the naming conventions), then the choice of which process is actually enrolled is nondeterministic.

We impose the following structure on enrollments, avoiding some ambiguities because of complex scoping: all processes enrolling to (the same instance of) a script must be roles in (an instance of) another script. As a result, the main program is regarded as a script. This restriction, together with another one imposed on basic communication within the bodies of the roles (described later) ensure that no process not enrolled in a script can affect the computations of that script.

Nested Enrollments

If a group of roles in (an instance of) a script S_1 enroll into (an instance of) another script S_2, the corresponding part of the performance of S_1 is delayed until the performance of S_2 terminates.

In particular, in the recursive case, a new instance is opened upon a recursive enrollment. In direct recursion, all the roles of S must enroll (in some permutation) back into S. Mutual recursion is also permitted. Note that in direct recursion a role can recursively enroll into *any* role of the script. Thus, in a recursive enrollment, the new roles always form a permutation of the current roles.

Script Initiation and Termination

A basic question related to the execution of a script is "when will it start?". Again, two major possibilities can be distinguished.

- *Delayed initiation* - According to this method, processes must first enroll in *all* the roles of a given instance of a script; only then the execution of the script may begin. A process enrolled in a given role is delayed until all other partners are also enrolled.

  In the broadcast script, a delayed initiation will activate the script only after the transmitter and all recipients have enrolled.

  This method enforces global synchronization between large groups of processes (as a possible extension to CSP's synchronized communication between two processes).

A consequence of this initiation strategy is that there is a one-to-one correspondence between (formal) roles and (actual) enrolling processes. No process may enroll in more than one role in one activation (of an instance) of a script.

- *Immediate initiation* - The script is activated upon the enrollment of its first participating process. Other processes may enroll while the script is in progress. A role is delayed only if it attempts to communicate with an unfilled role. This method may be easier to implement in existing host languages.

  Thus, in the broadcast example, after a transmitter has enrolled, each enrolling recipient may receive x independently of any other recipient having enrolled. This has a consequence that no role may assume that its script partner has sensed any effects of the script, unless it has communicated directly with that partner.

Similar considerations apply to the problem of terminating a script. A *delayed termination* will free (together) all the process enrolled in a script after all the roles are finished. An *immediate termination* will free each process when it completes its role. This distinction is crucial if script enrollment is to be allowed to act as a guard.

Note that immediate initiation combined with immediate termination allows a given process to enroll in several roles of the same script, where those roles do not communicate directly. With the combination of delayed initiation and delayed termination, the body of the script is treated as a closed concurrent block, similar to a **cobegin** ... ‖ ... ‖ ... **coend** construct. Delayed initiation is the more natural choice for partners-named enrollment. The kind of initiation and termination strategy used has consequences on the possibility of deadlock, as discussed in Section VII.

The declaration section of each script specifies the kind of initiation and termination strategies used in that script.

We call the collective activation of all the roles of an instance of a script a *performance*. If a performance has begun and some other process attempts to enroll in the script, a new instance of the script is invoked: a parallel performance begins.

We make no requirements about the fairness of script enrollments in the case of repeated attempts to enroll. We assume that the fairness properties are inherited from the host language. For example, in CSP no fairness is assumed. In Ada, repeated enrollments are serviced in order of arrival.

Critical Role Set

For a performance of a script, it may not be necessary that all roles of the script be filled. Different subsets of the roles could participate in different performances. For example, in the database example, it is sufficient that all the lock-manager roles be filled, as well as, either the reader or the writer (or both). So that such partially-filled performances do not conflict with the initiation and termination strategies, we add the *critical role set* to the declaration of the script. It specifies the possible subsets of roles that will enable a performance to begin. Thus the initiation and termination policies are always considered as relative to the appropriate critical role sets. If no such set is specified, it is taken to mean that the entire collection of roles is critical.

For example, consider a script S with roles p, q, and r and delayed initiation. If the critical role sets are (p, q) OR (q, r), then should processes enroll in p and q, then the performance could begin, with no r. If instead the roles are filled in the order p, r, q, then all the roles would be filled before the performance begins.

The critical role sets creates a problem: when can a performance, which was initiated upon enrollment of a critical set, be terminated? In principle, the performance would wait, possibly forever, for the enrollment of processes to the roles *not* in the critical set. We therefore assume a *critical moment*, after which no further enrollments to the current performance are allowed. This moment succeeds, but does not necessarily coincide with, the moment all processes in the critical role set have enrolled. Termination will depend only on roles that have enrolled up to that critical moment. A role not fulfilled up to the critical moment is considered to have terminated.

The use of critical role sets introduces yet another problem: individual roles do not know which of their partner roles are participating in a particular performance. When some of the roles of a script are not filled, then attempts to communicate with the unfilled roles would block. Similarly, roles waiting to service requests from unfilled roles would never terminate.

There are many solutions to this problem, none of which are fully satisfying. If a centralized mechanism is controlling enrollments and performances, then it could inform the active roles of the names of the inactive roles.[3] Alternatively, attempting to communicate with an unfilled role could return a distinguished value. Our database example will follow the latter solution.

Inter-role Communication

Communication among the various roles of a script is described using the inter-process communication primitives of the host language. Every communication between roles causes, at run time, a corresponding communication among the processes enrolled to the roles. In particular, the naming conventions of the host-languages apply to the roles: a role may name another role explicitly, or may communicate with an anonymous role in exactly the same way that actual processes do.

Note: We prohibit roles from communicating with any process other than the roles of the script. This restriction is intended to avoid the deadlock caused by a role trying to communicate with itself as the enrolling process.

III. Sample Scripts

In this section we present several example scripts. Our language is Pascal-like with extensions for communication (synchronized *send* and *receive* with the same semantics as the **!** and **?** instructions of CSP) and non-deterministic guarded commands (**if** and **do**). Role parameters will be designated *IN* for value parameters, *OUT* for result parameters, and *IN OUT* for value-result parameters. Comments will be use the PL/I and C convention of /* */. Sets are indicated by curly brackets { }.

Synchronized Star Broadcast

Our first example provides for a simple extension of the synchronized send and receive in the host language; it is shown in Figure 1. The broadcast script has one transmitter and five recipients; a more general example would use a general indexed family of recipients. The script is fully synchronized, because of the initiation and termination clauses. When all participants are enrolled, the data passed to the sender is sent, in turn, to each of the recipients. All wait until the last copy is sent. Note that the sender is never blocked while waiting for a recipient, because all the recipients are available and not waiting for any other I/O operations. The notation

$$\overset{5}{\underset{i=1}{\text{ROLE}}}\ \text{recipient}_i\ (\ \dots\ )$$

is an abbreviation for five copies of the recipient role. Within the role, i is replaced by the actual index.

A process would enroll as the transmitter by

```
ENROLL IN broadcast AS transmitter(expression);
```

A process would enroll as the first recipient by

```
ENROLL IN broadcast AS recipient1 (variable);
```

Pipeline Broadcast

---

3 The notion of a central administrator for a script, however, does not preserve our goal of not generating additional processes when executing a script.

```
SCRIPT StarBroadcast;
   INITIATION: DELAYED;
   TERMINATION: DELAYED;

   ROLE transmitter (IN r : item);
      BEGIN
         SEND r TO recipient1;
         SEND r TO recipient2;
         SEND r TO recipient3;
         SEND r TO recipient4;
         SEND r TO recipient5
      END transmitter;

    5
   ROLE recipient_i (OUT t : item);
   i=1

     BEGIN
        RECEIVE t FROM transmitter
     END recipient
END StarBroadcast
```

Figure 1. Synchronized Star Broadcast

Our second example, shown in Figure 2, is similar to the first in form, but not in action. Here the sender gives the message to the first recipient and is then finished. The first recipient waits for the second recipient to arrive, passes the message along, and finishes, and so on. The immediate initiation and termination permit processes to spend much less time in the script, than in the previous example. However, this technique allows roles to block at send or receive operations if the neighboring role is not available.

Database

Our third example implements a distributed, replicated database locking scheme. The script consists of k lock managers roles, one reader role, and one writer role. Each lock manager maintains a table of locks granted. Readers and writers can request or release lock on data items. Depending on the locking scheme, readers and writers may need permission from more than one lock manager to access a particular data item. Our example requires one lock to read, k locks to write. One performance of this script would result in either a reader or a writer (or both) attempting to lock or release a data item.

Between performances of the script the identity of the lock managers may change, but we assume that the lock tables are preserved by such a change (so that, for example, if a reader is granted a read lock in one performance, some lock manager will have a record of that lock on a subsequent performance). There would be a separate script for lock managers to negotiate the entering and leaving of the active set. The database example is shown in Figure 3 through Figure 5.

We assume that the lock tables are abstract data types with the appropriate functions to lock and release entries in the table and to check whether read or write locks on a piece of data may be added. We also assume that each processor, when enrolling provides its unique processor identifier, so that locks may be identified unambiguously.

In Section II we discussed critical role sets and the termination problem. In this example we have made available the function r.terminated, which returns true if role r has terminated or if the role r

```
SCRIPT PipeBroadcast;
    INITIATION: IMMEDIATE;
    TERMINATION: IMMEDIATE;
    CONST n = 5;

    ROLE transmitter (IN t : item);
        BEGIN
            SEND t TO recipient_1
        END transmitter;

    ROLE recipient_1 (OUT r_1 : item);
        BEGIN
            RECEIVE r_1 FROM transmitter;
            SEND r_1 TO recipient_2
        END recipient_1;

     n-1
    ROLE recipient_i (OUT r_i : item);
     i=2

        BEGIN
            RECEIVE r_i FROM recipient_{i-1};
            SEND r_i TO recipient_{i+1}
        END recipient_{2...n-1};

    ROLE recipient_n (OUT r_n : item);
        BEGIN
            RECEIVE r_n FROM recipient_{n-1}
        END recipient_n
END PipeBroadcast
```

Figure 2. Pipeline Broadcast

will not be filled. Before the critical role set is filled, r.terminated is false for all unfilled roles. Once the critical set is filled, all unfilled roles have r.terminated set to true.[4]

Accent Port Communication Facility

Our final example models the Accent port communication facility [22] as specified and verified in [10]. Accent is a communication-oriented operating system for a collection of processors connected by a network. Many processes can exist at each node (processor). Three goals of Accent are (1) the location of resources in the distributed system should be transparent, (2) it should be possible for any feature provided by the operating system kernel to be provided instead by a process, and (3) all services, except the basic communication primitives, should appear to processes as being provided through a message-passing interface.

Process communicate through *ports*. Associated with each port is a *queue* of messages sent to that port, but not yet received. Only one process at a time can have receive access to a given port, though many processes can have send access to it. We do not deal here with process or port creation or destruction. We assume the existence of processes and ports. We also assume there is a static binding between process and ports. We will implement ports as scripts.

Because messages are sent to ports, rather than to processes, intermediate processes can be used to manage communication between distinct process groups. A prime example is a network server: if process A runs on node X and process B runs on node Y, the network server N can provide mirror

[4] We make no claim that this termination function would be simple to implement without a central administrator for the script.

```
SCRIPT lock;
  INITIATION: IMMEDIATE;
  TERMINATION: IMMEDIATE;
  CRITICAL ROLES: (manager_1...k, reader) OR (manager_1...k, writer);

       k
  ROLE manager_i (IN OUT LockTable : LockType);
     i=1

      BEGIN
          DO ¬ (reader.terminated AND writer.terminated) →
              IF RECEIVE release(data, id) FROM reader →
                  LockTable.ReadUnlock(data, id)
              □ RECEIVE release(data, id) FROM writer →
                  LockTable.WriteUnlock(data, id)
              □ RECEIVE lock(data, id) FROM reader →
                  IF LockTable.AbleToRead(data) →
                      LockTable.ReadLock(data, id);
                      SEND granted TO reader
                  □ ¬ LockTable.AbleToRead(data) →
                      SEND denied TO reader
                  FI
              □ RECEIVE lock(data, id) FROM writer →
                  IF LockTable.AbleToWrite(data) →
                      LockTable.WriteLock(data, id);
                      SEND granted TO writer
                  □ ¬ LockTable.AbleToWrite(data) →
                      SEND denied TO writer
                  FI
              FI
          OD
      END manager;
```

Figure 3. Database Lock Manager

ports in X and Y so that A and B can communicate. Consider the situation of A sending a message to B. The network server N on X has an alias port B_N also on X. Process A believes that B_N belongs to B, but in fact it belongs to N. Messages sent to B_N are read by N and forwarded to the actual input port of B on Y.

The example specified in [10] deals with a distributed virtual memory system. That is, paging can be done across the network. We will restrict our discussion to the port and network server portions of this system.

A port is a FIFO buffer that accepts transmissions from any number of senders, but sends them onto a single receiver. Hence, two-way communication requires two ports. We model the FIFO buffer portion of the port as a queue process. The communication portion of the port is implemented as a script. This port script has three roles: sender, buffer, and receiver. We associate the identity of the port with the queue process. That is to select a port, the sender or receiver names the queue process in a partners-named enrollment. Simultaneous non-interfering communications are allowed through parallel performances.

A (generic) queue process, contains a FIFO data structure (assumed to be a primitive data type of the language). The process repeatedly enrolls in the port script, in case its sender or receiver are attempting to speak with it. Optionally, it could name the receiver process in its enrollment. For the sake of simplicity, we will leave the naming of the queue to the sender and receiver processes. The body of the queue process is

```
ROLE reader (IN id : ProcessId; IN data : object; IN request : (lock, release);
        OUT status : (granted, denied));
    VAR
        done : ARRAY [1..k] OF boolean;
    BEGIN
        done := false;  /* array assignment */
        IF request = release →

                  k
            DO    □  ¬ done[i]; SEND release(data, id) TO manager_i →
                 i=1

                done[i] := true
            OD

        □ request = lock →
            status := denied;

                  k
            DO    □  (status ≠ granted)∧ ¬done[i];
                 i=1

                SEND lock(data,id) TO manager_i →

                    RECEIVE status FROM manager_i;
                    done[i] := true
            OD
        FI
    END reader;
```

Figure 4. Database Lock Manager (continued)

```
TYPE PROCESS QUEUE;
      VAR q : FIFO_BUFFER OF BaseType;
      BEGIN
            q := empty;
            WHILE true DO
                  ENROLL IN PortScript AS buffer(q);
      END;
```

The port script allows enrollment in pairs: sender and buffer, receiver and buffer. It must allow also for the case that all three roles are filled. As in the database example, we use the *terminated* attribute of a role name to determine if that role is inactive. The port script is shown in Figure 6. It should be reasonably clear that the port script maintains the FIFO property of the underlying buffer data type and that the script will not deadlock on empty or full buffers. The most important feature of the port script, from the Accent point of view, is that the identities of the sender and receiver are hidden from each other.

The implementation of the net server is now straight forward. If we assume one net server per remote node, then each server scans through the ports it maintains. If a message appears it appends the true location of the server (at the remote node) and passes that message to the network interface (through a port). If the net server detects a message from the network interface, it strips off the destination address and puts the message in the appropriate user port. If we are permitted only one net server on each node, then it must also maintain a table corresponding to its input ports, of the destination node id of the remote server.

```
ROLE writer (IN id : ProcessId; IN data : object; IN request : (lock, release);
        OUT status : (granted, denied));
    VAR
        done : ARRAY [1..k] OF boolean;
        who : SET OF [1..k];
    BEGIN
        done := false;  /* array assignment */
        IF request = release →

                  k
            DO   □   ¬ done[i]; SEND release(data, id) TO manager_i →
                 i=1
                done[i] := true
            OD

        □ request = lock →
            who := φ;

                  k
            DO   □   ¬ done[i]; SEND lock(data, id) TO manager_i →
                 i=1
                RECEIVE status FROM manager_i;
                done[i] := true;
                IF status = granted → who := who ∪ {i}
                □ status = denied → done := true /* one denial implies failure */
                FI
            OD;

            IF status = denied →

                      k
                DO   □
                     i=1
                    i ∈ who; SEND release(data,id) TO manager_i → who := who - {i}
                OD
            □ status = granted → SKIP
            FI
        FI
    END writer
END lock
```

Figure 5. Database Lock Manager (continued)

IV. Sample Script in CSP, Ada, and with Monitors

In this section, we describe how scripts could be added to existing programming languages. The rules and examples given are intended to be existence proofs that such additions could be made without extending the base language in any way. As a result, not every language supports all features. Ideally, scripts would be added as an integral part of the base languages; these scripts would support all the options and features described above. In each of the examples of this section we extend the syntax of the native language to include scripts. These extensions include script declarations, role declarations, and enrollment statements. The syntax of these extensions were intended to conform to the normal syntax of the language.

Scripts in CSP

```
SCRIPT PortScript;
    INITIATION : IMMEDIATE;
    TERMINATION : IMMEDIATE;
    CRITICAL ROLES (sender, buffer) OR (receiver, buffer);

    ROLE sender (IN d : BaseType; OUT success : boolean);
        BEGIN
            SEND d TO buffer;
            RECEIVE success FROM buffer
        END sender;

    ROLE receiver (OUT d : BaseType; OUT success : boolean);
        BEGIN
            SEND "fetch" TO buffer;
            RECEIVE (d, success) FROM buffer
        END receiver;

    ROLE buffer (IN OUT q : FIFO__BUFFER OF BaseType);
        VAR d : BaseType;
        BEGIN
            DO ¬sender.terminated; RECEIVE d FROM sender →
                IF q.full → SEND false /*failed*/ TO sender
                □ ¬q.full →
                    q.enque(d);
                    SEND true /*ok*/ TO sender
                FI
            □ ¬receiver.terminated; RECEIVE "fetch" FROM receiver →
                IF q.empty → SEND (empty, false) /*failed*/ TO receiver
                □ ¬q.empty →
                    q.deque(d);
                    SEND (d, true) /*ok*/ TO receiver
                FI
            OD
        END buffer
END PortScript
```

Figure 6. Accent Port Script

CSP [14] imposes strict naming conventions, where in every communication both parties explicitly name each other. We, therefore, adopt a restricted named-enrollment policy: each process, besides naming the role to which it enrolls, names the processes for all other roles in the script with which the role will directly communicate. All inter-role communication will also use explicit role naming.

The initiation policy will be immediate initiation, because CSP cannot synchronize more than two processes at a time. Similarly, the termination policy will be immediate. We will use the ability of CSP to define named arrays of processes that know their indices, to "implement" arrays of roles. We take some notational liberties considering whole-array assignments. Figure 7 shows a broadcast script in CSP.

Now consider a parallel command [... ‖ p ‖ ... ‖ q ‖ ...], where p contains an enrollment of the form

```
ENROLL IN broadcast AS transmitter (exp) WITH
  [ qa AS recipient1, qb AS recipient2, q AS recipient3,
   qd AS recipient4, qe AS recipient5 ]; ...
```

```
SCRIPT broadcast::
  INITIATION : IMMEDIATE;
  TERMINATION : IMMEDIATE;
  [ ROLE transmitter (x: item):: VAR sent: ARRAY[1..5] OF boolean := 5*false;

     5
   *[□ ¬sent[k];recipient_k!x → sent[k]:=true]
    k=1

   ||

    5
   ROLE recipient_i (y:item):: transmitter?y
    i=1
  ].
```

Figure 7. Broadcast in CSP

Here qa, qb, qd, and qe are other process names in the same concurrent command.

In process q, we will have the following enrollment

`ENROLL IN broadcast AS recipient`$_3$`(u) WITH p AS transmitter; ...`

The use of arrays of roles here is rather strict: a process always enrolls to a specific role in an array. A suggestive idea is to allow the en bloc enrollment of an array of processes to an array of roles. The explicit, strict naming conventions make it difficult to hide details of communication. For example, if the body of the broadcast script were to be implemented as a pipeline, where $recipient_i$ $(1<i<5)$ receives the value of x from $recipient_{i-1}$ and transfers it to $recipient_{i+1}$ and $recipient_1$ receives x from the transmitter, then the enrollment would have to be different.

Translation into CSP

We now show that scripts with the restrictions mentioned above, do not transcend the direct expressive power of CSP. Since CSP is not explicit about local (intraprocess) procedures, we use an in-line translation. To avoid unintended matching between communication commands arising from the translation, we shall use unique, new message tags, which are assumed not to occur anywhere in the original program. Because CSP does not have instances of processes, we cannot implement parallel performances, instead we cause each performance of a script to execute separately. We therefore associate with each script s another process p__s, which will coordinate enrollments to s. Since this translation is only for the sake of proving expressibility in CSP, the centralized nature of the resulting implementation does not imply that the actual implementation needs to be centralized. One of the major directions of future research is to discover distributed algorithms to achieve such multiple synchronization based on a generalization of the current distributed algorithms for binary handshaking.

Consider $P = [p_1 \| \dots \| p_n]$ and a script s, with roles $r_1, \dots, r_m$.

Rules of Translation: Replace every enrollment within a process p_i of the form

`ENROLL IN s AS r (params) WITH [`p_{i_1} `AS` r_1`;...` p_{i_m} `AS` r_m`],`

by the following:

1. An output command p__s!start__s()
2. The body of role r (in script s) with:
   a. each role name r_j replace by process name p_{i_j} according to the correspondence specified in the enrollment.
   b. the actual parameters, *params*, substituted for the formal script data parameters (as in call-by-value-result semantics).

```
p__s:: ready: ARRAY[1..m] of boolean := m*true;
    done: ARRAY[1..m] of boolean := m*false;

       m    n
   *[  □    □
      k=1  j=1

           [ready[k];p_j?start__s() → ready[k]:=false
           □
           ¬ready[k];p_j?end__s() → done[k]:=true
           ]

         m
    □   ∧   done[k] → ready:=m*true; done:=m*false
        k=1
   ].
```

Figure 8. CSP Script Supervisor

c. every communication command tagged with the script name, for example, $r_1!(x + y)$ becomes $p_{i_1}!s(x + y)$ and $r_2?u$ becomes $p_{i_2}?s(u)$.

3. An output command p__s!end__s().

The process p__s will be concurrently composed with the enrolling processes, and is defined in Figure 8. Note that the script supervisor p__s must address all other processes, since every process is a potential enroller to every role. This is another example of the usefulness of the extended naming conventions described in [6].

We defer discussion of enrollments with unspecified parties to the next section. It describes the incorporation of scripts in Ada, where such enrollments fit more naturally.

Scripts in Ada

One feature that distinguishes CSP from Ada is that Ada supports server tasks that need not know the names of the processes that call them, whereas in CSP each process must know the name of every process with which it communicates. We extend this notion of a server task to a server script, that is a script with a partners-unnamed enrollment policy. Of course, the partners-named policy could be accomplished in Ada as in CSP, using local procedures to represent the roles and a supervising task to coordinate entries.

Figure 9 shows a broadcast script in Ada. The script consists of six roles: a sender and five recipients. The recipients all share the same code, so a template (role type) is used. Note that the script body contains a "reverse broadcast" because the recipients call the transmitter, rather than the other way around. This is a result of Ada's naming conventions: calls to a task must name that task. But receptions of calls (entries) do not name the calling task. In addition, selections between alternative entries are allowed, but not selections between alternative calls. See [7] for the problems caused by the absence of such selections.

Translation into Ada

We now show how a subset of scripts can be added to Ada with the following translation to Ada (without scripts). Each role becomes a task and one additional task is created to coordinate the enrollments. Because each role is represented by a task, the other roles can know its name. Each role is given a number, which it uses to call the start and stop (family of) entries of the supervisor. Figure 10 gives the general form of the supervisor, for a script s, where m is the number of roles in the script. We assume that the "macro expansion" prevents Ada tasks from calling any task of the script except through enrollment. This task per role translation is similar to the procedure per role translation to provide Ada procedure variables in [17].

```
SCRIPT broadcast IS
    INITIATION : IMMEDIATE;
    TERMINATION : IMMEDIATE;
    ROLE sender (data : IN item);
    ROLE TYPE recipient (data : OUT item);
    r1, r2, r3, r4, r5 : recipient;
END SCRIPT;

SCRIPT BODY broadcast IS
    ROLE sender (data : IN item) IS
        ENTRY receive (d : OUT item);
        completed : integer := 0;
        BEGIN
            WHILE completed < 5 LOOP
                ACCEPT receive (d : OUT item) DO
                    d := data;
                END;
                completed := completed + 1;
            END LOOP;
        END sender;

    ROLE recipient (data : OUT item) IS
        BEGIN
            sender.receive(data);
        END recipient;
END broadcast;

TASK s IS ... ENROLL IN broadcast AS sender(expression);... END s;

TASK r IS ... ENROLL IN broadcast AS r1(variable); ... END r;
```

Figure 9. Broadcast in Ada

Consider processes $p_1, \ldots, p_n$ and script instance s, with roles $r_1, \ldots, r_m$.

Rules of Translation:

1. Replace every enrollment within a process p of the form

   ```
   ENROLL IN s AS r(in-param, out-param, inout-param);
   ```

   by the following

   ```
   s_r.start(in-param, inout-param);
   s_r.stop(out-param, inout-param);
   ```

2. Replace each role r_i of script s by a task s__r_i.

   a. The role r_i has the form shown in the top half of Figure 11.

   b. Task s__r_i has all the entries of r_i plus two additional entries

      ```
      ENTRY start (v1 : IN t1; v3 : IN t3);
      ENTRY stop (v2 : OUT t2; v3 : OUT t3);
      ```

   c. Task s__r_i has all the local variables of r_i, without initialization, and one new local variable, $v1'$, $v2'$, $v3'$, for each formal parameter of the start/stop entry calls, v1, v2, v3.

3. Let B bet the body of r_i.

   a. The body of s__r_i is shown in the bottom half of Figure 11.

   b. In the body B, occurrences of v1, v2, v3 are replaced by $v1'$, $v2'$, $v3'$.

   c. Calls to role entry r_j.x(y, z) become calls to task entry s__r_j.x(y, z).

```
TASK s__supervisor IS
    ENTRY start(1..m);
    ENTRY stop(1..m);
END s__supervisor;

TASK BODY s__supervisor IS
    ready : ARRAY (1..m) OF boolean := (1..m => true);
    done : ARRAY (1..m) OF boolean := (1..m => false);
    all__done : ARRAY (1..m) OF boolean := (1..m => true);
    BEGIN
       LOOP
          SELECT
            WHEN ready(1)=>ACCEPT start(1) DO ready(1):=false; END;
          OR ...
          OR WHEN ready(m)=>ACCEPT start(m) DO ready(m):=false; END;
          OR WHEN ¬ done(1)=>ACCEPT stop(1) DO done(1):=true; END;
          OR ...
          OR WHEN ¬ done(m)=>ACCEPT stop(m) DO done(m):=true; END;
          OR WHEN done = all__done =>
              done := (1..m => false);
              ready := (1..m => true);
          END SELECT;
       END LOOP;
    END s__supervisor;
```

Figure 10. Ada Script Supervisor

d. Accept statements of the body undergo no special change.

This translation has two unfortunate consequences. First, the number of processes grows from n (in the script) to n+m+1 in the translation; this growth makes it difficult to associate the execution of a role with the same processor that enrolls in the script. Second, the translation can convert a terminating program into a non-terminating one, because of the infinite loops in the role tasks. A realistic implementation would also require non-centralized coordination of roles, as mentioned in the section on CSP.

Scripts with Monitors

Monitors can serve two purposes: encapsulation (abstraction) of information and mutual exclusion. Using monitors for data abstraction may lead to unnecessary restrictions on concurrency. Combining scripts and monitors allows the programmer to have the advantages of abstraction, without sacrificing all concurrency to the single-thread control of the monitor.

Consider a broadcast with mailboxes for each recipient. There are two monitor implementations of this scheme: the first uses a single monitor to house all the mailboxes, the second uses one monitor per mailbox. The first implementation is a unified abstraction, all details hidden in a single black box, but all access to any mailbox is serialized. The second implementation eliminates the unnecessary concurrency restrictions, but the components of the broadcast are no longer packaged together. Our script solution follows the multiple monitor scheme, but with the script providing the top-level packaging. The monitor implementation of a star broadcast, similar to Figure 2 is shown in Figure 12. Note that in this implementation, we assume that the critical role set includes the sender and all five recipients; this prevents the sender from waiting on a full mail box. A monitor-based supervisor would most easily implement immediate initiation and termination. No translation rules are given, as they would be similar to those for Ada and CSP.

```
ROLE r_i (v1 : IN t1; v2 : OUT t2; v3 : IN OUT t3) IS
    ENTRY e (parameter__list); ... -- entries to be called by other roles
    v4 : t4 := value4; ...        -- local variables
    BEGIN ...
        ACCEPT e(b,c) DO ... END; -- entry
        r_j.x(y,z); ...      -- call to entry in another role
    END r_i;
```

Ada Role (before translation)

```
LOOP
    v4 := value4;          -- initialize local variables
    s__supervisor.start(i); -- synchronize with supervisor
    ACCEPT start(v1 : IN t1; v3 : IN t3) DO  -- synchronize with
        v1' := v1;            --    enrolling task
        v3' := v3;
    END;
    B;
    ACCEPT stop(v2 : OUT t2; v3 : OUT t3) DO -- synchronize with
        v2 := v2';            --    enrolling task
        v3 := v3';
    END;
    s__supervisor(i).stop; -- synchronize with supervisor
END LOOP;
```

Ada Role (after translation)

Figure 11. Ada Role - Before and After

V. Proof Rules for Partial Correctness of Scripts

In this section we present a more formal definition of the script concept. We define *proof rules* for proving partial correctness assertions about concurrent programs using scripts. There are two main aspects of the script that dictate an approach toward the formulation of the required rules.

1. The script, viewed as an abstractions, is a multi-party communication and synchronization construct. It generalizes the primitives found in most concurrent languages that involve *binary* communication and synchronization.

2. The (joint) script enrollment of process to roles in a script can be viewed as a generalization of the procedure-call mechanism. In the script case, a *distributed call* consists of each process calling its piece of a procedure, namely a role in the script. The overall effect of a script is achieved through parameter passing.

The task is to find a proper amalgam of proof rules, dealing with concurrency, communication, and procedures, to form a uniform proof system defining the script construct.

As far as concurrency and communication are involved, our system is a natural extension of what is known as *cooperation proofs*. We generalize both the sequential proof rules for a process (role), to deal with enrollment, and the notion of cooperation, to deal with concurrent composition. A major design goal is to introduce into the proof system the same degree of modularity induced by the script construct on the program.

```
SCRIPT broadcast;
    TYPE mailbox : MONITOR
        VAR contents : item;
            status : (full, empty);
        PUBLIC PROCEDURE put (i : item);
            BEGIN
                WAIT UNTIL status = empty;
                contents := i;
                status := full;
            END put;
        PUBLIC FUNCTION get : item;
            BEGIN
                WAIT UNTIL status = full;
                get := i;
                status := empty;
            END get;
        BEGIN
            status := empty;
        END mailbox;

    ROLE sender (data : item);
        VAR k : integer;
        BEGIN
            FOR k := 1 TO 5 DO recipient_k.mbox.put(data);
        END sender;

      5
    ROLE recipient_i (VAR data : item);
     i=1

        VAR PUBLIC mbox : mailbox;
        BEGIN
            mbox.get(data);
        END recipient;
END broadcast;
```

Figure 12. Mailbox Broadcast

We adopted the idea, derived from the proof theory of procedures, to prove a *parametric assertion* about a script which is then adapted to the enrolling environment by a generalization of a rule for procedure calls.

This section consists of two parts. The first part presents the verification ideas in a way that is independent of the host language. In the second part, we assume that CSP is the host language, and consider an augmentation of the proof system presented in [1] to our needs. CSP was chosen because of its natural suitability for our context, the availability of established proof systems for it, and our familiarity with both. We devote a small discussion to adapting the ideas to a subset of Ada that deals with concurrency, for which cooperating proofs also exist. Nowhere is the dependency on the host language essential.

Because of the similarity between our proof system and that of CSP, we will use a a more CSP-like notation for scripts, for the rest of the paper. In particular, note that roles are treated syntactically as processes; they are prefixed with *name::* and are separated by $\|$.

In this section we assume that the actual parameters, transferred by an actual process to a role, are expressions referring to distinct identifiers, thereby avoiding aliasing. We will not treat the case where both initiation and termination are immediate. We do not assume CSP's convention for distributed termination of loops. Finally, to avoid cumbersome presentation, we consider only scripts that use exclusively either inter-role communication or enroll commands (not both in the same script). External processes can communicate only by enroll commands. The extension to any mixture of primitive inter-process communication and script enrollment is possible, but rather technical. The possibility of having nested enroll commands within the body of an accept in the extension to arbitrary mixtures when using Ada is discussed at the end of the section.

Proving Properties of Script Bodies

The way we intend to prove partial correctness of programs that use scripts is closely related to the way procedures are treated in [2, 9, 13]. For each body of a script some assertion, relating pre- and post-conditions is proved. Using these script assertions, an assertion about the main program is proved.

In case of nested enrollments, a script regards another script that enrolls in it as main program, while it is regarded as a main program by a script it enrolls in. Hence to avoid the artificial distinction, we use only the term script. Everything we say about it relates to the main program as well.

With each script we associate an invariant *SI* called the *script invariant*. Each SI expresses global information about its script. A script invariant may refer to the formal parameters and local variable of all the roles in the script.

When a script uses only primitive inter-role communication, the pre- and post-assertions associated with its body are proved using a proof system for the host language. When it uses enroll commands (that is, there are nested enrollments) the system described below is used.

The procedure inference rule [13] is used as the interface between the procedure call and its body. Similarly, we present a new proof rule for scripts that is a generalization of the procedure rule.

The notation

$\mathtt{ROLE}\ r_j(\mathtt{IN}\ \bar{x}_j;\ \mathtt{IN\ OUT}\ \bar{y}_j;\ \mathtt{OUT}\ \bar{z}_j)::B_j$

defines a role r_j with value (IN) parameters $\bar{x}_j$, value-result (IN OUT) parameters $\bar{y}_j$, result (OUT) parameters $\bar{z}_j$, and body B_j. For a script s with roles as defined above, we use the notation

$\mathtt{SCRIPT}\ s\ (\bar{x}, \bar{y}, \bar{z})::B_s$

to define a script. Here $\bar{x}, \bar{y}, \bar{z}$ denote the formal parameters of the roles $\bar{x}_1, \ldots, \bar{x}_{ns}; \bar{y}_1, \ldots, \bar{y}_{ns}; \bar{z}_1, \ldots, \bar{z}_{ns}$ respectively, where $ns = |s|$ denotes the number of roles in the script s. Also, B_s denotes the script body $\left(\overset{ns}{\underset{j=1}{\|}} B_j\right)$.

As mentioned above, an assertion

$$\{pre(s)\}\ B_s\ \{post(s)\}$$

can be associated with any given script s. Both pre(s) and post(s) are constructed by conjoining, respectively, the preconditions and postconditions of the various roles with the script invariant.

The formal data parameters referred to by the predicates pre(s) and post(s) may only be $\bar{x}$, $\bar{y}$ and $\bar{y}$, $\bar{z}$, respectively. The predicates may also refer to constants and *free variables* to describe initial and final values (called *logical variables* in [9]). Note that $\bar{z}$ must be initialized inside B_s, which explains why pre(s) may not refer to the result parameters. After termination of a performance, the value parameters, $\bar{x}$, have "returned" to their initial state. Hence, they can not affect the final values of the script. Therefore, post(s) may not refer to the value parameters. Note that the initial value of the value parameters can be accessed by post(s) through free variables. These restrictions are motivated similarly to the analogous restrictions regarding procedures and do not restrict generality.

When applying the proof system presented in [1] (summarized in an appendix) to a script s, which uses CSP's primitive communication commands, the script roles and the predicate pre(s) correspond,

[ROLE r_1 :: $\{x_1 = C\}$ sent[2..3] := false;
LI: $\{x_1 = C\}$

$*[\mathop{\Box}\limits_{k=2}^{3} \neg sent[k]; r_k!x_1 \rightarrow sent[k] := true \{LI\}]$

{LI}

$\|$

$\mathop{ROLE}\limits_{i=2}^{3} r_i :: \{true\}\ r_1?z_i\ \{z_i = C\}$

]

In this case, SI $\equiv$ true.

For establishing cooperation we have to prove (for k = i):

$\{x_1 = C\}\ r_k!x_1 \| r_1?z_i\ \{x_1 = C \wedge Z_i = C\}$

which is done by applying
- communication and preservation axioms
- conjunction, parallel composition, and consequence rules.

Figure 13. Broadcast Proof

respectively, to the processes and a precondition over the initial state in CSP programs. Consider again the broadcast example with only two recipient roles. Using the proof system for CSP described in [1], we may prove

$$\{x_1 = C\}\ B_{broadcast}\ \{z_2 = z_3 = C\}.$$

See Figure 13 for a proof outline. The free variable C *freezes* the initial value of the transmitter and final values of all the roles. Because $\{x_1 = C\}\ B_{broadcast}\ \{z_2 = z_3 = C\}$ is universally true, C may be replaced by any term to yield another universally true statement.

A process p_i can enroll as role r_j in script s using the command $E_j^s(\bar{a}_i, \bar{b}_i, \bar{c}_i)$, where the variables $\bar{a}_i, \bar{b}_i$, and $\bar{c}_i$, are the arguments corresponding to the parameters x_j, y_j, and z_j, respectively. The value arguments $\bar{a}_i$ can be expressions. The notation E_j^s is shorthand for ENROLL IN s AS r_j.

We define $E_1^s, \ldots, E_{ns}^s$ to be *(syntactically) matching enrollments*. By the assumption that initiation and termination are not both immediate, no two E_i^s, E_j^s, $i \neq j$ belong to the same process. This notion is a natural generalization of matching communication commands, used in verifying CSP programs [1]. Recall that by the restriction of enrollments in the script definition, matching enrollments consist only of enroll commands that are all made by roles from the same script.

We now introduce a new inference rule used as an interface between the enrolling processes and the script. This rule naturally generalizes the *procedure rule* [2, 9, 13].

Enrollment Rule: for a script s and matching enrollments $E_1^s, \ldots, E_{ns}^s$.

$$\frac{\{pre(s)\}\ B_s\ \{post(s)\}}{\{pre(s)[\bar{a};\ \bar{b}/\bar{x};\ \bar{y}]\}\ [\ \mathop{\|}\limits_{j=1}^{ns} E_j^s(\bar{a}_{k_j}, \bar{b}_{k_j}, \bar{c}_{k_j})]\ \{post(s)[\bar{b};\ \bar{c}/\bar{y};\ \bar{z}]\}}$$

where $\bar{a}$, $\bar{b}$, $\bar{c}$ denote $(a_{k_1}, \ldots, a_{k_{ns}})$, $(b_{k_1}, \ldots, b_{k_{ns}})$, $(c_{k_1}, \ldots, c_{k_{ns}})$, respectively. By definition all the processes p_{k_j} $(k_j = 1 \ldots n)$ and the roles r_j $(j = 1 \ldots ns)$ are disjoint. Here $p[\bar{u}/\bar{v}]$ denotes the assertion obtained from p by substituting (simultaneously) $\bar{u}$ for all free occurrences of $\bar{v}$.

In other words, the script s operates on the actual parameters $\bar{a}$; $\bar{b}$; $\bar{c}$ in exactly the same way as the body B_s would do with the formal parameters $\bar{x}$; $\bar{y}$; $\bar{z}$. Thus it is expected that post(s)$[\bar{b}; \bar{c}/\bar{y}; \bar{z}]$ is true after execution of the script if pre(s)$[\bar{a}; \bar{b}/\bar{x}; \bar{y}]$ was true beforehand.

Furthermore, let SI be the script invariant for B_s referring to the formal parameters. Then after passing the actual parameters, SI remains invariant (that is, parameter passing does not affect the invariance of SI).

As an example consider a program $P::[P_1 \| P_2 \| P_3]$ using the broadcast script specified above, where $P_1::E_1(5)$; $P_2::E_2(c_2)$; $P_3::E_3(c_3)$. Let E abbreviate $E^{broadcast}$. We can prove

$$\{true\}\ [P_1 \| P_2 \| P_3]\ \{c_2 = c_3 = 5\}.$$

Using the proof that

$$\{x_1 = C\}\ B_{broadcast}\ \{z_2 = z_3 = C\}$$

which was given before we take C to be 5 and get

$$\{x_1 = 5\}\ B_{broadcast}\ \{z_2 = z_3 = 5\}.$$

By the enrollment rule we get

$$\frac{\{x_1 = 5\}\ B_{broadcast}\ \{z_2 = z_3 = 5\}}{\{x_1 = 5[5/x_1]\}\ [E_1(5) \| E_2(c_2) \| E_3(c_3)]\ \{z_2 = z_3 = 5[c_2,\ c_3/z_2,\ z_3]\}}$$

After substitution we obtain

$$\{5 = 5\}\ [E_1(5) \| E_2(c_2) \| E_3(c_3)]\ \{c_2 = c_3 = 5\},$$

which completes the proof.

Note that, like the procedure-call rule [9], the enrollment rule is independent of the script body. It depends only on the specification of the body, namely the pre- and post-conditions of the script body. This is a strong argument supporting the use of scripts as an abstraction mechanism.

Before continuing, we would like to examine the meaning of the enrollment rule as a semantic definition of enrollments. As the rule uses substitutions into global states, one may falsely conclude that both delayed initiation and delayed termination are implied.

Enrolling processes need to be synchronized in order for such a global state to be an actual state in the computation. This actual state satisfies the script invariant (after substitution), so that the usual inductive argument can be applied to deduce the invariant upon total termination.

We need not, however, require synchronization at both initiation and termination. It suffices that at least one event, either initiation or termination be delayed (synchronized). The other one may be immediate. The argument for showing this is a variation on the one used in [5], as each performance of a script under such conditions satisfies similar properties to those of communication-closed layers. The only difference is that these layers do not form a cross-section of the whole program, only of the participating processes. We refer the reader to [5] for further discussions.

The restrictions we have presented induce a pattern of execution: processes do local activities until all face enrollments, then, a whole group, forming a matching enrollment, advancing in one "big step". This generalizes the execution of CSP programs induced by the [1] system, where processes are advanced one pair at the time. For a proof that an arbitrary execution is equivalent to such a serialized one, see [3].

Next we add an inference rule to deal with recursive scripts. It is a natural generalization of the rule for recursive procedures [13, 2]. Consider a (recursive) script declaration

$$\text{SCRIPT } s(\vec{x}, \vec{y}, \vec{z}) :: B_s,$$

where B_s may include recursive enrollments. The rule refers to recursive script s and matching enrollments $E_1^s, \ldots, E_{ns}^s$.

Recursion Rule:

$$\frac{\{pre(s)\}\ [\ \overset{ns}{\underset{j=1}{\|}} E_j^s(\vec{x}_j, \vec{y}_j, \vec{z}_j)]\ \{post(s)\} \vdash \{pre(s)\}\ B_s\ \{post(s)\}}{\{pre(s)\}\ [\ \overset{ns}{\underset{j=1}{\|}} E_j^s(\vec{x}_j, \vec{y}_j, \vec{z}_j)]\ \{post(s)\}}$$

That is, we infer

$$\{pre(s)\}\ [\ \overset{ns}{\underset{j=1}{\|}} E_j^s(\vec{x}_j, \vec{y}_j, \vec{z}_j)]\ \{post(s)\}$$

from the fact that $\{pre(s)\}B_s\{post(s)\}$ can be proved (using the other rules and axioms) from the assumption

$$\{pre(s)\}\ [\ \overset{ns}{\underset{j=1}{\|}} E_j^s(\vec{x}_j, \vec{y}_j, \vec{z}_j)]\ \{post(s)\}.$$

This is the usual circularity encountered when treating recursion. The generalization to mutual recursion is clear.

Finally, we introduce two new proof rules which are also a natural generalization of those for procedures. The names chosen for the rules are the same as those used for procedures [2]. Both of them refer to script s and matching enrollments $E_1^s, \ldots, E_{ns}^s$.

Parameter Substitution Rule:

$$\frac{\{p\}\ [\ \overset{ns}{\underset{j=1}{\|}} E_j^s(\vec{x}, \vec{y}, \vec{z})]\ \{q\}}{\{p[\vec{d};\ \vec{e}/\vec{x};\ \vec{y}]\}\ [\ \overset{ns}{\underset{j=1}{\|}} E_j^s(\vec{d}_{k_j}, \vec{e}_{k_j}, \vec{f}_{k_j})]\ \{q[\vec{e};\ \vec{f}/\vec{y};\ \vec{z}]\}}.$$

where $var(\vec{d};\ \vec{e};\ \vec{f}) \cap free(p,q) \subseteq \{\vec{x}, \vec{y}, \vec{z}\}$.

$p[\vec{d};\ \vec{e}/\vec{x};\ \vec{y}]$ stands for simultaneous substitution of the expressions from $\vec{d}$ and $\vec{e}$ for the variables x and y,

$var(\vec{d};\ \vec{e};\ \vec{f})$ denotes the set of all variables appearing in $\vec{d}$, $\vec{e}$, and $\vec{f}$.

free(p,q) denotes the set of all free variables of p and q. A similar restriction appears and is explained in [2, p. 464].

Variable Substitution Rule:

$$\frac{\{p\}\ [\ \big\|_{j=1}^{ns} E_j^S(\vec{a}_{k_j},\ \vec{b}_{k_j},\ \vec{c}_{k_j})]\ \{q\}}{\{p[\vec{t}/\vec{r}]\}\ [\ \big\|_{j=1}^{ns} E_j^S(\vec{a}_{k_j},\ \vec{b}_{k_j},\ \vec{c}_{k_j})]\ \{q[\vec{t}/\vec{r}]\}}$$

where $var(\vec{t};\ \vec{r}) \cap var(\vec{a};\ \vec{b};\ \vec{c}) = \phi$

The variable substitution rule is used to rename free variables which are not used as actual parameters. Those free variables are typically used to freeze the value of the parameters before enroll command.

Both rules are necessary only when recursion is allowed. Examples using the rules appear below.

Proving Properties of Enrollments

We now introduce the method for proving pre- and post- assertions about a script that uses enroll commands. This proof system is structured similarly to the one for CSP introduced in [1].

We use the term *process* for both a role and an external process. A proof of pre- and post- assertions about a script is done in two stages:

1. separate proofs are constructed in isolation for each component process.
2. the separate proofs are combined by showing that they *cooperate*.

To generate separate proofs for each process we need the following axiom:

Enrollment Axiom: Let E denote any *enroll* command

$$\{p\}\ E\ \{q\}.$$

where p and q refer only to variables local to the process from which E is taken.

This axiom implies that *any* post-assertion q can be deduced after an enroll command. Note, however, that q cannot be arbitrary since at stage (2) it must pass the cooperation test. This axiom is a natural generalization of the input/output axioms introduced for CSP's communication commands [1]. There the arbitrariness of q is explained in more detail.

Using the enrollment axiom and the first eight rules of inference (I1-I8), which are listed in the appendix, we can establish separate proofs for each process. This is presented, as in [21], by a *proof outline* in which each sub-statement of a process is preceded and followed by a corresponding assertion.

In this proof outline a process *guesses* the value its parameters will receive after enrollment. When the proofs are combined, these guesses have to be checked for consistency using a cooperation test.

Note the role of the "guess" in this proof rule. We may distinguish three levels of "guessing":

1. "small guess" - as present in proof system for CSP in the form of a communication axiom [1]. The "guess" is over the effect of a single communication.
2. "moderate guess" - as presented in the proof system for an ADA subset (for concurrency) using the call-accept primitives [8]. Here the "guess" is over a chain of entry calls, when an *accept* or *call* appears within the body of another *accept*.
3. "big guess" - as present in our system, where we "guess" the effect of an enrollment, which may involve an unbounded number of primitive communications.

We now explain how, at stage (2), the separate proofs are combined. First we need the concept of *bracketing*. We define a process P_i to be *bracketed* if the brackets "$<$" and "$>$" are interspersed in its text so that

1. for each program section $<B>$, B is of the form B_1; E; B'_1 where B_1 and B'_1 do not contain any enroll commands, and
2. all enroll commands appear only within brackets as above.

The purpose of the brackets is to delimit the script sections within which the script invariant need not necessarily hold. Again, a generalization of the situation in the script-free programs is easily recognizable [1].

With each proof of $\{p\}[P_1 \| \ldots \| P_n]\{q\}$ we associate a script invariant SI and an appropriate bracketing. The proof rule concerning parallel composition has the following form:

Parallel Composition Rule:

$$\frac{\text{proofs of } \{p_i\}P_i\{q_i\},\ i = 1, \ldots, n, \text{ cooperate}}{\{p_1 \wedge \ldots \wedge p_n \wedge SI\}[P_1 \| \ldots \| P_n]\{q_1 \wedge \ldots \wedge q_n \wedge SI\}}$$

provided no variable free in SI is subject to change outside a bracketed section.

Intuitively proofs cooperate if each performance of a script validates all the post-assertions ("guesses") of the enroll-commands enrolling in this performance.

We now define precisely when proofs cooperate. Assume a given bracketing of a script $[P_1 \| \ldots \| P_n]$ and a script invariant SI associated with it. We define $< B_1 >, \ldots, < B_{ns} >$ to be matching bracketed sections if they contain matching enrollment $E^s_1, \ldots, E^s_{ns}$ to some script s.

We further define the proofs $\{p_i\}P_i\{q_i\}$, $i = 1, \ldots, n$, to *cooperate* if

1. the assertions used in the proof of $\{p_i\}P_i\{q_i\}$ have no free variables subject to change in P_j for $i \neq j$;
2. The statement

$$\{\bigwedge_{j=1}^{ns} pre(B_j) \wedge SI\}\ [\ \big\|_{j=1}^{ns} B_j]\ \{\bigwedge_{j=1}^{ns} post(B_j) \wedge SI\}$$

   holds for all matching bracketed sections $< B_1 >, \ldots, < B_{ns} >$.

The following axiom and proof rules are needed to establish cooperation: enrollment axiom, enrollment rule, recursion rule, parameter substitution rule, and variable substitution rule as described above.

Rearrangement Rule:

$$\frac{\{p\}\ B_1; \ldots; B_{ns}\ \{p_1\},\quad \{p_1\}\ [\ \big\|_{j=1}^{ns} E^s_j]\ \{p_2\},\quad \{p_2\}\ B'_1; \ldots; B'_{ns}\ \{q\}}{\{p\}\ [\ \big\|_{j=1}^{ns} (B_j;\ E^s_j;\ B'_j)]\ \{q\}}.$$

provided $B_1, B'_1, \ldots, B_{ns}, B'_{ns}$ do not contain any enroll commands and $E^s_1, \ldots, E^s_{ns}$ above are matching enrollments.

The rearrangement rule reduces the proof of cooperation to sequential reasoning, except for an appeal to the enrollment rule. Note that the rearrangement of $B_1, \ldots, B_{ns}$, and $B'_1, \ldots, B'_{ns}$ is arbitrary, since they are disjoint in variables. This is a generalization of the binary rearrangement used for CSP, called the "formation rule" in [1].

For proving cooperation we also need the preservation rule (I9. in the appendix). Finally to complete the proof system the substitution rule (I10) and the auxiliary variable rule (I11) are needed.

For example, Consider the program $P::[P_1 \| P_2 \| P_3]$, where

$P_1::E_2(a_1)$

$P_2::a_2: = 5;\ E_1(a_2 + 1)$

$P_3::E_3(a_3)$

for the rest of the section $E \equiv E^{broadcast}$.

Note that P_2 enrolls as the transmitter and P_1, P_3 enroll as recipients. Using the system above we can prove:

$$\{true\}\ [P_1 \| P_2 \| P_3]\ \{a_1 = a_3 = 6 \wedge a_2 = 5\}$$

The proof outline is:

P_1: $\{true\}\ E_2(a_1)\ \{a_1 = 6\}$

P_2: $\{true\}\ a_2: = 5\ \{a_2 = 5\}\ E_1(a_2 + 1)\ \{a_2 = 5\}$

P_3: $\{true\}\ E_3(a_3)\ \{a_3 = 6\}$

and we may choose $SI \equiv true$. There is only one matching enrollment, so for cooperation we must prove:

$$\{a_2 = 5\}\ [E_1(a_2 + 1) \| E_2(a_1) \| E_3(a_3)]\ \{a_1 = a_3 = 6 \wedge a_2 = 5\}$$

Using the proof that

$$\{x_1 = C\}\ B_{broadcast}\ \{z_2 = z_3 = C\}$$

which was given above, we take C to be 6 and get

$$\{x_1 = 6\}\ B_{broadcast}\ \{z_2 = z_3 = 6\}.$$

By the enrollment rule we get

$$\frac{\{x_1 = 6\}\ B_{broadcast}\ \{z_2 = z_3 = 6\}}{\{x_1 = 6[a_2 + 1/x_1]\}\ [E_1(a_2 + 1) \| E_2(a_1) \| E_3(a_3)]\ \{z_2 = z_3 = 6[a_1,\ a_3/z_2,\ z_3]\}}.$$

and after substitution

$$\{a_2 + 1 = 6\}\ [E_1(a_2 + 1) \| E_2(a_1) \| E_3(a_3)]\ \{a_1 = a_3 = 6\}.$$

By the preservation axiom, we can prove

$$\{a_2 = 5\}\ [E_1(a_2 + 1) \| E_2(a_1) \| E_3(a_3)]\ \{a_2 = 5\}.$$

Using the conjunction rule the required cooperation is obtained. The proof is finished by applying the parallel composition rule.

The cooperation test between proofs requires comparisons of all syntactically matching enrollments, even though some of them will never take place during any performance of the script considered.

In this context, the main role of the script invariant SI is to carry global information helping to determine which of the syntactic matches also match semantically. This information is expressed using *auxiliary variables* (different from the program variables) [21].

Consider the enrollments shown in Figure 14. In this example there are four syntactically matching enrollments (denoted 1, 2, 3, 4). Two of them, namely 3 and 4, are not semantically matching enrollments (that is, they will *never* take place). The other two, namely 1 and 2, are se-

P$_1$ :: | P$_2$ :: | P$_3$ ::
E$_1$(5); ---- 3 ---- E$_2$(a$_2$); ---- 3 ---- 4 ---- E$_3$(a$_3$);
E$_2$(a$_1$) ---- 4 ---- E$_1$(a$_2$ + 1) ---- E$_3$(a$_3$)

Figure 14. Matching Enrollments

mantically matching. To verify the program, three auxiliary variables i, j, and k are used. See the proof outline in Figure 15. We choose $SI \equiv i = j = k$.

We now show that the two semantically matching enrollments (1,2) pass the cooperation test. In the other syntactic matching enrollment (3,4), the conjunction of the preconditions contradicts the invariant, so it trivially passes the cooperation test.

(1) We must prove

$$\{SI \wedge i = j = k = 0\}$$
$$[< E_1(5);\ i := 1 > \| < E_2(a_2);\ j := 1 > \| < E_3(a_3);\ k := 1 >]$$
$$\{SI \wedge a_2 = 5 \wedge i = j = k = 1\}$$

Taking C to be 5, we get by the enrollment rule

$$\{true\}\ [E_1(5) \| E_2(a_2) \| E_3(a_3)]\ \{a_2 = a_3 = 5\}.$$

By the assignment and preservation axioms.

$$\{a_2 = 5\}\ i := 1;\ j := 1;\ k := 1\ \{i = j = k = 1 \wedge a_2 = 5\}.$$

By applying the consequence and rearrangement rules the proof of (1) is finished.

(2) We must prove

$$\{SI \wedge a_2 = 5 \wedge i = j = k = 1\}$$
$$[< E_1(a_2 + 1) > \| < E_2(a_1) > \| < E_3(a_3) >]$$
$$\{SI \wedge a_1 = a_3 = 6 \wedge a_2 = 5\}$$

From the previous example, we know that

$$\{a_2 = 5\}\ [E_1(a_2 + 1) \| E_2(a_1) \| E_3(a_3)]\ \{a_1 = a_3 = 6 \wedge a_2 = 5\}.$$

We finish the proof of (2) by applying the preservation axiom and the conjunction rule. Hence, by the parallel composition, consequence, and auxiliary variables rules

$$\{i = 0 \wedge j = 0 \wedge k = 0\}\ [P_1 \| P_2 \| P_3]\ \{a_1 = a_3 = 6 \wedge a_2 = 5\}.$$

Finally by applying the substitution rule we obtain

$$\{true\}\ [P_1 \| P_2 \| P_3]\ \{a_1 = a_3 = 6 \wedge a_2 = 5\},$$

which completes our proof.

Before ending this section we want to clarify a point concerning the extension of the proof system for ADA [8], to any mixture of primitive call-accept communications and script enrollments. Such an extension enables the possibility of having occurrences of enroll commands within the body of an accept; such a phenomenon is not possible in extending the rule to mixtures in CSP.

A similar problem, of having occurrences of calls or accepts, within the body of another accept was resolved in [8, sec. 3] by restricting the notation of bracketing in such way that the invariant also holds when such inner calls or accepts are reached.

$P'_1 ::$	$P'_2 ::$	$P'_3 ::$
$\{i = 0\}$	$\{j = 0\}$	$\{k = 0\}$
$< E_1(5);\ \{true\}\ i: = 1 >$	$< E_2(a_2);\ \{a_2 = 5\}\ j: = 1 >$	$< E_3(a_3);\ \{true\}\ k: = 1 >$
$\{i = 1\}$	$\{a_2 = 5 \wedge j = 1\}$	$\{k = 1\}$
$< E_2(a_1) >$	$< E_1(a_2 + 1) >$	$< E_3(a_3) >$
$\{a_1 = 6\}$	$\{a_2 = 5\}$	$\{a_3 = 6\}$

Figure 15. Proof Outline For Bracketed Program

Applying that method in exactly the same way to enroll commands nested within accept gives an easy and smooth solution. We present bellow a modified definition for a bracketed task; the rest of the details in the extension are rather technical.

A task is called *bracketed* if the brackets '<' and '>' are interspersed in its text, so that:

1. for each bracketed section, <B>, B is of the form
   a. B_1; CALL T.a(arguments); B_2,
   b. B_1; ENROLL IN s AS r_j(arguments); B_2,
   c. ACCEPT b(parameters) DO B_1,
   d. B_2 ENDACCEPT;

   where B_1 and B_2 do not contain any entry call or accept or enroll, and may be null statements.
2. each call, accept and enroll is bracketed as above.

Example: Rotate

We now present a script and two different patterns of enrollment to this script, yielding two different effects in the enrolling program. The script *Rotate* consists of m roles arranged as a ring configuration. Each role R_i has a formal parameter x_i with an initial value denote by the free variable C_i. Each role R_i non-deterministically sends its own initial value to its right neighbor R_{i+1} and receives the initial value of its left neighbor R_{i-1}. (In this section, + and - are interpreted cyclically in {1,...,m}). The effect of each role transferring its initial value to its right neighbor is called rotate right. The script is shown in Figure 16.

Using the CSP proof system, we prove $\{\bigwedge_{i=1}^{m}(x_i = C_i)\}\ B_{rotate}\ \{\bigwedge_{i=1}^{m}(x_i = C_{i-1})\}$.

To verify the script, two auxiliary variables s_i and r_i are introduced for each role R_i . The proof outline for the Rotate script is shown in Figure 17. We choose the script invariant to be

$$SI \equiv \bigwedge_{i=1}^{m}\left[(s_i \wedge r_{i+1}) \rightarrow temp_{i+1} = C_i\right]$$

Note that SI can refer to local variables. The meaning of SI is "whenever R_i has sent and R_{i+1} has received, then $temp_{i+1}$ holds the value C_i ."

Matching bracketed sections consist of the first alternative of some R_i and the second alternative of R_{i+1}, so for establishing cooperation we have to prove

$$\{\neg send_i \wedge \neg receive_{i+1} \wedge LI_i \wedge LI_{i+1} \wedge SI\}$$
$$[\ < R_{i+1}!x_i \rightarrow s_i: = true;\ send_i: = true > \ \|\ < R_i?temp_{i+1} \rightarrow r_{i+1}: = true;\ receive_{i+1}: = true >\ ]$$
$$\{LI_i \wedge LI_{i+1} \wedge SI\}$$

By the arrow rule [1], it remains to be proved that

```
SCRIPT rotate ::

 m
[ROLE R_i (IN OUT x_i : integer) ::
i=1

  VAR send_i,  receive_i : boolean; temp_i : integer;
  send_i := false; receive_i := false;
  *[¬ send_i; R_{i+1}!x_i → send_i := true
  □
   ¬ receive_i; R_{i-1}?temp_i → receive_i := true
  ];
  x_i: = temp_i
].
```

Figure 16. Rotate Script

$$\{\neg send_i \wedge \neg receive_{i+1} \wedge LI_i \wedge LI_{i+1} \wedge \bigwedge_{\substack{j=1 \\ j \neq i}}^{m} [(s_j \wedge r_{j+1}) \rightarrow temp_{j+1} = C_j] \wedge temp_{i+1} = x_i\}$$

$$s_i: = true; \; send_i: = true; \; r_{i+1}: = true; \; receive_{i+1}: = true$$

$$\{LI_i \wedge LI_{i+1} \wedge SI\}$$

holds, where the above precondition is the postcondition of $R_{i+1}!x_i \parallel R_i?temp_{i+1}$. It is inferred from the axioms of communication and preservation.

Using the assignment axiom and consequence rule the required cooperation is obtained. By using the parallel composition rule we obtain

$$\{SI \wedge \bigwedge_{i=1}^{m} [x_i = C_i \wedge s_i = r_i = false]\} \; B_{rotate} \; \{SI \wedge \bigwedge_{i=1}^{m} [r_i \wedge s_i \wedge x_i = temp_i]\}$$

The post-assertion $(SI \wedge \bigwedge_{i=1}^{m} [r_i \wedge s_i \wedge x_i = temp_i])$ implies $(\bigwedge_{i=1}^{m} [x_i = C_{i-1}])$. So, finally, by the consequence, auxiliary variables, and substitution rules the required result is obtained.

We now show two enrollment patterns of m processes arranged as a ring configuration. In the first program, using the rotate-script, the effect of "rotate right" is achieved. In the second program, using a different pattern of enrollment to the rotate-script, the effect of "rotate left" is achieved. For the rest of this section let $E \equiv E^{rotate}$.

Rotate Right

The rotate right enrollment is

```
P :: [ || P_i ]   (i=1 .. m)

P_i :: a_i: = i; E_i(a_i)
```

We prove that: $\{true\} \; P \; \{\bigwedge_{i=1}^{m} (a_i = i - 1)\}$.

The proof outline is: $P_i : \{true\} \; a_i: = i \; \{a_i = i\} \; E_i(a_i) \; \{a_i = i - 1\}$

and we may choose $SI \equiv true$.

For cooperation we must prove

$$\{\bigwedge_{i=1}^{m} (a_i = i)\} \; [\; \Big\Vert_{i=1}^{m} E_i(a_i)] \; \{\bigwedge_{i=1}^{m} (a_i = i - 1)\}.$$

$R_i : \{x_i = C_i \wedge s_i = r_i = \text{false}\}$
$\quad send_i := \text{false};\ receive_i := \text{false};$
$\quad LI_i : \{x_i = C_i \wedge send_i = s_i \wedge receive_i = r_i\}$
$\quad *[\neg\, send_i;\ \ < R_{i+1}!x_i \rightarrow s_i := \text{true};\ send_i := \text{true} > \{LI_i\}$
$\quad \Box$
$\quad \neg\, receive_i;\ \ < R_{i-1}?temp_i \rightarrow r_i := \text{true};\ receive_i := \text{true} > \{LI_i\}$
$\quad]\ \{LI_i \wedge receive_i \wedge send_i\}$
$\quad x_i := temp_i\ \{s_i \wedge r_i \wedge x_i = temp_i\}$

Figure 17. Proof Outline for Rotate

We take C_i to be i and get

$$\{\bigwedge_{i=1}^{m}(x_i = i)\}\ B_{rotate}\ \{\bigwedge_{i=1}^{m}(x_i = i - 1)\}.$$

By the enrollment rule, we obtain

$$\frac{\{\bigwedge_{i=1}^{m}(x_i = i)\}\ B_{rotate}\ \{\bigwedge_{i=1}^{m}(x_i = i - 1)\}}{\{\bigwedge_{i=1}^{m}(x_i = i)[a_i/x_i]\}\ [\ \mathop{\|}_{i=1}^{m} E_i(a_i)]\ \{\bigwedge_{i=1}^{m}(x_i = i - 1)[a_i/x_i]\}}.$$

which after substitution yields the required result. By the parallel composition rule the proof is finished.

Rotate Left

The rotate left enrollment is

$$P :: [\mathop{\|}_{i=1}^{m} P_i]$$

$$P_i :: a_i := i;\ E_{m-i+1}(a_i)$$

For simplicity, we denote m – i + 1 by k_i. Note that $\{k_1, \ldots, k_m\}$ is permutation of $\{1, \ldots, m\}$, so P has exactly one matching enrollment.

We prove that: $\{\text{true}\}\ P\ \{\bigwedge_{i=1}^{m}(a_i = i + 1)\}$

The proof outline is: $P_i : \{\text{true}\}\ a_i := i\ \{a_i = i\}\ E_{k_i}(a_i)\ \{a_i = i + 1\}$

and we may choose $SI \equiv \text{true}$.

Note that $[\mathop{\|}_{i=1}^{m} E_{k_i}(a_i)]$ is the same as $[\mathop{\|}_{i=1}^{m} E_i(a_{k_i})]$, so we can interchange them.

For cooperation we must prove

$$\{\bigwedge_{i=1}^{m}(a_i = i)\}\ [\ \mathop{\|}_{i=1}^{m} E_i(a_{k_i})]\ \{\bigwedge_{i=1}^{m}(a_i = i + 1)\}.$$

We take C_i to be k_i and get

$$\{\bigwedge_{i=1}^{m}(x_i = k_i)\}\ B_{rotate}\ \{\bigwedge_{i=1}^{m}(x_i = k_{i-1})\}.$$

Because $k_{i-1} = m - (i - 1) + 1 = k_i + 1$,

$$\{\bigwedge_{i=1}^{m}(x_i = k_i)\}\ B_{rotate}\{\bigwedge_{i=1}^{m}(x_i = k_i + 1)\}.$$

By the enrollment rule, we obtain

$$\frac{\{\bigwedge_{i=1}^{m}(x_i = k_i)\}\ B_{rotate}\ \{\bigwedge_{i=1}^{m}(x_i = k_i + 1)\}}{\{\bigwedge_{i=1}^{m}(x_i = k_i)[a_{k_i}/x_i]\}\ [\ \big\|_{i=1}^{m} E_i(a_{k_i})]\ \{\bigwedge_{i=1}^{m}(x_i = k_i + 1)[a_{k_i}/x_i]\}}.$$

After substitution we get

$$\{\bigwedge_{i=1}^{m}(a_{k_i} = k_i)\}\ [\ \big\|_{i=1}^{m} E_i(a_{k_i})]\ \{\bigwedge_{i=1}^{m}(a_{k_i} = k_i + 1)\}.$$

which is clearly the same as the required conclusion. The proof is finished by the parallel composition rule.

Other definitions of k_i can cause interesting results, such as rotate k positions.

A Recursive Example: The Towers of Hanoi

The *Towers of Hanoi* is a game played with three poles, named *source*, *destination*, and *spare*, and a set of discs. Initially all the discs are on the source pole such that no disc is placed on top of a smaller one. The purpose of the game is to move all of the discs onto the destination pole. Each time a disc is moved from one pole to another, two constrains must be observed:

1. Only the top disc on a pole can be moved.
2. No disc may be placed on top of a smaller one.

The spare pole can be used as temporary storage.

The well-known conventional solution to the game makes use of a recursive procedure with four parameters. Three of the parameters represent the poles and the fourth is an integer specifying the number of discs to be moved. The algorithm consists of three steps. In step one, N-1 discs are moved, using a recursive call, from the source to the spare using the destination as temporary. In step two, a single disc is moved from the source to the destination. In step three, N-1 discs are moved, using a recursive call, from the spare to the destination, using the source as temporary.

We now introduce a solution using a recursive script. It is similarly structured to the conventional one, and makes use of the same three steps. Although it is distributed, no parallel computation is involved. Parallel computation may take place in a generalization of the game where more then three poles are allowed.

The recursive script, named *hanoi*, implementing a winning strategy for the game, is defined as follows. Each one of the three poles is "in possession" of a different role, represented as a stack of discs. Due to this stack representation the first constraint is observed trivially. Each of the three roles has two parameters. The first parameter is the number of discs to be moved and the second parameter is the stack itself. We also use an auxiliary simple script named *move*, which has two roles, named give and take. Each move role has one parameter of type stack of disks. The purpose of this script is to move a single element (disc) from the give-role stack onto the take-role stack.

The strategy of the hanoi script with three roles (named source, destination, and spare) and N discs is described by the same three steps used in the conventional solution.

1. If N>1 then N-1 discs are moved from the source to the spare using the destination as temporary. This is done by the source, destination, and spare roles *recursively* enrolling to the source,

```
SCRIPT hanoi ::
 INITIATION : DELAYED;
 TERMINATION: DELAYED;
 [ ROLE source (IN n1 : integer, IN OUT A : stack of discs) ::
    [ n1 ≠ 1→ENROLL IN hanoi AS source(n1 – 1, A) □ n1 = 1→skip];
    ENROLL IN move AS give (A);
    [ n1 ≠ 1→ENROLL IN hanoi AS spare(n1 – 1, A) □ n1 = 1→skip]
 ||
  ROLE destination (IN n2 : integer, IN OUT B : stack of discs) ::
    [ n2 ≠ 1→ENROLL IN hanoi AS spare(n2 – 1, B) □ n2 = 1→skip];
    ENROLL IN move AS take (B);
    [ n2 ≠ 1→ENROLL IN hanoi AS destination(n2 – 1, B) □ n2 = 1→skip]
 ||
  ROLE spare (IN n3 : integer, IN OUT C : stack of discs) ::
    [ n3 ≠ 1→ENROLL IN hanoi AS destination(n3 – 1, B) □ n3 = 1→skip];
    [ n3 ≠ 1→ENROLL IN hanoi AS source(n3 – 1, C) □ n3 = 1→skip]
 ].
```

Figure 18. Towers of Hanoi Script

spare, and destination roles respectively, with first parameter equal to N-1, while the second parameter is the stack that the role possesses.

2. A single disc is moved from the source to the destination. This is done by the source and destination roles respectively enrolling to the give and take roles in the move script.
3. If N>1 then N-1 discs are moved from the spare to the destination, using the source as temporary. This is done by the source, destination, and spare roles *recursively* enrolling to the spare, destination, and source roles respectively, with first parameter equal N-1, the second parameter, as before, is the stack.

The hanoi script is shown in Figure 18. The move script is shown in Figure 19.

We now verify this example. First consider the script move. Using the proof system for CSP [1], we can prove

$$\{X = s \bullet X_0 \wedge Y = Y_0\}\ \mathrm{Body}_{move}\ \{X = X_0 \wedge Y = s \bullet Y_0\},$$

where X_0 and Y_0 represent ordered stacks of discs and s denotes a single disc. They are used to freeze the initial state of stacks X and Y. By $s \bullet X_0$ we mean that s is placed on top of the stack of discs denoted by X_0.

It is required that the s disc be smaller than any disc in the stacks X_0 or Y_0 and that initially no disc is placed on top of a smaller one. Note that those requirements are satisfied (by the actual parameters) when the move script is used (in step 2) by the hanoi script. The proof outline of move is shown in Figure 20. It is simple to see that the constraint that "no disc may be placed on top of a smaller one" is observed by this script if the initial requirements are satisfied.

Finally we verify the hanoi script. We first prove formula (*)

$$\{A = A[1..W] \wedge B = B_0 \wedge C = C_0 \wedge n_1 = n_2 = n_3 = N\}$$

$$[E^{hanoi}_{source}(n_1,\ A) \parallel E^{hanoi}_{dest}(n_2,\ B) \parallel E^{hanoi}_{spare}(n_3,\ C)]$$

$$\{A = A[N+1..W] \wedge B = A[1..N] \bullet B_0 \wedge C = C_0 \wedge n_1 = n_2 = n_3 = N\}$$

where $A[1..W]$, B_0, C_0 are used to freeze the initial state of the stacks A, B, and C. The term $A[1..W]$ denotes an ordered stack of W discs, where for each i, j such that $1 \leq i < j \leq W$, disc $A[i]$ is smaller than disc $A[j]$. The term N is an integer such that $1 \leq N \leq W$.

```
SCRIPT move ::
  INITIATION : DELAYED
  TERMINATION: DELAYED
  [ ROLE give (IN OUT X : stack of discs) ::
       VAR temp1 : integer;
       temp1 := pop(X);
       take ! temp1;
  ||
    ROLE take (IN OUT Y : stack of discs) ::
       VAR temp2 : integer;
       give ? temp2;
       push (Y, temp2)
  ].
```

Figure 19. Move Script

For the sake of the proof we assume that any one of the A[1..W] discs is smaller than any disc of B_0 or C_0. Later we explain why that assumption can be removed. Based on the game definition we assume that, initially, no disc is placed on top of a smaller one.

By the recursion rule it suffices to prove that

$$(*) \vdash \{A = A[1..W] \wedge B = B_0 \wedge C = C_0 \wedge n_1 = n_2 = n_3 = N\}$$

$$Body_{hanoi}$$

$$\{A = A[N+1..W] \wedge B = A[1..N] \bullet B_0 \wedge C = C_0 \wedge n_1 = n_2 = n_3 = N\}$$

The proof outline of the hanoi script is given in Figure 21.

There are exactly three matching enrollments corresponding to steps 1-3, which must be shown to pass the cooperation test.

step (1): We must prove formula (1):

$$\{A = A[1..W] \wedge B = B_0 \wedge C = C_0 \wedge n_1 = n_2 = n_3 = N\}$$

$$[E^{hanoi}_{source}(n_1 - 1,\ A) \parallel E^{hanoi}_{dest}(n_3 - 1,\ C) \parallel E^{hanoi}_{spare}(n_2 - 1,\ B)]$$

$$\{A = A[N..W] \wedge B = B_0 \wedge C = A[1..N-1] \bullet C_0 \wedge n_1 = n_2 = n_3 = N\}$$

The proof starts with (*).

By the variable substitution, preservation, conjunction, and consequence rules (exchanging N with N-1),

$$\{A = A[1..W] \wedge B = B_0 \wedge C = C_0 \wedge n_1 = n_2 = n_3 = N - 1\}$$

$$[E^{hanoi}_{source}(n_1,\ A) \parallel E^{hanoi}_{dest}(n_2,\ B) \parallel E^{hanoi}_{spare}(n_3,\ C)]$$

$$\{A = A[N..W] \wedge B = A[1..N-1] \bullet B_0 \wedge C = C_0 \wedge n_1 = n_2 = n_3 = N - 1\}$$

Now by the parameter substitution rule (B, C, n_2, n_3 for C, B, n_3, n_2) and variable substitution rule (B_0, C_0 for C_0, B_0),

$$\{A = A[1..W] \wedge B = B_0 \wedge C = C_0 \wedge n_1 = n_2 = n_3 = N - 1\}$$

$$[E^{hanoi}_{source}(n_1,\ A) \parallel E^{hanoi}_{dest}(n_3,\ C) \parallel E^{hanoi}_{spare}(n_2,\ B)]$$

$$\{A = A[N..W] \wedge B = B_0 \wedge C = A[1..N-1] \bullet C_0 \wedge n_1 = n_2 = n_3 = N - 1\}$$

```
[ give : {X = s • X_0}
        temp_1 := pop(X);
        {temp_1 = s ∧ X = X_0}
        take ! temp_1;
        {X = X_0}
 ||
  take : {Y = Y_0}
        give ? temp_2;
        {temp_2 = s ∧ Y = Y_0}
        push(Y, temp_2);
        {Y = s • Y_0}
].
```

The script invariant is SI ≡ true.
Cooperation is proved easily using:
the communication axiom, the preservation axiom, and the consequence rule.
All that remains is the application of the parallel composition rule.

Figure 20. Move Script Proof Outline

Finally, by the parameter substitution rule ($n_1 - 1,\ n_2 - 1,\ n_3 - 1$ for n_1, n_2, n_3), the required result is obtained. **end step (1)**

step (2): We must prove formula (2):

$$\{A = A[N..W] \wedge B = B_0 \wedge n_1 = n_2 = N\}$$
$$[E^{move}_{give}(A) \parallel E^{move}_{take}(B)]$$
$$\{A = A[N+1..W] \wedge B = A[N] \bullet B_0 \wedge n_1 = n_2 = N\}$$

Using the proof that

$$\{X = s \bullet X_0 \wedge Y = Y_0\}\ Body_{move}\ \{X = X_0 \wedge Y = s \bullet Y_0\},$$

which was given earlier, we take s, X_0, Y_0 to be A[N], A[N+1..W], B_0, and get

$$\{X = A[N..W] \wedge Y = B_0\}\ Body_{move}\ \{X = A[N+1..W] \wedge Y = A[N] \bullet B_0\}.$$

Note that A[N], A[N+1..W], B_0 satisfy the precondition of the move script.

By the enrollment rule we get

$$\frac{\{X = A[N..W] \wedge Y = B_0\}\ Body_{move}\ \{X = A[N+1..W] \wedge Y = A[N] \bullet B_0\}}{\begin{array}{c}\{X = A[N..W] \wedge Y = B_0[A,\ B/X,\ Y]\} \\ [E^{move}_{give}(A) \parallel E^{move}_{take}(B)] \\ \{X = A[N+1..W] \wedge Y = A[N] \bullet B_0[A,\ B/X,\ Y]\}\end{array}}$$

and after substitution

$$\{A = A[N..W] \wedge B = B_0\}$$
$$[E^{move}_{give}(A) \parallel E^{move}_{take}(B)]$$
$$\{A = A[N+1..W]\ B = A[N] \bullet B_0\}$$

By the preservation axiom

$$\{n_1 = n_2 = N\}\ [E^{move}_{give}(A) \parallel E^{move}_{take}(B)]\ \{n_1 = n_2 = N\}$$

Using the conjunction rule, the required cooperation is obtained. **end step (2)**

step (3): We must prove formula (3):

Assume (*).
Let $\alpha(k) \equiv A = A[k..W] \land n_1 = N$.
$\beta_1 \equiv B = B_0 \land n_2 = N$.
$\beta_2 \equiv B = A[N] \bullet B_0 \land n_2 = N$.
$\beta_3 \equiv B = A[1..N] \bullet B_0 \land n_2 = N$.
$\gamma_1 \equiv C = C_0 \land n_3 = N$.
$\gamma_2 \equiv C = A[1..N-1] \bullet C_0 \land n_3 = N$.

[source : $\{\alpha(1)\}$
$[n_1 \neq 1 \rightarrow E^{hanoi}_{source}(n_1 - 1,\ A)\ \{\alpha(N)\}$
$\square\ n_1 = 1 \rightarrow skip\ \{\alpha(N)\}$
$]\ \{\alpha(N)\}$
$E^{move}_{give}(A);\ \{\alpha(N+1)\}$
$[n_1 \neq 1 \rightarrow E^{hanoi}_{spare}(n_1 - 1,\ A)\ \{\alpha(N+1)\}$
$\square\ n_1 = 1 \rightarrow skip\ \{\alpha(N+1)\}$
$]\ \{\alpha(N+1)\}$
||
dest : $\{\beta_1\}$
$[n_2 \neq 1 \rightarrow E^{hanoi}_{spare}(n_2 - 1,\ B)\ \{\beta_1\}$
$\square\ n_2 = 1 \rightarrow skip\ \{\beta_1\}$
$]\ \{\beta_1\}$
$E^{move}_{take}(A);\ \{\beta_2\}$
$[n_2 \neq 1 \rightarrow E^{hanoi}_{dest}(n_2 - 1,\ B)\ \{\beta_3\}$
$\square\ n_2 = 1 \rightarrow skip\ \{\beta_3\}$
$]\ \{\beta_3\}$
||
spare : $\{\gamma_1\}$
$[n_3 \neq 1 \rightarrow E^{hanoi}_{dest}(n_3 - 1,\ C)\ \{\gamma_2\}$
$\square\ n_3 = 1 \rightarrow skip\ \{\gamma_2\}$
$]\ \{\gamma_2\}$
$[n_3 \neq 1 \rightarrow E^{hanoi}_{source}(n_3 - 1,\ C)\ \{\gamma_1\}$
$\square\ n_3 = 1 \rightarrow skip\ \{\gamma_1\}$
$]\ \{\gamma_1\}$
].

The script invariant is $SI \equiv true$

Figure 21. Hanoi Script Proof Outline

$$\{A = A[N+1..W] \land B = A[N] \bullet B_0 \land C = A[1..N-1] \bullet C_0 \land n_1 = n_2 = n_3 = N\}$$

$$[E^{hanoi}_{source}(n_3 - 1,\ C) \parallel E^{hanoi}_{dest}(n_2 - 1,\ B) \parallel E^{hanoi}_{spare}(n_1 - 1,\ A)]$$

$$\{A = A[N+1..W] \land B = A[1..N] \bullet B_0 \land C = C_0 \land n_1 = n_2 = n_3 = N\}$$

The proof starts with (1).

By the parameter substitution rule (A, B, C for B, C, A; and n_1, n_2, n_3 for n_2, n_3, n_1) and the variable substitution rule (A[N+1..W], A[n] • B_0, C_0 for B_0, C_0 , A[N..W]) the required result is obtained. **end step (3)**

By applying the parallel composition rule, the required result about the body of the hanoi script is obtained. Finally by the recursion rule, the proof of (*) is obtained.

Consider, again, the constraint that no disc may be placed on top of a smaller one. The only place where that constraint has to be checked is within the move script. It was pointed out that if the initial requirements of the move script are satisfied, this constraint is observed. Furthermore, the requirements (step 2) are always satisfied. Thus we informally proved that the constraint is observed within the hanoi script, which means that it is an invariant.

Consider, again, the definition of the game. The claim we have just proved is stronger than needed. So, if we now take (*) and use the consequence rule and variable substitution rule to substitute, "empty, empty, empty" for A[N+1..W], B_0, C_0, where "empty" denotes an empty stack, we get

$$\{A = A[1..N] \wedge B = C = \text{empty} \wedge n_1 = n_2 = n_3 = N\}$$

$$[E^{hanoi}_{source}(n_1,\ A) \parallel E^{hanoi}_{dest}(n_2,\ B) \parallel E^{hanoi}_{spare}(n_3,\ C)]$$

$$\{A = \text{empty} \wedge B = A[1..N] \wedge C = \text{empty}\}$$

which is exactly what was defined as the object of the game.

Note that the last formula cannot be proved directly using the recursion rule because of step 3. Note also that when we have assumed empty stacks for B_0 and C_0, the assumption that any one of the A[1..W] discs is smaller than any disc of B_0 or C_0 is vacuous.

VI. Deadlock Freedom

In this section we deal only with the case where both initiation and termination are delayed. When there exist matching enrollments to a script, one of its instances (transparent to the enrolling processes) starts a performance, despite the possibility that other performances of that script are taking place at this moment. From the enrolling processes point of view the script is always available, and there is no need to wait till one performance terminates in order to start a new one. The multiplicity of instances is essential for the deadlock-freedom proof system presented below.

We show how the proof system can be used for proving deadlock freedom of a given program. We assume that there exists a deadlock freedom proof system for the host language (for example, the proof systems presented in [1, 8] for CSP and ADA, respectively).

As in [8] we use a notion called *frontiers of computation* (f.o.c), which characterizes the set of all commands executing at a given moment. Note that these commands may belong to different scripts. Their number is bounded by the number of the (main) program processes. No two commands may belong to the same process. A script that started a performance and has not terminated yet is called an *active* script. A process of an active script, which has not terminated yet, is called an *active* process.

Deadlock means a state in which execution can not proceed, although the program is still active. In the context of scripts this means that at least one process is active, each active process waits in front of a communication command (either an enroll command or a communication primitive of the host language), and no process can proceed. Thus, at the f.o.c., neither primitive communication nor matching enrollment are present in a deadlock.

We define a program P to be *deadlock free relative to a precondition p* if no execution of P, starting in an initial state satisfying p, ends in a deadlock. The approach we use in proving freedom of deadlock is similar to that of the previous section. Each script s is proved to be deadlock free relative to some assertion denoted by df(s).

Note that df(s) and pre(s) (from the partial correctness proof) need not be the same. For example for each script s, {true} s {true} holds but if there exist an initial state in which s ends in a deadlock, then for proving deadlock freedom df(s) has to be stronger then "true." As with pre(s),

```
SCRIPT s ::
[ROLE r1 (IN OUT x1 : integer)::
   [x1 > 5 → r2!x1 □ x1 ≤ 5 → r2?x1]
 ||
 ROLE r2 (IN OUT x2 : integer)::
   [x2 > 5 → r1?x2 □ x2 ≤ 5 → r1!x2]
].
```

Figure 22. Demonstrating df(s)

the df(s) predicate may refer only to value parameters, value-result parameters and constants. It may not refer to free variables.

The approach we introduce is slightly different from the one introduced in [1, 8, 21] where, in order to prove deadlock freedom, first all possible deadlock situations (also called blocked situation in [1, 21] and blocked f.o.c. in [8]) are showed to be unreachable. Using such a method would have forced us to give up modularity handling all the scripts at once instead of separating them, as we wish.

The main idea is that before a script can end in a deadlock it has to pass through a situation which we call a *potentially blocked situation* (p.b.s.). A necessary condition (but not sufficient) for a situation to be p.b.s. is that each of the script's own active processes is waiting in front of an enroll command. Note that in contradiction with the f.o.c., which may include commands from different scripts, the p.b.s. is characterized only by the process belonging to one script. We prove deadlock freedom of a script by identifying all its p.b.s. and showing that they are unreachable.

When a script uses only primitive inter-role communication its deadlock-freedom proof is done using a proof system for the host language. In case it uses an enroll command, the system described below is used.

An example, show in Figure 22will demonstrate a df(s) predicate associated with a script s that uses CSP's primitive communication only. It is also used later to illustrate the concept of p.b.s. Using the CSP proof system it is easy to prove that s is deadlock free relative to

$$df(s) \equiv (x_1 > 5 \land x_2 > 5) \lor (x_1 \leq 5 \land x_2 \leq 5).$$

The rest of this section is devoted to the formulation of a theorem which provides a sufficient condition for a script, using enroll commands, to be deadlock free. We assume that a specific proof outline is given for each process P_i, $i = 1, \ldots, n$, and SI is the script invariant associated with that proof.

We define a matching enrollment, $E^t_1, \ldots, E^t_{nt}$, to be a *df-matching enrollment* if

$$\bigwedge_{i=1}^{nt} [pre(E^t_i(\vec{a}_{k_i}, \vec{b}_{k_i}, \vec{c}_{k_i}))] \land SI,$$

(the conjunction of all the preassertions of the enroll commands and the script invariant of the enrolling processes) implies

$$df(t)[\vec{a}, \vec{b}/\vec{x}, \vec{y}].$$

It is easy to see that a performance initiated by a df-matching enrollment will not end in a deadlock.

We define $< B_1 >, \ldots, < B_{ns} >$ to be *df-matching bracketed sections*, if they contain a df-matching enrollment $(E^s_1, \ldots, E^s_{ns})$ to some script s.

We now introduce the concept of *potential blocking*. Consider a situation of an active script where each of its own active processes waits in front of an enrollment command. Although the processes can not continue at the moment, the state is not necessarily a deadlock because there may be matching enrollments among the enroll commands.

Such a situation is characterized by an n-tuple of *enrollment capabilities* (e.c.) associated with the corresponding processes and defined as follows.

Assume that each process waits in front of enroll command or has terminated; then

1. if it has terminated its e.c. is empty.
2. if it waits in front of an enroll command then its e.c. consists of the bracketed section surrounding this enroll command.

The bracketed sections forming an n-tuple may be partitioned in different ways to form matching bracketed sections. Such a composition of bracketed sections is called a *combination*. A number of different combinations may be obtained from an n-tuple, each one indicating a possible path of execution. Note that a combination which does not include any df-matching bracketed sections indicates an execution path which may end in a deadlock, where the script is still in the same situation.

A situation, as described above, is called a *p.b.s* if the following two conditions hold

1. Among the combinations obtained from the n-tuple of an e.c. there exists a combination that does not include any df-matching bracketed sections.
2. Not all processes have empty e.c.'s.

Formally, condition (1) of p.b.s. is:

$$\exists C \in \text{combination}(\text{n\_tuple}) \ \forall_{\text{match}} < B_1 >, \ldots, < B_{nt} > \in C$$

$$[\neg(\bigwedge_{i=1}^{nt}(\text{pre}(< B_i >)) \wedge SI \rightarrow \text{df}(t))]$$

where combination(n_tuple) is the set of all combination obtained from the n-tuple of e.c.'s that characterize the above situation, C describes one of those combinations and $< B_1 >, \ldots, < B_{nt} >$ are some matching bracketed sections belonging to C.

To illustrate the concept of potential blocking, consider the following examples with their proof outlines. All the enroll commands refer to the script s introduced in the previous example. The invariant is identically true in all the examples. In all the examples we consider the situation in which *each* process waits to enroll, so condition (2) holds trivially.

1. let $P :: [\{a_1 = 6\}E_1\{true\} \parallel \{a_2 = 6\}E_2\{true\}]$. There exists one combination only, including a matching enrollment which is a df-matching enrollment. Hence, condition (1) does not apply, and it is not a p.b.s.
2. let $P :: [\{a_1 = 6\}E_1\{true\} \parallel \{a_2 = 6\}E_1\{true\}]$. There exists one combination only, which does not include any matching enrollments. Hence, condition (1) holds, and the situation is a p.b.s.
3. let $P :: [\{a_1 = 6\}E_1\{true\} \parallel \{a_2 = 4\}E_2\{true\}]$. There exists one combination only, including a matching enrollment, which is not a df-matching enrollment. Hence, condition (1) holds, and again we have a p.b.s.
4. let $P :: [\{a_1 = 4\}E_1\{true\} \parallel \{a_2 = 6\}E_1\{true\} \parallel \{a_3 = 6\}E_2\{true\}]$. Two combinations can be obtained. In the first combination, the third and second processes form a df-matching enrollment, while in the second combination the third and first processes can also form a matching enrollment, which is not a df-matching enrollment. Hence condition (1) holds, and it is a p.b.s.
5. let $P :: [\{a_1 = 4\}E_1\{true\} \parallel \{a_2 = 4\}E_1\{true\} \parallel \{a_3 = 6\}E_2\{true\} \parallel \{a_4 = 6\}E_2\{true\}]$. Two combinations can be obtained, both include exactly two matching enrollments, which are not df-matching enrollments. Hence condition (1) holds, and it is a p.b.s.

6. let $P :: [\{a_1 = 6\}E_1\{true\} \parallel \{a_2 = 4\}E_1\{true\} \parallel \{a_3 = 6\}E_2\{true\} \parallel \{a_4 = 6\}E_2\{true\}]$. Two combinations can be obtained, both include exactly two matching enrollments where one of them is a df-matching enrollment. Hence condition (1) does not hold, and it is not a p.b.s.
7. let $P :: [\{a_1 = 4\}E_1\{true\} \parallel \{a_2 = 6\}E_1\{true\} \parallel \{a_3 = 4\}E_2\{true\} \parallel \{a_4 = 6\}E_2\{true\}]$. Two combinations can be obtained. In the first combination, the first and third processes and the second and fourth processes form two df-matching enrollments, but the second combination includes two matching enrollments which are both not df-matching enrollments. Hence condition (1) holds, and it is a p.b.s.

Note that if the n-tuple may form only one combination, which does not include any matching bracketed sections, then it is a state of deadlock (as in example (2)).

With each p.b.s. we associate an n-tuple of assertions, consisting of the assertions associated with the corresponding processes. The assertion p_i associated with a blocked process P_i is either post(P_i) if it has an empty e.c., or it is the preassertion of the bracketed section in front of which it waits. We call an n-tuple $< p_1, \dots , p_n >$ of assertions associated with a p.b.s. a *potentially-blocked n-tuple*.

It is now clear that a script has to pass through a p.b.s. before it can end in deadlock. Thus, if it can be proved that all p.b.s.'s are not reachable then deadlock cannot occur and the script is proved to be deadlock free. This argument is formally expressed in a theorem (similar to theorem 1 in [1, sec. 4]).

Theorem: Given a proof of {df(s)} s {q} with a script invariant SI, s is deadlock free (relative to df(s)) if for every potentially blocked n-tuple $< p_1, \dots , p_n >$, $\neg \left(\bigwedge_{i=1}^{n} p_i \wedge SI \right)$ holds.

This theorem provides a method for proving deadlock freedom. The expressed condition is not a necessary one since it depends on a *given* proof.

In order to prove that s is deadlock free, we have to identify all potentially blocked n-tuples, and the SI should be such that a contradiction can be derived from the conjunction of the SI and the given potentially blocked n-tuple. The arguments supporting this theorem are similar to those appearing in previous discussions of proof of absence of deadlocks [1, p. 378].

In the recursive case, we must show how to prove that a recursive script s is deadlock free relative to some assertion df(s). The problem that arises is how to decide if a recursive matching enrollment is a df-matching enrollment. Such a decision is based on knowing the assertion relative to which the script is deadlock free, where "the script" is the one the matching enrollments enroll to. In the case of recursive matching enrollments, df(s) is the assertion that must be proved. The solution is the standard one when treating recursion: permit the use of the desired conclusion about an enrollment as an assumption in the proof of the body.

Thus to decide if a recursive matching enrollment to script s is a df-matching enrollment, we assume that s is deadlock free relative to df(s). After all the recursive matching enrollments have been decided, we "forget" the assumption and continue as usual. If from that point, using the known proof system, it is provable that s is deadlock free relative to df(s), then indeed it is.

VII. Future Work

More work needs to be done with scripts to explore their potential for simplifying the programming of concurrent systems. Other issues such as distributed control of performances and practical implementation within various host languages have to be addressed.

There are many natural extensions to scripts. One such is a dynamic arrays of roles, where the number of roles is not fixed until run-time. We term these dynamic arrays *open-ended scripts*. They would allow different instances of a script to take place with somewhat different role structures. The question of the completeness of the proof system and the extension of the system for proving termination should be studied. Another issue involves extending the enrollment mechanism to serve as a guard. Enrolling to computed scripts, extending [6], is worth considering.

Acknowledgments

We would like to thank the attendees of the 1983 IFIP Working Group 2.2 Meeting on Formal Description of Programming Concepts for their comments and suggestions on a early draft of this report. We also thank Shmuel Katz and Amir Pnueli for various discussions concerning the proof rules. Thanks are also due to K. R. Apt and an anonymous referee for their comments on an earlier draft of this paper.

References

1] K. R. Apt, N. Francez, and W. P. De Roever. A proof system for communicating sequential processes. *ACM Transactions on Programming Languages and Systems* **2**(3): 359-385, July 1980.

2] K. R. Apt. Ten years of Hoare logic: A survey (part 1). *ACM Transactions on Programming Languages and Systems* **3**(4): 431-483, October 1981.

3] K. R. Apt. Formal justification of a proof system for communicating sequential processes. *Journal of the ACM* **30**(1): 197-216, January 1983.

4] P. Brinch Hansen. The programming language Concurrent Pascal. *IEEE Transactions on Software Engineering* **SE-1**(2): 199-207, June 1975.

5] T. Elrad and N. Francez. Decomposition of distributed programs into communication-closed layers. *Science of Computer Programming*, North Holland. **2**: 155-173, 1982.

6] N. Francez. Extended naming conventions for communicating processes. *Proceedings of the Ninth Annual ACM Symposium on Principles of Programming Languages* (Albuquerque), pages 40-45, January 1982.

7] N. Francez and S. Yemini. A fully abstract and composable inter-task communication construct. Submitted to *ACM Transactions on Programming Languages and Systems*. Draft, 1983.

8] R. Gerth and W. P. de Roever. A proof system for concurrent Ada programs. To appear in *Science of Computer Programming*, North Holland.

9] D. Gries and G. Levin. Assignment and procedure call proof rules. *ACM Transactions on Programming Languages and Systems* **2**(4): 564-579, October 1980.

10] B. Hailpern and S. Owicki. Modular verification of concurrent programs. *Proceedings of the Ninth ACM Symposium on Principles of Programming Languages* (Albuquerque), pages 322-336, January 1982.

11] P. Hilfinger, G. Feldman, R. Fitzgerald, I. Kimura, R. L. London, KVS Prasad, VR Prasad, J. Rosenberg, M. Shaw, and W. A. Wulf (editor). An informal definition of Alphard (preliminary). Technical report CMU-CS-78-105, Carnegie-Mellon University, February 1978.

12] P. N. Hilfinger. Implementation strategies for Ada tasking idioms. *Proceedings of the ACM-AdaTEC Conference on Ada* (Arlington), October 1982.

13] C. A. R. Hoare. Procedures and parameters: An axiomatic approach. In E. Engler, editor, *Symposium on Semantics of Algorithmic Languages*, pages 102-116. *Notes in Mathematics*, volume 188. Springer Verlag, 1971.

14] C. A. R. Hoare. Communicating sequential processes. *Communications of the ACM* **21**(8): 666-677, August 1978.

15] M. Joseph. Schemes for communication. Technical report CMU-CS-81-122, Carnegie-Mellon University, June 1981.

16] H. F. Korth. Edge locks and deadlock avoidance in distributed systems. *Proceedings of ACM Symposium on Principles of Distributed Computing* (Ottawa), pages 173-182, August 1982.

17] D. A. Lamb and P. N. Hilfinger. Simulation of procedure variables using Ada tasks. *IEEE Transactions on Software Engineering* **SE-9**(1):13-15, January 1983.

18] L. Lamport. Specifying concurrent program modules. *ACM Transactions on Programming Languages and Systems* **5**(2):190-222, April 1983.

19] B. H. Liskov, R. A. Atkinson, T. Bloom, J. E. Schaffert, R. W. Scheifler, and A. Snyder. *CLU Reference Manual. Lecture Notes in Computer Science*, volume 114. Springer-Verlag, 1981.

20] J. G. Mitchell, William Maybury, and Richard Sweet. Mesa language manual (version 5.0). CSL-79-3, Xerox Palo Alto Research Center, April 1979.

21] S. S. Owicki and D. Gries. An axiomatic proof technique for parallel programs. *Acta Informatica* **6**: 319-340, 1976.

22] Richard Rashid and George Robertson. Accent: A communication oriented network operating system kernel. *Proceedings of the Eight Symposium on Operating Systems Principles* (Asilomar), pages 64-75, ACM, December 1981.

23] L. G. Reid. Control and communication in programming systems. Technical report CMU-CS-80-142, Carnegie-Mellon University, September 1980.

24] J. Skansholm. Multicast and synchronization in distributed systems. Research report, Department of Computer Science, University of Goteborg, 1981.

25] United States Department of Defense. *Reference Manual for the Ada Programming Language*. ACM-AdaTEC, July 1982.

26] D. W. Wall. *Mechanisms for Broadcast and Selective Broadcast*. Ph.D. Thesis, Stanford University, 1980. Available as technical report 190, Computer Systems Laboratory, Stanford University, June 1980.

27] N. Wirth. Modula: A language for modular multiprogramming. *Software Practice and Experience* **7**(1): 3-35, January-February 1977.

Appendix

Notation

S -- script named S.

| S | , ns -- number of roles in the script S.

$E_j^S(\bar{a})$ -- enroll in S as $R_j(\bar{a})$.

$R_j^S(\bar{x}_j)$ -- role R_j in script S with formal data parameters $\bar{x}_j$, and body B_j.

B_S -- body of S $\left(\overset{ns}{\underset{j=1}{\|}} B_j \right)$.

pre(R_j^S) -- pre-condition of R_j^S.

post(R_j^S) -- post-condition of R_j^S .

SI -- script invariant.

pre(S) -- pre-condition of B_S.

post(S) -- post-condition of B_S. $\left(\bigwedge_{j=1}^{ns} \text{post}(R_j^S) \wedge SI \rightarrow \text{post}(S) \right)$

df(S) -- predicate relative to which S is proved to be deadlock free

Axioms and Proof Rules

I1. **Assignment Axiom**:

$$\{p[t/x]\}\ x:=t\ \{p\}$$

I2. **Skip Axiom**:

$$\{p\}\ \text{skip}\ \{p\}$$

I3. **Alternative Command Rule**:

$$\frac{\{p \wedge b_i\}\ S_i\ \{q\},\ i=1,\ldots,m}{\{p\}\ [\underset{i=1}{\overset{m}{\Box}} b_i \rightarrow S_i]\ \{q\}}$$

I4. **Repetitive Command Rule**:

$$\frac{\{p \wedge b_i\}\ S_i\ \{p\},\ i=1,\ldots,m}{\{p\}\ {*}[\underset{i=1}{\overset{m}{\Box}} b_i \rightarrow S_i]\ \{p \wedge \neg(b_1 \vee \ldots \vee b_m)\}}$$

I5. **Composition Rule**:

$$\frac{\{p\}S_1\{q\},\ \{q\}S_2\{r\}}{\{p\}\ S_1;\ S_2\ \{r\}}$$

I6. **Consequence Rule**:

$$\frac{p \rightarrow p_1,\ \{p_1\}S\{q_1\},\ q_1 \rightarrow q}{\{p\}\ S\ \{q\}}$$

I7. **Conjunction Rule**:

$$\frac{\{p\}S\{q\},\ \{p\}S\{r\}}{\{p\}\ S\ \{q \wedge r\}}$$

I8. **Disjunction Rule**:

$$\frac{\{p_1\}S\{q\},\ \{p_2\}S\{q\}}{\{p_1 \vee p_2\}\ S\ \{q\}}$$

I9. **Preservation Axiom**:

$$\{p\}\ S\ \{p\}$$

provided no free variable of p is subject to change in S. Note that the skip axiom is subsumed by the preservation axiom.

I10. **Substitution Rule**:

$$\frac{\{p\}\ S\ \{q\}}{\{p[t/z]\}\ S\ \{q\}}$$

provided z does not appear free in S and q. The substitution rule is needed to eliminate auxiliary variables from the pre-assertion.

I11. **Auxiliary Variables Rule**:

Let AV be a set of variables such that $x \in AV$ implies x appears in S' only in assignments $y := t$, where $y \in AV$. The if q does not contain free any variables from AV, and S is obtained from S' by deleting all assignments to variables in AV,

$$\frac{\{p\}\ S'\ \{q\}}{\{p\}\ S\ \{q\}}$$

I12. **Communication Axiom**:

$$\{true\}\ P_i?x \parallel P_j!y\ \{x = y\}$$

provided $P_i?x$ and $P_j!y$ are taken from P_j and P_i, respectively.

I13. **Arrow Rule**:

$$\frac{\{p\}\ (\alpha;\ S) \parallel S_1\ \{q\}}{\{p\}\ (\alpha \rightarrow S) \parallel S_1\ \{q\}}$$

where α stands for any input/output command.

I14. **Parallel Composition Rule**:

$$\frac{\text{proofs of } \{p_i\}P_i\{q_i\},\ i = 1, \ldots, n, \text{ cooperate}}{\{p_1 \wedge \ldots \wedge p_n \wedge SI\}[P_1 \parallel \ldots \parallel P_n]\{q_1 \wedge \ldots \wedge q_n \wedge SI\}}$$

New Rules

Enrollment Rule: for a script s and matching enrollments $E_1^s, \ldots, E_{ns}^s$.

$$\frac{\{pre(s)\}\ B_s\ \{post(s)\}}{\{pre(s)[\vec{a};\ \vec{b}/\vec{x};\ \vec{y}]\}\ [\ \|_{j=1}^{ns} E_j^s(\vec{a}_{k_j},\ \vec{b}_{k_j},\ \vec{c}_{k_j})]\ \{post(s)[\vec{b};\ \vec{c}/\vec{y};\ \vec{z}]\}}$$

Parameter Substitution Rule:

$$\frac{\{p\}\ [\ \|_{j=1}^{ns} E_j^s(\vec{x},\ \vec{y},\ \vec{z})]\ \{q\}}{\{p[\vec{d};\ \vec{e}/\vec{x};\ \vec{y}]\}\ [\ \|_{j=1}^{ns} E_j^s(\vec{d}_{k_j},\ \vec{e}_{k_j},\ \vec{f}_{k_j})]\ \{q[\vec{e};\ \vec{f}/\vec{y};\ \vec{z}]\}}.$$

$$\text{where } var(\vec{d};\ \vec{e};\ \vec{f}) \cap free(p,q) \subseteq \{\vec{x},\ \vec{y},\ \vec{z}\}$$

Variable Substitution Rule:

$$\frac{\{p\}\ [\ \|_{j=1}^{ns} E_j^s(\vec{a}_{k_j},\ \vec{b}_{k_j},\ \vec{c}_{k_j})]\ \{q\}}{\{p[\vec{t}/\vec{r}]\}\ [\ \|_{j=1}^{ns} E_j^s(\vec{a}_{k_j},\ \vec{b}_{k_j},\ \vec{c}_{k_j})]\ \{q[\vec{t}/\vec{r}]\}}$$

$$\text{where } var(\vec{t};\ \vec{r}) \cap var(\vec{a};\ \vec{b};\ \vec{c}) = \phi$$

Enrollment Axiom:

$$\{p\}\ E\ \{q\}.$$

Rearrangement Rule:

$$\frac{\{p\}\ B_1; \ldots;\ B_{ns}\ \{p_1\},\quad \{p_1\}\ [\ \|_{j=1}^{ns} E_j^s]\ \{p_2\},\quad \{p_2\}\ B'_1; \ldots;\ B'_{ns}\ \{q\}}{\{p\}\ [\ \|_{j=1}^{ns} (B_j;\ E_j^s;\ B'_j)]\ \{q\}}.$$

Recursion Rule:

$$\frac{\{pre(s)\}\ [\ \|_{j=1}^{ns} E_j^s(\vec{x}_j,\ \vec{y}_j,\ \vec{z}_j)]\ \{post(s)\}\ \vdash\ \{pre(s)\}\ B_s\ \{post(s)\}}{\{pre(s)\}\ [\ \|_{j=1}^{ns} E_j^s(\vec{x}_j,\ \vec{y}_j,\ \vec{z}_j)]\ \{post(s)\}}$$

THE COOPERATION TEST :
a syntax-directed verification method

by

Willem P. de Roever Jr.
Department of Computer Science,
University of Nijmegen1)/
University of Utrecht2)
(preliminary version)

The cooperation test was originally conceived to capture the proof theoretical analogue of distributed message passing between disjoint processes, as opposed to the interference test, being the proof theoretical analogue of concurrency based on interference by jointly shared variables. Since then the cooperation test has been applied to characterize concurrent communication in Hoare's Communicating Sequential Processes, Ichbiah's ADA, and Brinch Hansen's Distributed Processes, supported by soundness and completeness proofs. An overview is given of the rationale underlying this characterization, culminating in the development of proof systems for monitor based programming languages for concurrency which combine distributed message passing between processes with interference through local variables of a process which are shared between its subprocesses.

Acknowledgements: This paper is the result of cooperation between Nissim Francez, Krzysztof Apt, Nick van Diepen, Marly Roncken, Mark Kramer, Rob Gerth and myself. These colleagues have contributed to shape the cooperation test directly or indirectly to the best of their ability, varying from person to person.
Their collaboration with me spans a period of eight years, in which the research leading up to the cooperation test and its ramifications constituted the dominant theme of my research. To all of them I wish to express my deeply felt gratitude for this privilege and their trust.

---

1) Adress: Toernooiveld 1, 6525 ED Nijmegen, the Netherlands
2) Adress: Budapestlaan 6, 3508 TA Utrecht, the Netherlands

NATO ASI Series, Vol. F13
Logics and Models of Concurrent Systems
Edited by K. R. Apt

TABLE OF CONTENTS

1. Introduction

2. A proof system for CSP

3. A proof system for concurrent ADA
   - 3.1 THE SUBSET, ADA-CF
   - 3.2 A proof system for ADA-CF
   - 3.3 Characterization of safety properties

4. Owicki's proof system for shared variable concurrency

5. A proof system for Distributed Processes
   - 5.1 Why develop a proof system for Distributed Processes ?
   - 5.2 The proof system: notation and problems
   - 5.3 The proof rules
     - 5.3.1 Rule for the when statement: the when rule
     - 5.3.2 The external request rule.
     - 5.3.3 Parallel composition rule
     - 5.3.4 The interference freedom test

6. References

7. Appendix: the dutch national torus (reproduced from [GdeRRo2])

1. *Introduction*

The **cooperation test** [Apt, Francez & de Roever] was originally conceived to capture the proof theoretical analogue of distributed message exchange between disjoint processes, as opposed to the **interference freedom test** [Owicki & Gries], being the proof theoretical analogue of concurrent communication by means of interference through jointly shared variables. Some authors ([Levin & Gries, Lamport & Schneider, Schlichting and Schneider]) stress that both forms of communication can be proof theoretically characterized using interference freedom only, since proofs for both ultimately amount to an invariance proof of a big global assertion [Ashcroft], invariance of whose parts amounts to interference freedom. Yet I feel that the characteristic nature of the cooperation test is still preserved in the analysis of these authors, because in their analysis of CSP the part dealing with interference freedom specializes to maintenance of a global invariant, the expression of which requires per process the introduction of auxiliary variables which are updated in *that* process *only,* thus preserving the concept of disjointness (as opposed to sharing), since now *all* variables from different processes are disjoint.

The cooperation test has been applied to characterize concurrent communication as occurring in Hoare's Communicating Sequential Processes (CSP) [Hoare 2], Ichbiah's ADA [ARM], and Brinch Hansen's Distributed Processes (DP) [Brinch Hansen]. This characterization has been certified through soundness and completeness proofs [Apt 2, Gerth]. As in the interference freedom test this characterization consists of two stages, a **local** sequential stage and a **global** stage.
In the local stage one constructs purely sequential **proof outlines** for the component processes in isolation, disregarding communication. Proof outlines associate every statement with appropriate pre- and postconditions, such that Hoare's axiom and rules for sequential programming constructs are satisfied.
In the global stage these proof outlines are checked for mutual consistency by means of a cooperation test, because communication between processes forces proof outlines to make **assumptions** about the behaviour of the **environment** of a process, prior to combining these stages to a proof for the overall, concurrent, program using a parallel composition rule. The interaction between processes is captured by introduction of a *general invariant* GI, which keeps track of the values communicated between processes during their execution. The expression of GI requires introduction of auxiliary quantities called **auxiliary** variables (also called mathematical, or logical, or ghost, or fanthom variables by other authors). Since these auxiliary variables must be updated when communication occurs, GI may be temporarily violated. Therefore **bracketed sections** are introduced to confine the assignments to the free variables of GI syntactically. By postulating that these variables are updated in bracketed sections only, once proof of invariance of GI over all bracketed sections has been established, it suffices to assume GI in the precondition of a concurrent program in order to conclude GI

in its postcondition. (Of course the introduction of these auxiliary quantities is paralleled by their elimination via various auxiliary variable elimination rules, auxiliary variable substitution rules, and parameter substitution rules. This is the subject of [Apt 1], and is not discussed in the present paper; consult [deR] for the foundations of the link between concurrency and proof theory.)

The present paper stresses the uniform nature of the strategy outlined above. First the cooperation test is reviewed in its original form for CSP, in part II. Then it is combined with the notion of a **canonical** proof outline for procedure bodies (originally due to [Hoare 1]) in order to capture the mechanism of remote procedure calls. On account of the possibility of nesting of these calls inside procedure bodies, this canonical nature of proof outlines is **mandatory,** since, otherwise, every entry call or rendezvous would require a new proof outline for the appropriately modified procedure body, which, in case it contains in its turn a nested call, would require another proof outline for the nested call, etc..
That these chains of calls cannot become infinite, is due to the fact that:

- no recursion is allowed,
- execution of a remote procedure call represents an atomic statement w.r.t. the calling process and, hence, is indivisable, involving waiting in that process until the call has been executed,
- only a fixed finite number of processes can be declared.

In fact, this in itself indicates that, theoretically, one still might have done without canonical proof outlines for procedure bodies, since, as a result of these facts, only a finite number of such calling chains are syntactically possible; of course, this would not have resulted in a proof system applicable in practice.
Also, the possibility of nesting of procedure calls results in a refinement of the notion of bracketed section, since at a nested call new communication will occur and, therefore, GI has to hold again, implying that a nested call should not occur inside a bracketed section. This is the subject of part III, containing a proof theoretical characterization of the ADA rendezvous concept; also the proof of general safety properties, such as the possibility of proving absence of deadlock, is discussed by characterizing the overall state associated with such chains of calls as a conjunction of GI and the assertions associated with each of these calls in their respective proof outlines, a so-called **multicontrol point assertion.**
Part IV contains an overview of the interference freedom test of [Owicki & Gries] since this test has to be incorporated in the proof system for DP in part V.

In Distributed Processes distributed message exchange between processes through remote procedure calls between processes is combined with interference through shared variables between the subprocesses inside a process, a characteristic feature of monitor based languages. Owicki's concept of interference freedom is now taken over, but has to be generalized, because:

- an atomic action now extends from one programmer defined synchronization point to another, and is therefore not anymore a syntactically determined action as in Owicki's case, but is *semantically* determined,
- the number of subprocesses active at a certain time within a process is *dynamically* varying, corresponding as it does with all incarnations of its entry procedures from outside that process at that time,
- accepting an entry call results in a *new* procedure **incarnation** being *created* and executed.

This results in a coroutine mode of execution of (the atomic actions of) these subprocesses. Now the fact is that canonical proof outlines for procedure bodies have been introduced comes us to good stead. For the fact that the proof of an entry procedure is canonical implies that this proof characterizes the behaviour of each incarnation, implying that also interference freedom tests can be made canonical in principle. As in the case of multicontrol point assertions, the coexistence of various incarnations inside a process at specific locations is expressed by the conjunction of GI with the assertions attached to those locations in the various proof outlines, thus enabling the expression of the precondition pre of an interference freedom test, since pre expresses the dynamic coexistence of procedure incarnations inside a process. **Incarnation counters** have to be wired into the proof system to express the coexistence of incarnations of the *same* procedure. Finally, the fact that procedure bodies are canonical also implies that the locations at which our grains of interleaving (atomic actions) may start or end due to synchronization, i.e. the monitor lock being on or off, can be syntactically characterized in canonical fashion. This happens by combining in these proof outlines assertions expressing wheter the monitor lock is on or off with the conjunction of (i) the assertion to be proved invariant with (ii) the above assertion pre which expresses coexistence of the respective incarnations.
Part VI contains a list with references, and part VII is an appendix consisting of a correctness proof of a distributed priority queue appearing in Brinch Hansen's original DP article. When trying to prove that program a bug was discovered, and subsequently removed.

Many additions to the literature concerning the cooperation test are not discussed; of these the following are mentioned:

- Francez' proof system for a modified version of CSP, called CSP+, in which one-sided naming, as in ADA, and global broadcast are expressible [Francez],
- Apt's overview of the CSP proof system in which the cooperation test is simplified by taking the syntactically possible synchronization histories into account when expressing the general invariant [Apt 3].

2. *A proof system for CSP*

We first give an overview of some ideas of this proof system as used in the sequel. The following three facts concerning the syntax and semantics of CPS suffice for our purpose:

1) The basic command of CSP is $[P_1 \| \ldots \| P_n]$ expressing concurrent execution of the (sequential) processes $P_1 \ldots P_n$.
2) Every P_i refers to a statement S_i by $P_i{::}S_i$. No S_i contains variables subject to change in S_j $(i \neq j)$.
3) Communication between P_i and P_j $(i \neq j)$ is expressed by the receive and send primitives $P_j?x$ and $P_i!t$, respectively. Execution of $P_j?x$ (in $P_i{::}S_i$ and $P_i!t$ (in $P_j :: S_j$) is synchronized and results in the assignment of the value of expression t to the variable x (such a pair $P_i!t$, $P_j?x$, is called a **syntactically** matching **communication pair).**

In the proof system, the component processes are first proven correct in isolation, thus giving proof outlines in which each component statement is associated with appropriate pre- and postconditions. These pre- and postconditions satisfy Hoare's assignment axiom and proof rules for sequential programming constructs. They also satisfy the following two axioms, which are introduced to separate this first sequential stage of the proof from the second global stage, required by the nonsequential nature of process communication:

(1) $\{p\}\ P_i!t\ \{q\}$ and (2) $\{p\}\ P_j?x\ \{q\}$.

This implies that the assumption on (i.e. the postconditions of) the communication actions in the component proofs must be tested for compatibility, in order for these outlines to be combined; this is the **cooperation test.** For this test a **general invariant** (GI) is needed which expresses globally which of these communications occur, i.e., which of the syntactically matching communication pairs match **semantically;** to define GI, *auxiliary variables* are introduced.

As the variables appearing free in GI have to be updated at times, GI cannot be expected to hold throughout the program. However, GI only concerns the communication actions, so updating of the GI variables can be restricted to *bracketed sections* $<S_1; \alpha; S_2>$ each of which is associated with a (unique) send or receive primitive α (the statements S_1 and S_2 perform the updating of the GI variables). One of the functions of the cooperation test is to check whether GI is left invariant by the updating of its variables in each bracketed section. Basically, the test is the following:

Suppose we have proof outlines for the component processes of a CSP program. Then these proof outlines cooperate w.r.t. GI iff for any communication pair α, $\bar{\alpha}$ with associated bracketed sections and assertions $\{p\}<S_1; \alpha; S_2>\{q\}$, $\{\bar{p}\}<\bar{S}_1; \bar{\alpha}; \bar{S}_2>\{\bar{q}\}$ in the respective proof outlines, the following condition holds:

$\{p \wedge \bar{p} \wedge GI\}\ S_1; \bar{S}_1; x{:=}t; S_2; \bar{S}_2\ \{q \wedge \bar{q} \wedge GI\}$, where x:=t is the result of performing the communication.

The definition can be paraphrased informally as follows: if execution in process P_i resp. P_j arrives at the communication α, resp., $\bar{\alpha}$ (or rather, at the associated bracketed sections), as expressed by satisfaction of p, resp., $\bar{p}$ and if additionally, these can occur simultaneously, as expressed by satisfaction of $p \wedge \bar{p} \wedge GI$, then the processes P_i and P_j communicate by executing α and $\bar{\alpha}$, and after this action (and after leaving the bracketed sections) both the assumptions q and $\bar{q}$, made about the value transfer in the respective proof outlines, and GI should hold again.

For examples which show the *necessity* of something like GI and a cooperation test for a Hoare style proof system for CSP (lest one wants to lose the idea of component proofs) the reader is referred to [AFdeR]; these examples however are fully applicable to the current model.

In the remainder of this paper, the analogues of the above ideas will be developed for communication through remote procedure calls, specifically for characterizing ADA's rendezvous mechanism and for the communication by external request mechanism for Distributed Processes. In particular, as the reader will notice, the cooperation test and the bracketed sections reappear in the rendezvous and the external request rules.

3. *A proof system for concurrent ADA*

3.1 *THE SUBSET, ADA-CF*

The syntax of our concurrency fragment of ADA, called ADA-CF, is described by the following augmented BNF-grammar. The conventions used are similar to those in [ARM]: *Italicized* prefixes in the non-terminals are irrelevant; "[...]" denotes an optional part, "{...}" denotes repetition, zero or more times. We have taken some liberties with the ADA syntax, which is somewhat verbose.

program ::= **begin** task {task} **end**
task ::= **task** *task* _id decl **begin** stats **end**
decl ::= {entry_decl}{var_decl}
entry_decl ::= **entry** *entry* _id (formal_part)
var_decl ::= var_id_list: **int** | var_id_list: **bool**
var_id_list ::= var_id{,var_id}

formal_part ::= [var_id_list][# var_id_list]
stats ::= stat{;stat}
stat ::= **null** | ass_st | if_st | while_st | call_st | ass_st | sel_st
ass_st ::= var_id := expr
if_st ::= **if** bool_expr **then** stats **else** stats **end if**
while_st ::= **while** bool_expr **do** stats **end while**
call_st ::= **call** *task* _id. *entry* _id (actual_part)
actual_part ::= {expr}[# var_id_list]
acc_st ::= **accept** *entry* _id (formal_part) **do** stats **end accept**
sel_st ::= **select** sel_br { **or** sel_br} **end select**
sel_br ::= bool_expr : acc_st [;stats]
expr ::= "expression"
bool_expr ::= "boolean expression"
id ::= "identifier"

Thus, an ADA-CF program consists of a fixed set of tasks. These tasks are all activated simultaneously and executed in parallel. When execution reaches the end of the task body, the task terminates. Each task can have declarations for entries, which may be called by other tasks. The actions to be performed, when such an entry is called, are specified by corresponding accept statements. Executions of an accept is synchronized with the execution of a corresponding entry call. Consequently, a task executing an accept or entry call, will be suspended until another process reaches a corresponding entry call or accept, after which the statements of the accept body are executed by the called task, while the calling task remains suspended. This action is called a **rendezvous** and is the primary means of communication between and synchronization of tasks; in particular, there are no global variables. After a rendezvous, the two tasks continue their execution in parallel.

Apart from the synchronization, an entry call is executed as an ordinary procedure call. An entry declaration may specify a formal_part. Only parameters of type **int** are allowed. The first set of parameters, closed off by the '#'-sign, is of mode **in;** the second set is of mode **in out.** Hence, in the actual_part of a corresponding call, the first set of actual parameters may be expressions, the second set must be variables.

The formal_part of an accept statement must match the one of the corresponding entry declaration. A task may only contain accept statements for one of its own entries, but it may contain more than one accept statement for the same entry.

The select statement allows a task to wait for synchronization with one of a set of alternatives. First, all boolean expressions are evaluated to determine which branches of the select statement are open. If all are closed, the statement aborts. Otherwise, the task, if necessary, waits until a rendezvous corresponding with one of the open branches is possible. (Notice that each branch starts with an accept statement.) If more than one rendezvous is possible, one is selected arbitrarily.

Two more or less implicit changes w.r.t. the ADA semantics are the following:

- The removal of entry queues. This is not serious, as in ADA-CF entry queues cannot be used explicity within programs on account of the lack of queue interrogation operations, and can therefore be removed; this is proved in [PdeR].
- Deadlock instead of abortion in case an entry is called of an already terminated task.

3.2 A proof system for ADA-CF

The proof system for ADA-CF is similarly structured as that of [OWICKI & GRIES] for shared variable languages, and that of [APT, FRANCEZ & De ROEVER] for CSP in that a proof of a concurrent program is split into a local stage and a global stage. In the local stage one constructs purely sequential proof (outline)s for the component tasks in isolation. In the global stage these proof outlines are checked for mutual consistency by means of a **cooperation** test, before combining them to a proof of that program using the parallel composition rule, because communication between tasks forces proof outlines to make **assumptions** about the behaviour of the **environment** of a task.
Using appropriate notions of cooperation and of bracketed sections, the parallel composition rule for ADA-CF has the following form:

[Parallel composition rule]

proof outlines of $\{p_i\}$ **task** T_i $\{q_i\}$ for i=1,...n cooperate w.r.t. GI

--,

$\{\bigwedge_{i=1}^{n} p_i \wedge GI\}$ [**task** T_1 $\|\ldots\|$ **task** T_n] $\{\bigwedge_{i=1}^{n} q_i \wedge GI\}$

provided: no free variables of GI are updated outside a bracketed section, and, GI does not contain actual or formal parameters occurring in entry calls or accept bodies as free variables (to prevent aliasing).

In case of ADA-CF the separation between the local and global stage of a proof is brought about by the following axiom and rule:

- [Call axiom for ADA-CF]

  {pre} **call** $T.e(\vec{t}\ \#\ \vec{x})$ {post}, where $FV(pre) \cap \{\vec{x}\} = \emptyset$

  In a proof outline any postcondition may be the result of an entry call. The cooperation test in the parallel composition rule enforces that a rule for the ADA rendezvous is used to relate this postcondition to the postcondition q_1 of the accept body below, since post expresses an assumption about the behaviour of the accept statement. The restriction on the free variables of precondition pre is essential to the ADA-CF proof system since pre expresses state properties which are invariant under the call.

- [Accept rule] $\{p_1\}$ S $\{q_1\}$

  --,

  $\{p\}$ **accept** e $(\vec{u}\#\vec{v})$ **do** S **endaccept** $\{q\}$

  provided $(\vec{u} \cup \vec{v}) \cap FV(p,q) = \emptyset$.

  This rule expresses that a proof outline for the accept body is needed to obtain a proof outline for the corresponding accept statement.

  Note that the formal parameters of S do not occur in p or q. The cooperation test checks (via the rendezvous rule) that p, expressing properties of the local state, and pre as in the axiom above, expressing properties of the actual parameters of a call, are correctly related to p_1, the precondition of the accept body. Postcondition q_1 of the accept body is similarly related to postconditions q of the accept statement and post of the actual call.

Similarly as in the CSP proof system, a general invariant GI is introduced to model synchronization globally, and also a set AV of auxiliary variables, in order to express GI: AV is a set of variables such that $x \in AV$ if x appears only in assignments $y := t$ where $y \in AV$. (Notice that AV is defined relative to a particular program and that variables in AV do not influence the value of the 'real' program variables during execution of the program).

Bracketed sections are introduced to confine assignements to the free variables of GI. First a (pseudo-)translation of a rendezvous into CSP is given; using this translation, bracketed sections are defined:

	ADA−CF	**translated** CSP version
P_i:	**call** $P_j.pr(\vec{t},\vec{x})$	$P_j!(\vec{t},\vec{x})$; $P_j?\vec{x}$
P_j:	**accept** $pr(\vec{u}\ \#\ \vec{v})$ **do** T **endaccept**	$P_i?(\vec{u},\vec{v})$; T; $P_i!\vec{v}$

The translation clearly shows that a rendezvous results in *two* CSP-like communication actions. This suggests that *two* bracketed sections be associated with both the call and the accept body, which is in essence what we shall do:

A *bracketed section* is a construct of the form

(1) $<S_1$; **call** $P_j.pr(\vec{t},\vec{x})$; $S_2>$ or

(2) **accept** $pr(\vec{u}\ \#\ \vec{v})$ **do** T_1 ;> T <;T_2 **endaccept** such that S_1, S_2, T_1 and T_2 do not contain any call- or accept statements. The T_1 resp. T_2-part of the accept body will also be referred to as the *prelude* resp. *postlude* of the body.

The pieces of program over which GI must be proven invariant for each call will then be: S_1; $\vec{u}:=\vec{t}$; $\vec{v}:=\vec{x}$; T_1 and T_2; $\vec{x}:=\vec{v}$; S_2 (compare this with the CSP translation of the entry-call).

Apart from what is suggested by the translation, there is a more pressing reason why the accept bodies have been extended by pre- and postludes; after all, why not show invariance of GI simply over S_1; $\vec{u}:=\vec{t}$; $\vec{v}:=\vec{x}$; T; $\vec{x}:=\vec{v}$; S_2? This would reduce the number of cooperation tests, and the accept body must be proven anyway. Moreover, the fact that two communication actions are within the same bracketed section does not matter, because they take place during the *same* synchronization period. The catch is of course the appearance of other call statements within the accept body. The idea is that GI must hold when a (new) synchronization action takes place, i.e., at a new call statement (or rather, at the entrance of the bracketed section surrounding it). Were the above suggestion to be accepted, the validity of GI would not have been assured for call statements within the accept body, because GI would not have been required to hold within the body.

The notion of cooperation appropriate to ADA-CF is as follows:
Definition The proof outlines of $\{p_i\}$ **task** T_i $\{q_i\}$ (i=1..n) cooperate w.r.t. GI if

(1) for any syntactically matching pair, <C> and <A>, where

$C \equiv S_1$; **call** $T_j.a(\vec{e}\#\vec{x})$; S_2 and

$A \equiv$ **accept** $a(\vec{u}\#\vec{v})$ **do** S_1';> S; <S_2' **endaccept** (A within T_j),

the formula

$\{pre(C) \wedge pre(A) \wedge GI\}\ C \parallel A\ \{post(C) \wedge post(A) \wedge GI\}$

as defined below, holds,

(2) the assertions of the proof outline of $\{p_i\}$ T $\{q_i\}$ contain no free variables subject to change in any T_j $(j \neq i)$,

for i=1..n. □

Having obtained the correct notion of bracketing and cooperation, the last task is to define formally how to prove the formulae of the cooperation test. During the remainder of this section, the following entry call and matching accept will be fixed, with pre and postconditions as indicated;

$\{p_1\}$ <S_1; $\{\bar{p}_1\}$ **call** T'.$a(\vec{e}\#\vec{x})$ $\{\bar{q}_1\}$; S_2> $\{q_1\}$

$\{p_2\}$ < **accept** $a(\vec{u}\#\vec{v})$ **do** $\{p_2'\}$ S_1';> $\{\bar{p}_2\}$ S $\{\bar{q}_2\}$; <S_2' $\{q_2'\}$ **endaccept** > $\{q_2\}$..(1)

These bracketed sections are denoted by <C> and <A> respectively (the call is part of a task T).

The question is, how to prove

$\{p_1 \wedge p_2 \wedge GI\}\ C \parallel A\ \{q_1 \wedge q_2 \wedge GI\}$? ...(2)

According to the semantics of a rendezvous and the intention of the bracketing and the cooperation test, proof of this formula requires that the following partial proof outline can be completed:

$\{p_1 \wedge p_2 \wedge GI\}$

S_1; $\vec{u},\vec{v} := \vec{e},\vec{x}$; S_1'; $\{p \wedge GI\}$ S $\{q \wedge GI\}$; S_2'; $\vec{x} := \vec{v}$; S_2

$\{q_1 \wedge q_2 \wedge GI\}$ ...(3)

Next, observe that when synchronization is ignored, an entry call behaves like an ordinary procedure call. Hence, to describe the effect of executing the body of an accept statement, one must look at ordinary procedure call rules.

This brings us to an important point. In order to obtain a usable proof system a notion of proof outline is required which guarantees that for an accept statement *only one proof outline* is needed, irrespective of the particular characteristics of the caller. I.e., both the accept body and the cooperation test should not need additional ones, notwithstanding the fact that every call is associated with its own characteristic synchronization behaviour and its own characteristic parameters. This means that the proof outline of the body of some accept must be *canonical* in the sense that its constituent assertions must be strong enough to justify the assumptions of each matching call, and, symmetrically, must be weak enough to remain valid under the 'value-injection' of each matching call.

Disregarding synchronization, a rendezvous is equivalent to an ordinary procedure call. A similar quest for canonical proofs can be found in the literature dealing with proof rules for procedure calls in sequential programming. There, the simplest approach is the simulation of parameter transfer by syntactic substitution of actual for formal parameters. To achieve this, restrictions must be imposed on the actual parameters allowed. The same approach is adopted in the current case.

To be exact, we want the following:

For each accept statement

accept pr($\vec{u}$ # $\vec{v}$) **do** S **endaccept** ($\vec{u}$,$\vec{v}$ denote the parameter lists)

in a task P and for each call statement

call P.pr($\vec{t}$,$\vec{x}$):

if {p} S {q} holds, then {p[.]} **call** P.pr($\vec{t}$,$\vec{x}$) {q[.]} holds, where $[.] \equiv [\vec{t},\vec{x}/\ \vec{u},\vec{v}]$

and denotes substitution of the actual for the formal parameters.

This implies that in order to prove {r} **call** P.pr($\vec{t}$, $\vec{x}$) {s}, one only has to prove the implications $r \rightarrow p[.]$ and $q[.] \rightarrow s$ (after having proved {p} S {q} once and for all). We can achieve this by placing the following restrictions on the actual parameters of a call (cf. § 6.1 of [Apt1]:

(i) the variable parameters x_i are pairwise disjoint,

(ii) $FV(\vec{t}) \cap \vec{x} = \emptyset$, i.e. no variable parameter appears free in a value expression,

(iii) $(FV(\vec{t}) \cup \vec{x}) \cap FV(S) \subseteq \vec{u} \cup \vec{v}$, i.e. no variable in the actual parameter list may have the name of a variable appearing free in S, unless this is a formal parameter.

Only (ii) is a real restriction; the other two have to be made anyhow; firstly, our model does not specify a particular order in which the values computed in a procedure are assigned to the variables in the call statement. Hence, if two of these variable parameters are the same, their value is undefined after execution of the procedure, whence restriction (i). Secondly, because the proofs of the component tasks will be combined at a later stage, variable clashes must be avoided, so that the variables which appear in assertions of a proof outline cannot appear in assertions of another proof outline. Hence a reasonable assumption is:

(iii')

a variable appearing free in some task (and hence in the assertions of the corresponding proof outline) may not be subject to change in any other process.

This assumption implies restriction (iii) above. In the sequel we will assume (i), (ii) and (iii') to apply to each program.

This approach is justified by the following theorem:

Theorem Let S be some ADA-CF statement, p and q two assertions; $\vec{u}$, $\vec{v}$ and $\vec{x}$ denote sequences of distinct variables and $\vec{e}$ denotes a sequence of expressions.

If (a) $FV(\vec{e}) \cap \{\vec{x}\} = \emptyset$, $\{\vec{u}\} \cap \{\vec{v}\} = \emptyset$, $(FV(S) \cup \{\vec{u}, \vec{v}\}) \cap (FV(\vec{e}) \cup \{\vec{x}\}) = \emptyset$,

(b) the variables in $\vec{u}$ do not appear on the left-hand side of any assignment in S or as value or result parameter of any call in S:

Then (1) $\{p\}\ S\ \{q\} \Rightarrow \{p[.]\}\ S[.]\ \{q[.]\}$, provided $FV(q) \cap \{\vec{x}\} = \emptyset$

([.] denotes the variable substitution $\{\vec{e},\vec{x}/\vec{u}, \vec{v}]$),

(2) $\{p\}\ S[.]\ \{q\} \Rightarrow \{p\}\ \vec{u},\vec{v}:=\vec{e},\vec{x};\ S;\ \vec{x}:=\vec{v}\ \{q\}$

provided $FV(p,q) \cap \{\vec{u},\vec{v}\} = \emptyset$. □

Having formulated the condition subject to which parameter transfer can be modeled by (syntactic) substitution, we proceed with an informal deduction of the rendezvous rule, to be used in proving the formulae in the cooperation test.

The theorem above suggests that instead of completing proof outline (3) above one might try and complete

$\{p_1 \wedge p_2 \wedge GI\}$

$s_1;\ s_1'[.];\ \{p[.] \wedge GI\}\ S[.]\ \{q[.] \wedge GI\};\ s_2'[.];\ s_2$

$\{q_1 \wedge q_2 \wedge GI\}$ (4)

(remember that $FV(p_1,q_1,p_2,q_2,GI,S_1,S_2) \cap \{\vec{u},\vec{v}\} = \emptyset$; p and q still have to be determined).

Now consider the proof outline in (1) for $\{\bar{p}_2\}\ S\ \{\bar{q}_2\}$. The theorem implies the existence of a proof (outline) for $\{\bar{p}_2[.]\}\ S[.]\ \{\bar{q}_2[.]\}$, too. This proof outline is not yet strong enough to be used in (4) because p and q have to contain state information of both T' (containing the accept of (1)) and T (containing the call).

During execution of S, the state of T remains fixed and (hence) is characterized by the precondition of the call, $\bar{p}_1$. Consequently, $\bar{p}_1$ is invariant over S; $\bar{p}_1$ is even invariant over S[.], because $FV(\bar{p}_1) \cap \{\vec{x}\} = \emptyset$ (this explains the role of the restriction in the call axiom). GI, too, may be assumed to be invariant over S and hence over S[.] (remember, GI does not contain formal parameters as free variables) because inner calls or accepts are dealt with separately. Now, it is a fact that, using auxiliary variables and GI, an assertion such as p, 'talking' about the state of two different tasks, T' and T, can always be split into two assertions, $\bar{p}_1$ and $\bar{p}_2$, each talking about the state of only one task (i.e., $\bar{p}_1$ about T and $\bar{p}_2$ about T'); see e.g., the completeness proof in [Apt 2]. Consequently, formula (4) can be rewritten as:

$\{p_1 \wedge p_2 \wedge GI\}$

$\quad S_1;\ S_1'[.];\ \{\bar{p}_1 \wedge \bar{p}_2[.] \wedge GI\}\ S[.]\ \{\bar{p}_1 \wedge \bar{q}_2[.] \wedge GI\}\ S_2'[.];\ S_2$

$\{q_1 \wedge q_2 \wedge GI\}$.

And, as far as the accept body is concerned, there only remains the proof of $\{\bar{p}_2[.]\}\ S[.]\ \{\bar{q}_2[.]\}$ for which it suffices to prove $\{\bar{p}_2\}\ S\ \{\bar{q}_2\}$ which is already part of the proof outline of T'. These arguments lead up to the rendezvous rule below:

[Rendezvous rule]

$$\frac{\{pre(C) \wedge pre(A) \wedge GI\}\ S_1;\ S_1'[.]\ \{pre('call') \wedge pre(S)[.] \wedge GI\} \qquad \{pre('call') \wedge post(S)[.] \wedge GI\}\ S_2'[.];\ S_2\ \{post(C) \wedge post(A) \wedge GI\}}{\{pre(C) \wedge pre(A) \wedge GI\}\ C \parallel A\ \{post(C) \wedge post(A) \wedge GI\}},$$

where $C \equiv S_1$; **call** T'.a($\bar{e}$ # $\bar{x}$); S_2 (within a task T)

A $\equiv$ **accept** a($\bar{u}$ # $\bar{v}$) **do** S_1';> S; <S_2' **endaccept** (A within T') ,

$[.] \equiv [\bar{e}, \bar{x} / \bar{u}, \bar{v}]$,

'call' denotes the entry call within C.

Finally, a graphical interpretation of this rule is suggested below:

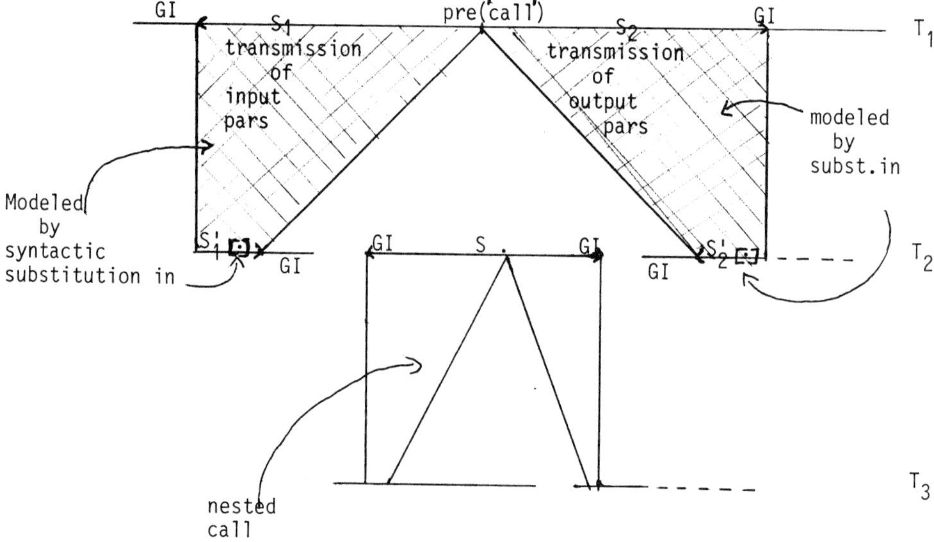

3.3 Characterization of safety properties

The parallel composition rule allows one to deduce partial correctness properties, i.e., properties of the *output* state of a set of communicating tasks [**task** T_1 || ... || **task** T_n]. But how does one express and prove, properties of the *intermediate* states, while computation of [T_1 || ... || T_n] is in progress?
We shall concentrate on **safety** properties, expressing, in Lamport's parlance, "that nothing bad happens during computation". Examples of such properties are properties of never terminating (service) programs, absence of deadlock, and absence of failure (abortion).
So when we determine which combinations of locations occur in snapshots of the computations of [T_1 || ...|| T_n], we are done. Technically, the only problem is that the, necessarily canonical, proof outlines of accept bodies have to hold for any call of the related entry. Hence, on their own, they cannot specify the actual values of the formal parameters occurring during a particular rendezvous, and, consequently, they do not fully characterize the state when reaching a particular location.

We suggest the following picture of these snapshots.
Due to the possibility of nesting of entry calls, execution of a particular statement, say, S in task T_i, which is contained in an accept body for an entry a, although immediately caused by execution of a call T_i.a(e#x) in task T_j, may be ultimately "provoked" by a whole chain of nested entry calls, since call T_i.a(e#x) may, on its turn, be contained in an accept body for entry b, which is called by call T_j.b(t#x) in task T_k, and so on. Such a maximal chain of calls, ending at a location in task T_i which is not necessarily associated with a call statement, is called a **multicontrol point** with **frontier** task T_i, and is suggested below:

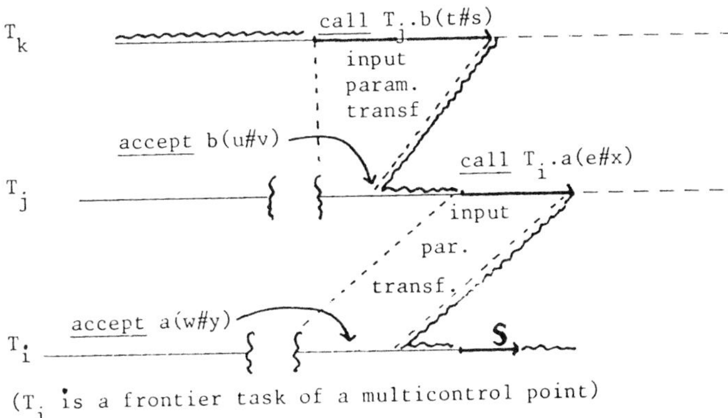

(T_i is a frontier task of a multicontrol point)

Consequently, the combination of locations occurring during concurrent execution can be split into disjoint multicontrol points.

Let an occurrence of a syntactic entity S be uniquely labeled by label 'S', then a multicontrol point is *syntactically* characterized by a chain of locations of the form at('C'), with 'C' labeling an entry call, which ends at a location at('S') with S denoting a task T, a statement S or a bracketed call <C>.
In the associated proof outlines these locations are paired to assertions. Typically a location at('C') is paired to an assertion pre('C') in the terminology of the rendezvous rule of the preceding section, which is invariant over execution of call 'C' (as stipulated by the call axiom). Hence, a first approximation to a *semantic* characterization of a multicontrol point is a conjunction of assertions of the form

$$pre('C_1') \wedge pre('C_2') \wedge \ldots \wedge pre('C_k') \wedge pre/post('S') \ldots (*)$$

However, two refinements must be incorporated in this characterization.
Firstly, the preassertions all encode local computation histories, which, therfore, should be checked for compatibility. I.e., it should be checked whether the local histories are compatible with the global calling history which is encoded in GI. This check is expressed by "anding" (*) with GI, resulting in the **multicontrol point assertion:**

$$pre('C_1') \wedge pre('C_2') \wedge \ldots \wedge pre('C_k') \wedge pre/post('S') \wedge GI \ldots (**)$$

Secondly, the values of the actual parameters should be included in these state descriptions since in proof outlines no specific incarnations are considered. So it seems that the assertions making up the multicontrol point assertion must be modified by substituting the formal parameters of each entry by the actual parameters of each call $'C'_i$. And indeed we may !
However, by strengthening GI sufficienctly one obtains that in fact multicontrol point assertion (**) already incorporates these values, because it is one of the functions of GI (so obtained) to encode which values are communicated during a particular rendezvous via the use of auxiliary variables ! Notice that this observation is a straightforward generalization of the precondition of the cooperation test of two processes to k+1 processes.

Thus, the combination of locations occurring during concurrent execution can be semantically characterized by associated multicontrol point assertions.
In [GdeR] this characterization is used to prove safety properties such as absence of deadlock and absence of failure (abortion). E.g., a proof of absence of deadlock is obtained by considering all multicontrol points in which the frontier tasks cannot proceed due to blocking, and proving that these points do not occur during actual program execution because their associated assertions evaluate to false.
Also ADA's **terminate** statement is characterized using these techniques.

In [GdeR] the following examples of ADA-CF correctness proofs are given:

- A carefully selected series of "simplest" paradigms indicating why a global invariant and the definition of bracketed sections, as given above, are needed. These examples illustrate that without these concepts our proof system would be both incomplete and unsound.

- A proof of partial correctness, of termination, of absence of deadlock, and absence of failure, of a bounded buffer program.
- Correctness proofs of similar properties of a distributed priority queue.

4. *Owicki's proof system for shared variable concurrency*

Owicki's proof system for concurrency with communication by means of shared variables is reviewed for her **General Programming Language (GPL).**
Concurrency is introduced in GPL by the *cobegin* statement:
cobegin S_1 ||...|| S_n **coend.** Here, S_1 through S_n are sequential statements, called the component processes of this statement. A set of variables is *shared* between $S_1,\dots,S_n$, and the processes are executed in parallel. However, Owicki makes an essential restriction on the parallellism in GPL; this restriction is worked out in [deR].
To simplify matters, this restriction is paraphrased as follows:
the assignment and tests within the S_i*'s are executed as* **atomic** *indivisible actions.* This means that the execution of a cobegin statement amounts to an arbitrary **interleaving** of these assignments and tests within the component processes.

In the GPL proof system, the components of a cobegin statement are proven correct in isolation, and, as in the CSP system of [AFdeR], a consistency check is therefore needed when these separate proofs are combined. This check is in fact straightforward.

Consider the program **cobegin** x:=1; x:=x+1 || x:=2 **coend** and the (valid) isolated proof outlines {**true**} x:=1; {x=1}x:=x+1 {x=2} and {**true**} x:=2 {x=2}. A quick inspection of the program shows that after termination, the value of x is either 2 or 3. However, restricting one's attention to these component proofs in isolation might lead one to conclude that {x=2} holds after termination. Now consider the precondition {x=1} of the action x:=x+1, which is also the postcondition of x:=1. This assertion holds immediately after the assignment x:=1 has terminated, but this does not imply that {x=1} holds whenever the second assignment, x:=x+1, is executed; The statement x:=2 could have been executed first. Hence, the necessary consistency check simply is the test whether each assertion in the proof outline of a component process is invariant over all atomic actions of the other processes which can be interleaved at that point. This check implies that *the postcondition of some action can safely be taken as the precondition of the following action in the component process.* The following **interference freedom test** formalizes this idea:

> Consider a program **cobegin** S_1 ||...|| S_n **coend** and proof outlines for the component processes. For each statement T, let pre(T) respectively post(T) denote the pre- respectively postcondition of T within the proof outline. For any statement A in S_i and

assignment B in S_j, $i \neq j$, the following Hoare formulae should be valid:

(1) {post(A) ∧ pre(B)} B {post(A)}

(2) {pre(S_i) ∧ pre(B) B {pre(S_i)}

The preconditions in this test may be interpreted as stating the possibility to be both at(A) and at(B), respectively at(S_i) and at(B).
In Owicki's case this test is complicated by the presence of await statements (which resemble the when statement of Distributed Processes somewhat).
This simple expression of the interference freedom test changes drastically when considering Distributed Processes, next. There, the grain of interleaving, being an assignment in the present section and hence syntactically determinable, is determined semantically. Also the number of concurrent subprocesses varies dynamically in case of Distributed Processes, necessitating **canonical** interference freedom tests. Thus dynamic variation is again captured syntactically, as in case of ADA's rendezvous rule.

5. *A proof system for Distributed Processes*

5.1 *Why develop a proof system for Distributed Processes ?*

In this part, a Hoare style proof system is developed for proving safety properties of concurrent programs which are written in a programming language which is based on the wellknown monitor concept of Hoare's and Brinch Hansen's, such as Distributed Process, Concurrent Pascal, Mesa, and Modula(-2). The actual language for which a proof system is developed is Brinch Hansen's Distributed Process(DP). The basic structure of this proof system can be adapted to these other languages, and combines and generalizes two approaches to the verification of concurrent programs:

- the Owicki-Gries approach for shared variable languages based on the concept of interference freedom, and
- the de Roever-Gerth approach for remote procedure calls, e.g., as occurring in ADA, based on the concept of cooperation.

A DP program consists of a fixed set of concurrently executing processes $[P_1 \| \ldots \| P_n]$.
A process does not contain other nested concurrent processes, and neither do shared variables occur. The syntax of a process is:
process *<name>: <private variables>; <common procedures>; <initial statement>* **end**

A process P is executed by starting execution of its initial statement, which may then be interleaved with execution of calls of other processes to the common procedures of P. These calls are named **external requests** ; their execution is identical to ADA's rendezvous, except that synchronization in DP is subject to less restrictions than in ADA, and therefore harder to handle when programming. Accepting an external request represents the only form of communication between processes, and results in a new **procedure incarnation** being created and executed. Similar to ADA's entry call, during execution of an external request the caller is suspended until the callee has finished execution of the corresponding incarnation.

The syntax of a procedure is:
proc *<name>* (*<input parameter list>* # *<output parameter list>) <statement>*
The parameter mechanism is call-by-value-result; within a procedure body no assignments to input parameters are allowed.
Synchronization is established, primarily, by **when statements** of the form:
when b_1: S_1 /.../ b_n: S_n **end**
with meaning: *wait* until at least one of the boolean guards b_i is true, then select one of the corresponding S_i arbitrarily for execution.
Synchronization occurs in a process:

- when waiting at a when statement, because its guards were false on arrival,
- when waiting after execution of its initial statement,
- upon completion of an external request to one of its common procedures.

These points are called **waiting points.**
By synchronization we mean:

- either the act of honouring an, arbitrarily selected, external request, or
- the act of resuming execution of a when statement (having been a waiting point earlier on, whose execution needs still to be resumed) as a result of a guard being **true;** this resembles a **coroutine mode of execution** within the process.

The main characteristic of DP, on which the proof system is built, is the *synchronization-at-waiting-points,* in particular the interplay between (execution of) external requests and the coroutine mode of operation. A clear picture of this is essential for understanding the proof system. The figure below shows the execution of 3 processes, P_1, P_2 and P_3. The horizontal lines represent the time axes for each of the respective processes, along which execution proceeds. During execution of P_1 an external request is made, the action of which is atomic w.r.t. P_1, as indicated by the brackets '<' and '>'. Execution of P_2 proceeds until a waiting point is encountered, denoted by the (leftmost) vertical wriggles, at which synchronization takes place. P_2 continues by honouring P_1's request and starting execution of a new incarnation of pr_2. During this execution, other waiting points are encountered and external requests are made. Finally execution arrives at the end of procedure body, after which P_1 and P_2 proceed independently. At parameter passing, external information from the caller (P_1) will be injected into the callee (P_2) by the input parameters at the beginning of the procedure execution and vice versa at the end.

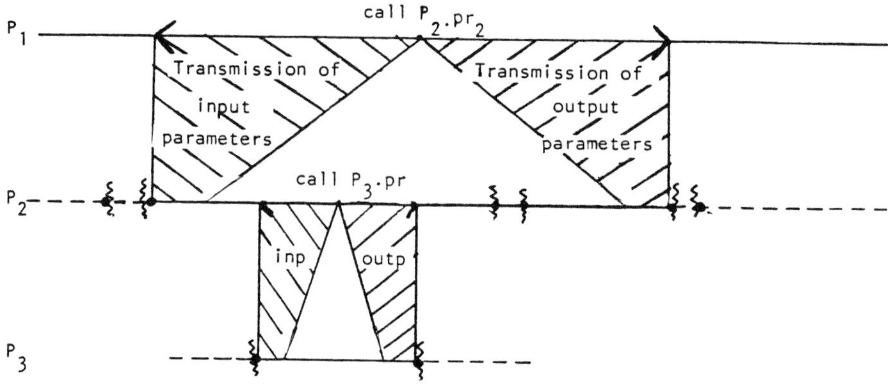

The **internal** coroutine mode of execution of each DP process can be viewed as the concurrent execution of a set of subprocesses - its initial statement and its procedure incarnations - sharing the local variables of that DP processes between them; this execution is **concurrent** in the sense that a possible execution of these subprocesses is an arbitrary nondeterministic interleaving of certain "atomic" actions of these processes.

Owicki's concept of interference freedom can be taken over, but has to be generalized, because:

- an atomic action extends now from one waiting point to another, and hence is *not anymore a* **syntactically** *determined action* as in Owicki's case, and
- the number of subprocesses, active at a certain time, is **dynamically varying,** as it comprises all incarnations of the common procedures.

(Especially this last idea of viewing a DP process as a shared variable program and, consequently, of introducing the concept of interference freedom, is missing in previous attempts to devise proof rules for monitor based languages and this is what makes their resulting proof systems incomplete in the technical sense of the word.)

The differences with ADA are as follows:

- At a waiting point, a process in DP has no choice as to which procedure call is accepted, or whose call continues.
- In a process, *more than one procedure incarnation* can coexist.

Thus, more than one multicontrol point (in the terminology of section 3.3) can be active inside a process.

The similarity of DP with monitors is that a monitor can be considered as a DP process whose initial statement does not contain external requests.

5.2 The proof system: notation and problems

The proof system captures the interaction between processes by introduction of a **general invariant** GI, which keeps track of the values communicated during execution of the external requests, and is expressed using auxiliary variables. As usual, updating the variables of GI is restricted to bracketed sections.
While GI describes synchronization globally, a **process invariant** PI (one for each process) describes the coroutine mode of execution inside a process, i.e., PI expresses the conditions on the process state at the moment new requests can be accepted or not yet finished pending older incarnations or, possibly, a pending remaining part of the initial statement, can be resumed.

The structure of process invariants is discussed next.
To characterize the relationship between the local variables of a process which are shared between the aforementioned subprocesses, and, a fortiori, to characterize the initial state for entry calls, for each process P_j a **monitor** invariant MI_j is introduced.
However, MI_j is not sufficient for characterizing the assertions to be proved invariant at waiting points.
E.g., consider the following fragment:

process P
  u:int; b:bool
  proc a(#x); x:=u; b:= **false; when** b:x:=x-u **end** {x=o} **end**
  ...
end

As indicated, we want to have {x=0} as postcondition of the procedure body.
This implies that {x=u} must hold when execution resumes at the when statement, but as the when statement is blocked, x=u must be implied as precondition for x:=x-u in the when rule by b $\wedge$ MI. Since x is a local variable of the procedure incarnation, x should not appear in assertions not belonging to the proof of the procedure body, and can therefore certainly not appear free in MI, which must hold at **every** waiting point. Therefore special assertions must be attached to a when statement 'W' in case that when statement blocks. This assertion - notation PI: at('W') - must be proven invariant over the operations which can be interleaved at this point.
Secondly, a special assertion - notation PI: after (Init) - is attached to the point after the initial statement, since this point is special, on account of the process becoming a passive object, only reacting to outside requests.

Similarly, a special assertion - notation PI: at(Init) - is attached to the point just before an initial statement.

Finally, pre- and postconditions of the bodies proper of common procedures pr_i (i.e., of the bodies without pre- and postludes) - notation:

PI: at(pr_i) and PI: after(pr_i) - are required to get canonical proofs.

This characterization of control flow is illustrated below.

Consider $[P_1 \| P_2 \| P_3]$, declared by:

```
process P1
begin ... call P2.pr2(x,y) end

process P3
proc pr3( )
...
end

process P2
proc pr2(u # v)
... c:= true
(1) when ¬c: ...c:=true end
end (2)
begin b:=true;c:= false
  do b: (3) when c: ...call P3.pr3(r,s)
  ... c:= false;b:=false end
  end
end (4)
```

Execution of $[P_1 \| P_2 \| P_3]$ can be graphically represented by:

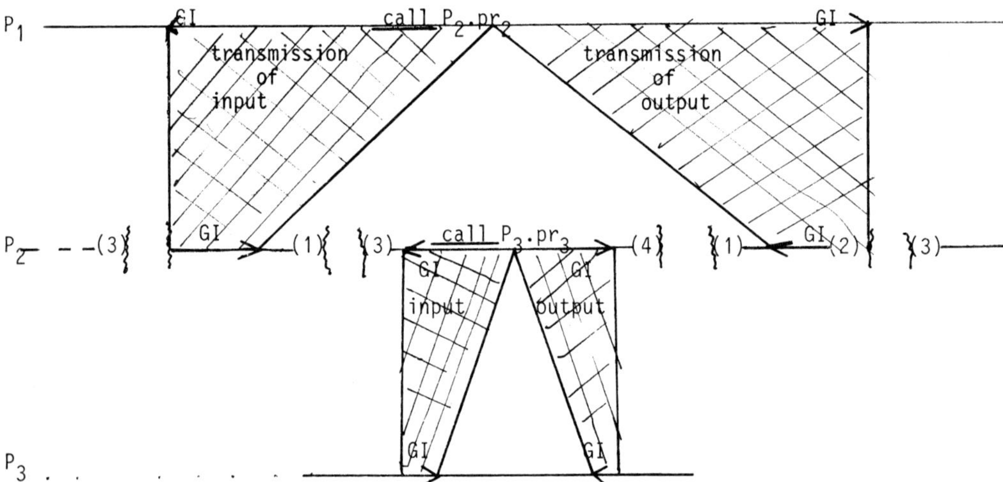

First the initial statements of P_1, P_2, P_3 are executed, leading to external request $P_2.pr_2(x,y)$ in P_1 and waiting point (3), then pr_2 is executed leading to waiting point (1); c being **true,** at (3) execution is resumed, leading to external request $P_3.pr_3$ and waiting point (4); upon which, c

being false, execution of $P_2.pr_2$ resumes at (1) and finishes at (2). Consequently, MI_2, characterizing the initial state for external requests to P_2, should be first established at (3), then at (1), then at (4), and thereafter at (2). Both (1) and (3) label waiting points to which assertions PI_2: at (1) and PI_2: at (3) are attached, which should be proved invariant.
After substitution of actuals for formals, PI: at pr_2 and PI: after pr_2 should hold immediately before, respectively, after execution of pr_2.
By overlaying the previous picture with these assertions, the following picture is obtained, taking GI which should hold before and after bracketed sections into account:

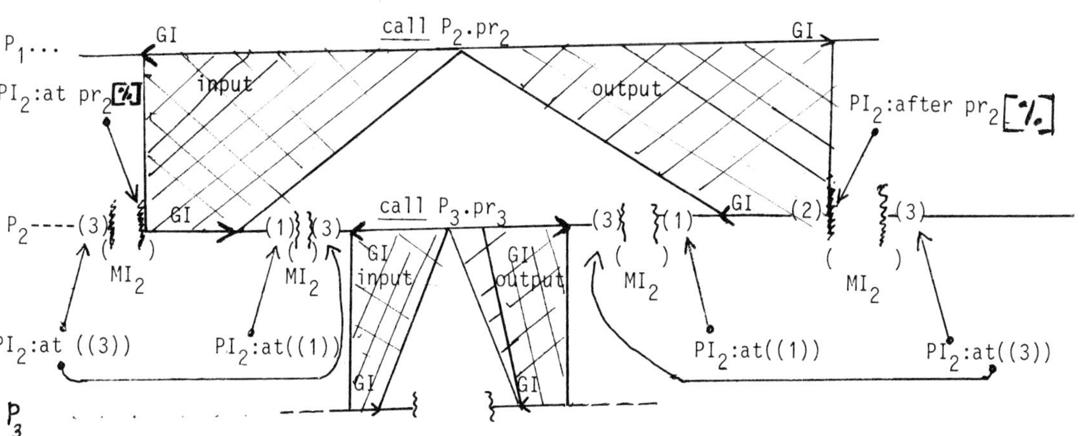

We end this section by discussing the main technical problems involved in designing the DP proof system qualitatively. The actual rules follow in later sections.

1) Proof outlines capture the sequential part of a proof. Hence, as explained in section 3.2 one proof outline per common procedure body is needed, and used. Also assertions over the complete program state at waiting points are needed (e.g., to prove absence of deadlock, see also point 3.a below). These are characterized using multicontrol point assertions, combining assertions from different proof outlines, as in section 3.3.

2) How to combine the cooperation test which has to be performed for every call with canonical proof outlines for procedure bodies? By restricting the range of this test to a small prelude and postlude of every procedure body, as in 3.2.

3) Interference freedom test (IFT).

   [a] Procedure incarnations are created dynamically. Hence, how to check whether two incarnations coexist? In principle, this is done using different multicontrol point

assertions for chains of nested calls which ultimately end at the potentially coexisting waiting points, for all syntactically possible chains of calls and waiting points. However, this can be simplified considerably.

[b] We have canonical procedure proofs. Do we need to check each of the incarnations separately, or can we formulate a canonical IFT, too? Yes, we can, but must be careful.

[c] IFT-checks have the form $\{p \wedge pre(S)\}\ S\ \{p\}$.
In Owicki's case S is basically an assignment, and hence *syntactically* determined. In DP, S is an arbitrary statement delimited by waiting points, and hence semantically determined. How do we cope with that? Primarily, using predicate transformers, predicating the values of guards in when statements. However, by using auxiliary variables, the predicates to be proved invariant over some statement can be trivialized in case the associated syntactically possible waiting points do not occur semantically, thus trivializing the IFT-checks for statements ending at those points. Hence, using appropriate proof outlines, IFT-checks are again syntactically expressible (this idea is well explained in [GdeRRo1]).

5.3 *The proof rules*

We only discuss the rules that are characteristic for DP.

5.3.1 *Rule for the when statement: the when rule*

$$\{p \wedge b_1\}\ S_1\ \{q\},\ \ldots,\ \{p \wedge b_n\}\ S_n\ \{q\},$$
$$p \wedge \neg \bigvee_{j=1}^{n} b_j \rightarrow PI\text{: } at(S),$$
$$\{b_1 \wedge PI\text{: } at(S)\}\ S_1\ \{q\},\ \ldots,\ \{b_n \wedge PI\text{: } at(S)\}\ S_n\ \{q\}$$

$$\{p\}\ \textbf{when}\ b_1 : S_1\ \|\ \ldots\ \|\ b_n : S_n\ \textbf{end}\ \{q\} \qquad \square$$

This rule is of interest, because the **when** statement may serve as a waiting point, and hence enable the process to synchronize. In the preceding section, we demanded that at this moment PI holds, which is expressed by the second premiss. Whenever the statement is resumed again, precondition p need not hold anymore. However, in this case process-control has arrived at "another" waiting point, which has made PI valid again. Thus, we have arrived at a situation equivalent to the guarded conditional with pre-assertion PI: at(S), hence the third premiss. Here PI: at(S) specializes to that part of PI applicable to S. The first premiss covers the case that the **when** statement does not act as a waiting point. Observe that the specialization in PI to locations introduces the notion of *interference freedom test.*

5.3.2 The external request rule.

The external request rule for DP is almost the same as the rendezvous rule for ADA. Differences are that for the process state, in which execution of an external request starts, the monitor invariant can be assumed, and that the bodies of the common procedures are separately declared.

Thus, call $<S_1$; **call** $P_j.pr(\vec{t},\vec{y})$; $S_2>$ in P_i

to common procedure

proc $pr(\vec{u}\#\vec{v})$ **begin** T_1; $>$ T $<$; T_2 **end** in P_j, $j \neq i$

using the simplifying assumption

begin new $\vec{u},\vec{v}$; $\vec{u}:=\vec{t}$; $\vec{v}:=\vec{y}$; S; $\vec{y}:=\vec{v}$ **end** "=" $S[\vec{t}/\vec{u}, \vec{y}/\vec{v}]$,

as in ADA-CF,

satisfies the **external request rule :**

$\{p \wedge MI_j \wedge GI\}\ S_1;\ T_1[\%]\{p_1[\%] \wedge p_2 \wedge GI\}$

$\{p_1\}\ T\ \{q_1\}$

$\{p_2 \wedge q_1[\%] \wedge GI\}\ T_2[\%];\ S_2\ \{q \wedge MI_j \wedge GI\}$

$\{p\}< S_1$; **call** $P_j.pr(\vec{t},\vec{y})$; $S_2 > \{q\}$

where (1) $[\%] = [\vec{t}/\vec{u}, \vec{y}/\vec{v}]$,

(2) p, p_2, q belong to the proof of P_i,

(3) $p_2 \equiv$ pre('call') and free variables $(p_2) \cap \vec{x} = \emptyset$,

(4) $p_1 \equiv PI_j$: at(pr), $q_1 \equiv PI_j$: after(pr),

(5) S_1, S_2, T_1, T_2 do not contain any external request or when statement. □

The conclusion of the rule is valid because there is only one procedure body per procedure name.

Because of (4), the proof of the procedure body is canonical. This rule will be strengthened in section 5.3.4 in order to formulate a canonical interference freedom test.

5.3.3 Parallel composition rule

$\{PI_i$: at$(Init_i)\}$ $Init_i$ $\{$ PI_i: after$(Init_i)\}$ for i=1,...n

are interference free

$\{\bigwedge_{i=1}^{n} PI_i$: at$(Int_i) \wedge GI\}$ $[P_1 \| \ldots \| P_n]\{\bigwedge_{i=1}^{n} PI_i$: after$(Init_i) \wedge GI\}$

where (1) PI_i denotes the process invariant of process P_i,

(2) $Init_i$ is the initial statement of process P_i. □

This rule should be clear, except for the interference freedom test which is explained in 5.3.4.

5.3.4 *The interference freedom test*

The contents of this section represent, w.r.t. part 3, the main technical achievement which is required for the development of a proof system for DP.
Two problems must be faced:

- *How to obtain a workable, and hence canonical, interference freedom test (IFT) for DP ?*
- *How to obtain a syntactic characterization of the semantically determined grains of interleaving (atomic actions) associated with the coroutine model of execution of the dynamically determined incarnations of the common procedures and of the initial statement of a DP process ?*

As regards to the first problem: By imposing a number of simple restrictions we have obtained canonical proofs for DP's common procedures. This implies that the behaviour of *every* incarnation has been characterized, thus making a canonical IFT feasible, as argued below.
Consider the program [P || Q || R] declared by:

```
process P                                        process Q
  proc pr(u#)                              begin call P.pr(1) end
                          when b: S2 end
    S1; b:= false; ⌊______________________⌋
                               'W'1
  end
  proc qr                                        process R
            when c: S4 end
    S3; ___________________                 begin call P.qr end
                 'W'2
  end
begin skip end
```

From which procedures incarnations can be interleaved, depends on the environment. Consider the waiting point at('W_1'): At this point actions from an incarnation of qr can be interleaved, indeed, but this is not the case for actions from pr, because:

- There may exist incarnations of pr and qr s.t. control is at('W_1') in one incarnation, and simultaneously (somewhere) in the body of qr in the other one.
- There do *not* exist *two* incarnations of pr s.t. control is at('W_1') in one incarnation, and simultaneously (somewhere) in the body of pr in the other one.

Let $<$ 'C_1', ... 'C_k', 'S' $>$: p denote the multicontrol point assertion p determined by multicontrol point $<$ 'C_1',... 'C_k', 'S' $>$. The informal statement above concerning interleaving at 'W_1' can be formalized using multicontrol point assertions. Assume for the moment that at('W_2') was a waiting point in the past, subsequently execution blocked at 'W_1', and now execution is resumed at 'W_2'. Then the IFT at 'W_1' for the interleaving starting at 'W_2' can be characterized by:

if there exist $<'C_1',\ldots,'C_k', 'W_1'>$: p and $<'\bar{C}_1',\ldots,'\bar{C}_l', 'W_2'>$:q *s.t.* $p \wedge q$ *holds then*
$\{PI: at('W_1') \wedge PI: at('W_2') \wedge c\}\ S_4\{PI: at('W_1')\}$.

Our first technical claim is that we can simplify this expression to:

$\{PI: at('W_1') \wedge PI: at('W_2') \wedge c \wedge GI\}\ S_4\{PI: at('W_1')\}$, by strengthening of the general invariant GI.

Assuming this claim to be correct, the following three tests express interference freedom of PI: at('W_1') over the body of qr:

(1) $\{PI: at('W_1') \wedge PI: at(qr) \wedge GI \wedge wp(S_3,c)\}$
S_3; 'W_2': **when** c: S_4 **end** $\{PI: at('W_1')\}$

(2) $\{PI: at('W_1') \wedge PI: at(qr) \wedge GI \wedge \neg\ wp(S_3,c)\}\ S_3\ \{PI: at\{'W_1')\}$

(3) $\{PI: at('W_1') \wedge PI: at('W_2') \wedge GI \wedge c\}$ **when** c: S_4 **end** $\{PI: at('W_1')\}$

(In this example it has been assumed that S_3 and S_4 introduce no additional waiting points). Observe that in order to formulate this IFT, all atomic actions have been listed separately, using weakest preconditions.
Thus, we are faced again by two problems:

- How to justify our technical claim?
- Our characterization of IFT is "impractical" in case of interleaving by loops, since then an infinite list of atomic actions may have to be considered.

First our technical claim is discussed.

The multicontrol point assertion (m.p.a.) is a generalization of the pre- and postconditions of the cooperation test. How can an m.p.a. be understood? In a process an assertion encodes an abstraction of the history of execution of that process leading up to the point labeled by that assertion. This history is the private history of computation inside that process, only. The general invariant encodes an abstraction of the (partial) order in which the private process histories relate to each other, as the overall computation in the concurrent program proceeds. Therefore the conjunction of assertions from different processes with the general invariant expresses whether the abstractions of these private histories are compatible w.r.t. each other, i.e., whether the point labeled by those assertions form a (partial) frontier of the overall computation.
Our claim is that the same principle applies to assertions from proof outlines of different common procedures inside the same process, by making the general invariant sufficiently strong. Again, such an assertion characterizes an abstraction of the process history leading up to the point labeled. Two such assertions from different procedure outlines are compatible if there coexist multicontrol points ending in the points labeled. *Thus, our claim amounts to the fact that the possible coexistence of these multicontrol points can be encoded in the general invariant.*

Observe that we still face the problem of expressing the coexistence of two multicontrol points leading to assertions in an outline of the *same* procedure.

Next, our formulation of the IFT is simplified.
Consider our example, again, and the proof outline

{PI: at{$'W_1'$) $\wedge$ PI: at(qr) $\wedge$ GI}
    S_3; {A} **when** c: S_4 **end** {PI: at($'W_1'$)}

According to the when rule: A $\wedge$ $\neg$c $\rightarrow$ PI: at($'W_2'$) and
{PI: at($'W_2'$) $\wedge$ c} S_4 {PI: at($'W_1'$)} must be proved.
Our second technical claim, that our formulation of IFT can be simplified, is suggested by the following observation:

If inside this proof outline PI: at($'W_2'$) $\Leftrightarrow$ PI: at($'W_1'$) $\wedge$ PI: at($'W_2'$) $\wedge$ GI *holds, then this outline replaces IFT's (1),(2) and (3) above, because (2) and (3) are anyhow generated when applying the when rule.*

This leads to the following idea: to show invariance of an assertion over (parts of) some procedure body 'S', one can construct a proof outline for 'S', in which the process invariant PI to be used in the when rule is suitably adapted.
Definition [INV(p,'S')] Let 'S' label the body of some procedure pr (or an initial statement), and p denote an assertion. Then the atomic actions in 'S' do not interfere with p iff a (valid) proof can be constructed for {p $\wedge$ PI: at(pr) $\wedge$ GI} S {p} (or {p $\wedge$ PI: at(Init) $\wedge$ GI} S {p}) such that the process invariant PI', used in the when rule is

$$PI' \equiv \bigwedge_{'W_i' \text{ in } 'S'} at('W_i'): (p \wedge PI: at('W_i') \wedge GI)$$

□

Now a syntactic characterization of the IFT w.r.t. atomic actions which are dynamically determined can be given.

Definition [Interference freedom test for DP]
Process P with common procedures $pr_1,\ldots,pr_n$ and process invariant PI is interference free w.r.t. a proof outline of P and GI iff:

- For all terms at($'W_i'$): p_i in PI,
  INV(p_i, pr_1.body) $\wedge \ldots \wedge$ INV(p_i, pr_n.body).
- For all terms at($'W_i'$): p_i in PI s.t. $'W_i'$ occurs in a procedure body, INV(p_i, $Init_p$).
- For the term after($Init_p$):q, INV(q, pr_1.body) $\wedge \ldots \wedge$ INV(q,pr_n.body).

□

Notice, that all these tests are required because one must first check whether an interleaving is anyhow possible. If this is not the case, PI': at($'W_i'$) reduces to **false** and the test is trivialized. Observe that this does not imply that subsequent tests are trivialized, too, because the when rule forces us to use PI': at($'W_j'$) as a precondition for a subsequent statement $'W_j'$.

This finishes the mainstream of our characterization of IFT.

However, three details have been glossed over:

(i) How to avoid clashes between variable names ?

(ii) In general, an assertion p, which is to be proved invariant, contains (auxiliary) variables which may be updated in the bracketed sections of a common procedure. However, the precondition of the proof outline in the definition of INV is only meaningful in case 'S' starts after the prelude of pr, because GI occurs in this precondition, and only holds *outside* bracketed sections. Yet, **in case that prelude updates a variable of p must be part of the interleaving over which p** (Observe that, by definition, p never occurs inside bracketed sections).

(iii) How to define IFT in case of assertions labeling points in the proof of the **same** common procedure ?

Ad(i):

These clashes can be avoided by requiring on beforehand that the formal parameters and local variables in common procedures are all differently named (this can be done due to the absence of recursion).

Ad(ii):

First the definition of INV(p,'S') is modified in that 'S' labels the body of some common procedure pr *without pr's prelude.* Yet the effect of updating those free variables of p occurring inside the prelude of pr must be taken into account. The incorporation of this aspect is straightforward.

Construct in INV's definition a proof for

{p('S') ∧ PI: at(pr) ∧ GI} S {p}, using PI', as defined, in the when rule, and define p('S') by:

p('S') ≡ sp(p,R),i.e. the **strongest postcondition** of p w.r.t. R, where

- R ≡ T, in case 'S' is the body of a procedure with prelude T,
- R ≡ skip, otherwise. □

Ad(iii):

Consider program [P ‖ Q] declared by:

process P; **proc** pr **begin** S; 'W': **when** c: T **end;** U **end**
begin ... **end**

process Q; **begin** call P.pr **end,**

where 'W' is the only when statement.

Let p ≡ PI: at('W'). Clearly p need not be invariant over pr.body, since there are no coexisting multicontrol points, and *hence INV(p,pr.body) should trivially hold.* But does it ...?

The following formula must be proved:

$\{p \wedge PI: at(pr) \wedge GI\}$ pr.body $\{p\}$ (*)

using $PI' \equiv at('W'): (p \wedge PI: at('W') \wedge GI)$

The preassertion of (*) can be made to yield **false,** certainly. So the IFT of p over atomic actions starting at 'S' has been made trivial.

Next, consider the atomic action starting at 'W':

PI' : at('W') should yield **false,** too.

But PI' : $at('W') \Leftrightarrow p \wedge PI: at('W') \wedge GI \Leftrightarrow PI: at('W') \wedge GI$ does not yield **false** at all !

Conclusion: *We cannot distinguish between one incarnation of pr in has reached at('W') and two incarnations of pr, in control has reached at('W').*

(This is the result of *not* using multicontrol point assertions in IFT !)

This, our last, problem can be overcome as follows, by introducing **incarnations counters:**

- For each procedure pr, a proof variable **pr'inc** is introduced which counts the number of coexisting incarnations of pr.
- pr'inc is a reserved name, not occurring in the program text.
- pr'inc may only appear in GI and in assertions in the proof outline of pr. □

Now INV (p,'S') can be redefined, by requiring the proof of

$\{p('S') \wedge PI: at(pr) \wedge GI \wedge \textbf{pr'inc} \geq \textbf{n}\}\ S\ \{p\}$

where the process invariant PI' used in the when rule is

$$PI' \equiv \bigwedge_{'W_i' \text{ in } 'S'} at('W_i'): (p \wedge PI: at('W_i') \wedge GI \wedge \textbf{pr'inc} \geq \textbf{n})$$

and

- n=1, in case p and 'S' do *not* belong to the same procedure outline
- n=2, in case they do. □

This leaves us with the question of expressing the updating of incarnation counters. Obviously, this should occur in the external request rule, which is redefined as follows:

[**External request rule,** final version]

$\{p \wedge MI_j \wedge GI\}$ S_1; **pr'inc:= pr'inc+1;** $T_1[\%]$ $\{PI_j: at(pr)[\%] \wedge p_2 \wedge GI\}$

$\{PI_j: at(pr)\}$ T $\{PI_j: after(pr)\}$

$\{p_2 \wedge PI_j: after(pr)[\%] \wedge GI\}$ $T_2[\%]$; **pr'inc:= pr'inc-1;** S_2 $\{q \wedge MI_j \wedge GI\}$

$\{p\} < S_1$; **call** $P_j.pr(\vec{t},\vec{y})$; $S_2 > \{q\}$,

with restrictions as in 5.3.2, observing that pr'inc:= pr'inc+1 expresses that the number of incarnations of pr is increased, and pr'inc:= pr'inc-1 that the number of incarnations of pr has decreased. □

Example: Consider [P || Q || R] declared by:

```
process P; int x; bool c;          process Q
  proc pr                          begin call P.pr end
    begin x:=x+1; c:=¬c;
      when c:skip end
    end                            process R
begin x:=0;c:= true end            begin call P.qr end
```

We sketch the proof of { **true** } [P || Q || R] {x=1}.
Only application of the external request rule between Q and P, and the IFT of PI_P: at('W') over pr.body is shown. The following proof outlines are used:

```
process P; int x; bool c                              process Q
  proc pr begin h:=1>                                 {h=0} begin
{h̄=1 ∧ x=0} x:=x+1; c:=¬c {x=1 ∧ h̄=1}                 < h:=1; call P.pr >
  'W': when c: skip end {x=1}                         end {h=1}
  < end {x=h}
  proc qr begin c:=¬c end
{h̄=0} begin x̄:=0; c:= true end {x=h̄}
```

$GI \equiv h=\bar{h} \wedge pr'inc \leq h$

$PI_P \equiv MI_P \wedge (at(pr): x=0 \wedge \bar{h} = 1) \wedge (after(pr): x=1) \wedge (at('W'): x=1 \wedge h=1)$

$MI_P \equiv x=\bar{h}$

In order to apply the external request rule for **call** P.pr, its three clauses need to be checked:

first clause: $\{\frac{h=0}{p} \wedge \frac{x=\bar{h}}{MI_P} \wedge \frac{h=\bar{h} \wedge pr'inc \leq h}{GI}\}$

$\frac{h:=1}{S_1}$; pr'inc:= pr'inc+1; $\frac{\bar{h}:=1}{T_1[\%]}$

$\{\frac{h=1}{p_2} \wedge \frac{\bar{h}=1 \wedge x=0}{PI:at(pr)[\%]} \wedge \frac{h=\bar{h} \wedge pr'inc \leq h}{GI}\}$,

which is clearly correct.

second clause: $\{x=0 \wedge \bar{h}=1\}$ x:=x+1; c:=¬c; **when** c: **skip end** $\{x=1\}$

third clause: $\{h=1 \wedge x=1 \wedge h=\bar{h} \wedge pr'inc \leq h\}$

$\frac{skip}{T_2[\%]}$; pr'inc:= pr'inc-1; $\frac{skip}{S_2}$

$\{h=1 \wedge x=\bar{h} \wedge h=\bar{h} \wedge pr'inc \leq h\}$

IFT of PI: at('W') over pr.body, with p ≡ at('W') and S ≡ pr.body:
INV(p,S) requires proof of

$$\underbrace{\{\underbrace{x=1 \wedge h=1}_{p(\bar{h}:1')} \wedge \underbrace{x=0 \wedge h=1 \wedge \ldots}_{PI:\ at(pr)}\}}_{\textbf{false}} S \ \{x=1\}$$

with PI′ ≡ at('W'): $\underbrace{\underbrace{x=1 \wedge h=1}_{p} \wedge \underbrace{x=1 \wedge h=1}_{PI:at('W')} \wedge \underbrace{h=\bar{h} \wedge pr'inc \leq h}_{GI} \wedge pr'inc \geq 2}_{\textbf{false}}$

This proof is trivial indeed:
{false} x:=x+1; c:=¬c; {false} **when** c: **skip end** {x=1} is obviously a valid proof outline, because the first clause of the when rule requires proving {*false* ∧ c} **skip** {x=1}, and the second and third clause are equally trivial, PI′ being **false.**
□

A nontrivial example, **the dutch national torus,** has been given in [GdeRRo2] and is reproduced in the appendix; the problem, "inspired by the Dutch National Flag", originally appeared in Dijkstra's [EWD 608] in a version written in CSP.
A correctness proof of a distributed priority queue has been given in [GdeRRo1], concerning a program given in Brinch Hansen's original DP article [BH]. When trying to prove this program an error was discovered, which was subsequently mended.

Utrecht, "Christmas holidays 84/85"

6. *References*

[ARM] ADA, The Programming Language ADA Reference Manual, LNCS 155 (1983).

[Apt 1] Apt, K.R., Ten Years of Hoare's Logic - Part I, Toplas 3 (1981), 431-484.

[Apt 2] Apt, K.R., Formal Justification of a proof system for Communicating Sequential Processes, JACM 30 (1983), 197-216.

[Apt 3] Apt, K.R., Proving correctness of CSP Programs - a tutorial, Technical report 84-24, LITP, Université Paris 7 (1984).

[AFdeR] Apt, K.R., Francez, N., and de Roever, W.P., A proof system for communicating sequential processes, Toplas 2 (1980), 359-385.

[A & S] Andrews, G.R., and Schneider, F., Concepts and notations for concurrent programming, ACM Comp. Surveys 15 (1983), 3-43.

[Ashcroft] Ashcroft, E., Proving assertions about parallel programs, JCSS 10 (1975), 110-135.

[BH1] Brinch Hansen, P., Distributed Processes: A concurrent programming concept, CACM 21 (1978), 934-941.

[BH2] Brinch Hansen, P., The programming language concurrent Pascal, IEEE Trans.S.E. 1 (1975), 99-207.

[EWD] Dijkstra, E.W., An exercise inspired by the Dutch National Flag, EWD-608, Burroughs, Nuenen, the Netherlands, 1977.

[Francez] Francez, N., Extended naming conventions for communicating sequential processes, in Proc. POPL 1982, ACM, New York, pp 40-45.

[Gerth] Gerth, R.T., A sound and complete Hoare axiomatization of the ADA rendezvous, Technical Report, Univ. of Utrecht (1984).

[GdeR] Gerth, R.T., and de Roever, W.P., A proof system for Concurrent ADA Programs, SCP 4 (1984), 159-204.

[GdeRRo1] Gerth, R.T., de Roever, W.P., and Roncken, M., Procedures and Concurrency: A study in proof, Proc. 5th ISOP, LNCS 137 (1982), 132-163.

[GdeRRo2] Gerth, R.T., de Roever, W.P., and Roncken, M., A study in Distributed Systems and Dutch Patriotism, Proc. of the 2nd conf. on Foundations of Software Technology and Theoretical Computer Science, Bangalore, India, 13-15 Dec. 1982, M. Joseph (Ed.), NCSDCT, Tata Research Institute, Bombay (1982).

[Hoare1] Hoare, C.A.R., Procedures and Parameters: an axiomatic approach, in: Symposium on Semantics of Algorithmic Languages, Lecture Notes in Mathematics 188, Springer (1971), 102-116.

[Hoare2] Hoare, C.A.R., Communicating Sequential Processes, CACM 21 (1978), 666-677.

[Howard] Howard, J.H., Proving monitors, CACM 19 (1976), 273-279.

[L & S] Lamport, L., and Schneider, F.B., The "Hoare Logic" of CSP, and all that, Toplas 6 (1984), 281-296.

[Le & G] Levin, G.M., and Gries, D., A proof technique for communicating sequential processes, Acta 15 (1981), 281-302.

[MMS] Mitchell, J.G., Maybury, W., and Sweet, R., Mesa Language Manual, XEROX, Palo Alto Research Center (1979).

[O & G] Owicki, S.S., and Gries, D., An axiomatic proof technique for parallel programs, Acta 6 (1976), 319-340.

[PdeR] Pnueli, A., and de Roever, W.P., Rendezvous with ADA - a proof theoretical view, Proc. ACM ADA-TEC Conference (1982).

[deR] de Roever, W.P., The quest for compositionality - a survey of assertion-based proof systems for concurrent programs, Part I: Concurrency based on shared variables, to appear in: Proc. of the IFIP Working Conference 1985: "The role of abstract models in computer science", E.J. Neuhold (Ed.), North-Holland; also as Technical Report, Univ. of Utrecht (1985).

[RoDKdeR] Roncken, M., van Diepen, N., Kramer, M., and de Roever, W.P., A proof system for Brinch Hansen's distributed processes, Technical Report RUU-CS-81-5, Univ. of Utrecht (1981).

[S & S] Schlichting, R.D., and Schneider, F.B., Using Message Passing for Distributed Programming: Proof rules and Disciplines, Toplas 6 (1984), pp 402-432.

[Wirth] Wirth, N., Programming in Modula-2, Springer-Verlag, 1982.

7. Appendix: the dutch national torus (reproduced from [GdeRRo2])

Edsger W. Dijkstra designed the following problem, "inspired by the Dutch National Flag" [Dijkstra, 1977]:

Consider a program comprising 3 + 3 processes in a cyclic arrangement; three main processes, called R(ed), W(hite) and B(lue), and three buffer processes RW, WB and BR, in between:

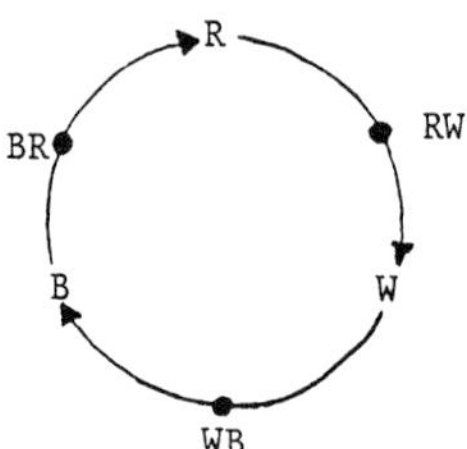

Each main process contains initially a number of red, white and blue pebbles. Its goal is to collect from the system all pebbles of its own colour, thus constructing a neatly coloured Dutch National Torus. Communication takes place along the directed channels as indicated in the figure. In particular, process B cannot communicate directly with process W to transmit its white pebbles. Moreover, per communication (at most) one pebble can be transmitted.

Below, we will give a DP version of Dijkstra's solution. Readers who want to see more of the original draft are referred to [Dijkstra, 1977].

The solution, as proposed in Dijkstra, implemented in DP.

The program contains three main processes R(ed), W(hite) and B(lue) respectively, and three buffer processes RW, WB and BR, in between.

Each buffer process is synchronized with its left neighbour for the input of pebbles. After each single input the process is synchronized with the main process at its righthand side, to get rid of the pebble again. The private variable y takes care of buffering the pebble. The main process on the left can only have its pebble buffered in y when y contains no other pebble; this is controlled by means of a when-statement. Each main process transmits the value ω to its right buffer process when it has transmitted all foreign coloured pebbles, to signal that the buffer process may terminate. A specific buffer process BR is as follows:

```
process R
r,w,b:bag_of_pebble; acc,term:bool
proc p(x:pebble)
   if x=ω: term:=true
      x≠ω: "place x in appropriate bag"; acc:=true
   end
begin
   r,w,b:=r0,w0,b0; acc,term:=true, false;
   do #b>0:
       b-:=b; acc:=false; call RW.p(b);
       when term∨acc:skip end
   end;
   do #w>0:
       w-:=w; acc:=false; call RW.p(w);
       when term∨acc:skip end
   end;
   call RW.p(ω)
end
```

The starting problem.

Unfortunately, the program lined out above does not fullfill its purpose for every input. Consider an initial division of pebbles such that process R has no white and blue pebbles. Execution in R starts with Init_R, where the loop statements are skipped because their guards are false. Consequently, Init_R terminates before external requests to procedure p_R can be honoured. Such a request may introduce a white pebble in R (as process B initially may have a white pebble). This pebble will never be sent to its collector process W, since sending only takes place in Init_R, which has terminated.

Clearly, the problem is that Init_R is allowed to terminate without checking whether it has to pass on pebbles from its left neighbour. This suggests, inserting just before the two guarded loops, the statement:

if $\#b_0+\#w_0=0$: when term∨acc:skip end | $\#b_0+\#w_0\neq 0$:skip end end.

An easier solution, not modifying the elegant algorithm, is demanding that each main process contains at least one foreign pebble. This is what Dijkstra proposed and we shall follow in his footsteps.

The general invariant now becomes:

$$GI\equiv\widehat{KL\in\{RW,WB,BR\}}(\bar{h}_{KL}=h_L\wedge\bar{h}_K=h_{KL}\wedge(z_{KL}=\varepsilon\supset I_K))$$

Proof outline of process BR.

The following monitor and process invariants are used

$MI_{BR}\equiv h_{BR}=\bar{h}_{BR}\hat{\ }y_{BR}\hat{\ }z_{BR}\wedge(trm_{BR}\rightarrow hd(\bar{h}_{BR})=\omega)\wedge h_{BR}\in\omega^{*}\pi^{*}(\varepsilon+\omega)\wedge(\omega\in h_{BR}\rightarrow\#h_{BR}\geq 2)$

$PI_{BR}\equiv$ at(BR.p):$(z_{BR}=x_{BR}\wedge MI_{BR})\wedge$after(BR.p): $MI_{BR}[\varepsilon/z_{BR}]\wedge$

at($Init_{BR}$):$(z_{BR}=\varepsilon\wedge h_{BR}=\bar{h}_{BR}=\varepsilon)\wedge$after($Init_{BR}$):$(MI_{BR}\wedge trm_{BR}\wedge y_{BR}=\varepsilon)\wedge$

at('W'):$(z_{BR}=x_{BR}\wedge MI_{BR})$

The first term of MI_{BR} just expresses that BR is a buffer (taking account of the lag). The second term is needed to prove that no calls occur once the value ω has been been received. The last two terms describe the behaviour of processes B (as seen from BR). This is needed to prove the calls to process R correct.

Here follows the proof outline:

```
process BR
   y,z:pebble; h,h̄:seq of pebble; trm:bool
   proc p(x:pebble) {MI}
   begin h^:=x; z:=x>{z=x∧MI}
     'W':when y=ε:{MI∧z=x∧y=ε}
            {MI[ε/y, x/z]} y:=x
          end {MI[ε/z]}
   <z:=ε end {MI}

   {z=ε∧h=h̄=ε}
   begin y:=ε; trm:=false {MI∧y=ε}
     do   trm:{MI∧y=ε}
          when y≠ε:{MI∧y≠ε}
             <h̄^:=y; {MI[ε/y, y=ω/trm]} call R,p(y)>
             trm:=(y=ω); y:=ε
          end {MI∧y=ε}
     end
   end {MI∧y=ε∧trm}
```

The proof outlines and invariants for the other buffers are similar and will not be spelled out.

```
process R
   r,w,b:bag of pebble; inc,term,l:bool; h,h̄:seq of pebble
   proc p(x:pebble) {MI}
   begin h^:=x;>{hd(h)=x∧MI[tl(h)/h]∧h∈w*r*(ε+ω)∧#h≥min(1,#h̄)}
     if x=ω:term:=true | x≠w:"place in appropriate bag"; acc:=true end
   {MI}<end {MI}

   {#(r0+w0)>0∧l=true∧h=h̄=ε}
   begin r,w,b:=r0,w0,b0; acc,term:=true, false; {MI∧h̄∈b*∧l∧LI1∧(term∨acc)}
     do #b>0:b-:=b; acc:=false; {MI[h̄^b/h̄]∧h̄∈b*∧l∧LI1[#b-1/#b]∧¬acc}
           <l:=false; h̄^:=b; {MI∧h̄∈b+∧¬l∧LI1} call RW.p(b); l:=true>;
           {MI∧h̄∈b+∧l∧LI1} 'W1':when term∨acc:skip end
     end; {MI∧#b=0∧h̄∈b*w*∧l∧(#b0>0→b∈h̄)∧LI2∧(term∨acc)}
     do #w>0:w-:=w; acc:=false; {MI[h̄^w/h̄]∧h̄∈b*w*∧l∧LI2[#w-1/#w]∧#b=0∧(#b0>0→b∈h̄)}
        <l:=false; h̄^:=w; {MI∧h̄∈b*w+∧¬l∧LI2∧#b=0∧(#b0>0→b∈h̄)} call RW.p(w); l:=true>;
        {MI∧h̄∈b*w+∧l∧LI1∧#b=0∧(#b0>0→b∈h̄)} 'W2':when term∨acc:skip end
     end; {MI∧#(b+w)=0∧h̄∈b*w*∧l∧#h̄≥1∧(term∨acc)}
     <l:=false; h̄^:=ω; call RW.p(ω); l:=true>
   end {MI∧#(b+w)=0∧l∧hd(h̄)=ω∧h̄≥2∧(term∨acc)}
```

Before the parallel composition rule can be applied, we need to check for cooperation (i.e. we need to check whether the external request rule has been properly used) and for interference freedom. First the

Cooperations tests:

We only check the call in process BR and the first call in process R; the other ones are analogously proven. For each call we have to prove the three premisses of the external request rule

A. call R.p(y) in BR:

1. $\{MI_{BR} \wedge y_{BR} \neq \varepsilon \wedge MI_R \wedge GI\}$

   $\bar{h}_{BR}\hat{}:=y_{BR};\ h_R\hat{}:=y_{BR}$

   $\{MI_{BR}[\varepsilon/y_{BR},\ y_{BR}=\omega/trm_{BR}] \wedge hd(h_R)=y_{BR} \wedge MI_R[tl(h_R)/h_R] \wedge h_R \in w^* r^* (\varepsilon+\omega) \wedge$
   $\#h_R \geq min(1,\#h_R) \wedge GI\}$

   the relevant part of GI is $\bar{h}_{BR}=h_R$, so GI is trivially invariant;

   the transformation of the BR-assertions is easily worked out, similar for the rest.

2. Canonical proof of the body of R.p: see proof outline

3. $\{MI_{BR}[\varepsilon/y_{BR}=\omega/trm_{BR}] \wedge MI_R \wedge GI\}$

   skip

   { idem }

   evident

2. PI:after(Init). To check invariance over R.p no global information is needed.

Hence we prove

$\{hd(h)=x \wedge MI[tl(h)/h] \wedge h \in \omega^* r^* (\varepsilon+\omega) \wedge \#b+\#w=0 \wedge hd(\bar{h})=\omega \wedge (term \vee acc) \wedge l \wedge \#\bar{h} \geq 2\}$

<u>if</u> x=ω:term:=<u>true</u> | x≠ω:"place in appropriate bag"; acc:=<u>true</u> <u>end</u>

$\{\#b+\#w=0 \wedge hd(\bar{h})=\omega \wedge (term \vee acc) \wedge l \wedge \#\bar{h} \geq 2\}$.

Only "#b+#w=0" and "term∨acc" can be affected by execution of R.p. Invariance of the latter term is trivial, so we concentrate on the first one.

First assume term holds:

In that case $MI[tl(h)/h] \wedge \#h \geq 2 \rightarrow hd(tl(h))=\omega$, so the pre-assertion implies $hd(tl(h))=\omega \wedge h \in \omega^* r^* (\varepsilon+\omega)$ which is false.

Assume ¬term holds:

Then acc must hold. As #w=0, $MI[tl(h)/h] \wedge \#h \geq 2 \rightarrow hd(tl(h)) \in r+\omega$.

The pre-assertion implies that $h \in \omega^* r^* (\varepsilon+\omega)$, hence $hd(h) \in r+\omega$.

So after termination, we still have #b+#w=0.

This concludes the interference freedom tests and the parallel composition rule may safely be applied:

$$\{\#(b_{OR}+w_{OR})>0 \wedge \#(r_{OW}+b_{OW})+\#(r_{OB}+w_{OB})>0 \wedge \widehat{\textstyle (k,K)\in\{(r,R),(w,W),(b,B)\}} \#k_{OK} \geq 0 \wedge GI\}$$

$$[R \| RW \| \ldots \| B \| BR]$$

$$\{\widehat{\textstyle (k,K)\in\{(r,R),(w,W),(b,B)\}} (\#k_K=\#(k_{OR}+k_{OW}+k_{OB})) \wedge \#(w_R+b_R)+\#(r_W+b_W)+\#(r_B+w_B)=0 \wedge GI\}$$

<u>Derivation of the required post-assertion:</u>

$(\widehat{\textstyle K\in\{R,W,B\}} PI_K:after(Init_K)) \rightarrow \#(w_R+b_R)=0 \wedge \#(b_W+r_W)=0 \wedge \#(w_B+r_B)=0$,

whence the second part of the post-assertion.

Of the first part of the post-assertion, we will only show $\#r_R=\#r_{OR}+\#r_{OW}+\#r_{OB}$:

$MI_R \rightarrow \#r_R=\#(r_{OR}+r(h_R))$ (1)

we show that $\#r(h_R)=\#(r_{OW}+r_{OB})$: (2)

$GI \rightarrow h_R=\bar{h}_{BR} \wedge h_{BR}=\bar{h}_B \wedge (l_B \rightarrow z_{BR}=\varepsilon)$ (3)

$PI_B:after(Init_B) \rightarrow l_B$ (4)

$PI_{BR}:after(Init_{BR}) \rightarrow y_{BR}=\varepsilon \wedge MI_{BR}$ (5)

from (3), (4) and (5) follows $h_R=\bar{h}_B$, hence $\#r(h_R)=\#r(\bar{h}_B)$

PI_B:after($Init_B$)$\rightarrow MI_B \wedge \#r_B=0$, or $\#r(\overline{h}_B)=\#(r_{0B}+r(h_B))$

which turns the last result into $\#r(h_R)=\#(r_{0B}+r(h_B))$

Remains to show $\#r(h_B)=\#r_{0W}$:

a similar reasoning as in (3), (4), (5) for the processes W and WB shows that $\#r(h_B)=\#r(\overline{h}_W)$.

PI_W:after($Init_W$)$\rightarrow MI_W \wedge \#r_W=0$, or $\#r(\overline{h}_W)=\#r_{0W}$, whence $\#r(h_B)=\#r_{0W}$

Finally $(1)\wedge(2)\rightarrow \#r_R=\#r_{0R}+\#r_{0W}+\#r_{0B}$.

Using the consequence, substitution and AV-rule, allows us to remove all unnecessary information and the auxiliary variables, thus concluding the proof.

If this proof is compared with the original proof in [Dijkstra, 197], the reader undoubtedly will notice the greater length and complexity of our proof. He should however bear in mind that ours is completely formal, whereas Dijkstra's proof is based on informal (albeit sound) reasoning.

B. <u>call</u> RW.p(b) in R:

1. $\{MI_R[\overline{h}_R\hat{\ }b/\overline{h}_R]\wedge\overline{h}_R\in b^*\wedge l_R\wedge LI_{R1}[\#b_R-1/\#b_R]\wedge\neg acc\wedge MI_{RW}\wedge GI\}$

   l_R:=<u>false</u>; $\overline{h}_R\hat{\ }:=b$; $h_{RW}\hat{\ }:=b$; $z_{RW}:=b$

   $\{MI_R\wedge\overline{h}_R\in b^+\wedge\neg l_R\wedge LI_{R1}\wedge\neg acc\wedge MI_{RW}\wedge z_{RW}=b\wedge GI\}$

   relevant part of GI:$\overline{h}_R=h_{RW}\wedge(z_{RW}=\varepsilon\rightarrow l_R)$ which is clearly invariant; transformation of R-assertions: clear

   RW-assertions: we only need to check the invariance of MI_{RW}:

   beforehand $z_{RW}=\varepsilon\wedge h_{RW}=\overline{h}_{RW}\hat{\ }y_{RW}$, hence afterwards: $h_{RW}=\overline{h}_{RW}\hat{\ }y_{RW}\hat{\ }z_{RW}$;

   also $\overline{h}_R=h_{RW}$(GI) and $\overline{h}_R\in b^+$ afterwards, so $h_{RW}\in b^+$ afterwards,

   hence $h_{RW}\in b^*w^*(\varepsilon+\omega)\wedge\omega\notin h_{RW}$; trm_{RW} and $\overline{h}_{RW}$ are left unchanged

2. Canonical proof of the body of R.p: see proof outline

3. $\{MI_R\wedge\overline{h}_R\in b^+\wedge\neg l_R\wedge LI_{R1}\wedge\neg acc\wedge MI_{RW}[\varepsilon/z_{RW}]\wedge GI\}$

   $z_{RW}:=\varepsilon$; l_R:=<u>true</u>

   $\{MI_R\wedge\overline{h}_R\in b^+\wedge l_R\wedge LI_{R1}\wedge\neg acc\wedge MI_{RW}\wedge GI\}$

   cf. the definition of GI

<u>Interference freedom tests.</u>

As expected, only the buffer process BR and the main process R are checked.

A. process BR

1. PI:at('W'). Invariance over $Init_{BR}$ is trivial, because

   $FV(PI:at('W'))\cap FV(Init)=\emptyset$

   Invariance over BR.p is trivial too on syntactic grounds: no two calling chains can coexist.

2. PI:after(Init). We show that no incarnation of BR.p can exist once BR's initial statement is terminated. The only global information that is needed, is that the actual parameter of a call to BR.p is either w, r or ω. Hence

   $act(at(BR.p))\wedge act(after(Init_{BR}))(BR.p)\rightarrow$
   $MI\wedge z\in(w+r+\omega)\wedge trm\wedge y=\varepsilon\rightarrow$
   $z\in(w+r+\omega)\wedge h=\overline{h}\hat{\ }z\wedge hd(\overline{h})=\omega\wedge h\in w^*r^*(\varepsilon+\omega)\rightarrow false.$

   As $at(BR.p)\equiv at('W_{BR}')$, this takes care of the second test.

B. process R

1. PI:at('W_i') (i=1,2). The invariance checks over R.p are trivial and are left to the reader. Here too, no global information is needed.

Proof outline of process R.

The following monitor invariant is used:

$$MI_R \equiv \bar{h}_R \in b^* \omega^* (\varepsilon+\omega) \wedge ((term_R \vee acc_R) \rightarrow \#h_R \geq min(1,\#\bar{h}_R)) \wedge (\neg acc_R \rightarrow \#h_R \geq min(1,\#\bar{h}_R-1)) \wedge$$
$$((acc_R \wedge \#w_R=0 \wedge \#h_R \geq 1) \rightarrow hd(h_R) \neq \omega) \wedge (term_R \rightarrow hd(h_R)=\omega) \wedge \#(b_{OR}+w_{OR})>0 \wedge$$
$$\#b(\bar{h}_R)+\#b_R=\#b_{OR} \wedge \#w(\bar{h}_R)+\#w_R=\#w_{OR}+\#w(h_R) \wedge \#r_R=\#r_{OR}+\#r(h_R)$$

The first term describes the sequence of pebbles that the process transmits. The next two terms are necessary to prove that after termination of the process, at least one pebble has been received. Together with the fourth and fifth term, they are used to prove that after termination no white pebbles can be received. The last three terms are important and describe the relationship between the pebbles within the bags and the pebbles received resp. transmitted at any time.

The process invariant is as follows:

$$PI_R \equiv at(R.p):(hd(h_R)=x_R \wedge MI_R[tl(h_R)/h_R] \wedge h_R \in \omega^* r^* (\varepsilon+\omega) \wedge \#h_R \geq min(1,\#\bar{h}_R)) \wedge after(R.p):MI_R \wedge$$
$$at(Init_R):(\#b_{OR}+\#w_{OR}>0 \wedge \#b_{OR} \geq 0 \wedge \#w_{OR} \geq 0 \wedge l_R \wedge h_R=\bar{h}_R=\varepsilon) \wedge$$
$$after(Init_R):(MI_R \wedge \#b_R+\#w_R=0 \wedge hd(\bar{h}_R)=\omega \wedge (term \vee acc) \wedge l_R \wedge \#\bar{h}_R \geq 2) \wedge$$
$$at('W_1'):(MI_R \wedge \bar{h}_R \in b^* \wedge l_R \wedge LI_{R1}) \wedge at('W_2'):(MI_R+\#b_R=0 \wedge \bar{h}_R \in b^* \omega^* \wedge l_R \wedge (\#b_{OR}>0 \rightarrow b \in \bar{h}_R) \wedge LI_{R2})$$

In the proof outline, the following two loop invariants are used:

$$LI_{R1} \equiv \exists k(\#b_R=\#b_{OR}-k \wedge (k>0 \rightarrow b \in \bar{h}_R))$$
$$LI_{R2} \equiv \exists k(\#w_R=\#w_{OR}-k \wedge (k>0 \rightarrow \omega \in \bar{h}_R))$$

These are needed to show that at least one foreign pebble will be transmitted by the process.

Now follows the proof outline of process R (the other proof outlines and corresponding invariants are analogous):

Correctness proof of the Dutch National Torus.

First some conventions and notation are introduced.

(1) To avoid name-clashes, the variables of each process are indexed by the process' name. However, this index will not be written if it is clear from the context, which process a variable belongs to.

(2) The notation "$\#b(h)$" is shorthand for "the number of blue pebbles in h" (where h is a bag, sequence, set etc.), "$\#(b_R+w_R)$" for "the number of blue and white pebbles in R" and so on.

(3) "hd(h)" denotes the head element of the sequence h; "tl(h)" denotes the rest of the sequence.

(4) "$r^* w^+ (\varepsilon+\omega)$" denotes a sequence of zero or more red pebbles, followed by at least one white pebble and possibly closed-off by an ω. (ε denotes the empty sequence).

(5) "h^k" denotes the concatenation of the two sequences h and k.

We want to prove the following Hoare formula:

$$\{\#(b_{OR}+w_{OR})>0 \wedge \#(r_{OW}+b_{OW})>0 \wedge \#(r_{OB}+w_{OB})>0 \wedge \bigwedge_{(k,K)\in\{(r,R),(w,W),(b,B)\}} \#k_{OK}\geq 0\}$$

$$[R \| RW \| W \| WB \| B \| BR]$$

$$\{\bigwedge_{(k,K)\in\{(r,R),(w,W),(b,B)\}} (\#k_K=\#(k_{OR}+k_{OW}+k_{OB})) \wedge \#(w_R+b_R)+\#(r_W+b_W)+\#(r_B+w_B)=0\}$$

To express the necessary assertions, some auxiliary variables are introduced. For each process we introduce variables h and $\overline{h}$ which keep track of the pebbels having been received resp. dispatched by the process. Using these, the fact that no pebble is lost during execution can be expressed. Next, consider a buffer process. With a little thought, it becomes clear that such a buffer has a maximal lag of 2 between the pebbles received and the pebbles already sent off. Therefore, an auxiliary variable z is introduced, remembering the pebble received last, as long as this pebble has not yet been put into the buffer-variable y. This is linked with the fact that the (last) call to the buffer, having transmitted the pebbly now in z, has not been completed yet. To express this link, each main process gets an auxiliary boolean l, expressing the fact that no call (originating from this process) is in progress.

```
process BR
y:pebble; trm:bool;
proc p(x:pebble)
   when y=ε:y:=x end
begin
   y:=ε; trm:=false
do ¬trm:
   when y≠ε:call R.p(y); trm:=y=ω; y:=ε end
end
```

Each main process has three bags of pebble, r(red), w(hite) and b(lue) initialized to resp. r_0, w_0 and b_0 (the pebbles themselves are denoted by r, w and b). Its goal is to collect from the system all pebbles of its own colour (in the correspondingly coloured bag). Its foreign pebbles it transmits, one at a time, via the buffer process on its right, thereby first emptying the bag that contains the pebbles with the larger travelling distance. When it has no more foreign pebbles left, it gives a signal ω, via the same buffer process (this introduces a starting problem, which will be discussed on the basis of the program text). Communication takes place in a lock-stepped fashion: after the process has sent a pebble to its right buffer process, it waits until its left buffer process has a new pebble to be submitted. When no more pebbles are to be submitted, expressed by the variable "term", the main process just empties its foreign coloured bags of pebble. This emptying takes place in a smooth way, by the set up of the communication: the right buffer process only finishes the request when it has already sent the former pebble to the next main process. Thus, no pebble vanishes. A variable "acc" keeps count of the last communication action of the process: acceptance or output of a pebble. Hence, our translation of a particular main process R (if g is a bag of pebbles, the cardinality of g is denoted by #g):

AROUND CCS, THEORETICAL CSP AND DISTRIBUTED SYSTEMS

NOTES ON ALGEBRAIC CALCULI OF PROCESSES

G. BOUDOL

INRIA - Sophia Antipolis
06560 Valbonne , France

Abstract

We gathered here some notes on Milner's calculi of processes. We interpret the terms of these calculi as transition systems. We intoduce a calculus called MEIJE built on a monoid of synchronized actions and illustrate some general semantic notions :

- we show the equivalence of this calculus with some others
- we give an implementation in a calculus restricted to purely atomic actions,
- we show the universality of MEIJE with respect to the notion of effective transition system and sketch its expressive power with regard to synchronization operators.

Finally the concept of subcalculus is illustrated through the description in our language of the class of rational parallel place machines.

Résumé

On présente quelques notes sur la notion de calcul algébrique de processus due à Milner. Ici les termes de ces calculs sont interpétés comme des systèmes de transitions. Ayant introduit un calcul appelé MEIJE, qui est construit sur un monoide d'actions synchronisées, on illustre quelques définitions générales concernant la sémantique :

- en montrant l'équivalence de ce calcul et de quelques autres,
- en donnant une implémentation dans un calcul à actions purement atomiques,
- en démontrant l'universalité de MEIJE par rapport à la notion de système de transition effectif et en esquissant son pouvoir d'expression quant aux opérateurs de synchronisation.

Enfin la notion de sous-calcul est illustrée par la description dans notre langage de la classe des machines à places rationnelles.

NATO ASI Series, Vol. F13
Logics and Models of Concurrent Systems
Edited by K. R. Apt

Contents

1. Introduction
2. Actions
3. Syntax
4. Operational semantics
5. Semantics
6. Equivalent formulations and implementation
7. Definability results
8. Subcalculi : rational parallel place machines
9. Conclusion

Foreword : This paper presents an overview, thus is not written according to the rules of mathematical rigour ; in particular it does not contain any proof.

1. Introduction

This paper sets some researches working on Milner's ideas about calculi of processes ([20] and especially [22]). We mainly address two questions regarding concurrent systems :

(1) what is a process ?

(2) how do systems compose one another and communicate ?

Concerning the first one we find a rather general concept at the cross-road of various approaches ([1,5,6,18,28]) : a process is a *labelled transition system* ([19]) or automaton (cf. [10]), in which states perform some discrete actions and become other states in doing so. This transition relation is denoted

$$p \xrightarrow{a} p'$$

However to be entitled to say that one has *parallel* systems, one must be able to take into account the global actions resulting from simultaneous activity of components. Moreover we shall assume that this activity is the only means to cooperate. Therefore actions themselves must carry out some kind of communication.

The first point is formalized by Milner in [21,22] by requiring that the set of actions is an abelian semigroup : to perform simultaneously two actions is to perform their product, obviously associative and commutative since it represents co-occurrence. It is perhaps more correct to understand composite actions as *non-interruptible* rather than *instantaneous* events (see § 6.2) and co-occurrence as the *synchronization* product, ensuring temporal atomicity. Composite actions are not just multisets : that some actions carry out communications means that their co-occurrence creates something new. Here, since we deal only with pure synchronization, not value passing (as in [20], but see also [22]), communication will be handshaking : some actions have an inverse, and they set the abelian group of signal exchanges. Notations : $a.b$ for the product, a^- for the inverse.

Hence parallel processes are transition systems where transitions are labelled by actions belonging to some abelian monoid. To compose systems or nets of processes, one usually put them into a synchronization structure or architecture. For instance the most basic way to combine two processes p and q is to build their *parallel composition* which we shall denote $(p \parallel q)$. More generally, any composition or synchronization mechanism appears to be a function on processes ; we call them *operators*, and given a family of primitive ones we construct compound systems by applying operators to constituents. This means that we describe processes by terms of a free algebra which sets up a *syntax* ; such an algebraic approach is now widely followed, even if semantical options differ (for instance see [6,8,15,22,25,26,30]).

On the semantical side we shall keep the informal hypothesis that "all happens through actions" : if the behaviour of a compound system depends on components, it only depends on their activity (no shared memory, for example). This is formalized by specifying the behavioural effect of an operator by means of structural rewriting rules, following Plotkin's style ([28,29]) of operational description. For instance in the "asynchronous" parallel composition we regard the arguments as independant. Thus the semantics of $(p \parallel q)$ is described by three rules according to the idea that either only one of the components runs, or both run synchronously :

if $p \stackrel{a}{\rightarrow} p'$ then $(p \parallel q) \stackrel{a}{\rightarrow} (p' \parallel q)$

if $q \stackrel{b}{\rightarrow} q'$ then $(p \parallel q) \stackrel{b}{\rightarrow} (p \parallel q')$

if $p \stackrel{a}{\rightarrow} p'$ and $q \stackrel{b}{\rightarrow} q'$ then $(p \parallel q) \stackrel{ab}{\rightarrow} (p' \parallel q')$

Moreover a transition $(p \parallel q) \stackrel{c}{\rightarrow} r$ must be deduced by means of one of these specification rules. As another example, we shall also use a synchronization operator called *ticking* and denoted $a * p$ by which each action of a process p is linked to a given action a :

if $p \stackrel{b}{\rightarrow} p'$ then $a * p \stackrel{ab}{\rightarrow} a * p'$

In most cases a will be an authorization signal sent by a synchronizer.

The first three technical sections of the paper set off the syntactical aspects of our MEIJE calculus : algebra of terms, built on a commutative monoid of action, and operational semantics. In such an algebraic setting, the above two questions become :

> what kind of transition systems and operators can we denote by expressions of our language ?

However we may only claim to describe the behavioural capabilities of transitions system or operators, even if they are operationally given. Indeed if one takes algebras of processes as an approach to programming languages (cf. [6,16,20]), this means that one wants to "program" for example synchronizers or synchronization mechanisms ignoring what are the internal states of such objects, provided they do their jobs. Therefore we have an informal postulate :

> nothing can be said about a system unless it results from observation of its actions.

This assumption may be interpreted in many ways (see for example [6,8,12,14]) ; here and in the work of Milner and others it is brought up through the notion of *bisimulation*, due to Park ([26], see also [5,22]). For we want to describe how systems operate, not how they can be observed. The idea of bisimulation on transition systems is the following : you have a (possibly infinite) set of colours ; then you paint each state of the system one colour. You get a bisimulation if your painting (partition) satisfies :

> if there is a transition from, say, a blue state to a green state performing the action **a** then from *every* blue state your can perform **a** reaching a green state.

In this formulation "performing the action **a**" is actually relative to an *abstraction criterion* (or set of experiments, see [12]) : **a** may be an abstract action realized by some sequences of concrete actions, including perhaps invisible ones.

This leads to our semantical universe of processes regarded as quotients by bisimulations, which are still transition systems, on abstract actions. We also introduce in this universe the notions of *morphism* (various other attempts have been made in this direction, see [11,18,31,35] and references in these papers) and *simulation*. The latter is here the central semantical concept ; simulations are "concrete" state mappings which are morphisms on an "abstract" level.

Regarding the operators we interpret the above postulate by assuming that a semantics is not only a bisimulation but also a congruence, compatible with the given operators. This means for instance that specifications and verifications of a compound system are modularized, coming from specifications and verifications of the components. Thus an algebraic calculus of processes consists in :

- a syntax, which is a family of operators (relative to some set of actions) building a free algebra of terms,
- an operational semantics specifying the behavioural effect of the operators. Thus we get a transition system, the states of which are terms,
- a semantics given through a bisimulation compatible with the algebraic structure.

Particularizing simulations to this algebraic framework we get definitions for (syntax directed) translations (cf. [13]) and the notions of

- realizability of a transition system in a calculus
- definability of an operator
- subcalculus

which evolve from Milner's work [20,22].

This technical apparatus is presented in the central section (which may be partially omited at first reading). The rest of the paper is devoted to illustrate these general definitions.

In section 6 we show that our calculus could be presented by means of other primitive operators, with the same expressiveness. We also show that parallelism involving global actions may be simulated, up to an abstract view on action, by interleaving. After these basic examples (others may be found in [2]) we return to the motivating questions in section 7. There we show that every effective transition system is realizable in MEIJE and give **de** Simone 's result [33] concerning operators.

The universality of our calculus, as it is stated here, means that in some respects it is too strong, entailing the undecidability of some basic questions. Therefore we have to search for less powerful subcalculi. Moreover it is too abstract : we would like to have more concrete interpretations such as transition systems determined by some kind of *parallel machine* for instance. The last technical section is an attempt to progress in these directions. There we introduce the *rational parallel place machines* which generalize Petri nets. We conclude in discussing some semantical aspects of our propositions.

2. Actions

MEIJE is a synchronization calculus parametrized by a *commutative monoid* $\mathbb{M}$ of actions : it intends to provide some tools for organizing the concurrent behaviour of processes which perform actions in $\mathbb{M}$. These actions may themselves be communications. If for instance an equation $u=v$ is valid in $\mathbb{M}$ we may understand this equation as a *law of interaction* reflecting some communication structure (a similar idea is that of Winskel's synchronization algebra [35]). In this paper we will not go very far beyond this allusion with regard to action monoids.

We have to formalize the idea of *global* action of concurrent system. This activity results from the behaviour of components running together. Thus a first approximation is that a global action is a *set* of particulate actions. But distinct components may perform the same action. Therefore global ones are rather **multisets**, and even finite such since we shall assume that there are only finitely many active components in a system. Let A be some set of **atomic actions** ; here atomicity is temporal as well as spatial. These may be for instance names of programs written in some language. If we use $a, b, c \ldots$ to range over A, a multiset on A is written

$\{a,\ldots,a,b,\ldots,b,c,\ldots,c\ldots\}$

But a more convenient notation is

$a^n b^m c^k \ldots$ (in any order)

where the positive integers $n, m, k \ldots$ are the respective numbers of occurrences. And union is the sum of respective exponents, thereafter denote as a product :

$$(a^n b^m c^k).(a^{n'} b^{m'} c^{k'}) = a^{n+n'} b^{m+m'} c^{k+k'}$$

with unit 1.

From this point of view, multisets on A (or $\mathbb{N}$-sets, in Eilenberg's terminology, [10] chap. VI) are elements of the commutative monoid $\mathbb{N}\langle A\rangle$. Technically $\mathbb{N}\langle A\rangle$ is the set of mappings f from A to the additive monoid of positive integers $\mathbb{N}$ such that $f(a)=0$ for almost all $a \in A$. This monoid of multisets on A is also well-known to be the *free commutative monoid* generated by A. This is our first example of commutative monoid of actions.

Another basic example is that of free commutative group $fcg(S)$ generated by some set S of **signals**. Each of the elements of S, say s, is here a synchronization action, endowed with an inverse s^-. The interaction law $s.s^-=1$ (together with freeness) says that the primitive communication act is a handshake between two participants temporarily unavailable for other interactions. For instance (see [20,22]) we may have ports $p, q, r \ldots$ such that for each value v of appropriate type there are two inverse actions p_v and p_v^- for sending and receiving the value v through the port p.

If we let for a while $s, p, q, \ldots$ range over S then the actions of $fcg(S)$ are written

$s^n p^m q^k \ldots$ (in any order)

with $n, m, k, \ldots$ integers. For it is well-known that $fcg(S)$ is isomorphic to $\mathbb{Z}\langle S\rangle$, the set of mappings f from S to the additive group of integers $\mathbb{Z}$ such that $f(s)=0$ for almost all $s \in S$. This will be our **synchronisation group** : our calculi are parametrized by product monoids

$$\Gamma(\mathbb{M}) = \mathbb{M} \times \mathbb{Z}\langle\Lambda\rangle$$

where

- $\mathbb{M}$ is any given commutative monoid
- $\Lambda = \{\lambda_n / n \in \mathbb{N}\}$ is a denumerable set of **signal identifiers** , or variables, disjoint from $\mathbb{M}$.

We shall use α,β,γ... and u,v,w,... to range over Λ and $\Gamma(\mathbb{M})$ respectively. A pair $(u,v) \in \Gamma(\mathbb{M})$ is also written as a product $u.v$. Thus actions may be denoted

$$u.\ \alpha^n \beta^m \gamma^k ... \text{ with } u \in \mathbb{M} \text{ and } n,m,k ... \text{ in } \mathbb{Z}.$$

We say that $\alpha \in \Lambda$ **occurs** in $u \in \Gamma(\mathbb{M})$ if α is an irreducible factor of u, that is :

$$\forall B \subseteq \Lambda\ .\ u \in \mathbb{M}\times\mathbb{Z}<B> \Rightarrow \alpha \in B$$

For instance α occurs in $a\alpha b\,\alpha^{-2}$ but not in $\alpha\beta\alpha a\,\alpha^{-2}$.

Let us recall that a morphism over $\Gamma(\mathbb{M})$ is a mapping φ such that

$\varphi(1) = 1$ (where 1 is the unit of $\Gamma(\mathbb{M})$.)

$\varphi(u.v) = \varphi(u).\varphi(v)$

Thus if $u \in \Gamma(\mathbb{M})$ has an inverse u^-,$\varphi(u^-)$ is the inverse of $\varphi(u)$. In the **pure** MEIJE calculus over $\mathbb{M}$ we only use *pure synchronization morphisms*. These are morphisms which change nothing but a finite number of signal identifiers into packs of other ones. Thus they are denoted

$$\varphi = <u_1/\alpha_1 ,..., u_k/\alpha_k> \text{ with } u_i \in \mathbb{Z}<\Lambda>$$

For instance if $\varphi = <\alpha\beta/\alpha>$ and $u \in \mathbb{M}$ then

$\varphi(u\alpha^2) = u\alpha^2\beta^2$ and

$\varphi(u\alpha^-\beta) = u\alpha^-$

In the **applied** version of our calculus the basic monoid $\mathbb{M}$ is a product

$$\mathbb{M} = \mathbb{N}<A> \times \mathbb{Z}<S>$$

where A is a set of atomic actions, S a set of signals (and A,S,Λ are assumed to be pairwise disjoint). Here we shall use (applied) *synchronisation morphisms* φ given as

$$<u_1/b_1 ,..., u_k/b_k>$$

for some finite subset $B = \{b_1 ,..., b_k\}$ of $A \cup S \cup \Lambda$.

It will also be convienient to work with finite sets of actions, thus with the semiring $\mathbb{K}(\mathbb{M})$ of finite subsets of $\Gamma(\mathbb{M})$. We ambiguously use u,v,w... to range over $\mathbb{K}(\mathbb{M})$ and denote as usual (cf. [10])

0 for the empty set of actions

u for the singleton $\{u\}$ when $u \in \Gamma(\mathbb{M})$

$u+v$ for the union of u and v

$u.v$ for the product $\{x.y / x \in u \text{ and } y \in v\}$

We assume well understood the notation $u \in v$ for $u \in \Gamma(\mathbb{M})$ and $v \in \mathbb{K}(\mathbb{M})$. Here again we say that $\alpha \in \Gamma$ **occurs in** $u \subseteq \Gamma(\mathbb{M})$ if

$$\forall B \subseteq \Gamma \qquad u \subseteq \mathbb{M} \times \mathbb{Z}<B> \Rightarrow \alpha \in B$$

(α is an irreducible factor of at least one element of u).

3. Syntax

Syntacticaly a calculus of processes is a free algebra of terms, relative to a commutative monoid $\mathbb{M}$ of actions. In order to define (by recursion) infinite processes we assume given a countable set

$$X = \{x_n / n \in \mathbb{N}\}$$

of variables or *identifiers*. We let $x, y, z \ldots$ to range over X. We have two versions of our calculus :

- a pure one, where we denote the set of terms by $\mathcal{M}_{\mathbb{M}}(X)$. In this case we only use pure synchronization morphisms : intuitively we only will be able to schedule processes in these calculi.
- an applied one, where the monoid $\mathbb{M}$ is a product $\mathbb{N}<A>\times\mathbb{Z}<S>$ and the set of terms is denoted $\mathcal{M}_{<A,S>}(X)$.

In this case we are allowed to use arbitrary synchronisation morphisms ; consequently we will be able to describe more discriminating synchronization mechanisms, depending on what actions are performed.

In both cases we use $p, q, r, \ldots$ to range over terms.

The syntax is the following :

(i) each identifier $x \in X$ is a term.

The constant $\mathbb{O}$ is a term

(ii) **action** : For each $u \in \mathbb{K}(\mathbb{M})$ if p is a term then $u : p$ is a term

(iii) **morphism** : if φ is a synchronization morphism and p is a term then φp is a term (if we only use pure morphisms, we are in a pure calculus, otherwise we are in an applied calculus, with the implicit hypothesis on the form of $\mathbb{M}$)

(iv) **recursive definitions** : if $x_{i_1}, \ldots, x_{i_k}$ are identifiers and $p, p_1, \ldots, p_k$ are terms then

$(p$ **where** $x_{i_1} = p_1, \ldots, x_{i_k} = p_k)$**is a term**

(v) **restriction** : for each signal identifier $\alpha \in \Lambda$ if p is a term then $p\backslash\alpha$ is a term.

These are, with slight lexical variations (but the same semantics, see below) among CCS's or SCCS's primitives. This is not the case of the following :

(vi) **asynchronous parallel composition** : if p and q are terms then $(p \parallel q)$ is a term

(vii) **ticking** : for each $u \in \mathbb{K}(\mathbb{M})$ if p is a term then $u * p$ is a term.

Let us have a words on static semantics (cf. [28]) : **bindings** in our language are recursive definitions and restriction. Therefore occurrences of variables (in X or Λ) may be free or bound and may accordingly be substituted or not. We shall not be very formalist on that matter since it is standard. We merely point out that :

- an occurrence of $\alpha \in \Lambda$ in a term comes through the action, morphism and ticking constructs. It is bound if it is under the scope of a restriction $\backslash\alpha$, that is in a subterm $q\backslash\alpha$.
- an occurrence of $x \in X$ in a term is bound if it is under the scope of a recursive definition, that is if it is an occurrence of an x_{i_j} in q or $p_1 \ldots$ or p_k in a subterm $(q$ **where** $x_{i_1} = p_1, \ldots, x_{i_k} = p_k)$.

- syntactic equality of terms is, as usual, the *conversion* equivalence, that is identity up to the name of some bound variables in some subterms. For instance

  $(x \textbf{ where } x = a : x) = (y \textbf{ where } y = a : y)$

  $((\alpha + \beta) * \alpha^- : \mathbb{O}) \backslash \alpha = ((\lambda + \beta) * \lambda^- : \mathbb{O}) \backslash \lambda$

- in the course of substitution, we may have to convert bound variables in order to avoid captures of free variables. For instance, in an applied calculus let

  $p = (z \textbf{ where } z = ((<\alpha.a/a>x \parallel <\alpha^-.b/b>y) \backslash \alpha \parallel \beta * z))$

  $q = \alpha * (a : z)\ ,\ r = \alpha^- * (b : y)$

  and let σ be the substitution $q/x\ ,\ r/y$. Then

  $p[\sigma] = (z' \textbf{ where } z' = ((<\gamma a/a>q \parallel <\gamma^- b/b>r) \backslash \gamma \parallel \beta * z')).$

We call **agent** any closed term (i.e. without any free variables) and **expression** any term without free signal identifiers. For instance

$(\alpha * x \parallel \alpha^- * y) \backslash \alpha$

is an expression, but not an agent.

We denote by $\mathcal{A}_{\mathbb{M}}$ and $\mathcal{E}_{\mathbb{M}}(X)$ respectively the sets of these terms (and $\mathcal{A}_{<A,S>}, \mathcal{E}_{<A,S>}(X)$ if we are in an applied calculus).

4. Operational semantics

In the operational interpretation each *agent* of the calculus is a state of a transition system, performing some actions in $\mathbb{M}$. Moreover these possible transitions only depend on the syntactic struture of the term. The word "operational" roughly means that we have a set of rules to get transitions $p \overset{u}{\to} q$ and a clause which says that valid transitions are only the ones we get after a finite game. Therefore it should be more correct to call operational semantics of an agent the set of proof trees of its transitions. In this setting a primitive operator or an expression without recursion determines a finite set of rules, thus a way to transform sets of proofs, and recursion comes through least fixed points.

A set of rules associated with an operator is its *semantic specification*, or operational description. In the following these rules will take the form :

$$\frac{p_1 \overset{u_1}{\to} q_1, \ldots, p_k \overset{u_k}{\to} q_k}{p \overset{u}{\to} q} \quad \text{(with some additional conditions on actions)}$$

also written as :

$$p_1 \overset{u_1}{\to} q_1, \ldots, p_k \overset{u_k}{\to} q_k \ (\ldots) \vdash p \overset{u}{\to} q$$

The consequence symbol $\vdash$ must be read, as usual, "if...then..." or more accurately "from...deduce...". The transition relation over MEIJE terms

$$\to \subseteq \mathcal{M}_{\mathbb{M}}(X) \times \Gamma(\mathbb{M}) \times \mathcal{M}_{\mathbb{M}}(X)$$

is the least one satisfying the following rule schemata :

(i) $R1 : u \in v \vdash v : p \xrightarrow{u} p$

This is the standard rule for action (or guarding) except that we allow finite sets of actions as guards. It means that $v : p$ is a process which may first perform an action in v and then behaves like p. The rule for morphisms is equally standard :

(ii) $R2 : p \xrightarrow{u} p' \vdash \varphi p \xrightarrow{\varphi(u)} \varphi(p')$

The most technical case is that of recursion. The behaviour of a term

$$(p \textbf{ where } x_{i_1} = p_1, \ldots, x_{i_k} = p_k)$$

is that of p in which the identifiers x_{i_j} stand for p_j. But this binding is recursive, thus in p_j itself an identifier x_{i_l} behaves like p_l. Therefore the rule is

(iii) let $r_j = (x_{i_j} \textbf{ where } x_{i_1} = p_1, \ldots, x_{i_k} = p_k)$

and

$$q_j = p_j[r_1/x_{i_1}, \ldots, r_k/x_{i_k}] \quad \text{for } 1 \leq j \leq k$$

Then

$$R3 : p[q_1/x_{i_1}, \ldots, q_k/x_{i_k}] \xrightarrow{u} p' \vdash (p \textbf{ where } x_{i_1} = p_1, \ldots, x_{i_k} = p_k) \xrightarrow{u} p'$$

The rule for restriction is also well-known ; the effect of the construct $\backslash\alpha$ is two-fold : from an external point of view it hides the signal α and from an internal point of view it constrains the exchange of the signal α

(iv) $R4 : p \xrightarrow{u} p'$ and α does not occur in $u \vdash p\backslash\alpha \xrightarrow{u} p'\backslash\alpha$

As we have already indicated there are three rules for the parallel composition which is thus a nondeterministic operator :

(v) $R5.1 : p \xrightarrow{u} p' \vdash (p \parallel q) \xrightarrow{u} (p' \parallel q)$

$$R5.2 : p \xrightarrow{u} p', q \xrightarrow{v} q' \vdash (p \parallel q) \xrightarrow{u.v} (p' \parallel q')$$

$$R5.3 : q \xrightarrow{v} q' \vdash (p \parallel q) \xrightarrow{v} (p \parallel q')$$

Finally :

(vi) $R6 : p \xrightarrow{u} p'$ and $v \in w \vdash w * p \xrightarrow{u.v} w * p'$

Examples 4

(1) No rule applies to $\mathbb{O}$. Thus this term does not perform any action. The same is true for $O : p$ and $O * p$.

(2) Let

$$p = (\alpha^- * (\alpha * a : \mathbb{O} \parallel \alpha * b : \mathbb{O}))\backslash\alpha$$

$$q = (\alpha^{-2} * (\alpha * a : \mathbb{O} \parallel \alpha * b : \mathbb{O}))\backslash\alpha$$

(with $\alpha \in \Lambda, a, b \in \mathbb{M}$)

Then

$$
\begin{array}{rc}
R1: & \overline{\qquad\qquad} \\
R6: & \overline{a:\mathbb{O} \xrightarrow{a} \mathbb{O}} \\
R5.1: & \overline{\alpha * a:\mathbb{O} \xrightarrow{\alpha.a} \alpha * \mathbb{O}} \\
R6: & \overline{(\alpha * a:\mathbb{O} \parallel \alpha * b:\mathbb{O}) \xrightarrow{\alpha.a} (\alpha * \mathbb{O} \parallel \alpha * b:\mathbb{O})} \\
R4: & \overline{\alpha^{-} * (\alpha * a:\mathbb{O} \parallel \alpha * b:\mathbb{O}) \xrightarrow{a} \alpha^{-} * (\alpha * \mathbb{O} \parallel \alpha * b:\mathbb{O})} \\
 & p \xrightarrow{a} \left[\alpha^{-} * (\alpha * \mathbb{O} \parallel \alpha * b:\mathbb{O})\right] \backslash \alpha
\end{array}
$$

Similarly one may prove, using R5.3, that

$$p \xrightarrow{b} (\alpha^{-} * (\alpha * a:\mathbb{O} \parallel \alpha * \mathbb{O})) \backslash \alpha$$

The reader can verify that the transition graph for p is

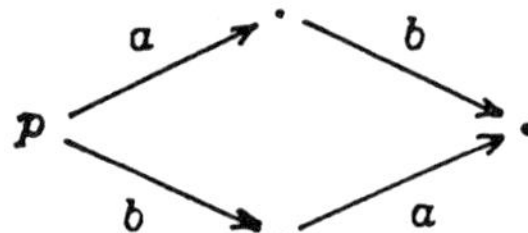

For q :

$$
\begin{array}{rcc}
R1: & \overline{\qquad\qquad} & \overline{\qquad\qquad} \\
R6: & \overline{a:\mathbb{O} \xrightarrow{a} \mathbb{O}} \, , & \overline{b:\mathbb{O} \xrightarrow{b} \mathbb{O}} \\
R5.2: & \alpha * a:\mathbb{O} \xrightarrow{\alpha a} \alpha * \mathbb{O} & \alpha * b:\mathbb{O} \xrightarrow{\alpha b} \alpha * \mathbb{O} \\
 & \multicolumn{2}{c}{\overline{(\alpha * a:\mathbb{O} \parallel \alpha * b:\mathbb{O}) \xrightarrow{\alpha^2 ab} (\alpha * \mathbb{O} \parallel \alpha * \mathbb{O})}} \\
R6: & \multicolumn{2}{c}{\overline{\alpha^{-2} * (\alpha * a:\mathbb{O} \parallel \alpha * b:\mathbb{O}) \xrightarrow{ab} \alpha^{-2} * (\alpha * \mathbb{O} \parallel \alpha * \mathbb{O})}} \\
R4: & \multicolumn{2}{c}{\overline{q \xrightarrow{ab} (\alpha^{-2} * (\alpha * \mathbb{O} \parallel \alpha * \mathbb{O})) \backslash \alpha}}
\end{array}
$$

The reader can verify that this is the only possible transition from q.

(3) Let

$p = (x \textbf{ where } x = a:x)$.then

$\vdash_{R_1} a:p \xrightarrow{a} p \vdash_{R_3} p \xrightarrow{a} p$

Thus the transition graph of p is $p \circlearrowleft a$.

Similarly if we let $q = (x \textbf{ where } x = (a+b):x)$ one easily checks (using R1 and R3) that the transition graph of q is

$b \circlearrowright q \circlearrowleft a$

More generally for each $u \in \mathbb{K}(\mathbb{M})$ we define the **clock on u** by

$$\boxed{h_u = (x \textbf{ where } x = u:x)}$$

Such processes will play a fundamental role. Their transition graphs are

$h_u \circlearrowleft v \in u$

i.e. they are processes which repeatedly perform some action in u (if any) and reconfigurate in themselves. As in [22] we denote :

$\mathbb{1} = h_1$

Another kind of "clock" is :

$p = (x \ \textbf{where} \ x = 1{:}(a * x))$

Here the number of a actions gives the current date, since we have :

$p \xrightarrow{1} a * p \xrightarrow{a} a * a * p \xrightarrow{a^2} \ldots \xrightarrow{a^n} \ldots$

(4) Let

$p = (x \ \textbf{where} \ x = (a{:}\mathbb{0} \parallel x)).$

Then we have a proof tree T_1 :

$\vdash_{R_1} a{:}\mathbb{0} \xrightarrow{a} \mathbb{0} \vdash_{R_{5.1}} (a{:}\mathbb{0} \parallel p) \xrightarrow{a} (\mathbb{0} \parallel p) \vdash_{R_3} p \xrightarrow{a} (\mathbb{0} \parallel p)$

With T_1 we build a proof tree T_2

$$R3{:}\dfrac{R5.2{:}\dfrac{R1{:}\dfrac{}{a{:}\mathbb{0} \xrightarrow{a} \mathbb{0}} \ , \ T_1}{(a{:}\mathbb{0} \parallel p) \xrightarrow{a^2} (\mathbb{0} \parallel (\mathbb{0} \parallel p))}}{p \xrightarrow{a^2} (\mathbb{0} \parallel (\mathbb{0} \parallel p))}$$

More generally if we have a proof tree T_n of a transition $p \xrightarrow{a^n} p_n$ we build, following the same scheme, a proof T_{n+1} of $p \xrightarrow{a^{n+1}} (\mathbb{0} \parallel p_n)$.

We shall see that semantically p denotes the process

$p \circlearrowleft a^n \quad (n > 0)$

This suggests to generalize the definition of clocks to subsets U of $\mathbb{M}$ (not necessarily finite). For instance we denote, for $u \in \mathbb{K}(\mathbb{M})$:

$$\boxed{h_{u^+} = (x \ \textbf{where} \ x = (u{:}\mathbb{0} \parallel x))}$$

We will see later for what U the clock h_U is actually definable in MEIJE.

(5) Another basic example is that of a <u>bag</u>. Let us assume two actions a and b respectively meaning putting and removing a token. Then the behaviour of a bag p_k initially containing k tokens is as such :

One can simultaneously

- put (performing a) as many token as one wishes
- remove (performing b) at most k tokens.

In figure :

$(k) \xrightarrow{a^n b^m} (k+n-m)$

for $m \leq k$, $n+m > 0$.

These processes are realized (see [3]) by

$$\begin{cases} p_0 = (x \ \textbf{where} \ x = (a{:}b{:}\mathbb{0} \parallel x)) \\ p_{k+1} = (b{:}\mathbb{0} \parallel p_k) \end{cases}$$

(p_0 may be seen as an infinite parallel juxtaposition of elementary cells).

(6) We let the reader find the initial transitions of

$$p = (x \textbf{ where } x = (a : \mathbb{O} \parallel <ab/a, b^2/b> x)).$$

Once provided this machinery we associate with each agent p a transition system, the states of which are terms reachable from p after a sequence of actions. The operational semantics of expressions is given by functions on these transition systems ; examples will be given in section 6 since this is only meaningful at an abstract level.

5. Semantics

5.1. Transition systems

We just have shown how operational semantics brings a structure of labelled transition system on the set of agents. Generally speaking a (labelled) **transition system** ([19]) (abbreviated t.s.) on a set **A** of actions is a triple

$$\Theta = (\mathbb{Q}, \mathbf{A}, T) \text{ where}$$

- $\mathbb{Q}$ is the set of *states*
- **A** is the set of *actions*
- T, the *transition relation*, is a subset of $\mathbb{Q} \times \mathbf{A}^* \times \mathbb{Q}$ where $\mathbf{A}^*$ is the set of finite sequences of actions.

We qualify Θ as **elementary** if $T \subseteq \mathbb{Q} \times \mathbf{A} \times \mathbb{Q}$

Notations : we abusively let $u, v, w, \ldots$ range over $\mathbf{A}^*$; the concatenation of v after u is $u : v$ and ε is the empty sequence. $p \overset{u}{\underset{T}{\to}} q$ stands for $(p, u, q) \in T$. We extend the transitions to sequences by

(i) $p \overset{\varepsilon}{\underset{T}{\Rightarrow}} p$

(ii) if $\exists q.\ p \overset{u}{\underset{T}{\to}} q \ \&\ q \overset{v}{\underset{T}{\Rightarrow}} r$ then $p \overset{u:v}{\underset{T}{\Rightarrow}} r$

and even to sets $u \subseteq \mathbf{A}^*$ of sequences by

(iii) if $\exists v \in u. p \overset{v}{\underset{T}{\Rightarrow}} q$ then $p \overset{u}{\underset{T}{\Rightarrow}} q$

Remark 5.1 : usually a transition system is given provided with some *initial state*. But such systems $\Theta = (\mathbb{Q}, \mathbf{A}, T, q)$ are themselves states in a "universal" t.s. if we define

$$\Theta \overset{u}{\to} \Theta' \text{ iff } \Theta' = (\mathbb{Q}, \mathbf{A}, T, q') \ \&\ q (\overset{u}{\underset{T}{\to}} q').$$

Nevertheless all the following definitions and considerations are trivially extended to transition systems with initial state provided that in this case we assume the set $\mathbb{Q}$ **reduced** to the states reachable from the initial one through the extended relation $\underset{T}{\Rightarrow}$.

As we have pointed out, it is necessary to somehow abstract from such systems. For instance one may remark that in the examples above agents such as $\mathbb{O}$, $0 : p$ and $0 * p$ or p and $(\mathbb{O} \parallel p)$ have the same behaviour. Therefore we want to regard them as "equal". Equality holds through an abstract view on actions which we call an abstraction (or observation) criterion. Such a criterion on a set **A** of actions is a set of **abstract actions** (or observables, or experiments, see [12]) which themselves are non-empty sets of sequences of actions. The intended meaning is that all sequences of a single experiment $e \subseteq \mathbf{A}^*$ are held to carry out the same abstract action. Thus it is natural to assume that elements of a given criterion are disjoint ; stated differently : an abstraction criterion is deterministic. But it needs not be total : some sequences may be invisible or meaningless from a given point of view ; similarly a prefix of an observable sequence of actions may be unobservable (deadlock). Thus an **abstraction criterion** on a set **A** of actions is a *partial partition* over $\mathbf{A}^*$, i.e. a set $\mathbb{C} = \{e_i / i \in I\}$ of disjoint abstract actions $e_i \subseteq \mathbf{A}^*$. We also say that a sequence $u \in \mathbf{A}^*$ is *observable from* $\mathbb{C}$ if $\exists e \in \mathbb{C}. u \in e$.

The best known examples of this are criteria defining the strong congruence and the observation equivalence of CCS ([20], see also [22]). Both are special cases of criteria obtained from projections : let $B \subseteq \mathbf{A}$ be a set of *visible* actions ; then two sequences are observationally equivalent if their visible content is the same. Therefore observables are here classes in the equivalence relation

$$u \equiv_B v \iff \mu_B(u) = \mu_B(v)$$

where $\mu_B : \mathbf{A}^* \to B^*$ is the *projection* on B. This projection is the morphism of monoid determined by

$$\mu_B(a) = \text{if } a \in B \text{ then } a \text{ else } \varepsilon$$

When $B = \mathbf{A}$ ($\mu_{\mathbf{A}}$ is the identity) we get the **strong criterion** on **A** in which each sequence of actions is observable and distinguishable from any other one.

We intend to define a concept of congruence of a transition system in such a way that we would be able to define the quotient as a transition system on abstract actions. A **congruence** of a transition system $\Theta = (\mathbb{Q}, \mathbf{A}, T)$ (abbreviated t.s.-congruence) is a pair $\rho = (\mathbb{C}, R)$ where :

- $\mathbb{C}$ is an abstraction criterion on **A** and
- R is an equivalence relation on $\mathbb{Q}$ such that two R-equivalent states can not be distinguished by means of the observations from $\mathbb{C}$. Formally :

$$\forall q \in \mathbb{Q} \ \forall e \in \mathbb{C} \ \forall p \in \mathbb{Q} \ \forall q' \in \mathbb{Q}$$

$$\textit{if } q \overset{e}{\underset{T}{\Rightarrow}} p \ \& \ (q, q') \in R$$

$$\textit{then } \exists p' \in \mathbb{Q}. q' \overset{e}{\underset{T}{\Rightarrow}} p' \ \& \ (p, p') \in R$$

This commutation property is usually drawn

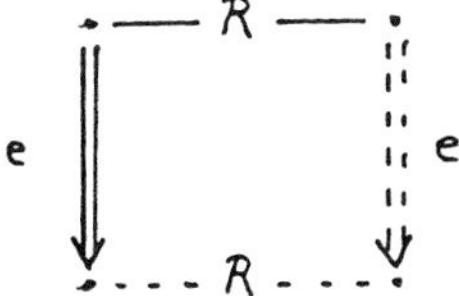

Brookes & Rounds [5] call such a relation R *invariant* ; it seems that these are *weak homomorphisms* of Ginzburg (see [26,31]). The terminological situation about "bisimulations" is rather confusing (compare for instance [5,22,26,31]).

Note that since we require R to be a symetric relation, the symetric schema also holds :

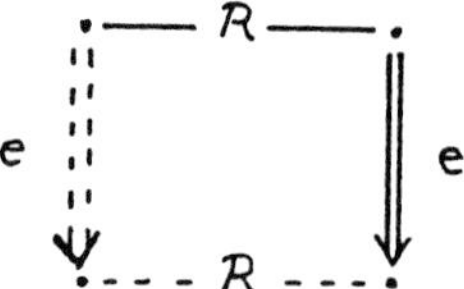

We call $\mathbb{C}$-congruence of transition system (or simply $\mathbb{C}$-congruence, and strong congruence when $\mathbb{C}$ is the strong criterion) an equivalence R on states such that $(\mathbb{C},R)$ is a t.s.-congruence.

For a congruence $\rho = (\mathbb{C},R)$ on $\Theta = (\mathbb{Q},\mathbf{A},T)$ we define the **quotient** system Θ/ρ to be

$$\Theta/\rho = (\mathbb{Q}/R,\mathbb{C},T/\rho)$$

where (denoting by $\pi_R : \mathbb{Q} \to \mathbb{Q}/R$ the canonical surjection)

$$\pi_R(p) \overset{e}{\underset{T/\rho}{\to}} \pi_R(q) \text{ iff } \exists r.\ p \overset{e}{\underset{T}{\Rightarrow}} r \ \&\ (r,q) \in R.$$

In diagrams :

A quotient of a system Θ may also be called a *reduction* of this system.

Remark 5.2 : if $\mathbb{C}$ is the strong criterion and Θ is elementary we shall regard Θ/ρ as an elementary transition system on **A**.

Examples 5.1

(1) With the strong criterion, the elementary transition system (where all the arrows are implicitely labelled by the same action)

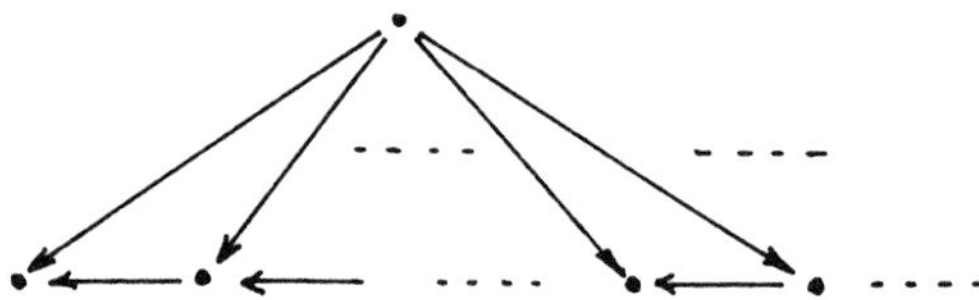

is a reduction of

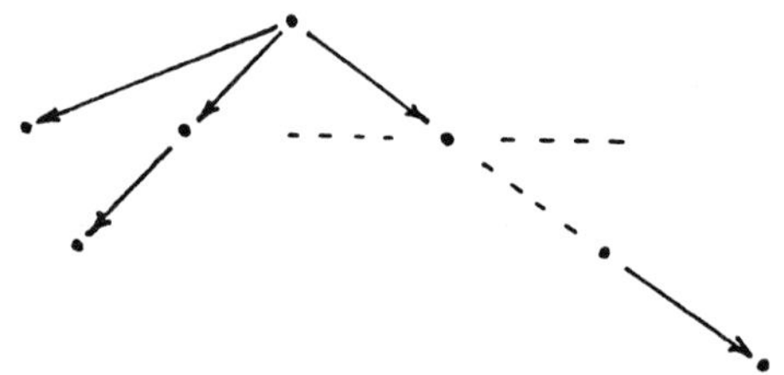

(2) With the criterion on $\mathbf{A} = \{a,b\}$ associated with the projection on $B = \{a\}$ in which observables are $\overline{\varepsilon} = \{b^n / n \in \mathbb{N}\}$, $\{b^{n_1}ab^{n_2}...b^{n_k}ab^{n_{k+1}} / n_i \in \mathbb{N}\} = \overline{a}^k$ the system

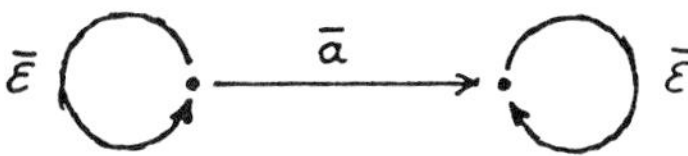

is a reduction of

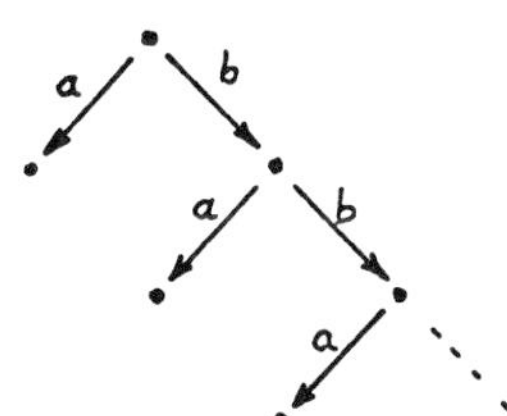

(3) In MEIJE the equivalence relations on agents generated by

$\{(p,(\mathbb{O} \parallel p)) / p \in \mathcal{A}_{\mathbf{M}}\}$

$\{(p \parallel q, q \parallel p) / p,q \in \mathcal{A}_{\mathbf{M}}\}$

$\{(p \parallel (q \parallel r),(p \parallel q) \parallel r) / p,q,r \in \mathcal{A}_{\mathbf{M}}\}$

are strong congruences.

An interesting fact (see [2,5,22]) is that an abstraction criterion $\mathbb{C}$ in itself determines a $\mathbb{C}$-t.s.-congruence in which the only means to distinguish states is observation of actions (for instance this constrasts with example (3) above where the "structure" of states is taken into account).

Lemma 5.1

For any transition system $\Theta = (\mathbb{Q},\mathbf{A},T)$ and for any observation criterion $\mathbb{C}$ on $\mathbf{A}$ there exists a coarsest $\mathbb{C}$-t.s.-congruence $\sim_{\mathbb{C}}$ on Θ i.e.

(i) $\sim_{\mathbb{C}}$ is a $\mathbb{C}$-congruence on Θ

(ii) For all $\mathbb{C}$-congruences R on Θ $(p,q) \in R \Rightarrow p \sim_{\mathbb{C}} q$

Notations : we shall use $\sim_{\mathbb{C}}$ uniformly disregarding the transition systems ; similarly the equivalence class of a state p in $\sim_{\mathbb{C}}$ is denoted $[\![p]\!]_{\mathbb{C}}$ (respectively $[\![p]\!]$ when $\mathbb{C}$ is the strong criterion). Following [5] we might use the name "$\mathbb{C}$-bisimulation" for $\sim_{\mathbb{C}}$; in order to avoid misunderstanding we prefer to call it $\mathbb{C}$-**equipollence**.

The above assertion may be stated as a very useful proof principle, which is nothing more than Park's induction :

Proposition 5.1 (the proof principle)

Let $\Theta = (\mathbb{Q},\mathbf{A},T)$ be a transition system and $\mathbb{C}$ an abstraction criterion on $\mathbf{A}$. Let S be a $\mathbb{C}$-congruence on Θ and R a symetric relation over $\mathbb{Q}$.

If *for all* $e \in \mathbb{C}$

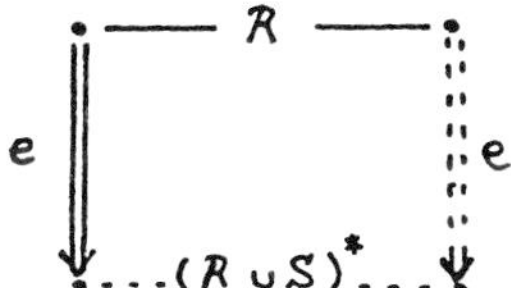

$i.e. p \overset{e}{\underset{T}{=>}} p'$ & $(p,q) \in R => \exists q'. q \overset{e}{\underset{T}{=>}} q'$ & $(p',q') \in (R \cup S)^*$

(where $(R \cup S)^*$ is the reflexive and transitive closure of $R \cup S$)

then $(R \cup S)^*$ is a $\mathbb{C}$-congruence

thus $(p,q) \in R => p \sim_{\mathbb{C}} q$ ▪

In this statement S is a set of already proved "equalities" which serve as hypotheses to prove $R \subseteq \sim_{\mathbb{C}}$.

The notion of *morphism* is usually strongly related to that of congruence. Here the intended intuitive meaning is that a morphism from a system Θ to another one Θ' is a *representation* of Θ in Θ'. Therefore it is natural to assume :

- *soundness* : if the representation of a state q of Θ can carry out the representation of a sequence of actions u then q actually carry out a sequence v with the same representation.
- *completeness* : if a state q of Θ can carry out a representable sequence of actions u then its representation actually carries out the representation of u.

Let $\Theta = (\mathbb{Q},\mathbf{A},T)$ and $\Theta' = (\mathbb{Q}',\mathbb{B},T')$ be to transition system. A **morphism** from Θ to Θ' is a pair (ψ,φ) such that

- ψ is a *partial mapping* from $\mathbf{A}^*$ to $\mathbb{B}^*$ which tells which sequences of actions in Θ are represented by sequences in Θ', and how
- $\varphi : \mathbb{Q} \to \mathbb{Q}'$ tells how states of Θ are represented in Θ'

and this pair is subject to satisfy the properties :

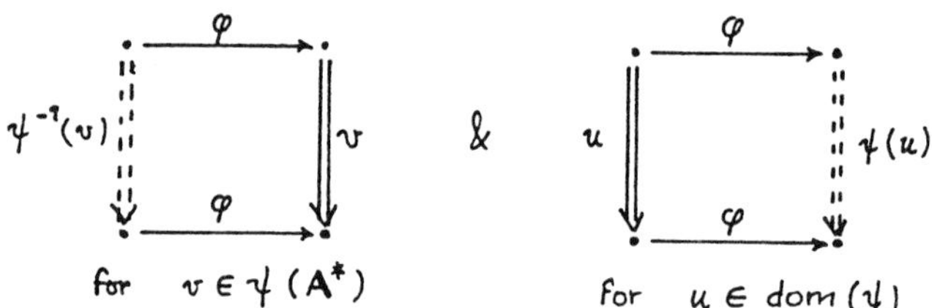

(we omit the formal statements)▪

This notion of morphism is only an attempt among others called reduction, abstraction, contraction... see references in [11,18,31]. It is easy to check that it fulfils the usual requirements :

(1) for each $\Theta = (\mathbb{Q},\mathbf{A},T)$ the pair of identities on $\mathbb{Q}$ and $\mathbf{A}^*$ is a morphism. The composition $(\psi o \psi', \varphi o \varphi')$ of two morphisms is a morphism.

(2) Let $\rho = (\mathbb{C},R)$ be a congruence on Θ and

$\psi : \mathbf{A}^* \to \mathbb{C}$ (partial) given by

$\psi(u) = e$ iff $u \in e$

Then (ψ,π_R) is a morphism from Θ onto the quotient Θ/ρ.

(3) Let $\mathbb{Q}' \subseteq \mathbb{Q}$, $\mathbb{B} \subseteq \mathbf{A}$ and Θ' be the subsystem $(\mathbb{Q}',\mathbb{B},T')$ where $T' = T \cap (\mathbb{Q}' \times \mathbb{B}^* \times \mathbb{Q}')$.

Then the pair of canonical injections is a morphism.

(4) If (ψ,φ) is a morphism from Θ to Θ' and

$\mathbb{C} = \{\psi^{-1}(\psi(u)) \,/\, u \in dom(\psi)\}$

$(p,q) \in R \iff \varphi(p) = \varphi(q)$

then $\mathbb{C}$ is an abstraction criterion on A and R is a $\mathbb{C}$-congruence. Moreover $\Theta\,/\,(\mathbb{C},R)$ is isomorphic to the image subsystem $(\psi,\varphi)(\Theta)$ of Θ'.

In these notes we regard **semantics** of a system Θ as a quotient by a congruence ρ. Therefore a question raises : how can we "concretely" define a representation of Θ by another system Θ' in order to get a semantically sound representation ? Or technically stated (with the previous notations) :

let

- $\rho' = (\mathbb{C}',S)$ *be a congruence on* Θ'
- ψ *a partial mapping from* $\mathbb{C}^*$ *to* $\mathbb{C}'$

We want to find "concrete" mappings $\vartheta : \mathbb{Q} \to \mathbb{Q}'$ such that there exists $\varphi : \mathbb{Q}/R \to \mathbb{Q}'/S$ satisfying

(i) (ψ,φ) is a morphism from Θ/ρ, the semantics of Θ, to Θ'/ρ'

(ii) the diagram

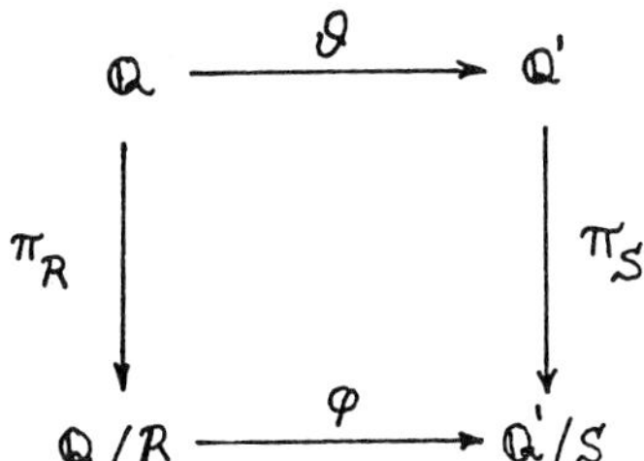

commutes $(\pi_S o \vartheta = \varphi o \pi_R)$

An immediate observation is that if such a φ exists then it is unique (notation : $\vartheta\hat{}$), thus "concretely determinded" by ϑ.

We call such a triple (ψ,ϑ,ρ') a **simulation** of (Θ,ρ) by or in Θ'.

Another observation is that a necessary and sufficient condition of exitence for φ satisfying (ii) is

$$(p,q) \in R \;\Rightarrow\; (\vartheta(p),\vartheta(q)) \in S$$

and if moreover the converse is true then φ is injective. (We have a "simulation criterion" analogous to proof principle for congruences, but it is rather technical ; and since we shall not give proofs explicitely using this criterion, we do not state it here).

The semantical notion of simulation is the central one of this paper, once particularized in two nested kinds :

- a simulation (ψ,ϑ,ρ') is a (correct) **implementation** of (Θ,ρ) in Θ' when ψ does not shade off the semantical criterion $\mathbb{C}$, i.e. is an injection from $\mathbb{C}$ to $\mathbb{C}'$, and similarly $\vartheta\hat{}$ is injective. Thus an implementation gives a concrete and semantically exact image of a system, up to an observation criterion on the target system, where actions of Θ/ρ are "implemented" as abstract actions.
- Let us assume that Θ and Θ' are t.s. on the same set A of actions and $\rho' = (\mathbb{C},S)$. Then ϑ is a **$\mathbb{C}$-realization** of (Θ,ρ) in (Θ',ρ') if $(id_{\mathbb{C}},\vartheta,\rho')$ is an implementation. Here we get a fully exact image of the semantics of Θ as a subsystem of (Θ',ρ') by means of the concrete state mapping ϑ. When $\mathbb{C}$ is the strong criterion we call ϑ a *strong realization*.

5. 2. Algebraic systems

In these notes we are mainly interested in **algebraic transition system** (abbreviated a.t.s.) $\Theta = (\mathbb{Q}, \mathbb{A}, T)$ with respect to a family F of operators. This means that the set of states is the domain of an F-algebra. Thus for all $f \in F$ of arity k we have a mapping

$$f_\Theta : \mathbb{Q}^k \to \mathbb{Q}$$

(we omit the reference to Θ if it is understood)

N.B. : we assume here some familiarity with the standard concepts of algebra ; see for instance P.M. Cohn, "Universal Algebra" (Harper and Row, New York, 1965).

Let us take F as a set of *operator symbols* and X as a set of variables or parameters. Then we get syntactic objects which are the terms built on X by means of the constructors $f \in F$. These set up the domain $\mathcal{T}_F(X)$ of the well-known free F-algebra on X.

Notation : $\mathcal{T}_F$ for $\mathcal{T}_F(\phi)$, the set of ground terms. For instance this is the way in which MEIJE agents and expressions are built.

As usual terms $t \in \mathcal{T}_F(X)$ are interpreted on an algebraic system Θ as functions t^Θ of *evaluations* of the parameters in $\mathbb{Q}$. These are mappings $\nu : X \to \mathbb{Q}$ assigning to each variable a value. Let us recall the definition :

$$\begin{cases} x^\Theta(\nu) = \nu(x) & \text{for } x \in X \\ f(t_1,\dots,t_n)^\Theta(\nu) = f_\Theta(t_1^\Theta(\nu),\dots,t_n^\Theta(\nu)) & \end{cases}$$

Obviously $t^\Theta(\nu)$ only depends on the value of variables occurring in t, thus t^Θ may also be regarded as a mapping from $\mathbb{Q}^k$ to $\mathbb{Q}$, if there are k distinct variables occurring in t.

Examples (in MEIJE) :

$t = (x$ **where** $x = (1{:}x \parallel y))$ will represent a function of one argument (named y) on processes, while

$t' = (\alpha^- * (\alpha * \alpha \parallel \alpha * y))\backslash\alpha$ will be a function of two arguments named x and y.

A value $t^\Theta(\nu)$ of such functions is called an *instance* in $\mathbb{Q}$ of the term t.

This allows to specify the transition relation of an algebraic system by a set of rules, as for the operational semantics of MEIJE (or CCS [20], SCCS [22] and so on). If we regard the operator f as a synchronization mechanism, each rule is one element of a non-deterministic strategy for f indicating

- which components of a system (composed by f) are allowed to proceed,
- what are the simultaneously permitted actions, and
- how the system recomposes a global transition (action and reconfigured state).

Therefore these rules take the following general format (cf. [33]) :

$$\mathbb{R} : \frac{x_{i_1} \xrightarrow{u_1} x'_{i_1},\dots,x_{i_k} \xrightarrow{u_k} x'_{i_k}, (u_1,\dots,u_k,u) \in U}{f(x_1,\dots,x_n) \xrightarrow{u} t}$$

(a rule for f on $\mathbb{A}$, also differently stated ...$\vdash$...) **where** :

– $x_1,\dots,x_n$, $x'_{i_1},\dots,x'_{i_k}$ *are distinct variables and* $\{x_{i_1},\dots,x_{i_k}\} \subseteq \{x_1,\dots,x_n\}$

We let for $1 \leq j \leq n$:

$$x'_j = \begin{cases} x'_{i_l} & \text{if } j = i_l \text{ for some } l \ (1 \leq l \leq k) \\ x_j & \text{otherwise} \end{cases}$$

– $U \subseteq \mathbf{A}^{k+1}$ *is a predicate on actions*

– t *is a term of* $\mathcal{T}_F(\{x'_1,\ldots,x'_n\})$ *in which each* x'_j *occurs at most once.*

(thus look-ahead in the future of the arguments is forbidden as well as duplications).

Examples 5.2

The generalized clocks h_U for $U \subseteq \mathbf{A}$ are specified by

$$u \in U \vdash h_U \overset{u}{\rightarrow} h_U$$

(considering h_U as a constant symbol)

We even generalize a little more to $U \subseteq \mathbf{A}^{k+1}$:

$$\frac{x_1 \overset{u_1}{\rightarrow} x'_1,\ldots,x_k \overset{u_k}{\rightarrow} x'_k, (u_1,\ldots,u_k,u) \in U}{h_U(x_1,\ldots,x_k) \overset{u}{\rightarrow} h_U(x'_1,\ldots,x'_k)}$$

(for instance ticking $u * x$ is such a synchronization mechanism)

We call **semantic specification** (of a set F of operators, on a set $\mathbf{A}$ of actions, abbreviated $(F,\mathbf{A})$-specification) a set Φ of such rules. We say rather informally that an *elementary* F-algebraic transition system $\Theta = (\mathbb{Q},\mathbf{A},T)$ **satisfies** this specification iff

for any state $q = f_\Theta(q_1,\ldots,q_n)$

$q \underset{T}{\overset{u}{\rightarrow}} q'$ **iff** this transition is the conclusion drawn from an instance in $\mathbb{Q}$ of a Φ rule.

Remark : a "specification" here is thus required to be exact and complete. We shall not study the interesting notion of "satisfaction of a specification up to an abstraction criterion on actions".

Now when $\Theta = (\mathbb{Q},\mathbf{A},T)$ is an F-algebraic transition system we obviously refine the concept of congruence : an **F-a.t.s.-congruence** (for short F-congruence or even congruence if no confusion is possible) on Θ is a pair $\rho = (\mathbb{C},R)$ such that

- ρ is a t.s.-congruence
- R is compatible with the algebraic structure, i.e.
  for all $f \in F$ if $(p_1,q_1) \in R,\ldots,(p_n,q_n) \in R$ then
  $(f_\Theta(p_1,\ldots,p_n), f_\Theta(q_1,\ldots,q_n)) \in R$

In this case, where we still qualify R as $\mathbb{C}$-congruence or $(F,\mathbb{C})$-congruence, the quotient system Θ/ρ is also an F-algebraic system. We recall the standard definition :

$$f_{\Theta/\rho}(\pi_R(p_1),\ldots,\pi_R(p_n)) = \pi_R(f_\Theta(p_1,\ldots,p_n))$$

(we recall that $\pi_R(p)$ is the equivalence class of p in the relation R).

And we have

Lemma 5.2

Let Θ be an elementary F-algebraic system satisfying a semantic specification Φ of F.

(i) if R is a strong F-congruence on Θ then the quotient system satisfy the same specification

(ii) the strong equipollence $\sim$ is also an F-congruence (i.e. compatible with the algebraic structure).

Let us now introduce the notion of algebraic calculus of processes. A *simple algebraic calculus of process* is a structure $\mathcal{A} = (F,\mathbf{A},\Phi,\rho)$ where as before

- F is a family of operators
- $\mathbf{A}$ is a set of actions
- Φ is a semantic specification of F on $\mathbf{A}$
- $\rho = (\mathbb{C},R)$ is a *semantics*

Let us see what a semantics is : first we call *agents* of the calculus the ground terms belonging to $\mathcal{T}_F$. Then we define an operational transition system on agents

$$Op(\mathcal{A}) = (\mathcal{T}_F,\mathbf{A},T)$$

where T is the least transition relation satisfying the specification Φ. Then ρ is a semantics if it is an F-congruence on $Op(\mathcal{A})$.

The semantical universe of the calculus $\mathcal{A}$ is the quotient system

$$Sem(\mathcal{A}) = Op(\mathcal{A})/\rho = (\mathcal{T}_F/R,\mathbb{C},T/\rho)$$

in which the states (equivalence classes of agents) are the **processes** of the calculus. Equivalently process determined by an agent p might be seen as a subsystem of $Sem(\mathcal{A})$ with $\pi_R(p)$ as initial state (cf. remark 5.1). The transition system $Sem(\mathcal{A})$ is also an F-algebraic one. Moreover it satisfies the specification Φ if $\mathbb{C}$ is the strong criterion. Expressions of $\mathcal{T}_F(X)$ give **derived operators** on this system with which the semantics is still compatible.

However these calculi are too simple : there are no binding operators. When we have such operators the semantics of expression is given by means of substitutions. It seems fairly easy to extend a simple calculus to another one with recursive definitions of processes (see Prop. 4.6 in [22]). The situation is more delicate concerning operators such as restriction. A more careful analysis of the syntactical aspects of the semantic specifications is needed here. In particular one has to bring out the action parameters of an operator, occurring in the corresponding syntactic construct. This point is not yet clearly elucidated.

Therefore we shall keep a rather vague notion of *algebraic calculus of processes*. Such an object is a structure

$$\mathcal{A} = (F,\mathbf{A},T,\rho)$$

where

- F is a set of operators. We assume that some are bindings with respect to a set X of process identifiers and a set of action identifiers (disjoint from the set $\mathbf{A}$ of actions). Accordingly one defines the sets $\mathcal{A}_F$ of *agents* and $\mathcal{E}_F(X)$ of *expressions*. As in MEIJE agents are closed terms and expressions are terms in which action identifiers are bound.

  We also assume defined the operation of substitution and denote $t[p_1,\dots,p_n]$ the term $t[p_1/x_{i_1},\dots,p_n/x_{i_n}]$ if $x_{i_1},\dots,x_{i_n}$ are the free process variables occurring in t.
- $T \subseteq \mathcal{A}_F \times \mathbf{A} \times \mathcal{A}_F$ is the transition relation
- $\rho = (\mathbb{C},R)$ is as before a *semantics*, i.e.
  (i) R is a $\mathbb{C}$-congruence on $(\mathcal{A}_F,\mathbf{A},T)$
  (ii) R is compatible with the expressions : for all expression t, for all agents $p_1,\dots,p_n,q_1,\dots,q_n$

$$(p_1,q_1)\in R \text{ ,..., } (p_n,q_n)\in R \;\Rightarrow\; (t[p_1,\dots,p_n],t[q_1,\dots,q_n])\in R$$

Then expressions t define *derived operators* $[\![t]\!]_{\mathcal{Q}}$ on the quotient semantical system

$$Sem(\mathcal{Q}) = (\mathcal{A}_F/R,\mathbb{C},T/\rho)$$

The extensional equivalence between expression is defined by

$$(t,t') \in \underline{R} \quad \text{iff} \quad [\![t]\!]_{\mathcal{Q}} = [\![t']\!]_{\mathcal{Q}}$$

(when R is the $\mathbb{C}$-equipollence $\sim_{\mathbb{C}}$ we get the notation $\simeq_{\mathbb{C}}$)

Obviously we regard simple calculi as special cases of algebraic calculi. Concerning MEIJE we have :

Proposition 5.2

the strong equipollence $\sim$ is a semantics of the MEIJE calculus.

In fact all the calculi considered in the following will be equipped with the **strong equipollence** as semantics. One may observe some apparently strange phenomena in MEIJE such as

$$x\backslash\alpha \simeq x$$

However this is not so surprising : since $t\backslash\alpha$ binds α in the "text" of the expression t, if α does not occur in t then obviously $t\backslash\alpha \simeq t$.

We conclude this section by particularizing the notions of implementation and realization to algebraic calculi of processes (an implementation of a calculus into another one might be called a compilation). Let $\mathcal{Q} = (F,\mathbf{A},T,\rho)$ and $\mathcal{B} = (G,\mathbb{B},T',\rho')$ be two calculi of processes where $\rho = (\mathbb{C},R)$ and $\rho' = (\mathbb{C}',R')$ respectively. Then

(1) we first want to formalize the idea of **syntax-directed implementation**. Here each primitive construct of the source calculus is "implemented" as derived operator, ie. expression, of the target one. Let

- $\rho'' = (\mathbb{C}'',R'')$ be a t.s.-congruence on the semantical system $Sem(\mathcal{B})$
- $\psi : \mathbb{C} \to \mathbb{C}''$ an injective mapping
- $\vartheta : F \to \mathcal{T}_G(X)$ a mapping such that if the arity of $f \in F$ is n then $\vartheta(F)$ has exactly n free variables.

This mapping is algebraically extended as ϑ^* from $\mathcal{T}_F(X)$ to $\mathcal{T}_G(X)$ by

$$\begin{cases} \vartheta^*(x) = x & \text{for} \quad x \in X \\ \vartheta^*(F(t_1,\ldots,t_n)) = \vartheta(F)[\vartheta^*(t_1),\ldots,\vartheta^*(t_n)] \end{cases}$$

(note : we keep the same notation for its restriction to agents)

We suppose that ϑ^* preserves the notions of agent and expression. Finally let

- φ be given by the commutative diagram

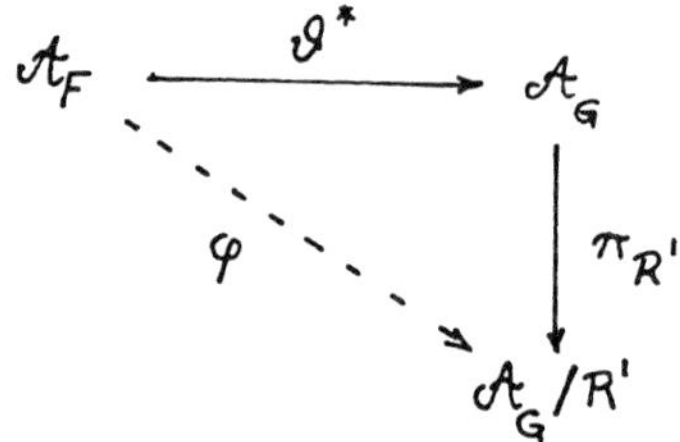

Then (ψ,ϑ,ρ'') is a **translation** (or a **syntax-directed implementation**) of the calculus $\mathcal{A}$ in the calculus $\mathcal{B}$ if (ψ,φ,ρ'') is an implementation of the "concrete" (or syntactic) system $(\mathcal{A}_F,\mathbf{A},T)$ in the system $Sem(\mathcal{B})$.

(2) the calculus $\mathcal{A}$ is a *subcalculus* of $\mathcal{B}$ if each primitive construct of $\mathcal{A}$ is definable as a derived operator of $\mathcal{B}$. Let us assume that $\mathbf{A} = \mathbb{B}$ and $\mathbb{C} = \mathbb{C}'$. Then $\mathcal{A}$ is a **subcalculus** of $\mathcal{B}$ if there exists a mapping ϑ as in the point above such that ϑ^* (restricted to agents) is a $\mathbb{C}$-realization of $\mathcal{A}$ in $\mathcal{B}$.

The remainder of these notes is devoted to illustrate all these abstract semantical concepts.

6. Equivalent Formulations and Implementation

6.1. Subcalculi

Our first example of MEIJE-definable operator is Milner's **synchronous product** [21,22] $(p \times q)$ given by the specification (on any monoid $\mathbb{M}$).

$$p \xrightarrow{u} p' ,\ q \xrightarrow{v} q' \vdash (p \times q) \xrightarrow{uv} (p' \times q')$$

This is a kind of parallel composition in which components are not allowed to proceed independently. To define this operator in MEIJE we have to "tick" the two component -a priori independent- by the reception of a signal and to place them in a context which sends two signals synchronously. Thus we let

$$\boxed{x \times y \simeq (\alpha^2 * (\alpha^- * x \ \| \ \alpha^- * y)) \backslash \alpha}$$

(for some $\alpha \in \Lambda$)

In [2] we gave other formulae :

$$x \times y \simeq (\alpha * x \ \| \ \alpha^- * y) \backslash \alpha$$

$$\simeq ((\alpha^- * x \ \| \ \alpha^- * y) \ \| \ h_{\alpha^2}) \backslash \alpha$$

Remarks : this is the first step to show the equivalence of some calculi, in the sense that each will be a subcalculus of the other. Thus we could have formally defined a translation

$$\vartheta(\times) = (\alpha^2 * (\alpha^- * x_1 \ \| \ \alpha^- * x_2)) \backslash \alpha$$

and so on ; however we shall stay at a more intuitive level. A second remark is that if we would not take the restriction as a binding operator, then we would not be able to define uniformly operators by formulae. For instance if $\backslash\alpha$ does not bind α then $e[\alpha:\mathbb{0},\alpha:\mathbb{0}]$ where $e = (\alpha^2 * (\alpha^- * x \parallel \alpha^- * y))\backslash\alpha$ does not perform the synchronous product of $\alpha:\mathbb{0}$ by itself. On the contrary we avoid here sorting considerations (for processes as well as for the semantical equivalences of expressions).

Obviously ticking is strongly related to the synchronous product since

$$\boxed{u * x \simeq h_u \times x}$$

With this fundamental operator we can define another one which was taken as primitive in [2], **triggering** $(u=>p)$ of p by u, for $u \in \mathbb{K}(\mathbb{M})$. This synchronization has the effect of linking each initial transition of p to some action in u and then vanishes :

$$p \overset{v}{\to} p',\ w \in u \vdash (u=>p) \overset{w.v}{\to} p'$$

The definition is :

$$\boxed{u => x \simeq (u:\mathbb{1}) \times x}$$

(let us recall that $\mathbb{1} = h_1$, cf. [22] and example 4.3).

This suggests to define for each $u \in \mathbb{K}(\mathbb{M})$ a process called the **trigger** (on u) by

$$\boxed{\tau_u = u:\mathbb{1}}$$

Then we derive an operator which is very often regarded as primitive, the well-known (binary) **sum** $(p+q)$:

$$p \overset{u}{\to} p' \vdash p+q \overset{u}{\to} p'$$

$$q \overset{v}{\to} q' \vdash p+q \overset{v}{\to} q'$$

In order to realize the sum, we have to trigger the two arguments on the reception of some signal and put them into a context which sends only one signal. The expression we gave in [2] was

$$x+y \simeq ((\alpha^- => x \parallel \alpha^- => y) \parallel \alpha:\mathbb{0})\backslash\alpha$$

Another one is :

$$\boxed{x+y \simeq (\alpha^- => (\alpha^- => x \parallel \alpha^- => y))\backslash\alpha}$$

Thus we see that in our calculus non-deterministic choice results (with the presence of confluent non-determinism in the parallel composition) from unarbitrated communications.

Remark 6.1 : at this point we must mention the fact that our primitive operators $u:p$ and $u*p$ might have been restricted to $u \in \Gamma(\mathbb{M})$. If we are in a calculus applied to $\langle A,S\rangle$ they even may be restricted to

$u \in Y$ where $Y = A \cup S \cup S^- \cup \Lambda \cup \Lambda^-$

(with $\Lambda^- = \{\lambda^- / \lambda \in \Lambda\}$ and similarly for S^-).

For we have :

$0:x \simeq 0*x \simeq \mathbb{O}\ ,\ 1*x \simeq x$

$1:x \simeq (\alpha^- : \mathbb{O} \parallel \alpha : x)\backslash\alpha$

$(u+v):x \simeq u:x + v:x$

$(u+v)*x \simeq h_{(u+v)}\times x$

$(u.v):x \simeq u=>(v:x)$

$(u.v)*x \simeq u*(v*x)$ ▪

Yet another derived operator : the **interleaving** parallel composition $(p \mid q)$ in which the components are not allowed to proceed synchronously :

$p \overset{u}{\to} p' \vdash (p \mid q) \overset{u}{\to} (p' \mid q)$

$q \overset{v}{\to} q' \vdash (p \mid q) \overset{v}{\to} (p \mid q')$

The expression defining this operator in MEIJE is similar to that which defines the product but obviously we have here to send only one occurrence of the signal to the components :

$$\boxed{x \mid y \simeq (\alpha * (\alpha^- * x \parallel \alpha^- * y))\backslash\alpha}$$

This operator allows to express a **desynchronization** construct similar to that used in [21] by which the behaviour of a process is at any time delayed :

$\vdash \nabla(p) \overset{1}{\to} \nabla(p)$

$p \overset{u}{\to} p' \vdash \nabla(p) \overset{u}{\to} \nabla(p')$

It is trivially given by

$$\boxed{\nabla(x) \simeq (x \mid \mathbb{1})}$$

As we shall just see the situation is summarized by saying that we have (at least) three equivalent formulations of our MEIJE calculi. That is we have three calculi $\mathcal{M}$ (MEIJE), $\mathcal{S}$ (a variant of the early SCCS [21]) and $\mathcal{C}$, each of which being a subcalculus of the others :

	$\mathcal{M}$	$\mathcal{S}$	$\mathcal{C}$
action $u:p$ $(u \in \Gamma(\mathbb{M}))$	all primitive		
restriction $p\backslash\alpha$			
recursive definitions			
morphism φp	optional		
ticking $u*p$ $(u \in \Gamma(\mathbb{M}))$		derived	derived
parallel composition $(p \parallel q)$		derived	derived
desynchronization $\nabla(p)$	derived		derived
product $p \times q$	derived		
interleaving $p \mid q$	derived	derived	

(the blank spaces ought to be filled with "primitive")

Remarks : implicitely

- all these calculi are relative to a monoid $\Gamma(\mathbb{M})$
- the common semantics is the strong equipollence

We have seen how to derive the primitive operators of $\mathcal{S}$ and $\mathcal{C}$ in MEIJE, and some other equations :

$$u * x \simeq h_u \times x$$

$$u => x \simeq \tau_u \times x \qquad (\text{ with } \tau_u = u : \mathbb{1})$$

$$\nabla(x) \simeq (x \mid \mathbb{1})$$

Thus for the other "inclusions" :

$$\boxed{(x \mid y) = (\nabla(h_{\alpha^-} \times x) \times \nabla(h_{\alpha^-} \times y) \times h_\alpha)\backslash\alpha}$$

This allows to define the sum in $\mathcal{S}$ (and in $\mathcal{C}$) :

$$x + y = (\alpha => (\alpha^- => x \mid \alpha^- => y))\backslash\alpha$$

Therefore we can define for example a clock

$$h_{\alpha+\alpha\beta+\beta} = (x \text{ where } x = \alpha : x + \alpha\beta : x + \beta : x)$$

Then

$$\boxed{((x \parallel y) = ((\alpha+\alpha\beta+\beta) * (\nabla(\alpha^- * x) \times \nabla(\beta^- * y)))\backslash\alpha,\beta}$$

The equivalence of $\mathcal{M}$ and $\mathcal{S}$ is that of two standpoints out of which

- the former sets an "asynchronous" parallel composition, where the components are priori independant and synchronized by some tools (ticking, restriction)
- The latter comprises a synchronous parallel composition and a construct to desynchronize (but also a synchronization mechanism : restriction).

The calculus $\mathcal{S}$ seems to be the "most primitive" one (exercice : write the exact formulation -without ticking and sum- of $\parallel$ in $\mathcal{S}$). The calculus $\mathcal{C}$ lies upon the distinction of the two fundamental aspects of parallel composition :

- mutual exclusion enforced in the interleaving operator, used as desynchronization
- temporal atomicity of global actions insured by the synchronous product

(see below, chapter 6.2)

We shall not distinguish these calculi, using the primitive of one or the other according to which is the more convenient.

Remark 6.2 : in SCCS [22] Milner uses some "infinitary" constructs : infinite sums or recursive definitions, and also more general restrictions parametrized by subsets of the action monoid :

$$p \overset{u}{\rightarrow} p', u \in B \vdash p \upharpoonright B \overset{u}{\rightarrow} p' \upharpoonright B$$

(this is a generalized clock, see example 5.2)

Here we want to have more "syntactical" (effective) constructs. We shall see what is lost in doing so. But pursing this spirit we might have define a calculus $\mathcal{M}'$ with

- action, parallel composition, recursive definitions and
- a unique synchronization construct called **interfacing**.

In such an operator $p \mid U$ (*p interfaced by U*) the given subset U of $\Gamma(\mathbb{M}) \times \Gamma(\mathbb{M})$ tells what actions are allowed to pass through the interface and how they are modified :

$$p \xrightarrow{u} p', (u,v) \in U \vdash p \mid U \xrightarrow{v} p' \mid U$$

This is a generalized clock (cf. example 5.2) which gathers restriction, morphism and ticking.

However such a construct is too abstract (for instance how does it bind signal identifiers ?).

Some other remarkable classes of processes are realized as subcalculi of MEIJE. A first example is that of finite processes, or finite automata but without terminal states. A **finite process** is given by a transition system with initial state $\Theta = (\mathbb{Q}, \mathbf{A}, T, q)$ such that $\mathbb{Q}$ and T are finite sets.. These are our *finite* objects in the semantical universe of transition systems. It might be rather clear that if $\mathbf{A} \subseteq \mathbb{M}$ then finite processes on $\mathbf{A}$ are strongly realized by agents of the subcalculus $\mathcal{F}_{\mathbb{M}}$ of MEIJE whose syntax is

- the constant $\mathbb{O}$
- action $u : p$ for $u \in \mathbb{K}(\mathbb{M})$
- sum $p + q$, recursive definitions

Indeed Milner [23] has given a complete (with respect to the strong equipollence) axiomatization of this calculus ; as usual completeness lies upon the existence of *normal forms* for agents of the calculus. These are terms of the form

$$(x_l \text{ where } \ldots, x_i = \sum_{1 \le j \le k} u_i^j : x_j, \ldots)$$

in which it is easy to recognize a finite automaton : $x_1, \ldots, x_k$ represent states (with x_l initial) while the system of equations is nothing else than a linear grammar representing the transition table.

For example the equations of

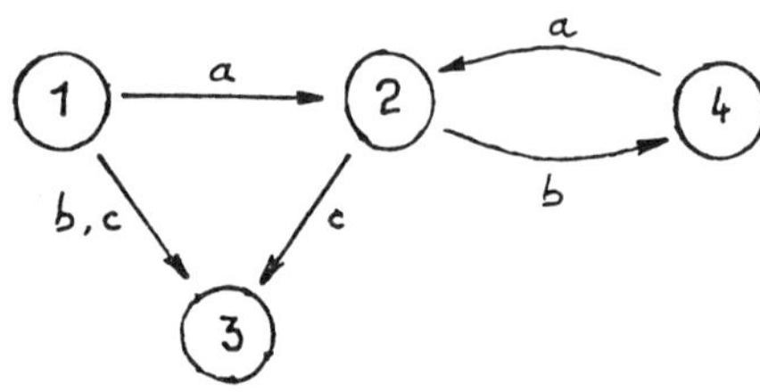

are

$$x_1 = 0 : x_1 + a : x_2 + (b+c) : x_3 + 0 : x_4$$

$$x_2 = 0 : x_1 + 0 : x_2 + c : x_3 + a : x_4$$

and so on.

With 1 as initial state, this process is also realized by the term

$$(b+c) : \mathbb{O} + a : (x \text{ where } x = c : \mathbb{O} + b : y, y = a : x)$$

In a similar way one may describe the context-free grammars by a subcalculus $\mathcal{N}$ of MEIJE called in [2] that of *sequential non-deterministic processes.* Its constructors are

- the constant $\mathbb{O}$
- action $u:p$ for $u \in \mathbb{K}(\mathbb{M})$
- sum $p+q$ and sequential composition $p;q$
- recursive definitions

Let us explain what our **sequential composition** is (s.a. [6,20]). Assume we are in calculus applied to $<A,S>$, where $s \in S$ is a distinguished **termination signal.** Then the specification of $p;q$ (implicitely parametrized by s) is

$$p \xrightarrow{u} p', s \text{ does not occur in } u \quad \vdash p;q \xrightarrow{u} p';q$$

$$\begin{array}{l} p \xrightarrow{us^-}, s \text{ does not occur in } u \\ q \xrightarrow{v} q' \end{array} \vdash p;q \xrightarrow{u_1} q'$$

This operator is expressed in MEIJE (cf. [2]) by means of another one $p \setminus s$

$$x \setminus s \simeq (\alpha * <\beta s/s> x \ || \ (y \text{ where } y = \alpha^- :y + \alpha^- \beta : \mathbb{O}))\backslash \alpha, \beta$$

(x *until* S, which kills X as soon as it has signaled its termination)

$$x;y \simeq (<\alpha/s>(x \setminus s) \ || \ \alpha => y)\backslash \alpha$$

Remarks : here we see a use of applied morphisms in order to synchronize on specific actions. Our formulation, compared to that of CCS [20], shows the fruitfulness of Milner's idea of action monoid : here we do not have to look at this synchronization upto an observation criterion hiding internal communications. Moreover we do not have to modify the *text* of the synchronized agents : we simply put them into synchronizing expression.

Then for example the well-known grammar for the language of sequences of n a's followed by n b's ($n \geq 0$) is translated as

$$(x \text{ where } x = s^- : \mathbb{O} + (a:x);(b:s^- : \mathbb{O}))$$

And for the Dyck's language on $\{a,b\}$

$$(x \text{ where } x = s^- : \mathbb{O} + (a:x);(b:x) + (b:x);(a:x))$$

(see [2]).

We have given in [3] another example of a class of process realizable as a subcalculus of MEIJE, that of systems determined by *labelled Petri nets.* From an informal point of view, a calculus seems to correspond to a *language* where one frelly uses the primitive constructs to "program" processes or synchronization mechanisms wheras we have an image of the idea of *architecture* as expressions built with some "static" operators. For instance in MEIJE the static operators are restriction, morphism, ticking and parallel composition : they set an immutable structure upon their arguments. Let us call for a while *"synchronizing net expressions"* the expressions got from this syntax. Then any such term t with free process variables $x_1,\ldots,x_k$ each occurring once only may be shown equivalent to a normal form

$$(u_1 * \varphi_1 x_1 \ || \ \ldots \ || \ u_k * \varphi_k x_k \ || \ syn)\backslash V$$

for some finite subset V of Λ, where $syn \in \mathcal{F}$ is a finite synchronizer

6.2. Implementation

It is often argued that parallelism is legitimately simulated by interleaving. Here we give a precise meaning to this assertion. It lies upon the duality of the notion of atomicity (= non-interruptibility) in the action monoid and the notion of abstraction criterion introducing atomicity at an abstract level.

A preliminary remark : in a MEIJE calculus (in any formulation) we may restrict the morphisms to be *alphabetic* , looking like relabellings of CCS, that is of the form $<\dots u/a \dots>$ where $u \in \Lambda$. This was already pointed out by Milner in [22]. We leave its proof to the reader (hint : use the clocks h_{v^+}). We want to implement the $\mathcal{C}$ calculus applied to $<A,S>$ (with a termination signal $s \in S$) in which the action constructs $u:p$ are restricted to $u \in Y \cup \{1\}$ (see remark 6.1. We recall that $Y = A \cup S \cup S^- \cup \Lambda \cup \Lambda^-$).

The crucial observation is simply that the commutative monoid

$$\Gamma(\mathbb{M}) = \mathbb{N}<A> \times \mathbb{Z}<S \cup \Lambda>$$

is nothing else than a quotient of the free monoid Y^* of sequences on Y^*. Namely by the congruence given by the relations :

$u:v = v:u$ for all u,v

$u:u^- = \varepsilon$ (the empty sequence) for $u \in S \cup \Lambda$

Notation : $\pi(u) \subseteq Y^*$ is the equivalence class of u in this congruence.

In the target calculus $\mathcal{C}'$ only "particulate" actions (cf. [22]), i.e. in Y, are allowed. Then in our translation of $\mathcal{C}$ into $\mathcal{C}'$ a composite action u of $\Gamma(\mathbb{M})$ is represented by any sequence v such that $\pi(v) = u$. But this is not yet sufficient since we also have to distinguish sequences of composite actions. Therefore we need two particulate actions d and f, not in Y, indicating respectively the *beginning* and the *end* of a non-interruptible action in $\mathcal{C}$. For instance a sequence $d : a : a^- : b : a : f$ represents $a.b$. Thus an action $u \in \Gamma(\mathbb{M})$ is represented by any sequence of the set

$$\psi(u) = \{d : v : f \;/\; u = \pi(v)\}$$

Let

$$\$ = \{ \{u\} \;/\; u \in \Gamma(\mathbb{M})\}$$

$$\mathbb{C} = \{\psi(u) \;/\; u \in \Gamma(\mathbb{M})\}$$

These are observation criteria respectively on $\Gamma(\mathbb{M})$ and $Y' = Y \cup \{d,f\}$. And $\psi : \$ \rightarrow \mathbb{C}$ is an injection.

Remarks : $\$$ determines the same equipollence $\sim$ as the strong criterion. Note also that some sequences of Y'^* are unobservable from $\mathbb{C}$.

Now in the target calculus $\mathcal{C}'$ the parallel composition acts as interleaving but with some rendez-vous mechanism in order to synchronize. Thus this calculus has some similarity with TCSP [6]. The syntax is :

(i) $\mathbb{O}$ is a term of $\mathcal{C}'$; each identifier $x \in X$ is a term of $\mathcal{C}'$

(ii) if $a \in Y'$ and p is a term then $a:p$ is a term

(iii) if p is a term and φ an alphabetic synchronization morphism then φp is a term

(iv) if p and q are terms of $\mathcal{C}'$ then $p+q$ and $p;q$ are terms of $\mathcal{C}'$

(v) if p and q are terms of $\mathcal{C}'$ and B is a finite subset of Y' then $p \mid_B q$ is a term of $\mathcal{C}'$

(vi) recursive definitions, as usual.

Note : the composition operator $|_B$ binds the identifiers $\alpha \in \Lambda$ such that $\alpha \in B$ or $\alpha^- \in B$.

The semantics of the parallel composition operator $|_B$ is that the two components are interleaved except when they perform actions in B, on which there is a rendez-vous. This is similar to Milner's conjunction $\&_B$, see [22,2] and to de Simone ' s "produit de mixage" [32] :

$$p \xrightarrow{u} p', u \notin B \vdash (p \mid_B q) \xrightarrow{u} (p' \mid_B q)$$

$$p \xrightarrow{b} p', q \xrightarrow{b} q', b \in B \vdash (p \mid_B q')$$

$$q \xrightarrow{u} q', u \notin B \vdash (p \mid_B q) \xrightarrow{u} (p \mid_B q')$$

In order to define a syntax directed implementation of $\mathscr{C}$ in $\mathscr{C}'$ we obviously need some synchronizers :

- the first one ensures the correct scheduling of abstract actions, excluding overlapping :

  $sem = (x \text{ where } x = d : f : x)$

This is just a simple semaphore, performing repeatedly the sequence $d : f$.

- the second one, used in the translation of restriction, controls the balance between occurrences of α and α^- ($\alpha \in \Lambda$) during the course of an abstract action :

$$syn_\alpha = (x \text{ where } x = (d : y);(f : x) ,$$
$$y = s^- : \mathbb{0} + (\alpha : y);(\alpha^- : y) + (\alpha^- : y);(\alpha : y))$$

(y performs sequences in a Dyck's language, in which α occurs as many times as α^-, and x is the iteration of y, see [2,6])

The translation ϑ is now fairly obvious :

(i) $\vartheta(\mathbb{0}) = \mathbb{0}$

(ii) $\vartheta(a : -) = d : a : f : x$ For $a \in Y$
and $\vartheta(1 : -) = d : f : x$

(iii) $\vartheta(\varphi -) = \varphi x$

(iv) $\vartheta(- \text{ where } x_{i_1} = -, \ldots, x_{i_k} = -) = (z \text{ where } x_{i_1} = y_1, \ldots, x_{i_k} = y_k)$

(v) $\vartheta(- \backslash \alpha) = (x \mid_{B_\alpha} syn_\alpha)$ with $B_\alpha = \{d, f, \alpha, \alpha^-\}$

(vi) $\vartheta(- \mid -) = ((x \mid y) \mid_B sem)$ with $B = \{d, f\}$ (and $\mid \; = \; \mid_\phi$)

(vii) $\vartheta(- \times -) = (x \mid_B y)$

Our purpose is achieved since

proposition 6.1

the triple $(\psi, \vartheta, (\mathbb{C}, \sim_\mathbb{C}))$ is a translation (syntax- directed implementation) of $\mathscr{C}$ in $\mathscr{C}'$.

The situation in this implementation is much simpler than, for instance, the more realistic problem of translating CSP in CCS (cf [13]).

7. Definability results

Until now we have seen only examples of what can be defined in MEIJE or any equivalent calculi, that is examples in the semantical universe of MEIJE processes and operators. But the two fundamental questions remain

- what is the class of MEIJE-realizable processes ?
- which operators can be defined by MEIJE expressions ?

To the first one we get, by means of de Simone ' s results [33,34], a rather complete answer. The second one is more difficult.

We study these problems in the particular case of processes on a free commutative monoid $\mathbb{N}\langle A\rangle$ of actions with $A = \{a_1,\ldots,a_m\}$.

It is well-known that such a monoid is isomorphic (by Parikh's mapping) to $\mathbb{N}^m$, the additive monoid of m-uples of positive integers. Thus we have a notion of recursively enumerable or computable subset of $\mathbb{N}\langle A\rangle$:

$U \subseteq \mathbb{N}\langle a_1,\ldots,a_m\rangle$ **is computable iff**

$\{(n_1,\ldots,n_m) \,/\, a^{n_1}{}_1 \ldots a^{n_m}{}_m \in U\}$ is a recursively enumerable subset of $\mathbb{N}^m$.

This definition is obviously extended to predicates, that is $U \subseteq \mathbb{N}\langle A\rangle^k$, corresponding to subsets of $\mathbb{N}^{k.m}$.

In the sequel we let $\mathbb{M} = \mathbb{N}\langle a_1,\ldots,a_m\rangle \times \mathbb{Z}\langle S\rangle$ (though the set S of signals does not play any rôle). The crucial result is :

Lemma 7.1 (de Simone [33,34])

Let $f : \mathbb{N}^k \to \mathbb{N}$ be a primitive recursive function, $a \in A$ and $\chi(a,f)$ the operator specified on $\Gamma(\mathbb{M})$ by the rule :

$$\left\{\begin{array}{l} x_1 \overset{u_1 a^{n_1}}{\rightarrow} x'_1 ,\ldots, x_k \overset{u_k a^{n_k}}{\rightarrow} x'_k , \\ u_i \in \mathbb{N}\langle A-\{a\}\rangle \times \mathbb{Z}\langle S \cup A\rangle , \\ v = u_1 \ldots u_k \, a^{f(n_1,\ldots,n_k)} \end{array}\right\}$$

$$\vdash \chi(a,f)(x_1, \ldots, x_k) \overset{v}{\rightarrow} \chi(a,f)(x'_1,\ldots,x'_k)$$

Then $\chi(a,f)$ is strongly definable in the MEIJE applied calculus $\mathcal{M}_{\langle A,S\rangle}$ ▪

The proof (see [33,34]) gives a construction of an expression e_f for f (we implicitely asssume a fixed) by induction on the scheme of definition of f :

(i) If f is the constant function $f(n_1,\ldots,n_k) = 0$ then

$$e_f = \langle 1/a\rangle\, x_1 \times \ldots \times \langle 1/a\rangle\, x_k$$

(ii) If f is a projection $f(n_1,\ldots,n_k) = n_i$ then

$$e_f = \langle 1/a\rangle\, x_1 \times \ldots \times x_i \times \ldots \times \langle 1/a\rangle\, x_k$$

(iii) If f is the successor function :

$$e_f = a * x_1$$

(iv) If f is a composition :

$$f(n_1,\ldots,n_k) = g(g_1(n_1,\ldots,n_k),\ldots,g_l(n_1,\ldots,n_k))$$

then

$$e_f = e_g[e_{g_1}/x_1,\ldots,e_{g_l}/x_l]$$

(v) If f is defined by primitive recursion, for instance

$$\left\{\begin{array}{l} f(0,n) = g(n) \\ f(l+1,n) = g'(f(l,n),l,n) \end{array}\right.$$

then

$$e_f = (<\alpha/a> x_1 \times <\beta/a> x_2 \times syn)\backslash\alpha,\beta$$

with

$$syn = (x \textbf{ where } x = e_g[t_1] + \alpha^- => (e_g[<\alpha\delta/\alpha,\lambda/\beta>x, t_2, t_3]\backslash\lambda,\delta))$$

where

$$t_1 = (y \textbf{ where } y = 1{:}y + \beta^- a => y)$$

$$t_2 = (y \textbf{ where } y = 1{:}y + \delta a => y)$$

and

$$t_3 = (u \text{ where } y = 1{:}y + \beta^- \lambda a => y) \quad \blacksquare$$

An easy corollary of this Lemma is :

Proposition 7.1

Let U be a computable subset of $\mathbb{N}<a_1,...,a_m>^{k+1}$ and H_U the operator specified on $\Gamma(\mathbb{M})$ by the rule

$$\left\{\begin{array}{l} x_1 \xrightarrow{u_1 v_1} x'_1,...,x_k \xrightarrow{u_k \cdot v_k} x'_k, v_i \in \mathbb{Z}<S \cup \Lambda> \\ \text{and } u_i \in \mathbb{N}<A> \ (\text{for } 1 \leq i \leq k), (u_1,...,u_k,u) \in U, \\ v = v_1 \ldots v_k u \end{array}\right\}$$

$$\vdash \ H_U(x_1,...,x_k) \xrightarrow{v} H_U(x'_1,...,x'_k)$$

Then H_U is strongly definable in $\mathcal{M}_{<A,S>}$ ▪

Remark 7.1 : in fact this is true in the restricted calculus $\mathcal{S}'_{<A,S>}$ which is $\mathcal{S}_{<A,S>}$ without the desynchronization operator ∇ but with sum as a primitive operator.

This result has quite a lot of consequences. For instance if $U \subseteq \mathbb{N}<A>$ it means that any **effective clock** h_U (with U computable) is strongly realizable in MEIJE. This contrasts with SCCS [22] in which one always may define :

$$h_U = fix\ x\ .\ \{x = \sum_{u \in U} u : x\}$$

even when U is not computable.

As we have seem clocks are related to ticking operators, thus we are able to generalize this construct :

$$\boxed{U * x \simeq h_U \times x}$$

Similarly every **effective trigger** τ_U is realizable :

$$\boxed{\tau_U \simeq (\alpha * h_U \ \| \ \alpha^- : \mathbb{1})\backslash\alpha}$$

and the associated triggering construct is

$$\boxed{U => x \simeq \tau_U \times x}$$

which allows to generalize the action operator :

$$\boxed{U : x \simeq U => (1 : x)}$$

When $U \subseteq \mathbb{N}\langle A\rangle^2$ the above proposition indicates the definability of some interfacing operators. For instance if B is a computable subset of $\mathbb{N}\langle A\rangle$ then the "restriction" operator $p \upharpoonright B$ which is $p \mid U$ for

$$U = \{(u.v, v.u) / u \in B, v \in \mathbb{Z}\langle S \cup \Gamma\rangle\}$$

is definable.

Yet another example : **effective pure scheduling**. A pure scheduling of a system of k processes is a context which tells at any discrete time $n \in \mathbb{N}$ what are the components allowed to proceed. Such a control is determined by a (recursively enumerable) subset V of $\{0,1\}^k \times \mathbb{N}$: the last component is the current date, the k first ones are boolean values (not allowed / allowed to proceed). We omit the obvious formal specification. Assuming that A contains an action a , the subset V is identified to a computable subset U of $\mathbb{N}\langle a\rangle^{k+1}$. Then the itended scheduling operator is defined by the expression

$$(\alpha_1 * x_1 \parallel \ldots \parallel \alpha_k * x_k \parallel synchro)\backslash\alpha_1,\ldots,\alpha_k$$

with

$$synchro = (\langle\alpha/a\rangle H_U[t_1,\ldots,t_k] \times t)\backslash\alpha$$

and

$$t_i = h_{(1+\alpha_i^- a)} \qquad (1 \leq i \leq k)$$

$$t = (x \text{ where } x = 1{:}(\alpha^- * x)) \quad \text{(seeexample 4.3)}$$

Here we do not have morphisms on the arguments since we do not care about synchronisation of specific actions.

Obviously the strong expressive power of our calculus immediately entails undecidability results :

Proposition 7.2

The (equivalent) questions of whether or not, for agents $p \in \mathcal{A}_{\langle A,S\rangle}$

(1) $p \sim \mathbb{O}$

(2) $\{u / \exists q.p \xrightarrow{u} q\} = \phi$

(3) $\{q / \exists u.p \xrightarrow{u} q\} = \phi$

are undecidable.

Indeed if B is a recursively enumerable but not recursive subset of $\mathbb{N}\langle A\rangle$ and $u \in \mathbb{N}\langle A\rangle$ we have

$$(u{:}\mathbb{O}) \upharpoonright B \sim \mathbb{O} \iff u \notin B \qquad \blacksquare$$

The main applications of proposition 7.1 are to answer the questions asked at the outset of this section. We define an **effective transition system** on $\mathbb{N}\langle A\rangle$ (with $A = \{a_1,\ldots,a_m\}$) to be a system $\Theta = (\mathbb{Q}, \mathbb{N}\langle A\rangle, T)$ such that

- $\mathbb{Q} = \{q_n / n \in \mathbb{N}\}$ is a denumerable set of states and
- the transition relation is effective with respect to the enumeration of $\mathbb{Q}$. That is

  $$V = \{(n, n_1, \ldots, n_m, k) / (q_n, a^{n_1}{}_1 \ldots a^{n_m}{}_m, q_k) \in T\}$$

  is a recursively enumerable subset of $\mathbb{N}^{m+2}$.

Theorem 7.1 (first definability theorem)

any effective transition system on $\mathbb{N}<A>$ (A finite) is strongly realizable in an applied MEIJE calculus.

The idea is the following : we introduce two new actions a and b (not in A) which will serve as "coloured sticks" to count the index of the starting state and target state of the transitions. Now let (with the previous notations)

$$U = \{a^n a^{n_1}{}_1 \ldots a^{n_m}{}_m b^k \ / \ (n, n_1, \ldots, n_m, k) \in V\}$$

By definition this is a computable subset of $\mathbb{N}<a, a_1, \ldots, a_m, b>$ if V is recursively enumerable. Thus if Θ is effective, we know by proposition 7.1 that the clock h_U is strongly realizable in MEIJE. Obviously we shall convert a and b to receiving of signals α and β; and it only remains to ensure the correct chaining of states. In order to do this we need a synchronizer t which satisfies :

$$\forall n \in \mathbb{N} \quad t \xrightarrow{\beta^n} (\alpha^n => t)$$

(in fact $\alpha^n => t$ is a "synchronous bag" containing initially n tokens, cf. example 4.5)

It is easily proved that we may let

$$t = (x \text{ where } x = (\beta : \alpha : \mathbb{1}) \times x + 1 : x)$$

Finally with each state q_n of Θ we associate

$$\vartheta(q_n) = (<\alpha^- / a, \beta^- / b> h_U \times (\alpha^n => t)) \backslash \alpha, \beta$$

and this is the intended strong realization ▪

Remark : this result holds in $\mathcal{J}'_{<A', S>}$ (with $A' = A \cup \{a, b\}$), see remark 7.1.

To conclude this section we quote de Simone ' s theorem about definability of operators. Let us call for a while **effective calculus of processes** any simple algebraic calculus $A = (F, \mathbb{M}, \Phi, \rho)$ such that

- F is a finite set of operator symbols
- $\mathbb{M} = \mathbb{N}<A>$ for some finite alphabet of actions A
- Φ is a finite semantic specification of F on $\mathbb{M}$ such that for each rule of Φ the predicate U on actions is computable (cf. § 31)
- ρ is the strong congruence

Theorem 7.2 (second definability theorem, de Simone [33])

any effective calculus of processes is a subcalculus of an applied MEIJE calculus.

To prove this de Simone builds a syntax-directed translation

$$\vartheta(f) = (\alpha_1 * \varphi_1 x_1 \ \| \ \ldots \ \| \ \alpha_k * \varphi_k x_k \ \| \ syn(f)) \backslash V$$

where the φ_i 's are applied morphisms and $syn(f)$ controls the correct application of the semantic rules for f.

Let us give some examples of definable operators. Let $w \in \mathbb{M}$ and U be a decidable (i.e. computable as well as its complement) subset of $\mathbb{M}$

(i) discriminated ticking :

$$p \xrightarrow{u} p', u \notin U \vdash w *_U p \xrightarrow{u} w *_U p'$$

$$p \xrightarrow{u} p', u \in U \vdash w *_U p \xrightarrow{w.u} w *_U p'$$

(ii) discriminated triggering :

$$p \xrightarrow{u} p', u \not\subset U \vdash w{=}{>}_U p \xrightarrow{u} w{=}{>}_U p'$$

$$p \xrightarrow{u} p', u \in U \vdash w{=}{>}_U p \xrightarrow{w.u} p'$$

(iii) discriminated sum :

$$p \xrightarrow{u} p', u \in U \vdash p \oplus_U q \xrightarrow{u} p'$$

$$q \xrightarrow{v} q', v \in U \vdash p \oplus_U q \xrightarrow{u} q'$$

and the rules of $(p \parallel q)$ with the additional hypotheses $u \not\subset U, v \not\subset U$:

$$p \xrightarrow{u} p', u \not\subset U \vdash p \oplus_U q \xrightarrow{u} p' \oplus_U q$$

$$p \xrightarrow{u} p', q \xrightarrow{v} q', u \not\subset U, v \not\subset U \vdash p \oplus_U q \xrightarrow{uv} p' \oplus_U q'$$

$$q \xrightarrow{v} q', u \not\subset U \vdash p \oplus_U q \xrightarrow{v} p \oplus_U q'$$

(iv) discriminated synchrony :

$$p \xrightarrow{u} p', q \xrightarrow{v} q', u \in U, v \in U \vdash p \oplus_U q \xrightarrow{uv} p' \oplus_U q'$$

and the rules of interleaving when $u \not\subset U$ or $v \not\subset U$.

(v) conjunction :

$$p \xrightarrow{u} p', q \xrightarrow{u} q', u \in U \vdash p \cap_U q \xrightarrow{u} p' \cap_U q'$$

and the rules of $(p \parallel q)$ when $u \not\subset U, v \not\subset U$

8. Subcalculi : rational parallel place machines

Owing to its universality the MEIJE calculus may appear too strong in some respects (undecidability problems). Therefore it is natural to look for less powerful calculi. We have already seen such a subcalculus, namely that of *finite processes* (par. 6 and [23]) in which one can only define finite transition systems. Many synchronization problems may be formulated in this calculus which is closed under many interesting operators (see [1,24,26]). But it disallows expressing dynamical creation of parallelism. A typical example of "unboundedly parallel" object is that of **bag** (cf. example 4.5 in § 4).

In this section we propose a generalization of finite processes following the usual mathematical step in which "finite" is generalized by "rational".

We have not emphasized algebraic properties of operators (see [22,2]) and their proofs in this notes. At least we may note that

$$\begin{cases} p+q \simeq q+p \\ p+(q+r) \simeq (p+q)+r \\ p+\mathbb{0} \simeq p \end{cases}$$

$$\begin{cases} p \times (q \times r) \simeq (p \times q) \times r \\ (p+q) \times r \simeq p \times r + q \times r \end{cases}$$

and also

$$p \times q \simeq q \times p$$

$$p \times \mathbb{1} \simeq p \ , \ p \times \mathbb{0} \simeq \mathbb{0}$$

and moreover

$$\begin{cases} (u+v)\text{=>}p \simeq u\text{=>}p + v\text{=>}p \\ u\text{=>}(p+q) \simeq u\text{=>}p + u\text{=>}q \\ 1\text{=>}p \simeq p \ , \ 0\text{=>}p \simeq \mathbb{0} \\ u\text{=>}(v\text{=>}p) \simeq (u.v)\text{=>}p \\ u\text{=>}(p \times q) \simeq (u\text{=>}p) \times q \end{cases}$$

Therefore the set $\mathcal{A}_{\mathbb{M}}/\sim$ of MEIJE processes is a $\mathbb{K}(\mathbb{M})$- algebra (see [10], chap. VII). Introducing a "star" or **cross** operator

$$\boxed{x^{\times} = (y \text{ where } y = x \times y + \mathbb{1})}$$

we may call, following Eilenberg (idem), the operators

$$p+q \ , \ p \times q \ , \ u\text{=>}p \ , \ p^{\times}$$

the **rational** ones over $\mathcal{A}_{\mathbb{M}}/\sim$.

Note that, using the notations of SCCS [22]

$$p^{\times} \simeq \sum_{n \in \mathbb{N}} p^{n} \quad \text{where } p^{0} = \mathbb{1}, p^{n+1} = p \times p^{n}$$

and that the usual identity $p^{\times} \simeq p \times p^{\times} + \mathbb{1}$ is valid.

Reminder : we recall that the family $Rat(\mathbb{M})$ of rational subsets of a monoid $\mathbb{M}$ is (cf. [9,10]) the closure of the family of finite subsets of $\mathbb{M}$ by the rational operations

- union, denoted $U+V$
- product $U.V = \{u.v / u \in U, v \in V\}$
- generated submonoid denoted $U^{\times}$ in order to avoid confusion with the set of sequences.

When $\mathbb{M}$ is a product monoid (for instance $\mathbb{N}^{k}$, with operation $(n_1,\ldots,n_k)\cdot(m_1,\ldots,m_k) = (n_1+m_1,\ldots,n_k+m_k)$) the rational subsets are usually called rational relations.

We might call *rational* the agents of the family $\mathcal{R}_{\mathbb{M}}$ closure of the calculus $\mathcal{F}_{\mathbb{M}}$ of finite processes by rational operators, but we shall not keep exactly this denomination.

Example 8.1 : in $\mathcal{R}_{\mathbb{M}}$ lie the **rational triggers** τ_U for U a rational subset of $\mathbb{M}$, since τ is a morphism :

$$\tau_0 = \mathbb{0} \ , \ \tau_1 = \mathbb{1}$$

(we recall that 0 stands for the empty set, and that a singleton $\{u\}$ is denoted u)

$$\tau_{U+V} \simeq \tau_U + \tau_V$$

$$\tau_{U.V} \simeq \tau_U \times \tau_V \ , \ \tau_{u.V} \simeq u\text{=>}t_V$$

$$\tau_{U^{\times}} \simeq (\tau_U)^{\times}$$

Let us try to see what the transition systems determined by agents in $\mathcal{R}_{\mathbb{M}}$ are. We start with finite processes, expressed by agent of $\mathcal{F}_{\mathbb{M}}$ in normal form :

$$(x_l \text{ where } \ldots, x_i = \sum_{1\le j\le k} u^j{}_i : x_j, \ldots)$$

The operators $p+q, p\times q$ and $u \Rightarrow p$ preserve finiteness, thus let us look at the effect of the cross operator. It may be (recursively) specified by

$$\begin{cases} \vdash p \overset{1}{\ } \mathbb{1} \\ p \overset{u}{\to} q \ , \ p^{\times} \overset{v}{\to} r \vdash p^{\times} \overset{uv}{\to} q\times r \end{cases}$$

or more explicitely :

$$p \overset{u_1}{\to} p_1, \ldots, p \overset{u_n}{\to} p_n \vdash p^{\times} \xrightarrow{u_1 \ldots u_n} p_1 \times \ldots \times p_n$$

(including the case $n=0$ where $p^{\times} \overset{1}{\to} \mathbb{1}$).

Thus starting with $p \in \mathcal{F}_{\mathbb{M}}$ the states of the transition system determined by $p^{\times}$ have the form

$$((x^{n_1}{}_1 \times \ldots \times x^{n_k}{}_k \ \textbf{where} \ \ldots, x_i = \sum_{1\le j\le k} u^j{}_i : x_j, \ldots)$$

(excepted for $p^{\times}$ itself)

This means that given the finite transition table, states may be regarded as belonging to $\mathbb{N}^k$. For example (8.2) if

$$p = (x \text{ where } x = a : y, y = b : x + c : y)$$

$$q = (y \text{ where } x = a : y, y = b : x + c : y)$$

the states reachable from $p^{\times}$ are the $p^n \times q^m$ and the transitions are given by

$$p^n \times q^m \simeq \sum_{k\le m} a^n b^{m-k} c^k : (p^{m-k} \times q^{n+k})$$

This suggests the following definition :

a **simple parallel place machine** on the monoid $\mathbb{M}$ of actions is a structure $\mathcal{Q} = (\mathbb{P}, \mathbb{M}, T, I)$ where

- $\mathbb{P} = \{p_1, \ldots, p_k\}$ is a finite set of **places**
- $T \subseteq \mathbb{P} \times \mathbb{M} \times \mathbb{P}$ is a finite set of **elementary transitions**
- I is the set of **initial markings** which is a rational subset of $\mathbb{N}^{\mathbb{P}}$.

Intuitively each place contains **tokens** and a marking μ sets tokens into place, i.e. is a mapping of $\mathbb{N}^{\mathbb{P}}$ which itself is identified to $\mathbb{N}^k$. The **states** of the machine are markings. Each elementary transition (p_i, u, p_j) removes one token from p_i and, performing u , put it in p_j. Then the behaviour is the following : given a marking μ , the machine performs synchronously elementary transitions. It thus performs a product of such transitions, by which all tokens are moved. Formally :

- each place p_i is identified to the marking where there is one token in p_i and no other one.
- T is identified to a subset of the product monoid $\mathbb{N}^{\mathbb{P}} \times \mathbb{M} \times \mathbb{N}^{\mathbb{P}}$.

For instance, the elementary transitions in the above example are :

$$(1,0) \overset{a}{\to} (0,1) \ , \ (0,1) \overset{b}{\to} (1,0) \text{ and } (0,1) \overset{c}{\to} (0,1).$$

Then the set of **transitions** of the machine $\mathfrak{A}$ is $T^{\times}$, the submonoid of $\mathbb{N}^{\mathbb{P}} \times \mathbb{M} \times \mathbb{N}^{\mathbb{P}}$ generated by T.

Example 8.2 (continued) :

$$T^{\times} = \{(n,m) \xrightarrow{a^n b^{m-k} c^k} (m-k, n+k) / n,m \in \mathbb{N}, k \leq m\}$$

In order to take into account the set of initial states, we define the transition system determined by a simple place machine $\mathfrak{A} = (\mathbb{P}, \mathbb{M}, T, I)$ by

$\Xi(\mathfrak{A}) = (\mathbb{Q}, \mathbb{M}, U)$ where

- $\mathbb{Q} = \mathbb{N}^{\mathbb{P}} \cup \{I\}$
- $(q,u,q') \in U \iff q = I \ \& \ \exists q'' \in I.\ (q'',u,q') \in T^{\times}$ or $(q,u,q') \in T^{\times}$

This definition yields the

Proposition 8.1

(1) For any simple parallel place machine $\mathfrak{A}$ on $\mathbb{M}$, $\Xi(\mathfrak{A})$ is strongly realizable in $\mathcal{R}_{\mathbb{M}}$

(2) any agent $p \in \mathcal{R}_{\mathbb{M}}$ strongly realizes $\Xi(\mathfrak{A})$ for some simple parallel place machine $\mathfrak{A}$.

From a semantical point of view, simple parallel place machines only correspond to a special kind of what might been called *rational transition systems*. These are $\Theta = (\mathbb{Q}, \mathbb{M}, T)$ *where*

- $\mathbb{Q}$ is a commutative monoid of states
- $\mathbb{M}$ is a commutative monoid of actions
- $T \subseteq \mathbb{Q} \times \mathbb{M} \times \mathbb{Q}$ is a rational relation

However these are rather abstract objects, thus we focus on the case where $\mathbb{Q}$ is the set of distribution of tokens in places. Therefore a **rational parallel place machine** (on $\mathbb{M}$) is

$\mathfrak{A} = (\mathbb{P}, \mathbb{M}, T, i)$ where

- $\mathbb{P} = \{p_1, \ldots, p_k\}$ is a finite set of places
- $\mathbb{M}$ is a commutative monoid of actions
- $T \subseteq \mathbb{N}^{\mathbb{P}} \times \mathbb{M} \times \mathbb{N}^{\mathbb{P}}$ is a rational relation
- $i \in \mathbb{N}^{\mathbb{P}}$ is the initial state

As before, this machine determines a transition system with initial state $\Xi(\mathfrak{A}) = (\mathbb{N}^{\mathbb{P}}, \mathbb{M}, T, i)$. It corresponds to a synchronous behaviour : all the tokens must be moved in a transition.

Example : bags are objects of this kind, determined by a one place machine. For if we denote :

$\varepsilon = (1) \xrightarrow{1} (1)$ (a "neutral" transition)

$t_1 = (0) \xrightarrow{a} (1)$ (to put a token)

$t_2 = (1) \xrightarrow{b} (0)$ (to remove a token)

the transition relation $T = \varepsilon^{\times} \bullet (t_1 + t_2) \bullet (t_1 + t_2)^{\times}$ is such that

$$T = \{(k) \xrightarrow{a^n b^m} (k+n-m) / n+m > 0, m \leq k\}$$

(cf. example 4.5)

The transitions ε, t_1, t_2 can be figured, with labelled barred lines to make the distinction with the transition system itself, by

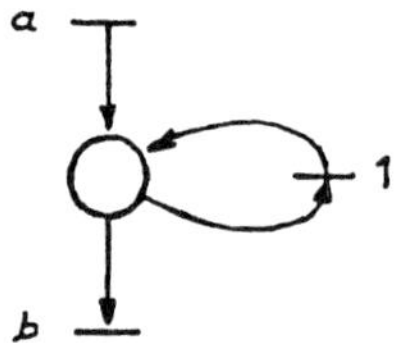

Obviously each **rational clock** i.e. h_U with U a rational subset of $\mathbb{M}$ is also defined by a rational machine (with one place and no tokens).

If we want to get an *asynchronous behaviour* we associate with $\mathcal{A}$ the transition system

$$\Delta(\mathcal{A}) = (\mathbb{N}^{\mathbb{P}}, \mathbb{M}, T', i)$$

where

$$T' = \{\varepsilon_1 + \ldots + \varepsilon_k\}^{\times} \bullet T$$

with

$$\varepsilon_j = (\mu_j, 1, \mu_j) \quad \mu_j(p) = \begin{cases} 1 & \textit{if } p = p_j \\ 0 & \textit{otherwise} \end{cases}$$

(elementary "neutral" transitions)

In the asynchronous system $\Delta(\mathcal{A})$ a transition of the machine may be performed as soon as there are enough tokens on the places since

$$(\mu_1, u, \mu_2) \in T' \iff \exists \mu'_1, \mu'_2 \bullet (\mu'_1, u, \mu'_2) \in T \;\&$$
$$\mu'_1 \leq \mu_1 \,\&\, \mu_2 = \mu_1 - \mu'_1 + \mu_2$$

For instance the bag is an example of asynchronous system.

Note : The sets $\{\mu' \,/\, \exists u. \mu \overset{u}{\rightarrow} \mu'\}$ and $\{u \,/\, \exists \mu'. \mu \overset{u}{\rightarrow} \mu'\}$ for $\mu \in \mathbb{N}^{\mathbb{P}}$ are rational (got from T by transductions).

We could have allowed a rational set I of initial states and devised $\Xi(\mathcal{A})$ as in the simple case ; but nothing is gained in doing so :

Lemma 8.1

Let $\mathcal{A} = (\mathbb{P}, \mathbb{M}, T, I)$ be a generalized rational place machine, i.e. $I \in Rat(\mathbb{N}^{\mathbb{P}})$. Then there exists a rational parallel place machine $\mathcal{A}' = (\mathbb{P}', \mathbb{M}, T', i)$ such that $\Xi(\mathcal{A})$ and $\Xi(\mathcal{A}')$, restricted to states reachable from the initial ones, are isomorphic.

In the proof one uses some results of Eilenberg & Schutzenberger [9]. We only mention the fact that *non-conservative* transitions, which lose some tokens, are introduced.

We have noted that rational clocks are determined by some rational parallel place machines. In order to define these clocks in MEIJE we have to introduce a new (temporal) **iterator**. Once remarked that

$$h_U \simeq \tau_U \times (1 : h_U)$$

we let

$$\boxed{x^{\square} = (y \textit{ where } y = x \times (1 : y))}$$

The specification of this operator is

$$p \overset{u}{\to} q \vdash p^{\square} \overset{u}{\to} q \times p^{\square}$$

For the rest of this section $\mathbb{M} = \mathbb{N}\langle A\rangle$ and $A = \{a_1,\dots,a_m\}$.

Let $\mathcal{H}_{\mathbb{M}}$ be the closure of $\mathcal{R}_{\mathbb{M}}$ by the family of operators

- $u \Rightarrow p$ for $u \in \mathbb{M}$
- φp for $\varphi = \langle u_1/a_1,\dots,u_m/a_m\rangle, u_i \in \mathbb{M}$
- $p \cap_{B^\times} q$ (see § 7) which is denoted $p \wedge_B q$, for $B \subseteq A$
- $p^{\square}$

For instance $h_U \in \mathcal{H}_{\mathbb{M}}$ for any $U \in Rat(\mathbb{M})$ since $h_U \simeq \tau_U{}^{\square}$.

Proposition 8.2

(1) for any rational place machine $\mathcal{Q}$ on $\mathbb{M} = \mathbb{N}\langle A\rangle, \Xi(\mathcal{Q})$ is strongly realizable in $\mathcal{H}_{\mathbb{N}\langle A'\rangle}$ for some A' $(A \subseteq A')$

(2) any agent $p \in \mathcal{H}_{\mathbb{M}}$ strongly realizes $\Xi(\mathcal{Q})$ for some rational place machine on $\mathbb{M}$.

For the first point, the argument is similar to that of Theorem 7.1. Let $\mathcal{Q} = (\mathbb{P},\mathbb{M},T,i)$ be a rational machine with $\mathbb{P} = \{p_1,\dots,p_k\}$, $\mathbb{M} = \mathbb{N}\langle a_1,\dots,a_m\rangle$.

Let $B = \{b_1,\dots,b_k,c_1,\dots,c_k\}$ be a set of new action symbols (not in A). Obviously $T \subseteq \mathbb{N}^{\mathbb{P}} \times \mathbb{M} \times \mathbb{N}^{\mathbb{P}}$ is isomorphic to a rational subset U of $\mathbb{N}\langle A \cup B\rangle$. We interpret b_i as the presence of an "input" token on the place p_i and similarly c_i as the presence of an "output" token. We have to control the flow of tokens in the clock h_U "realizing" the transitions. We need a synchronizer t such that

$$t \xrightarrow{c^{n_1}{}_1 \dots c^{n_k}{}_k} ((b^{n_1}{}_1 \dots b^{n_k}{}_k) \Rightarrow t)$$

for all $(n_1,\dots,n_k) \in \mathbb{N}^{\mathbb{P}}$

(in fact $(b^{n_1}{}_1 \dots b^{n_k}{}_k) \Rightarrow t$ is a "synchronous bag" containing $n_1,\dots,n_k$ coloured tokens).

This achieved if we let

$$t = (\sum_{1 \le i \le k} c_i : b_i : \mathbb{1})^{\times \square}$$

(which is in $\mathcal{H}_{\mathbb{N}}\langle A \cup B\rangle$)

Let φ_B be the projection $\langle 1/b_1,\dots,1/b_k,1/c_1,\dots,1/c_k\rangle$.

Then with each state $\mu = (l_1,\dots,l_k)$ in $\mathbb{N}^{\mathbb{P}}$ we associate

$$\vartheta(\mu) = \varphi_B(h_U \wedge_B ((b^{l_1}{}_1,\dots,b^{l_k}{}_k) \Rightarrow t))$$

and this is the claimed strong realization.

For the second point one uses Eilenberg & Schutzenberger ' s results [9] again and introduce *non-conservative* transitions which this time create tokens.

The proposed elements in this section do not allow to appreciate the practical and theoretical interest of rational parallel place machines. Moreover a similar study might be attempted for "rationally specified" operators. At least we may note that rational place machines generalize Petri nets -which we showed to be strongly realizable in MEIJE, in a more direct way, cf. [3]. Let us briefly face this. A **Petri net** (with which we assume the reader familiar, see for instance [27]) is a structure $(\mathbb{P},A,Pre,Post)$ where

- $\mathbb{P} = \{p_1,\dots,p_k\}$ is the finite set of places
- $A = \{a_1,\dots,a_m\}$ is the finite set of transitions
- $Pre : \mathbb{P}\times A \to \mathbb{N}$ and $Post : A\times\mathbb{P} \to \mathbb{N}$ are the numerical functions setting the preconditions and postconditions to the firing of transitions.

A transition $a \in A$ is *enabled* by the marking $\mu\in\mathbb{N}^{\mathbb{P}}$ if for all place $p\in\mathbb{P}$ $\mu(p)\geq Pre(p,a)$. And by firing a we get the marking μ' :

$$\mu'(p) = \mu(p)-Pre(p,a)+Post(a,p)$$

Let $t_i = (\mu_i,a_i,\mu'_i)$ for $1\leq i\leq m$ where $\mu_i(p) = Pre(p,a_i)$ and $\mu'_i = Post(a_i,p)$
Then the behaviour of the Petri net with initial marking μ is exactly that of the asynchronous transition system $\Delta(\mathcal{Q})$ (which obviously is also $\Xi(\mathcal{Q}')$ for some $\mathcal{Q}'$) associated with the machine

$$\mathcal{Q} = (\mathbb{P},\mathbb{N}\langle A\rangle,(t_1+\dots+t_m),\mu)$$

Remark : it is well-known (see [9]) that for any rational transition relation T there exists a *finite* set $U \subseteq \mathbb{N}^{\mathbb{P}}\times\mathbb{M}\times\mathbb{N}^{\mathbb{P}}$ of transitions such that T is a rational subset of $U^{\times}$. Such a finite set U may be represented as a labelled Petri net. Thus a rational parallel place machine may also be regarded as a (rationally) synchronized Petri net : a labelled Petri net provided with a rational expression on its transitions.

9. Conclusion

We chose to interpret our language in the semantical universe of transition systems. These are rather general and conceptually simple mathematical objects. As demonstrated by Plotkin [28] transition systems provide a general framework to express semantics. They also set up the natural universe in which to interpret formulae of some modal logics. For all these reasons the notion of transition system is a basis for comparison of various formalisms (see for example [4,5,18]. In these notes they have been mainly used to evaluate expressiveness of our MEIJE calculus - something which could not have been achieved without the very fruitful idea of monoid of actions due to Milner [21,22].

Obviously this is not the only possible approach to the question : what is a process ? A great variety of models may be found in the literature, among which we would like (unfairly) distinguish :

(1) models which lay "below" transition systems. One of the best known examples is that of formal languages. Although they are sometimes taken as a direct interpretation of some syntax or algebra (as in [16,17,25,30,32]), formal languages have been for a long time strongly linked to transition systems (or automata, see [10]). This is also the case in the area of parallelism (cf. [1,24,26]) where they are very often assorted by some relevant informations (see [6,7,8]). Indeed these models seem to correspond to some canonical kinds of transition systems. These models own the advantage to provide a direct semantics (without recourse to quotienting), with a direct definition of the operators ; this has not been achived here.

In the same category one may also put the observational semantics of Hennessy [14,15] which is near ours since it lies upon operational semantics. As Darondeau [8] points out this semantics contrasts with bisimulations in that backtracking along the behaviour of a process is not allowed. It seems also to be a question of linear **vs** branching time.

It is not very surprising that, among all the existing definitions of semantic equality, bisimulations are very strong as shown by Brookes and Rounds in [5]. However in some respects our equipollences determined by observation criteria on actions may appear to be too weak. To see why, let us say a few words about the second approach.

(2) On the other side one find models of the notion of processes which are "above" transition systems. The concept of machines or automata belongs here. They naturally determine transitions between states. In our domain this category is mainly represented by Petri nets (see [27]). The general idea is : how do things operate ?

In machines, the structure of states may carry some meaningful information (e.g. : boundedness in Petri nets) ; this structure requires a fine description. Therefore if one wants to show for instance that a calculus or language of processes corresponds to some class of machines (cf. for instance [3,23]) one has to carefully examine what properties are used in the proof of that correspondance. From that may emerge a complete axiomatization of the calculus ; we note that completeness is usually shown by means of normal forms, in which one recognizes the structure of a machine ([23]) or more generally of a concrete interpretation ([12,14]).

We have not paid much attention to proof theory in these notes. Many algebraic properties are valid in our calculi (cf. [2,22]) and the proof principle, i.e. Park's induction for congruences provides a very powerful tool. However we would like to have a more syntactical version, explicitely involving recourse to specifications of operators (a similar aim holds for proofs of simulation) ; this is a research in progress. More generally it should be clear that we have emphasized here an operational or "syntactical" point of view. Let us quote Milner about this subject : "operational semantics, since it can be set up with so few preconditions, must be the touchstone for assessing mathematical models rather than the reverse" ([22]). Not less clearly, much work remains to be done towards a smooth theory of that matter.

Acknoledgement : many ideas and results presented in these notes were elaborated with the contribution of R. de Simone, and some are his own.

REFERENCES

1 A. Arnold & M. Nivat : "Comportements de processus", Coll. AFCET "Les Mathématiques de l'Informatique" (AFCET, Paris, 1981)

2 D. Austry & G. Boudol : "Algèbre de processus et synchronisations", Theoret. Comput. Sci. 30 (1984) 91-131

3 G. Boudol, G. Roucairol & R. de Simone : "Petri nets and algebraic calculi of processes", Rapport de Recherche INRIA 292 (1984)

4 S.D. Brookes : "On the relationship of CCS and CSP", ICALP 83, Lecture Notes in Comput. Sci. 154 (1983) 83-96

5 S.D. Brookes & W.C. Rounds : "Behavioural equivalence relations induced by programming logics", ICALP 83, Lecture Notes in Comput. Sci. 154 (1983) 97-108

6 S.D. Brookes, C.A.R. Hoare & A.W. Roscoe : "A theory of communicating sequential processes", JACM 31 (1984) 560-599

7 Ph. Darondeau & L. Kott : "On the observational semantics of fair parallelism", ICALP 83, Lecture Notes in Comput. Sci. 154 (1983) 147-159
s.a. Rapport de Recherche INRIA 262 (1983)

8 Ph. Darondeau : "Infinitary languages and fully abstract models of fair asynchrony", Advanced Course on Logics and Models for Verification and Specification of Concurrent Systems, La Colle-sur-Loup (1984)

9 S. Eilenberg & M.P. Schutzenberger : "Rational sets in commutative monoids", Journal of Algebra 13 (1969) 173-191

10 S. Eilenberg : "Automata, Languages and Machines", vol.A, Academic Press (1974)

11 J.S. Gourlay, W.C. Rounds & R. Statman : "On properties preserved by contractions of concurrent systems", Intern. Symp. on Semantics of Concurrent Computations, Evian 79, G. Kahn Ed., Lecture Notes in Comput. Sci. 70 (1979) 51-65

12 M. Hennessy & R. Milner : "On observing nondeterminism and concurrency", ICALP 80, Lecture Notes in Comput. Sci. 85 (1980) 299-309
s.a. "Algebraic laws for nondeterminism and concurrency" CSR-133-83, Computer Science Dept., Edinburgh Univ. (1983)

13 M. Hennessy, Wei Li & G. Plotkin : "A first attempt at translating CSP into CCS", 2 nd Intern. Conf. on Distributed Computing Systems, Paris (1981) 105-115

14 M. Hennessy & R. de Nicola : "Testing equivalences for processes", ICALP 83, Lecture Notes in Comput. Sci. 154 (1983) 548-560
s.a. CSR-123-82, Comput. Sci. Dept., Edinburgh Univ. (1982)

15 M. Hennessy : "Modelling finite delay operators", CSR-153-83, Comput. Sci. Dept., Edinburgh Univ. (1983)

16 C.A.R. Hoare : "A model for communicating sequential processes", Techn. Rep. PRG-22, Programming Research Group, Oxford Univ. (1981)

17 M. Jantzen : "The power of synchronizing operations on strings", Theoret. Comput. Sci. 14 (1981) 127-154

18 K. Jensen : "A method to compare the descriptive power of different types of Petri nets", MFCS 80, Lecture Notes in Comput. Sci. 88 (1980) 348-361

19 R.M. Keller : "Formal verification of parallel programs", CACM 19 (1976) 371-384

20 R. Milner : "A Calculus of Communicating Systems", Lecture Notes in Comput. Sci 92 (1980)

21 R. Milner : "On relating synchrony and asynchrony", CSR-75-80, Comput. Sci. Dept., Edinburgh Univ. (1981)

22 R. Milner : "Calculi for synchrony and asynchrony", Theoret. Comput. Sci. 25 (1983) 267-310

23 R. Milner : "A complete inference system for a class of regular behaviour", J. of Computer and Systems Sciences 28 (1984) 439-466

24 M. Nivat : "Synchronization of concurrent processes", in "Formal Language Theory : Perspective and Open Problems", R.V. Book, ed., A.P. (1980) 429-454

25 W.F. Ogden, W.E. Riddle & W.C. Rands : "Complexity of expressions allowing concurrency", 5th ACM POPL (1978) 185-194

26 D. Park : "Concurrency and automata on infinite sequences", 5th GI Conf., Lecture Notes in Comput. Sci. 104 (1981) 167-183

27 J.L. Peterson : "Petri Nets", ACM Computing Surveys 9 (1977) 223-252

28 G. Plotkin : "A structural approach to operational semantics", Daimi FN-19, Comput. Sci. Dept., Aarhus Univ. (1981)

29 G. Plotkin : "An operational semantics for CSP", in "Formal Description of Programming Concepts II", D. Bjorner, ed, North- Holland (1982) 199-225

30 A.C. Shaw : "Software description with flow expressions", IEEE Trans. on Software Engineering 4 (1978) 242-254

31 J. Sifakis : "Property preserving homomorphisms of transition systems", Logics of Programs, Lecture Notes in Comput. Sci. 164 (1984) 458-473

32 R. de Simone : "Langages infinitaires et produit de mixage", Theoret. Comput. Sci. 31 (1984) 83-100

33 R. de Simone : "Calculabilité et expressivité dans l'algèbre de processus parallèles Meije", Thèse de 3e cycle, Univ. Paris 7 (1984)

34 R. de Simone : "Note on Meije and SCCS : infinite sum operators vs nonguarded definitions", Theoret. Comput. Sci. 30 (1984) 133-138

35 G. Winskel : "Synchronization trees", CMU-CS-83-139, Comput. Sci. Dept., Carnegie-Mellon Univ. (1983)
s.a. ICALP 83, Lecture Notes in Comput. Sci. 154 (1983) 695-711

DEADLOCK ANALYSIS IN NETWORKS OF COMMUNICATING PROCESSES

S. D. Brookes
Carnegie-Mellon University
Pittsburgh, Pa.
USA

A. W. Roscoe
Programming Research Group
Oxford University
Oxford
England

0. Abstract.

We use the failures model of Communicating Sequential Processes to describe the behaviour of a simple class of networks of communicating processes. This model is well suited to reasoning about the deadlock behaviour of processes, and we demonstrate this fact by proving some results which help in the analysis of deadlock in networks. In particular, we formulate some simple theorems which characterise the states in which deadlock can occur, and use them to prove some theorems on the absence of global deadlock in certain classes of systems. Some examples are given to show the utility of these results.

1. Introduction.

In [3,4,5] we described the failures model of communicating processes and used it to describe some interesting parallel programming examples. We stated there that the model was well suited, by its very construction, to reasoning about the potential or the absence of deadlock in systems of processes. In this paper we elaborate this point in some detail, developing some ideas which originated in Roscoe's thesis [15]. We provide some simple yet useful theorems which may be used to analyse networks for the potential of deadlock. We demonstrate the utility of these results by examining some examples from the literature. We compare our work briefly with earlier work by several other authors, and make some suggestions for future research.

The simplicity of the mathematical structure of the failures model lends itself to clean formulation of deadlock properties and to formal manipulation of process behaviour. We

NATO ASI Series, Vol. F13
Logics and Models of Concurrent Systems
Edited by K. R. Apt

assume familiarity with the material of either [3,4] or [5], where details were given of the syntax for processes in a version of CSP and of the mathematical construction of the failures model. We use P and Q to range over processes. A failure is a pair (s, X) consisting of a trace s (a finite sequence of events) and a refusal set X (a set of events). If (s, X) is a possible failure of a process P, we interpret this as saying that the process may refuse all of the events in X after having performed the sequence s; thus, if the process is placed in an environment which only wants to perform events from this set at that stage, deadlock is possible. The improved failures model of [5] also allows a treatment of the phenomenon of *divergence*, which occurs when a process is able to perform an unbounded number of internal actions without communicating with its environment. Processes were described as pairs $\langle F, D\rangle$, with F being a failure set and D a divergence set. We took in [5] a pessimistic view of divergence, regarding the possibility of divergence as catastrophic. In this view it is useless to try to prove absence of deadlock if there is a possibility of divergence. We will therefore assume in this paper that all processes are divergence-free (have empty divergence set), so that a process is fully described by its failure set. We use the notation $\mathcal{F}[\![P]\!]$ for the failure set of a process P. In [5] we also allowed for the possibility of infinite refusal sets when processes were able to use infinite alphabets. This is important since it allows cleaner statements and easier proofs for several results.

2. Networks of Communicating Processes.

Graphical representations of networks of processes have been used extensively in the literature, notably by Milne and Milner [13]. Almost every paper on deadlock analysis uses a more or less formal notion of network. Our notation will be as follows.

A network is a graph with nodes of the form (P_i, A_i), consisting of a process P_i and alphabet A_i, and with an arc (determined uniquely by the set of nodes) from (P_i, A_i) to (P_j, A_j) iff $A_i \cap A_j \neq \emptyset$ and $i \neq j$. Thus two processes are linked in the graph if and only if their alphabets indicate that there is an event representing a possible communication between them. Of course, this says nothing about whether or not such a communication will ever take place dynamically, and the network structure is static. It may be convenient to think of the arcs in a network as representing communication links. Since CSP treats communication in a more or less symmetric fashion, we do not assign directions to the arcs. Note that in the case of a system in which processes are defined by recursion, the network can be thought of as potentially infinite; a recursive expansion of a process definition can be viewed as replacing a node of the system by a new graph.

For a network $V = \{(P_i, A_i) \mid 1 \leq i \leq n\}$ we define the parallel composition PAR(V) to be

$$\mathrm{PAR}(V) = \|_{i=1}^{n} (P_i, A_i).$$

This is a *mixed parallel composition* as in [5], with process P_i using alphabet A_i. Note that for a network $V = \{(P_i, A_i) \mid 1 \leq i \leq n\}$ the behaviour after the trace s will be that of the network V after s defined by:

$$V \underline{\text{after}}\, s \;=\; \{(P_i \underline{\text{after}}\, s\restriction A_i, A_i) \mid 1 \leq i \leq n\},$$

because at this stage the process at node i has performed the sequence $s\restriction A_i$, obtained by including only the events in s which belong to the set A_i.

Examples.

Example 1. Dining Philosophers.

In this example due to Dijkstra, well known from the literature [9,12], there are five philosophers, PHIL_i, ($i = 0\ldots4$), five forks FORK_i ($i = 0\ldots4$), and a butler process BUTLER. In our version the alphabets of these processes are:

$$\begin{aligned} A_i &= \{\text{i.picks.i}, \text{i.puts.i}, \text{i.eats}, \text{i.enters}, \text{i.leaves}, \text{i.picks.i+1}, \text{i.puts.i+1}\}, \\ B_i &= \{\text{i.picks.i}, \text{i}-\text{1.picks.i}, \text{i.puts.i}, \text{i}-\text{1.puts.i}\}, \qquad (i = 0, \ldots, 4), \\ C &= \{\text{i.enters}, \text{i.leaves} \mid 0 \leq i \leq 4\}, \end{aligned}$$

and the process definitions are:

$$\begin{aligned} \text{PHIL}_i &= (\text{i.enters} \rightarrow \text{i.picks.i} \rightarrow \text{i.picks.i+1} \rightarrow \\ &\qquad\quad \text{i.eats} \rightarrow \text{i.puts.i} \rightarrow \text{i.puts.i+1} \rightarrow \text{i.leaves} \rightarrow \text{PHIL}_i), \\ \text{FORK}_i &= (\text{i.picks.i} \rightarrow \text{i.puts.i} \rightarrow \text{FORK}_i) \,\Box\, (\text{i}-\text{1.picks.i} \rightarrow \text{i}-\text{1.puts.i} \rightarrow \text{FORK}_i), \end{aligned}$$

for $i = 0, \ldots, 4$, and

$$\begin{aligned} \text{BUTLER} &= |||_{i=1}^{4} \text{ADMIT}, \\ \text{ADMIT} &= \Box_{i=0}^{4} (\text{i.enters} \rightarrow \text{i.leaves} \rightarrow \text{ADMIT}). \end{aligned}$$

In the definition of the butler process we have used the *interleaving* operation, as described in [3,4,5]. Addition and subtraction of indices is understood to be modulo 5. The system of butler, philosophers and forks corresponds to the following network:

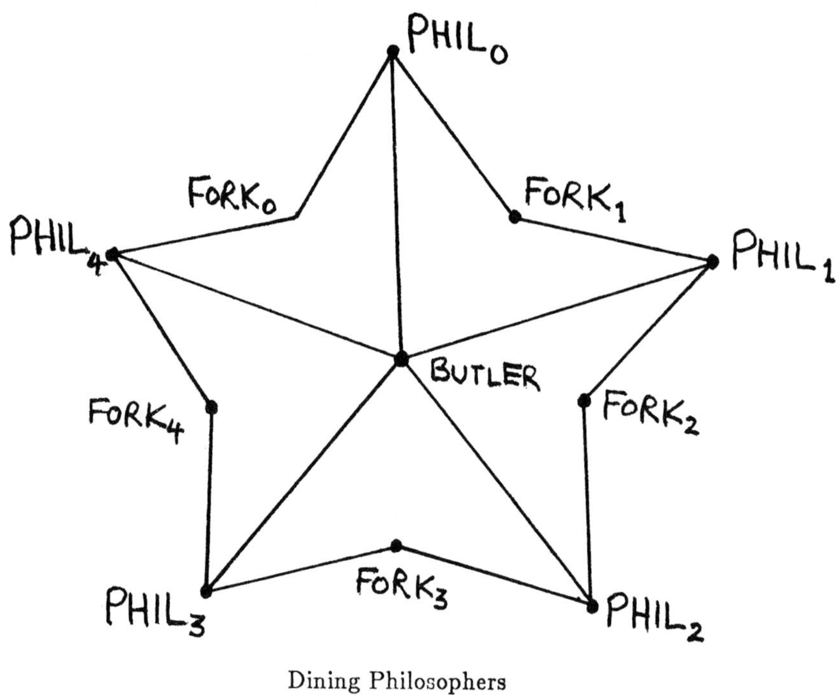

Dining Philosophers

Example 2. A chain of processes.

A simple chain of processes in which each one communicates solely with its immediate predecessor and successor is represented as a particularly simple form of network. The graphical notion of a chain thus corresponds to the use of the CSP chaining operation $\gg$, as defined in [5]. The following diagram illustrates a case when there are 3 processes:

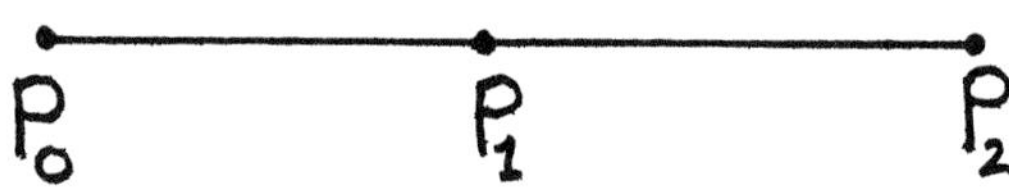

We will be particularly interested in a class of networks whose communication structure is especially simple.

Definition 1. A network V is a *tree* iff each of its connected components has one more vertex than arcs.

We are abusing notation slightly here, because it might be more conventional to term such a network a *forest*. In our terminology, a tree network is a collection of single trees. Trees arise naturally as the communication graphs of networks built with the master-slave operator $[P \parallel \mathrm{m}{:}Q]$. In such a combination P is the master process and it has a slave referred to by the name m. More generally, we can form a combination

$$[P \parallel \mathrm{m}_1{:}Q_1 \parallel \ldots \parallel \mathrm{m}_n{:}Q_n]$$

in which P has n slaves. In the network graph corresponding to this system the root node is the overall master process, and its sons are its immediate slaves. In a tree, each process communicates with its immediate predecessor (master) and with its immediate sons (slaves); the root process also may communicate with its environment. A chain is a special case of a tree. Note also that when recursion is used to define a process the corresponding network may be infinite.

In all of our systems we are considering only two-way communication, so that no single communication can involve more than two processes. This condition corresponds to a simple constraint on alphabets.

Definition 2. An indexed set $\{ A_i \mid 1 \leq i \leq n \}$ of alphabets is *triple-disjoint* if $A_i \cap A_j \cap A_k$ is empty whenever i, j, k are distinct.

Definition 3. A network $V = \{ (P_i, A_i) \mid 1 \leq i \leq n \}$ is *normal* if its alphabets are triple-disjoint and the traces of each process are generated by the corresponding alphabet:

$$\forall i.\ \mathrm{traces}(P_i) \subseteq A_i^*.$$

Definition 4. A network $V = \{ (P_i, A_i) \mid 1 \leq i \leq n \}$ is *unidirectional* if for all i and s there is at most one $j \neq i$ such that

$$\mathrm{initials}(P_i \ \underline{\mathrm{after}}\ s) \cap A_j \neq \emptyset.$$

In a unidirectional system at all times each process is prepared to communicate with at most one other process. Of course, the choice of communication partner may vary during an execution of the system. Many interesting example systems are unidirectional.

Definition 5. A property of networks is *hereditary* if whenever it holds of an entire network it also holds of all non-empty subnetworks.

Note that the properties introduced in Definitions 1, 3 and 4 are obviously hereditary.

Deadlock.

Now we are ready to begin an analysis of the deadlock properties of networks. We say that a process P *can deadlock* after s if $(s, \Sigma) \in \mathcal{F}[\![P]\!]$; this means that the process can refuse all events after performing the sequence s. Conversely, we say that P is *free of deadlock* if for all $s \in \Sigma^*$ we have $(s, \Sigma) \notin \mathcal{F}[\![P]\!]$. Note that this certainly requires that the process be also free of divergence, since in this semantics divergence is regarded as catastrophic [5].

These definitions generalise in the obvious way to a network of processes.

Definition 6. A network V is *free of deadlock* if PAR(V) is free of deadlock.

Definition 7. A network V is *strongly free of deadlock* if all non-empty subnetworks $U \subseteq V$ are free of deadlock.

Of course, strong freedom from deadlock implies the weaker condition, but the converse is not generally true.

Definition 8. In a network $V = \{(P_i, A_i) \mid 1 \leq i \leq n\}$, a *state* is a trace s of the system together with an indexed set $\langle X_1, \ldots, X_n \rangle$ of refusal sets X_i such that for each i

$$(s \upharpoonright A_i, X_i) \in \mathcal{F}[\![P_i]\!].$$

The state is *maximal* if each of the refusal sets is maximal. Note that the structure of our model guarantees that each state may be extended to a maximal state. A state is simply a cross-section of the network giving the local information about what each process in the system is refusing on the next step. We will define the *communication graph* of the network in this state as the (directed) graph in which there is an outgoing arc from node i to node j iff $(A_i - X_i) \cap A_j \neq \emptyset$. The following result shows how to characterise the states in which deadlock occurs.

LEMMA 1. *A network* $V = \{(P_i, A_i) \mid 1 \leq i \leq n\}$ *can deadlock after* s *iff there is a maximal state* $(s, \langle X_1, \ldots, X_n \rangle)$ *for which*

$$\bigcup_{i=1}^{n} A_i = \bigcup_{i=1}^{n} (A_i \cap X_i).$$

We will refer to such a (maximal) state as a *deadlock state.*

Definition 9. A *request* in a network $V = \{(P_i, A_i) \mid 1 \leq i \leq n\}$ is a triple of the form

$$\langle u, X, v \rangle, \qquad 1 \leq u, v \leq n, \quad X \subseteq \Sigma,$$

satisfying the condition

$$(A_u - X) \cap A_v \neq \emptyset.$$

This corresponds to a state in which the process P_u at node u wants to participate in an action from the alphabet of the process P_v at node v; X represents a refusal set of P_u, so that $A_u - X$ contains the events P_u may perform next; thus, it may also be possible for the process to perform events requiring the participation of processes other than P_v, depending on the set X. The request is *strong* if

$$\emptyset \neq (A_u - X) \subseteq A_v.$$

In this case, P_u is limited to performing a communication with P_v alone on the next step.

These notions generalise to sequences of requests, having the form

$$\langle u_1, X_1, u_2, X_2, \ldots, X_{n-1}, u_n \rangle.$$

Here we require that each of $\langle u_1, X_1, u_2 \rangle, \langle u_2, X_2, u_3 \rangle, \ldots, \langle u_{n-1}, X_{n-1}, u_n \rangle$ be a request. A sequence is *proper* if all of its nodes are distinct. A sequence is a *cycle* of requests when $u_n = u_1$; a *proper* cycle is one in which (apart from u_1 and u_n) the nodes are distinct. The length of this cycle is $n - 1$, which for a proper cycle is the number of distinct nodes involved.

We may thus speak of a state containing a cycle of requests. A connection between cycles of requests and deadlock is made by the following result. Note that it gives a simple characterisation of the communication graph of a system in a deadlock state: if the system satisfies the conditions of the theorem then deadlock corresponds to a cycle in the communication graph involving at least three distinct nodes.

THEOREM 1. *Let $V = \{(P_i, A_i) \mid 1 \leq i \leq n\}$ be a normal unidirectional network of processes and let $P = PAR(V)$ be their parallel composition. Suppose that the following conditions hold:*

(i) Each P_i is free of deadlock;

(ii) Each pair $[P_i\, {}_{A_i}\|_{A_j}\, P_j]$ is free of deadlock;

Then any deadlock state of P contains a proper cycle of strong requests of length at least 3.

Proof.

Let $(s, \langle Y_1, \ldots, Y_n \rangle)$ be a deadlock state of P. Then by Lemma 1,

$$\forall i. (s \restriction A_i, Y_i) \in \mathcal{F}[\![P_i]\!], \tag{a}$$

$$\bigcup_{i=1}^{n} A_i = \bigcup_{i=1}^{n} (A_i \cap Y_i). \tag{b}$$

By assumption, the Y_i are maximal refusal sets in (a). For each i let $Q_i = P_i \underline{\text{after}}\, s\lceil A_i$, so that $P \underline{\text{after}}\, s = \|_{i=1}^{n} (Q_i, A_i)$. We argue as follows.

• None of the Y_i can include A_i as a subset, as P_i is deadlock-free by assumption (i) and the system is normal. From (b) we see that for each i,

$$A_i - (\bigcup_{j \neq i} A_j) \subseteq Y_i, \qquad \text{FACT 1}$$

so that in this state of the system each process is refusing all events unique to its own alphabet. Hence,

$$A_i - Y_i \subseteq \bigcup_{j \neq i} A_j. \qquad \text{FACT 2}$$

• By maximality of Y_i we know that Y_i contains all of the *impossible* events from the set $A_i - \text{initials}(Q_i)$:

$$A_i - \text{initials}(Q_i) \subseteq Y_i.$$

Hence,

$$A_i - Y_i \subseteq \text{initials}(Q_i).$$

But there is at most one $j \neq i$ with

$$\text{initials}(Q_i) \cap A_j \neq \emptyset,$$

since the system is unidirectional. Hence there is at most one $j \neq i$ for which

$$(A_i - Y_i) \cap A_j \neq \emptyset. \qquad \text{FACT 3}$$

Putting these facts together, we see that there is a unique j (depending on i) such that $i \neq j$ and

$$\emptyset \neq A_i - Y_i \subseteq A_j.$$

Consider j as a function of i, mapping indices to indices. Note that $j(i) \neq i$, and it also happens that $j(j(i)) \neq i$, because if this were to happen we would have a pair of indices $i, j = j(i)$ with

$$A_i - Y_i \subseteq A_j, \qquad A_j - Y_j \subseteq A_i.$$

But by (b) and (3) we would then have

$$A_i \cap A_j \subseteq Y_i \cup Y_j,$$

which would in turn imply that

$$A_i - Y_i \subseteq Y_j, \qquad A_j - Y_j \subseteq Y_i.$$

Hence, we would get

$$(A_i \cap Y_i) \cup (A_j \cap Y_j) = A_i \cup A_j,$$

contradicting the assumption (ii) that the pair $[P_{i\,A_i} \|_{A_j} P_j]$ was free of deadlock.

The sequence

$$1, j(1), j^2(1), \ldots$$

must contain a first repetition, say $j^m(1) = j^{m+k}(1)$, since there are only finitely many indices. Define $n_r = j^{m+r}(1)$, for $r = 1 \ldots k$. Then $\langle n_1, Y_{n_1}, n_2, \ldots, Y_{n_{k-1}}, n_k \rangle$ is a cycle of strong requests. ▮

An intuitive interpretation of this theorem is that global deadlock (*i.e.* deadlock of the entire system) can only be caused in a unidirectional normal system by local deadlock or else by a cycle of at least three distinct nodes each demanding to communicate with its successor and refusing to communicate with its predecessor. Some important consequences of the theorem are:

Corollary. If a tree network satisfies the conditions above, then it is strongly free of deadlock.

Proof. A tree has no proper cycles, and all of the hypotheses of the theorem are hereditary properties. ▮

Corollary. In a unidirectional tree network, pairwise freedom of deadlock implies absence of global deadlock.

If a network has only a small number of cycles, it is often possible to prove absence of deadlock by performing a case analysis. For instance, in a *ring* of processes there are only two possible cycles to consider. To satisfy the preconditions of Theorem 3 we still need to prove pairwise freedom from deadlock. This may often be possible by a simple case analysis, and the amount of work involved in the analysis can often be reduced substantially by using the following lemma:

LEMMA 2. *If* $c \not\in A$, $c \not\in B$, *and* $C = A \cup \{c\}$, *then* $[P_C \|_B Q] \backslash c = [(P \backslash c)_A \|_B Q]$.

If c is an event whose hiding in P does not cause any divergence, then $P \backslash c$ can deadlock if and only if P can. Hence, if hiding c does not cause divergence and if $c \in A - B$, we see that $[P_A \|_B Q]$ is deadlock-free if and only if $[(P \backslash c)_A \|_B Q]$ is. This concealment of "irrelevant" communication can substantially reduce the complexity of the deadlock analysis. By hiding irrelevant communication we can reduce the amount of detail still further.

Here is an example to illustrate this type of reasoning.

Example 3. Privilege Rings (after Dijkstra [11]).

We consider a ring of n processes ($n \geq 3$) each of which wants to keep entering a critical section; to maintain mutual exclusion, a process is only allowed to enter its critical region when it has obtained a "privilege" token, which is passed around the ring. When a process wants to begin its critical region it first requests the privilege from its neighbour; when it is granted the privilege, the process performs its critical action and then releases the privilege token. Using mutual recursion, we may define the individual processes P_i ($i < n$) by

$$\begin{aligned} P_i &= (\text{i.get} \to \text{i+1.find} \to \text{i.priv} \to \text{i.crit} \to \text{i.rel} \to Q_i) \\ &\quad \Box\, (\text{i.find} \to \text{i+1.find} \to \text{i.priv} \to \text{i–1.priv} \to P_i) \\ Q_i &= (\text{i.get} \to \text{i.crit} \to \text{i.rel} \to Q_i) \Box (\text{i.find} \to \text{i–1.priv} \to P_i). \end{aligned}$$

All arithmetic here is modulo n. P_i represents a node without the privilege token and Q_i represents a node with the privilege. Thus, if P_i wants to get the privilege it must put in a request first to its successor, and wait for that process to find the token and pass it back; if P_i is asked to find the privilege it passes the request on to its neighbour. A Q_i process with the token may either allow the critical action or pass the token on to its predecessor.

Let A_i be the obvious alphabets for these processes. If we begin with the system $V = \{(Q_0, A_0), (P_1, A_1), \ldots, (P_{n-1}, A_{n-1})\}$, so that initially the 0 process has the token, we would like to prove that PAR(V) is free of deadlock. Here is the network graph for the system.

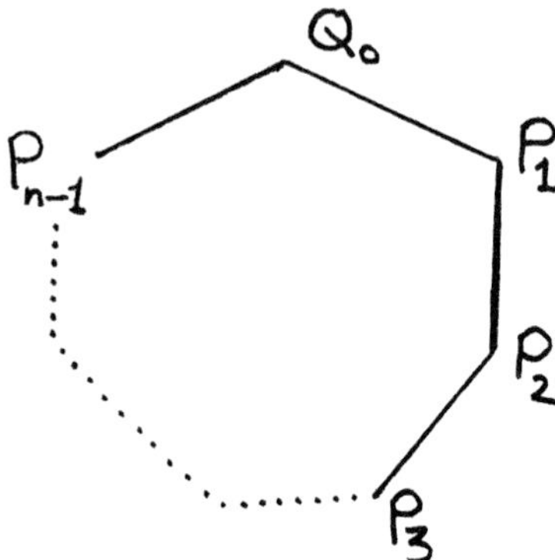

It is easy to see that the system is normal and unidirectional. It remains to prove pairwise freedom from deadlock. We must show that each of the pairs

$$\begin{aligned} &(Q_0, A_0) \,||\, (P_1, A_1), \\ &(P_i, A_i) \,||\, (P_{i+1}, A_{i+1}) \qquad (0 < i < n), \\ &(P_{n-1}, A_{n-1}) \,||\, (Q_0, A_0) \end{aligned}$$

is deadlock-free. These analyses are simplified by judicious use of Lemma 2, as follows. We can hide (without introducing divergence) the set $L_i = \{\text{i.get}, \text{i.rel}, \text{i.find}, \text{i--1.priv}\}$ in process P_i or Q_i when the process appears on the left of $\|$ in this list; and the same holds for the set $R_i = \{\text{i.crit}, \text{i.rel}, \text{i+1.find}, \text{i.priv}\}$ when on the right. Let $P_i^L = P_i \backslash L_i$ and $Q_i^L = Q_i \backslash L_i$, with similar notation P_i^R and Q_i^R for the other hiding operation. Also, let $A_i^L = A_i - L_i$, with similar notations for the R versions. We have, by definition, and using properties of the hiding operation,

$$\begin{aligned} P_i^L &= \text{i+1.find} \rightarrow \text{i.priv} \rightarrow Q_i^L, \\ Q_i^L &= (\text{i.crit} \rightarrow Q_i^L) \sqcap P_i^L, \\ Q_i^R = P_i^R &= (\text{i.find} \rightarrow \text{i--1.priv} \rightarrow P_i^R) \,\Box\, (\text{i.get} \rightarrow P_i^R). \end{aligned}$$

Using Lemma 2, now we have to prove freedom from deadlock in the pairs:

$$\begin{aligned} &(Q_0^L, A_0^L) \parallel (P_1^R, A_1^R), \\ &(P_i^L, A_i^L) \parallel (P_{i+1}^R, A_{i+1}^R), \\ &(P_{n-1}^L, A_{n-1}^L) \parallel (Q_0^R, A_0^R). \end{aligned}$$

This may be done by a simple case analysis. Therefore we can use the above theorem to deduce the existence, in any deadlock state, of a cycle. Thus, deadlock is possible only if either each process is waiting for its successor or each process is waiting for its predecessor. We can easily formalise and prove the property that there is always exactly one process with the token: either process 0 still has it and no other process has been granted it, or else exactly one process has been given the privilege but has not yet released it. But process i can only be waiting for process $i+1$ if it does not have the token; and, similarly, a process can only be waiting for its predecessor if it does not have the token. It follows that deadlock is impossible.

A modification of this argument goes through whenever the system is started with at least one token in the ring. Of course, in the case where no process initially has the privilege, deadlock must occur.

Example 4. A deadlocked chain.

Define a chain of $n+1$ processes for any $n > 1$ as follows. The processes will be $P_0, \ldots, P_n$, with alphabets A_i given by

$$\begin{aligned} A_0 &= \{\text{1.a}\}, \\ A_i &= \{\text{i.a}, \text{i.b}, \text{i+1.a}, \text{i+1.b}\}, \qquad 1 \le i < n, \\ A_n &= \{\text{n.b}\}. \end{aligned}$$

The process P_0 wants to keep receiving message a from process P_1, and P_n wants to keep receiving message b from P_{n-1}. Each of the intermediate processes $P_1, \ldots, P_{n-1}$

can repeatedly transmit a from its right to its left, and b from its left to its right. The definitions are:

$$\begin{aligned} P_0 &= (1.\mathrm{a} \rightarrow P_0) \\ P_n &= (\mathrm{n.b} \rightarrow P_n) \\ P_i &= \mathrm{T}_i^a \,|||\, \mathrm{T}_i^b, \qquad (1 < i < n), \\ \mathrm{T}_i^a &= (\mathrm{i{+}1.a} \rightarrow \mathrm{i.a} \rightarrow \mathrm{T}_i^a), \\ \mathrm{T}_i^b &= (\mathrm{i.b} \rightarrow \mathrm{i{+}1.b} \rightarrow \mathrm{T}_i^b). \end{aligned}$$

In the mixed parallel composition corresponding to this system, no event is initially possible. The reason is easy to see: although each of the interior processes in the chain is attempting to perform one of two actions, each of those actions is also in the alphabet of a neighbour who is not willing to cooperate. And although the end processes are trying to receive a message from their neighbours, their neighbouring processes are not initially able to send the message. The chain therefore deadlocks immediately. However, it is not difficult to see that every non-empty proper subnetwork is deadlock-free! This example shows that there exist chains in which deadlock is a global property.

3. A more general result.

The above theorem is only applicable when the system is unidirectional. More general results are needed to tackle some other interesting examples such as the Dining Philosophers. A useful technique is based on the concept of *competition* ("cliques" in the terminology of [15]).

Define a competition relation COMP on triples of nodes of V:

$$\begin{aligned} (i,j,k) \in \mathrm{COMP} \quad \Leftrightarrow \quad & i \neq j \,\&\, j \neq k \,\&\, k \neq i \\ & \&\ \exists s.(\mathrm{initials}(P_i\ \underline{\mathrm{after}}\ s) \cap A_j \neq \emptyset\ \&\ \mathrm{initials}(P_i\ \underline{\mathrm{after}}\ s) \cap A_k \neq \emptyset) \end{aligned}$$

Intuitively, $(i,j,k) \in \mathrm{COMP}$ iff at some stage P_j and P_k can find themselves in competition for the attention of P_i. We use the notation $\mathrm{COMP}(i,j) = \{\, k \mid (i,j,k) \in \mathrm{COMP} \,\}$. Thus, $k \in \mathrm{COMP}(i,j)$ means that P_k may compete at some time with P_j for the attention of P_i.

When $i \neq j$ we define $\mathrm{comp}_V(i,j)$ to be the smallest subset C of V containing i and j, and closed under COMP:

$$k, l \in C \ \&\ (k,l,m) \in \mathrm{COMP} \quad \Rightarrow \quad m \in C.$$

Where V is obvious from the context we will omit the subscript. The set $\mathrm{comp}(i,j)$ is an "upper bound" on the set of processes which might interfere or compete directly with communications between P_i and P_j, in that this set contains (at least) all of the processes which may dynamically find themselves competing with a communication between P_i and P_j. We will refer to $\mathrm{comp}(i,j)$ as the *competition set* of processes i and j, and to the members of this set other than i and j as *competitors*. Note that the definition depends on the processes as well as on the communication structure of the network, since it takes into account the dynamic behaviour of the processes and not just the static communication pattern of the alphabets. Of course, if $k \in \text{comp}(i,j)$ then there must be an arc between P_i and P_k and between P_j and P_k. The converse is not true in general.

Examples.

1. In the dining philosophers system (*Example 1*), two adjacent philosophers can find themselves competing for the same fork, and any two philosophers can compete for entry into the room via the butler process. The only interesting competition sets are

$$\begin{aligned} \text{comp}(\text{PHIL}_i, \text{FORK}_i) &= \text{comp}(\text{PHIL}_{i+1}, \text{FORK}_i) = \{\text{PHIL}_i, \text{FORK}_i, \text{PHIL}_{i+1}\}, \\ \text{comp}(\text{PHIL}_i, \text{BUTLER}) &= \{\text{PHIL}_0, \ldots, \text{PHIL}_4, \text{BUTLER}\}, \end{aligned}$$

for $i = 0 \ldots 4$. This is as expected: neighbouring philosophers can compete for the fork situated between them, and all philosophers compete for the attention of the butler.

2. In the privilege ring example (*Example 3*), there are no non-trivial competition sets.

3. In the deadlocked chain example (*Example 4*), the only whole system is a competition set, since any adjacent pair P_{i-1} and P_{i+1} can compete for the process P_i in between them.

4. In general, the competition sets of a tree network are particularly simple in structure. There are no nontrivial competitors for any two non-adjacent nodes. If nodes i and j are adjacent then $\text{comp}(i,j)$ forms a connected subtree of the network. Moreover, any two of these nontrivial competition sets either coincide or else have at most a single node in their intersection.

Of course, these properties of trees do not hold of general networks. The following simple property of competition sets, true in all networks, will be useful.

LEMMA 3. *If $U \subseteq V$ and $i, j \in U$, then*

$$comp_U(i,j) \subseteq comp_V(i,j).$$

Other properties of competition sets may be established in a fairly simple manner, and will be used without proof. Further details appear in [15]. Note in particular that

$$\begin{aligned} \text{comp}(i,j) &= \text{comp}(j,i), \\ k \in \text{comp}(i,j) &\Rightarrow \text{comp}(i,k) \subseteq \text{comp}(i,j), \\ A_i \cap A_j = \emptyset &\Rightarrow \text{comp}(i,j) = \{i,j\}. \end{aligned}$$

The use of competition sets in deadlock analysis is illustrated in the following result.

THEOREM 2. *For any normal network $V = \{(P_i, A_i) \mid 1 \leq i \leq n\}$, if every competition set $U \subseteq V$ is strongly free of deadlock, then any deadlock state $(s, \langle X_1, \ldots, X_n \rangle)$ of V must contain a cycle of requests not entirely contained in any single competition set, and satisfies the additional condition:*

$$\forall i, j.[i \neq j \Rightarrow \exists k \in comp(i,j).\ (A_k - X_k) \subseteq \bigcup \{A_r \mid r \not\in comp(i,j)\}].$$

Proof. Similar to that of Theorem 1. ∎

This theorem places a further constraint on the structure of a deadlocking cycle of requests: that it must contain nodes from at least two distinct competition sets. This makes it easier to analyse the network for possible deadlocks, since there are usually fewer cycles satisfying this condition and consequently fewer cases to check. The additional condition also helps to reduce the number of cycles to consider; it says that every pair of processes has a competitor who wants to communicate only outside of the competition set.

THEOREM 3. *For any normal tree V, if every competition set $U \subseteq V$ is strongly free of deadlock then V is strongly free of deadlock.*

Proof. By the previous theorem, deadlock is possible for V after a trace s only if there are (maximal refusal) sets $X_1, \ldots, X_n$ satisfying the conditions:

$$(s \upharpoonright A_i, X_i) \in \mathcal{F}[\![P_i]\!], \tag{1}$$

$$\bigcup_{i=1}^{n} A_i = \bigcup_{i=1}^{n} (A_i \cap X_i), \tag{2}$$

$$\forall i, j.[i \neq j \Rightarrow \exists k \in \text{comp}(i,j). (A_k - X_k) \subseteq \bigcup \{A_r \mid r \not\in \text{comp}(i,j)\}], \tag{3}$$

and such that this state $(s, \langle X_1, \ldots, X_n \rangle)$ includes a cycle of requests which does not lie wholly inside a single competition set. The indices of this cycle, say $i_1, \ldots, i_k$, satisfy the conditions:

$$(A_{i_r} - X_{i_r}) \cap A_{i_{r+1}} \neq \emptyset$$

for each r (counting modulo k). We claim that any such sequence must lie entirely within a single competition set; in particular, we will show that

$$\{i_1, \ldots, i_k\} \subseteq \text{comp}(i_1, i_2). \tag{4}$$

This will provide us with a contradiction, and therefore allow us to conclude that deadlock is impossible, given the preconditions of the theorem.

The result (4) is proved by induction on the size of the cycle, k. If $k = 2$ there is nothing to prove. Assume true for all cycles of requests of length less than k. There are two cases: either i_1 is repeated later in the sequence $i_2, \ldots, i_k$, or else there is no repetition.

• In the latter case, when i_1 is not repeated, we can see from the tree structure that $i_2 = i_k$, so that $\langle i_2, X_{i_2}, \ldots, i_{k-1}, X_{i_{k-1}}, i_k \rangle$ is a cycle of requests for the processes $\langle i_2, \ldots, i_k \rangle$. Thus, by inductive hypothesis we have

$$\{ i_2, \ldots, i_k \} \subseteq \mathrm{comp}(i_2, i_3).$$

Let $Q_i = P_i$ <u>after</u> $s \upharpoonright A_i$. By construction we have

$$\begin{aligned} &\mathrm{initials}(Q_{i_2}) \cap A_{i_3} \neq \emptyset, \\ &\mathrm{initials}(Q_{i_2}) \cap A_{i_1} \neq \emptyset, \end{aligned}$$

because $i_2 = i_k$. We also know that

$$(A_{i_2} - X_{i_2}) \cap A_{i_3} \neq \emptyset, \quad (A_{i_k} - X_{i_k}) \cap A_{i_1} \neq \emptyset,$$

and

$$(A_{i_2} - X_{i_2}) \subseteq \mathrm{initials}(Q_{i_2}), \quad (A_{i_k} - X_{i_k}) \subseteq \mathrm{initials}(Q_{i_k}).$$

This latter is by maximality of the X_i as in the proof of Theorem 1. Hence, $(i_2, i_1, i_3) \in r$, and $i_3 \in \mathrm{comp}(i_1, i_2)$. It follows that

$$\{ i_1, \ldots, i_k \} \subseteq \mathrm{comp}(i_1, i_2).$$

• In the other case, when i_1 is repeated, we have for some $1 < r < k$, $i_r = i_1$. Clearly there are two cycles of requests:

$$\begin{aligned} &\langle i_1, X_{i_1}, \ldots, i_{r-1}, X_{i_{r-1}}, i_r \rangle \\ &\langle i_r, X_{i_r}, \ldots, i_k, X_{i_k}, i_1 \rangle. \end{aligned}$$

By the inductive hypothesis,

$$\begin{aligned} &\{ i_1, \ldots, i_r \} \subseteq \mathrm{comp}(i_1, i_2) \\ &\{ i_r, \ldots, i_k \} \subseteq \mathrm{comp}(i_r, i_{r+1}) = \mathrm{comp}(i_1, i_{r+1}). \end{aligned}$$

However, by construction,

$$\mathrm{initials}(Q_{i_1}) \cap A_{i_2} \neq \emptyset \quad \text{and} \quad \mathrm{initials}(Q_{i_1}) \cap A_{i_{r+1}} \neq \emptyset,$$

as before, so that $i_{r+1} \in \mathrm{comp}(i_1, i_2)$. Thus, $\mathrm{comp}(i_1, i_{r+1}) \subseteq \mathrm{comp}(i_1, i_2)$, from which the result follows. Having established the truth of (4), that completes the proof of this theorem. ∎

Example: Absence of deadlock in the dining philosophers system.

We argue along the following lines, although we will omit details. Suppose that deadlock is possible, and consider the communication graph of the system in a deadlock state. We will reach a contradiction.

- If there is an edge from PHIL_i to FORK_i then FORK_i must have a unique outgoing edge, to PHIL_{i-1}; if PHIL_{i-1} has an edge leading to FORK_i then there is a unique outgoing edge, to PHIL_i.

- By looking at the parallel composition of PHIL_i and FORK_i, we see that: whenever FORK_i has a unique outgoing edge leading to PHIL_i, then PHIL_i has a unique outgoing edge leading to FORK_{i+1}. Similarly, whenever FORK_{i+1} has a unique outgoing edge to PHIL_i, then PHIL_i has a unique outgoing edge to FORK_i.

- By Theorem 2, there must be an edge leading out from the competition set $\{\text{PHIL}_0, \ldots, \text{PHIL}_4, \text{BUTLER}\}$. By the previous two properties this means that there must be a cycle of requests linking all of the philosophers and forks. Moreover, the edges of this cycle must be the only edges leading from these processes, so that the butler process is not involved.

- Use the definition of the butler process to demonstrate that this situation can never arise, by a simple counting argument: the butler is designed to ensure that no more than four philosophers can ever be seated simultaneously. In any trace of the system the number of *enter* events cannot exceed the number of *leave* events by more than 4.

4. Comparison with other work.

Many authors have worked on deadlock analysis in networks of processes, notably [6,7,8]. Our model has the advantage of providing a succinct and mathematically tractable representation of deadlock. We have been able to use the model in proofs of some interesting results on the analysis of deadlock in networks, and then to prove absence of deadlock in some well known examples such as the Dining Philosophers. The theorems of this paper are only a sample of a large class of general results which we will be able to derive for analysing the deadlock properties of networks. We have focussed here mainly on results pertaining to unidirectional systems and trees of processes. Dijkstra [8] proved some similar theorems on the absence of deadlock in unidirectional networks for the special case in which the patterns of communication were cyclic: each process rotated its communication requests in cyclic order through its immediate neighbours. Dijkstra stated that his results were applicable in a more general setting, and we have demonstrated that this is indeed the case. We also hope that we may be able to represent some of the results obtained by Chandy and Misra [6] in our setting. Other results related to ours are contained in [14], where Reisig considers a Petri net model and gives a characterization of deadlock states. The work of Apt et al. [1,2] on reasoning about partial correctness of CSP programs also contains some methods for analysing deadlock, using global invariants. Essentially, this work is based on a rather different approach from ours: typically, a CSP program is first transformed syntactically into a program in a *guarded command* language [10] which no longer involves communication, and matching pairs of communications from the original program are transformed (synchronized) into assignment statements. Then one reasons about the absence of deadlock by finding a global invariant which guarantees that no deadlock state can be reached, because it is false in deadlock states.

5. Future work.

As we stated earlier, the deadlock analysis theorems of this paper exemplify a class of general results on deadlock in networks of parallel processes. Theorem 1 concerns unidirectional networks, and Theorem 3 is applicable to tree networks. We hope to prove more results along these lines in the future and to use them to analyse the properties of a larger number of classes of networks. For instance, our definition of competition set provided a fairly crude bound on the set of processes which could be involved in causing a local deadlock; a more careful analysis may lead to sharper results. It would be especially useful to be able to refine the results on competition sets so as to minimise the amount of local checking that is required in order to establish freedom from deadlock. All the same, the competition set analysis described in this paper does seem to be fairly useful. Sharper results, although less generally applicable, may be obtained by focussing instead on a notion of *conflict* with respect to a set of events. Roughly speaking, two processes can conflict over a set C of events if they can reach a state in which they can only perform events in C next, each is requesting the other process to do something, but they cannot agree on any communication. Although we do not elaborate here, this notion can be used to modify the statement of Theorem 3 and its corollaries, so that slightly different hypotheses are used in deadlock analysis. This material will be developed further in future work and will appear in an extended version of this paper.

Another important topic for future work is the proof of absence of proper cycles of requests in networks. This will be vital if we are to apply these techniques to networks with large numbers of possible cycles. It seems likely that in many cases this will involve the discovery of global invariants and associated properties of the underlying graphs, and again we see the possibility of some connections with the ideas of [1,2].

Acknowledgements.

The authors would like to thank C. A. R. Hoare for his many helpful suggestions and discussions, and for his encouragement and guidance during the development of this work. Discussions with Krzysztof Apt, Jay Misra, Ernst-Rudiger Olderog, David Reed and Wolfgang Reisig have been very useful.

6. References.

[1] Apt, K. R., A Static Analysis of CSP Programs, in: Logics of Programs, Proceedings, Springer Verlag LNCS vol. 164, pp. 1-17 (1983).

[2] Apt, K. R., Francez, N., and de Roever, W. P, A proof system for communicating sequential processes, TOPLAS vol. 2 no. 3, pp. 359-385 (1980).

[3] Brookes, S. D., Hoare, C. A. R., and Roscoe, A. W., A Theory of Communicating Sequential Processes, Oxford University Computing Laboratory, Programming Research Group, Technical Report PRG-16.

[4] Brookes, S. D., Hoare, C. A. R., and Roscoe, A. W., A Theory of Communicating Sequential Processes, JACM July 1984.

[5] Brookes, S. D., and Roscoe, A. W., An Improved Failures Model for Communicating Processes, Proc. NSF–SERC Seminar on Concurrency, Springer Verlag LNCS (to appear, 1985).

[6] Chandy, K. M., and Misra, J., Deadlock Absence Proofs for Networks of Communica Processes, Information Processing Letters, Vol. 9, no. 4, Nov. 1979.

[7] Chandy, K. M., Misra, J., and Haas, L. M., Distributed Deadlock Detection, ACM TOPLAS Vol. 1 no. 2, pp 144-156 (1983).

[8] Dijkstra, E. W., A Class of Simple Communication Patterns, EWD643, in: Selected Writings on Computing, Springer Verlag (1982).

[9] Dijkstra, E. W., Hierarchical Ordering of Sequential Processes, Acta Informatica 1, pp 115-138 (1971).

[10] Dijkstra, E. W., Guarded Commands, Nondeterminacy and Formal Derivation of Programs, CACM, Vol. 18 No. 8, August 1975.

[11] Dijkstra, E. W., Invariance and non-determinacy, in: Mathematical Logic and Programming Languages, C. A. R. Hoare and J. C. Shepherdson, eds., Prentice-Hall International Series in Computer Science (1985).

[12] Hoare, C. A. R., Communicating Sequential Processes, CACM 1978.

[13] Milne, G., and Milner, R., Concurrent Processes and their Syntax, JACM vol 26 no. 2, pp 302-321 (1979).

[14] Reisig, W., Deterministic Buffer Synchronization of Sequential Processes, Acta Informatica 18, 117-134 (1982).

[15] Roscoe, A. W., A Mathematical Theory of Communicating Processes, Ph. D. thesis, Oxford University (1982).

A PARADIGM FOR DETECTING QUIESCENT PROPERTIES IN DISTRIBUTED COMPUTATIONS*

K. Mani Chandy and Jayadev Misra
Department of Computer Sciences
University of Texas at Austin
Austin, Texas 78712

1. Introduction

The problem of stability detection is one of the most widely studied problems in distributed computing [1-28]. A *stable property* is one that persists: if the property holds at any point, then it holds thereafter. Examples of stable properties are termination, deadlock and loss of tokens in a token-ring. The problem is to devise algorithms to be superimposed on the underlying computation to determine whether a specified stable property holds for the underlying computation. This paper presents a simple (almost trivial) algorithm to detect *quiescent properties*, an important class of stable properties including those mentioned above. Distributed snapshots [7] may be used to derive algorithms for these problems. However our approach in this paper is different and results in simpler algorithms.

2. Model of Distributed Systems

2.1. The Model

A distributed system is a set of processes and a set of directed communication channels. Each channel is directed from one process to another process. Processes send messages on outgoing channels and receive messages on incoming channels. A process sends a message along an outgoing channel by depositing it in the channel. A process receives a message along an incoming channel by removing the message from the channel. A process may receive a message some arbitrary time after it is sent. Initially, all channels are *empty*. At any time each process is in one of a set of process states and each channel is in one of a set of channel states.

---

*This work was supported in part by a grant from the Air Force Office of Scientific Research under AFOSR 810205.

NATO ASI Series, Vol. F13
Logics and Models of Concurrent Systems
Edited by K. R. Apt

The channel state for a first-in-first-out channel is the sequence of messages in transit along the channel. For channels which deliver messages in arbitrary order, the channel state is the set of messages in transit. A system has a set of states, an initial state from this set, and a set of state transitions. The system state at any time is the set of process and channel states. Let S, S^* be states of a system. S^* is *reachable* from S if and only if there exists a sequence of state transitions from S to S^*. We assume that all system states are reachable from the initial system state.

2.2. Quiescent Property

A *stable property* B of a distributed system is a predicate on system states such that for all S^* reachable from S:

$B(S)$ *implies* $B(S^*)$

In other words, once a stable property becomes *true* it remains *true*. A *quiescent* property of a distributed system is a special kind of stable property characterized by (1) a subset P^* of the set of processes, (2) for all processes p in P^*, a predicate b_p on the process states of p and (3) a subset C^* of the set of channels between processes in P^*. A process p in P^* cannot send messages along channels in C^* while b_p holds. Furthermore, if b_p is *true*, it must remain *true* at least until p receives a message along a channel in C^*. The quiescent property B is:

all channels in C^* are *empty* and for all processes p in P^*: b_p.

It is easily seen that B is also a stable property. A process p is a *predecessor* of a process q with respect to B if and only if p and q are both in P^* and there exists a channel in C^* from p to q. For brevity we shall say p is a predecessor of q and drop the phrase "with respect to B". If for some system state, we have for some process q in P^*:

b_q *and* all of q's incoming channels in C^* are *empty and*

for all predecessors p of q: b_p (1)

then this condition must persist at least until for some predecessor p of q, b_p

becomes *false*. This fact is useful in understanding quiescent properties and their detection.

2.3. Problem Definition

Let the system computation go through a sequence of global states S_i, $i \geq 0$, where S_0 is the initial state; this sequence of global states will be called the *underlying computation*. Given a quiescent property B we wish to superimpose a detection algorithm on the underlying computation to determine whether B holds. The detection algorithm sets a boolean variable *claim* to *true* when it detects that B holds, and *claim* is *false* until that point. The detection algorithm must guarantee:

(Safety) : *not claim or B*

(Liveness) : within finite time of B becoming *true, claim* is set to *true.*

We now present a brief discussion of three instances of quiescent properties: termination, database deadlock and communication deadlock.

2.4. Termination

A computation is defined to be *terminated* if and only if all processes are *idle* and all channels are *empty*. Thus C^* is the set of all channels, P^* is the set of all processes, and for each process p, b_p is: p is *idle*. Idle processes don't send messages and hence termination is a quiescent property.

2.5. Database Deadlock

A process is either *active* or *waiting*. A waiting state of a process p is specified by a pair (R_p, H_p) where R_p is a non-empty set of resources that p is waiting for and H_p is a set of resources that p needs and holds (where R_p and H_p have no common elements). Resources are sent as messages from active processes to other processes; a waiting process does not send any resource it needs and holds. A process p, in a waiting state specified by (R_p, H_p), takes the following action on receiving a resource r in R_p:

begin $R_p := R_p - \{r\}$; $H_p := H_p \cup \{r\}$;

  if $R_p = \{\ \}$ **then** become active **else** wait

end

Here { } is the empty set. When p transits from active to waiting state, R_p and H_p are set to values which are of no consequence to us here. A set P^* of processes is deadlocked if every process in P^* is waiting for resources held by other processes in P^*, i.e.

P^* is database deadlocked $\equiv$

for all p in P^*: p is waiting and there exists a q in P^* such that

$R_p \cap H_q \neq \{\}$

In this case, the predicate b_p is: p is waiting for R_p and p holds H_p. A channel c is in C^* if and only if c is from a process q to a process p where p and q are both in P^*, and q holds a resource required by p. Typically, P^* is not specified and it is required to obtain a P^* as part of the detection algorithm.

2.6. Communication Deadlock

As in database deadlock a process is *active* or *waiting*. A waiting process p is waiting on a set of incoming channels C_p; on receiving a message along *any* channel in C_p, process p becomes active. An active process may start waiting at any time. Until it receives a message along a channel in C_p, a waiting process p continues to wait on C_p. A waiting process cannot send messages. A set of waiting processes is deadlocked if no process in the set is waiting on a channel from a process outside the set, and all channels between processes in the set are *empty*, i.e.,

A set of processes P^* is communication deadlocked $\equiv$

for all p in P^*: p is waiting for a set of incoming channels C_p where each channel c in C_p is from a process in P^*, and c is *empty*.

In this case, b_p is: p is waiting on C_p. C^* is the union of all C_p for p in P^*.

As in database deadlock, the detection algorithm is required to find P^* if such a set exists. Next we consider two specific classes of distributed systems: (i) systems in which messages are acknowledged and (ii) systems in which channels are first-in-first-out, and show how to detect quiescent properties in each class. The latter class needs little description. We describe the former class next.

2.7. Systems with Acknowledgements

Let c be a channel from a process p to a process q. On receiving a message along c, process q sends an acknowledgement ack_c to p. We are not concerned with how *acks* travel from one process to another. An *ack* is not considered to be a message in that *acks* are not acknowledged in turn. Furthermore, the statement "channel c is *empty*" means that c contains no message; it may or may not contain *acks*. Let num_c be the number of unacknowledged messages p has sent along outgoing channel c, i.e.,

$num_c =$ number of messages sent by p along c −
number of ack_c acknowledgements received by p.

$num_c = 0$ *implies* c is *empty*.

We assume that every message sent is received in finite time and acknowledged in finite time. We also assume that every *ack* sent is received in finite time. Hence, an acknowledgement is received for each message within finite time of sending the message. Therefore,

if B becomes *true*, then within finite time of B becoming *true*:

$$\text{for all } c \text{ in } C^*: num_c = 0$$

3. The Paradigm

Our paradigm is based on observing each process computation for some period of time called an observation period. An *observation period* for a process p is specified by two integers, $start_p$ and end_p, $start_p \le end_p$, denoting that p's computation is observed at every S_i, $start_p \le i \le end_p$. An *observation period set* for a quiescent property B is a set of observation periods, one for each process in P^*.

An observation period set $obs'' = \{(start_p'', end_p'') \mid p \text{ in } P^*\}$ *is later than* an observation period set $obs' = \{(start_p', end_p') \mid p \text{ in } P^*\}$ if and only if all starting times in obs'' are after some starting time in obs', i.e.

$$\min_p \; start_p'' \quad > \quad \min_p \; start_p'$$

Let B^* be a predicate on observation period sets, defined as follows.

$B^* (obs) \equiv$ [for all p in P^* :

for all states S_i where $start_p \leq i \leq end_p$: b_p holds in S_i]

and

[for all p,q in P^* where p is a predecessor of q: all messages sent

by p at or before $start_p$ are received by q at or before end_q] (2)

Note: To ensure that messages sent by p at or before $start_p$ are received by q at or before end_q, we must have for all p,q in P^* where p is a predecessor of p : $start_p \leq end_q$ (3)

3.1. Quiescence Detection Paradigm

claim : = *false*; obtain an observation period set *obs*;

while *not* B^* *(obs)* **do**

obtain an observation period set *obs′* later than *obs*;

obs : = *obs′*

od;

claim : = *true*

We next prove the correctness of this paradigm and postpone discussion of techniques for implementing the paradigm to a later section.

3.2. Proof of Correctness

Safety : *not claim or B*

Safety holds while *claim* is *false*; therefore consider the final iteration of the while loop after which *claim* is set to *true*. For this iteration, we prove the following by inducting on *i*:

for all $i \geq 0$: for all p in P^* :

$[\, [\, i < start_p$ or b_p holds in $S_i\,]$ *and*

$[\, i < end_p$ or p's incoming channels in c are empty $]\,]$

This induction follows from (1), (2), and (3).

Liveness: If there exists an $i \geq 0$ such that B holds for S_i then there exists a $j \geq 0$ such that $claim = true$ in S_i . If B holds for S_i then for all observation period sets, *obs*, where $start_p \geq i$, for all p, B^* (*obs*) holds. From the paradigm, either *claim* is set *true* or later observation periods are chosen indefinitely. Hence if B holds for S_i for any $i \geq 0$, then *claim* will be *true* for some S_j , $j \geq 0$.

3.3. Implementation of the Paradigm

The key question for implementation is: How can we ensure that all messages sent by a predecessor p of a process q at or before $start_p$, are received by q at or before end_q?

3.3.1. Systems with Acknowledgements

The above question can be answered for systems with acknowledgements by ensuring the following condition: for all p,q in P^* where p is a predecessor of q and for all channels c from p to q :

$num_c{=}0$ at $start_p$ *and* $start_p \leq end_q$.

Proof of this condition is as follows. At $start_p$, $num_c{=}0$ implies that c is empty and hence all messages sent along c have been received. Hence all messages sent at or before $start_p$, along c, are received at or before $start_p$ and since $start_p \leq end_q$, the result follows.

For all p in P^*, let $quiet_p \equiv$ for all states S_i, where $start_p \leq i \leq end_p$: $[b_p$ and for all outgoing channels c in C^* : $num_c = 0]$.

In the paradigm we replace B^* (*obs*) by

[for all p in P^* : $quiet_p$] *and*

[for all p,q in P^* where p is a predecessor of q : $start_p \leq end_q$].

We show, in section 4, how $start_p \leq end_q$, can be maintained. num_c is maintained as a local variable of p and hence $quiet_p$ can be determined by p. Note that for systems with rendezvous, such as CSP and ADA, num_c=0 holds at all times.

3.3.2. Systems with First-In-First-Out Channels

To answer the key question posed at the beginning of this section, we use special messages called *markers*, which are sent and received along channels in C^*. They have no effect on the underlying computation other than that they occupy the same channels as regular messages. We use the following implementation rules.

R1. Every process p in P^* sends one marker along each outgoing channel in C^* some (finite) time after (or at) $start_p$ and,

R2. Every process p in P^* has received one marker along each incoming channel in C^* some time before (or at) end_p.

Since channels are first-in-first-out, all messages sent along a channel before the marker is sent on the channel must be received before the marker is received. Hence every message sent at or before $start_p$ is received at or before end_q, for all p,q in P^*, where p is a predecessor of q.

Each process p in P^* maintains a local boolean variable $quiet_p$ where

$$quiet_p \equiv \text{ for all states } S_i \text{ where } start_p \leq i \leq end_p : b_p.$$

In the paradigm we replace $B^*(obs)$ by : [for all p in P^* : $quiet_p$] and rules **R1**, **R2** are satisfied.

3.4. Notes on the Paradigm

Our constraints on observation period sets are weak. For instance it is possible that for a predecessor p of q, $start_q > end_p$ and there may be *no overlap* between

p's and q's observation periods. For a system with first-in-first-out channels, process p may send markers on some or all outgoing channels *after* end_p, and may receive markers on some or all incoming channels *before* $start_p$.

If the quiescent property never holds, the iteration in the paradigm will never terminate, i.e. an infinite sequence of observation period sets will be obtained.

4. Applications of the Paradigm

There are many problems to which the paradigm may be applied and many ways of applying the paradigm. We show two examples to demonstrate the power of the paradigm: termination detection and (both types of) deadlock detection, described earlier. We use termination detection as an example of the use of markers and deadlock detection as an example of the use of acks.

4.1. Termination Detection

Processes are labeled p_i, $0 \leq i < n$. We employ a *token* to transmit the values $quiet_p$. The token cycles through the processes visiting $p_{(i+1) mod\ n}$ after departing from p_i, all i. A cycle is initiated by a process p_{init}, called the initiator. If the token completes a cycle (i.e. returns to p_{init} after visiting all processes) and if all processes p return a value $quiet_p$ of *true* in this cycle then the initiator detects termination, i.e. it sets *claim* to *true.* If any process q returns a value $quiet_q$ of *false* in a cycle, then the current cycle is terminated and a new cycle is initiated with q as the initiator. A process ends one observation period and immediately starts the next observation period when it sends the token. The algorithm, described next in detail, shows how $quiet_p$ is set.

4.1.1. The Algorithm

The are no shared variables in a distributed system. However, *for purposes of exposition* we assume that *claim* is a shared global variable which has an initial value of *false* and which may be set *true* by any process. Such a global variable can be simulated by message transmissions; for instance, the process that sets *claim* to *true* may send messages to all other processes notifying them.

Two types of messages are employed in the termination detection algorithm.

<marker> : this type of message has already been discussed; it carries no other information (except its own type).

<token, initiator> : this is the token and its initiator, as described in Section 4·1.

Each process has the following constants and variables. These will be subscripted, by i, when referring to a specific process i.

ic: number of incoming channels to the process, a constant,

idle: process is idle,

quiet: process has been continuously idle since the token was last sent by the process; *false* if the token has never been sent by this process,

hold-token: process holds the token,

init: the value of initiator in the <token, initiator> message last sent or received; undefined if the process has never received such a message,

m: number of markers received, since the token was last sent by the process; initial value as given in the algorithm.

Initial Conditions

The token is at p_0.

m_i = the number of channels from processes with indices greater than i, for all i, i.e., the cardinality of the set, $\{c \mid c \text{ is a channel from } p_j \text{ to } p_i \textit{ and } j > i\}$.

(This initial condition is required because otherwise, the token will permanently stay at one process.)

$quiet_i = false$, for all i.

(The algorithm is slightly more efficient with different initial conditions, but for purposes of exposition we shall make the simpler assumption.)

$$hold\text{-}token_i = \begin{cases} true, \text{ for } i=0 \\ false, \text{ for } i \neq 0 \end{cases}$$

$init_i$ is arbitrary, for all i

Algorithm for a Process P_i

The algorithm for a process is a repetitive guarded command. The repetitive guarded command is a set of rules where each rule is of the form, *condition* $\rightarrow$ *action*. The algorithm proceeds as follows: one of the rules whose condition part evaluates to *true* is selected nondeterministically and its action part is executed. The repetitive guarded command consists of the following rules:

1. receive *marker* $\rightarrow$ $m_i := m_i + 1$;
2. $quiet_i$ *and* receive regular message (i.e. underlying computation's message) $\rightarrow$ $quiet_i := false$;
3. receive <*token, initiator*> $\rightarrow$ **begin** $init_i := initiator$; $hold\text{-}token_i := true$ **end**;
4. $hold\text{-}token_i$ *and* $(ic_i = m_i)$ *and* $idle_i$ $\rightarrow$

if $quiet_i$ *and* $(init_i = i)$ **then** {termination detected} $claim := true$;

if $quiet_i$ *and* $(init_i \neq i)$ **then** {continue old cycle}

begin

$m_i := 0$;

Send marker along each outgoing channel;

$hold\text{-}token_i := false$;

send <*token*, $init_i$> to $p_{(i+1) \bmod n}$

end

if $\sim quiet_i$ **then** {initiate new cycle}

begin

$m_i := 0$; $quiet_i := true$; $init_i := i$;

Send marker along each outgoing channel;

$hold\text{-}token_i := false$;

send $<token, init_i>$ to $p_{(i+1) mod\ n}$

end

4.1.2. Proof of Correctness

We need merely show that the algorithm fits the paradigm. A process p_i ends an observation period and starts the next one when the token leaves p_i. Initially, an observation period is started when the token leaves p_0; the values of m_i are so chosen initially that it is possible for the token to leave p_i, for the first time, when p_i has received markers from all lower numbered processes. We need to show the following {initial conditions should be treated slightly differently}:

1. $quiet_i \equiv p_i$ has been continuously idle in the current observation period, i.e. since the token last left p_i

2. Each process sends a marker on each outgoing channel upon starting an observation period.

3. Each process ends an observation period only after receiving exactly one marker along each incoming channel.

4. *claim* is set to *true* if and only if in one cycle of the token (which corresponds to an iteration of the paradigm all processes p_i return a value of $quiet_i = true$ at the end of their observation periods.

5. After termination, a cycle of the token is completed in finite time. To guarantee this we must ensure that each process receives a marker along each incoming channel in finite time.

Proofs of these assertions follow directly from the algorithm and the details are left to the reader.

4.1.3. Overhead and Efficiency

The most overhead is incurred in rule 4, when a process is idle. The overhead while a process is doing useful work in negligible. Also a process sends the token only when the process is idle; this controls the rate at which the token cycles through processes. For instance, if all processes are active, the token will not move at all. Also observe that termination will be detected within two cycles of after computation terminates.

4.2. Deadlock Detection

The following refinement of the paradigm is applicable to database deadlock and communication deadlock, under the assumption that messages are acknowledged.

A process which we call the *detector* sends *initiate* messages to all processes; on receiving an *initiate* message a process starts its observation period and acknowledges the *initiate* message. After receiving acknowledgements to all the *initiate* messages sent the detector sends *finish* messages to all processes. A process p ends its observation period after receiving a *finish* message and replies with a boolean value $quiet_p$ and a set $waiting\text{-}for_p$, where

$$quiet_p \equiv \text{for all states in the observation period :}$$
$$[p \text{ is } waiting \text{ } and \text{ for all outgoing channels } c : num_c = 0]$$

$$waiting\text{-}for_p = \begin{cases} \text{set of objects that } p \text{ is waiting for in the observation period, if } quiet_p. \\ \\ \text{arbitrary, if } not\ quiet_p \end{cases}$$

The *detector* determines whether there exists a set of processes P^*, such that for all p in P^* : $quiet_p$ and the sets $waiting\text{-}for_p$ are such as to constitute a deadlock. The proof of correctness is that the algorithm fits the paradigm.

The algorithm, as stated above, appears to be centralized rather than distributed. Note however, that the *detector* process could be different for different initiations and there could be multiple *detectors*. The function of the detector, i.e. sending messages, detecting deadlock, can be decentralized by having messages forwarded to their destinations by intermediate processes and deadlock detection computation carried out by intermediate processes.

5. Previous Work

The idea of observation periods is central to the works of Francez, Rodeh and Sintzoff on distributed termination [12-14], and Chandy, Misra and Haas on deadlock detection [6]. Dijkstra [11], Gouda [16] and Misra [26] have developed token based algorithms for termination detection, and these algorithms also use observations over a period. We have attempted to generalize these works to produce a particularly simple paradigm for detecting an important class of properties, quiescent properties, in distributed systems with asynchronous channels.

Acknowledgement: It is a pleasure to acknowledge extensive discussions with Shmuel Katz, who also carefully read and commented on earlier draft of this paper. Edsger W. Dijkstra and Hank Korth helped with constructive criticism.

References

1. C. Beeri and R. Obermarck, "A Resource Class Independent Deadlock Detection Algorithm", *Research Report RJ3077,* IBM Research Laboratory, San Jose, California, May 1981.

2. G. Bracha and S. Toueg, "A Distributed Algorithm For Generalized Deadlock Detection", *Technical Report TR 83-558,* Cornell University, June 1983.

3. K. M. Chandy and J. Misra, "Asynchronous Distributed Simulation Via a Sequence of Parallel Computations", *Communications of the ACM,* Vol. 24, No. 4, pp. 198-205, April 1981.

4. K. M. Chandy and J. Misra, "A Distributed Algorithm for Detecting Resource Deadlocks in Distributed Systems", *ACM SIGACT-SIGOPS Symposium on Principles of Distributed Computing,* Ottawa, Canada, August 1982.

5. K. M. Chandy and J. Misra, "A Computation on Graphs: Shortest Path Algorithms", *Communications of the ACM,* Vol. 25, No. 11, pp. 833-837, November 1982.

6. K. M. Chandy and J. Misra and L. Haas, "Distributed Deadlock Detection", *ACM Transactions on Computing Systems,* Vol. 1, No. 2, pp. 144-156, May 1983.

7. K. M. Chandy and L. Lamport, "Distributed Snapshots: Determining Global States of Distributed Systems", to appear in *ACM Transactions on Computing Systems.*

8. E. Chang, "Echo Algorithms: Depth Parallel Operations on General Graphs", *IEEE Transactions on Software Engineering,* Vol. SE-8, No. 4, pp. 391-401, July 1982.

9. S. Cohen and D. Lehmann, "Dynamic Systems and Their Distributed Termination", *ACM SIGACT-SIGOPS Symposium on Principles of Distributed Computing,* pp. 29-33, Ottawa, Canada, August 18-20, 1982.

10. E. W. Dijkstra and C. S. Scholten, "Termination Detection for Diffusing Computations", *Information Processing Letters,* Vol. 11, No. 1, August 1980.

11. E. W. Dijkstra, "Distributed Termination Detection Revisited", EWD 828, Plataanstraat 5, 5671 AL Nuenen, The Netherlands.

12. N. Francez, "Distributed Termination", *ACM Transactions on Programming Languages and Systems,* Vol. 2, No. 1, pp. 42-55, January 1980.

13. N. Francez, M. Rodeh, and M. Sintzoff, "Distributed Termination with Interval Assertions", *Proceedings of Formalization of Programming Concepts,* Peninusla, Spain, April 1981. Lecture Notes in Computer Science 107, (Springer-Verlag).

14. N. Francez and M. Rodeh, "Achieving Distributed Termination Without Freezing", *IEEE-TSE,* Vol. SE-8, No. 3, pp. 287-292, May 1982.

15. V. Gligor and S. Shattuck, "On Deadlock Detection in Distributed Data Bases", *IEEE Transactions on Software Engineering,* Vol. SE-6, No. 5, September 1980.

16. M. Gouda, "Personal Communication", Department of Computer Sciences, University of Texas, Austin, Texas 78712.

17. L. Haas and C. Mohan, "A Distributed Deadlock Detection Algorithm for a Resource-Based System", *Research Report RJ3765,* IBM Research Laboratory, San Jose, California, January 1983.

18. T. Herman and K. M. Chandy, "A Distributed Procedure to Detect AND/OR Deadlock", Computer Sciences Department, University of Texas, Austin, Texas 78712, February 1983.

19. T. Holt, "Some Deadlock Properties of Computer Systems", *Computing Surveys,* Vol. 4, No. 3, pp. 179-196, September 1972.

20. D. Kumar, Ph.D Theses (in preparation), Computer Sciences Department, University of Texas, Austin, Texas 78712.

21. L. Lamport, "Time, Clocks and the Ordering of Events in a Distributed System", *Communications of the ACM,* Vol. 21, No. 7, July 1978.

22. G. Le Lann, "Distributed Systems - Towards a Formal Approach", *Information Processing 77,* IFIP, North-Holland Publishing Company, 1977.

23. D. Menasce and R. Muntz, "Locking and Deadlock Detection in Distributed Data Bases", *IEEE Transactions on Software Engineering,* Vol. SE-5, No. 3, May 1979.

24. J. Misra and K. M. Chandy, "A Distributed Graph Algorithm: Knot Detection", *ACM Transactions on Programming Languages and Systems,* Vol. 4, No. 4, pp. 678-688, October 1982.

25. J. Misra and K. M. Chandy, "Termination Detection of Diffusing Computations in Communicating Sequential Processes", *ACM Transactions on Programming Languages and Systems,* Vol. 4, No. 1, pp. 37-43, January 1982.

26. J. Misra, "Detecting Termination of Distributed Computations Using Markers", *Proceedings of the ACM SIGACT-SIGOPS Symposium of Principles of Distributed Computing,* Montreal, Canada, August 17 - 19, 1983.

27. R. Obermarck, "Deadlock Detection For All Resource Classes", *Research Report RJ2955,* IBM Research Laboratory, San Jose, California, October 1980.

28. R. Obermarck, "Distributed Deadlock Detection Algorithm", *ACM Transactions on Database Systems,* Vol. 7, No. 2, pp. 187-208, June 1982.

ABOUT FAIR ASYNCHRONY

Philippe DARONDEAU
IRISA -Campus de Beaulieu-
F 35042 RENNES CEDEX

This paper studies the joint influence of fairness and asynchrony on the modelling of a CCS-like language. Programs in the language are provided with an implementation preorder which reflects their observational properties. A fully abstract model of the preorder is constructed in the framework of infinitary languages, preferred here to more classical domains. The case of bounded parallelism is analyzed : there, infinitary rational expressions may be used to specify the observationally meaningful properties of programs, and no induction is needed to prove those semantic properties.

1. INTRODUCTION

The opening section is a rather informal presentation of the topics addressed in the sequel. We choose as a starting point the pure version of CCS without value passing (Mi 2). Thus, no provision will be made for simultaneous events as are considered in SCCS (Mi 3). In this introduction, we adhere as much as possible to the usual conventions for the notation of CCS terms and programs.

The first concept we are concerned about is asynchrony. A particular program p is said to be asynchronous if $p \simeq \tau.p$, where τ is the CCS symbol of internal moves and $\simeq$ denotes some semantical identity. It is a well known fact that asynchrony does not hold in general for CCS, owing to the sum contexts. Although NIL and τ.NIL are equivalent, this is not the case for NIL + α.NIL and τ.NIL + α.NIL. Intending to reach full asynchrony of programs, we shall significantly depart from CCS by avoiding both τ's and the + operator, while providing in exchange polyadic guarding operators. This way, $\alpha.p + \beta.q$ will be translated into $\langle\alpha,\beta\rangle\ (p,q)$, but no sum of parallel expressions may be rendered.

Still more essential than asynchrony appears the concept of fairness. Our understanding of the term may be stated as follows : in a fair computation, no agent who infinitely often has opportunities to communicate with other agents may remain forever inactive. This definition is rather sketchy, for it does not specify the nature of the agents. But it is sufficient to

NATO ASI Series, Vol. F13
Logics and Models of Concurrent Systems
Edited by K. R. Apt

point out what fairness is not in our mind. Consider for instance program $(\alpha.NIL)$ $[/\alpha]$, then the empty execution appears as a fair computation, for the agent $(\alpha.NIL)$ has no opportunity to communicate with the environment. Hence, fairness has little to do with the constraint of finite delay of actions [Mi 4], which constraint would leave the above program with no execution at all ! Communication between agents makes it somewhat involved to grasp the precise implications of fairness, even in simple situations. For instance, even though the semantics of the parallel composition is based on the interleaving of actions, programs p and q given by $p = rec\ x.(\alpha.x + \beta\ .\ x)$ and $q = (rec\ y.(\alpha.y)) \mid (rec\ z.\ (\beta.z))$ do not appear equivalent. The difference between them is sensible for the observer r equal to $rec\ w.\ (\overline{\alpha}.w + \overline{\beta}.\gamma.NIL)$, in that not every fair computation of $(p|r)$ leads to a state where γ is available. Now, the eventual accessibility of γ is guaranteed by the system $(q|r)$, which incorporates three parallel agents instead of two. Thus, fairness might be seen as the ultimate distinction between sequential non-determinism and parallelism : it does not invalidate the expansion theorem of CCS [Mi 2] but nevertheless prevents some parallel programs, such as q above, from having any sequential equivalent. Two versions of fairness, namely strong fairness and weak fairness, are generally considered, depending on the use of "infinitely often" or "almost always" in the expression of the constraint. It may be observed that <u>weak fairness is in contradiction with full asynchrony</u>. If weak fairness were embodied into some composition operator $\|$, then an easy distinction between $rec\ x.\ (\tau.(\alpha.x + \beta\ .x))$ and
$rec\ y.\ (\alpha.y + \beta\ .y)$ could be obtained by respectively filling them into the context
$((\quad) \| \ ((rec\ z.(\overline{\alpha}.z)) \| \ (\overline{\beta}.\gamma\ .NIL)))$: the eventual availability of γ would be guaranteed for the second program, but not for the first.
From our assumption of full asynchrony, we must bar any way to get effective distinctions between p and $(\tau.p)$, and we shall therefore forget weak fairness and consider strong fairness only. Now, $\tau.p \simeq p \simeq p| (rec\ x.(\tau.x))$ will emerge as valid relations. (In fact, τ-programs and other programs used in this introduction have a very different syntax in the programming language considered in section2).

Our main interest in fair asynchrony is in what concerns the <u>observational semantics</u> of programs. A semantics of this type may be constructed as the model of an observational precongruence $\underset{\sim}{\sqsubset}$ defined as follows : $p \underset{\sim}{\sqsubset} q$ iff for every context $\mathcal{C}$, any information possibly obtained when observing $\mathcal{C}[p]$ may also be obtained when observing $\mathcal{C}[q]$. The precongruence does not necessarily coïncide with the observational preorder $\lesssim$ defined analogously for $\mathcal{C}$ the empty context. However,it seems a desirable property that the two relations coïncide : this guarantees that no operator upon programs is able to amplify semantic differences which observers are unable to detect by themselves. Hence, all the semantics may be captured by mere interaction.

Various questions arise as regards the way to perform interactive experiments, the way to extract informations from experiments, and the way to compare programs according to the resulting informations. Let us take the first point. Surely, observers should not be able to amplify semantic differences which make no sense for the operators upon programs. It then appears most important that programs are experimented upon in their ordinary working conditions. For instance, if the programming language does not provide for roll-back, an observer should not be able to run several experiments from a particular configuration of a program, if different from the initial configuration. To the implicitly backtracking observers of CCS will therefore be preferred on-line observers which interact with the observed program in linear runs from the initial state. Now, observers may have finite or infinite behaviours, they may be simple agents or systems of communicating agents, they may be restricted to program definable behaviour or may be endowed with arbitrary behaviours. Since fairness is mainly a property of infinite behaviours, we shall naturally choose observers with infinite behaviour. Now, under the assumption of fairness, infinite sequences of interactions between parallel observers may yield informations that no sequential observer can get alone. Given $p = (q|r)$ where $q = \text{rec } x.(\alpha.x)$ and $r = \text{rec } x.(\bar{\alpha}.x)$, consider for instance a pair of parallel observers $q' = q$ and $r' = r$. In a run of $p|(q'|r')$, an infinite sequence of direct interactions between q' and r' outside the observed system p will indicate that p may proceed forever without any of its component agents starving for α or $\bar{\alpha}$. Hence, observers should have the full generality of non-deterministic parallel programs, and we shall assume from now on, for the sake of concreteness, that they are given the effective form of programs.

Let us turn to consider what are the results of experiments and how the associated information may be used to compare programs. To define the result of an experiment upon p, performed as a run of $(p|q)$ for some q, we have a wide range of possibilities with extremes as follows :

- from a q-experiment upon p, extract the minimal information, that is a binary result,
- from a q-experiment upon p, extract the maximal information, and then identify the result of the experiment with the computation of q.

To the difference of M. Hennessy (He), we have chosen the second branch, but we are not yet sure that a more discriminative congruence is obtained this way. Nevertheless, the above alternative has strong implications on the way to compare programs. When experiments with binary results lead to compare programs according to some improvement ordering, the natural counterpart on the second branch is to compare programs according to some implementation ordering (Jo). In clear, p_1 is observationally less than p_2 $(p_1 \lesssim p_2)$ if every computation of q in $p_1|q$ coïncides with a computation of q in $p_2|q$, and p_1 implements p_2 $(p_1 \sqsubseteq p_2)$ if this relation is preserved by contexts, i.e. if $\mathcal{C}(p_1) \lesssim \mathcal{C}(p_2)$ for every context $\mathcal{C}$.

Once an observational preorder has been approved, it remains to provide it with a denotational model, and as far as possible with a fully abstract model (Mi 1). A meaning function $\mathcal{N}$ which takes its values in some domain with order relation < is fully abstract w.r.t. the observational preorder iff $(\mathcal{N}(p) < \mathcal{N}(q) \Leftrightarrow p$ implements $q)$.

Domains of denotational models are often chosen as c.p.o.'s, and even as ω-algebraic c.p.o.'s. The least element of the domain gives meanings to the undefined program Ω. The base elements give meanings to the finite terms which approximate programs according to the syntactic ordering. The semantics of recursively defined programs are given by least fixpoints of ω-continuous operators, computed as limits of ω-chains of base elements. Due to the very nature of fairness, it is quite clear that fixed points of ω-continuous operators are not sufficient in our case, for the parallel composition is certainly not ω-continuous. But this does not preclude fixpoints from being used, since least and greatest fixpoints still exist under the relaxed assumption of monotonicity of the operators (Pa). Now, we may question the introduction of the tricky program Ω : of what practical interest is it to introduce the concept of syntactic approximation when transfinite induction is needed to fit the computation rules of fixpoints ? Here, we shall avoid recourse to the undefined program Ω and thus seek for more direct ways to deal with infinity. Since results of experiments are infinite computations, we turn our mind to domains of infinitary languages, viewed as abstract representations of sets of computations. Consequently, we shall use greatest fixpoints of monotonic operators on languages, among which will appear an adapted version of the fair merge operator, central to the work of D. Park (Pa). It is also our opinion that this operator is at the very heart of fair asynchrony. As a drawback of dealing directly with infinity, we lack an axiomatization of the implementation preorder, but a decision procedure will be proved to exist for the restricted class of programs with bounded parallelism.

To end this introduction, some early indications may be given as regards the intuitive significance of our semantic objects. The considered languages are families of triples $<\delta,\rho,d>$ where :

- ρ represents the finite or infinite trace of the interactions between a program and an observer,
- δ represents some of the partial failures $(\alpha_1, \ldots ,\alpha_n)$ of the program, recognized as such by the observers for they cannot infinitely often offer the complementary actions $\bar{\alpha}_i$ without getting effective communications $\{\alpha_i , \bar{\alpha}_i\}$ with the program,
- d represents the set of the actions for which the observer may know with certainty that no component agent of the observed program is starving for them.

Such triples have a certain similarity with the failures used by S. Brookes (Br) , and our semantic ordering is defined like in that work by reverse inclusion of sets. No simple connection appears to exist between our implementation preorder $\sqsubset\!\!\!\sim$ and Hennessy's testing preorders (He) : at most can we say that $p \sqsubset\!\!\!\sim q$ implies $p \sqsubset\!\!\!\sim_1 q$ and $q \sqsubset\!\!\!\sim_2 p$.

2. A TOY PROGRAMMING LANGUAGE

The programming language which we present in this section is rather a toy language. It has been designed to fit the objective of finding out a model of the observational preorder which is fully abstract for every terms in a non trivial subset of fair asynchronous CCS. This requirement led us to avoid the use of variables in general recursive definitions, and to restrict recursion to ready made patterns embodied into built in iterators. Another motivation against general recursive definitions may be found in the CCS program rec $x.(\tau.(x|x))$ which we will identify with NIL, like we do for rec $x.(\tau.x)$, although another possible solution could be for instance x = rec $y.(\alpha.y)$, and NIL is not a least element ! Technically, we have turned CCS, or rather a subset of it, into a classical Σ-algebra (with the benefit of making our proofs easier to work out).

Some notations must be taken before a sketch of the operators in Σ. From now on, we assume given disjoint sets of complementary action names Δ and $\overline{\Delta}$, ranged over by α resp. $\overline{\alpha}$, such that there exist reciprocal bijections $\overline{}$: $\alpha \mapsto \overline{\alpha} \mapsto \alpha$. We let Ren, ranged over by π, denote the set of the domain finite injections over $\Lambda = \Delta \cup \overline{\Delta}$ such that :
$(\forall\lambda)(\pi(\lambda)$ defined $\Rightarrow \pi(\overline{\lambda}) = \overline{\pi(\lambda)})$ & $(\exists n)(\forall\lambda)(\pi^n(\lambda)$ undefined$)$.
The following operators are specific to our language.

- $\langle\lambda_1\ldots\lambda_n\rangle$ denotes a n-ary guarding operator, and $\langle\lambda_1\ldots\lambda_n\rangle\ (p_1\ldots p_n)$ reflects the CCS sum $(\lambda_1.p_1 + \ldots + \lambda_n.p_n)$,

- $[\lambda \triangleright \pi]$ denotes a unary network iterator, and $p\ [\lambda \triangleright \pi]$ acts as if it were the CCS term rec $x.(\lambda.((p|x)[\pi]))$,

- $\langle\lambda \Rightarrow \lambda_1 : \lambda'_1, \ldots, \lambda_n : \lambda'_n\rangle$ denotes a constant local iterator, whose CCS equivalent is rec $x.(\lambda.(\lambda_1.\lambda'_1.x + \ldots + \lambda_n.\lambda'_n.x))$.

Some comments follow . Program $p\ [\lambda \triangleright \pi]$ acts as a dynamic string of copies of p each of which, once started from the left by a λ, may further communicate with its left and right neighbours located at a distance less than n if π^n is the undefined function. The existence of such an n is crucial for our characterization of semantics by greatest fixpoints. But as a counter-part, network iterators applied to finite agents do not afford a way to simulate, for instance, finite automata with infinite behaviour. Opportunately, such behaviours may be rendered by asynchronous compositions of local iterators. Since local iterators are mere cycles, there will be no technical difficulty to state their correspondence with infinitary languages, without using at all the prefix order on words. The full power of the language comes from the application of network iterators to asynchronous compositions of local iterators. Of course, any Turing machine can be simulated this way by a dynamic string of finite state automata !

To make things quite clear, our programming language is the free term algebra T_Σ for the signature $\Sigma = \bigcup \Sigma_n$, $n \geqslant 0$, given by :

$\Sigma_0 = \{NIL\} \cup \{<\lambda \;\Rightarrow\; \lambda_1 : \lambda'_1, \ldots, \lambda_n : \lambda'_n > \mid \lambda, \lambda_i, \lambda'_i \;\varepsilon\; \Lambda\}$

$\Sigma_1 = \{<\lambda> \mid \lambda \;\varepsilon \Lambda\} \cup \{ (\pi) \mid \pi \;\varepsilon\; Ren\} \cup \{ (\lambda \triangleright \pi) \mid \lambda \;\varepsilon \Lambda, \pi \;\varepsilon\; Ren\}$

$\Sigma_2 = \{ \mid \} \cup \{ <\lambda_1, \lambda_2> \mid \lambda_i \;\varepsilon \Lambda\}$

$\Sigma_n = \{<\lambda_1 \ldots \lambda_n> \mid \lambda_i \;\varepsilon \Lambda\}$ for $n > 2$.

In Σ_2 , $\mid$ denotes the asynchronous composition operator.
In Σ_3 , (π) denotes a renaming/restriction operator.
Before we provide a formal definition of the operational semantics of T_Σ , we present a few sample programs.

Let S and S' denote disjoint sets of action names, interrelated by a pair of renaming functions π_1 , π_2 which have respective range S' and S and act as reciprocal bijections between S and S'. For p a program with sort S and $\alpha \notin$ S, one may build the following "τ-programs" which are equivalent to p :

$\{ \tau p \} = (<\alpha>(p) \mid <\bar{\alpha}> (NIL)) \; (\pi_1) \; (\pi_2)$

$\{ p \mid \tau^\omega \} = (p \mid (<\alpha \Rightarrow \alpha : \alpha> \mid <\bar{\alpha} \Rightarrow \bar{\alpha} : \bar{\alpha}>)) \; (\pi_1) \; (\pi_2)$

Let greek letters α to ε be taken in S, and let x, y, z $\notin$ S, then the CCS program

$\{ rec \; x \; y \; z \; . \; (\alpha.z + \beta.y, \varepsilon.x, \gamma.y + \delta.x) \}$

may be implemented by the Σ-term

$(<\bar{x}> (NIL) \mid (X \mid (Y \mid Z))) \;\; (\pi_1) \; (\pi_2)$

where

$X = < x \Rightarrow \alpha : \bar{z} \; , \beta : \bar{y} >$

$Y = < y \Rightarrow \varepsilon : \bar{x} >$

$Z = < z \Rightarrow \gamma : \bar{y} \; , \delta : \bar{x} >$

Clearly, any kind of recursive specification of a finite state machine may be implemented in the above fashion, and we shall return to that point in section 4. We come presently to a formal definition of the operational semantics.

A computation is a finite or infinite sequence of communications among the agents of a system, whose global state is described by a program in T_Σ. Each communication may be represented by an associated transition $p \xrightarrow{e} p'$ between program states, where e is a pair of complementary actions $\{\lambda_R , \bar{\lambda}_S\}$, or a pair of invisible actions $\{\tau_R , \tau_S\}$. Subscripts of actions identify processes, like in (Co). Along the computation, fresh identifiers are generated for new processes each time a new unguarded occurence of the asynchronous composition operator | appears in the program state, which is the case at each expansion of an iterator. Processes are therefore unable to perform infinite sequences of actions. Communications and actions of programs or processes may be specified together by an inference system in Plotkin style (P1). The rules read according to the following conventions.

- $\lambda \in \Lambda = \Delta \cup \overline{\Delta}$; $\tau = \overline{\tau} \notin \Lambda$ is the undefined action name, thus $\pi(\lambda) = \tau$ if λ is not in the definition domain of π and $\pi(\tau) = \tau$; $\mu \in \Lambda \cup \{\tau\}$
- $ID = \{\leftarrow, \rightarrow\}^*$ is the set of process identifiers, ranged over by R and S; arrows have a positional meaning with respect to the operator symbol |
- e denotes a singleton set $\{\lambda_R\}$ or a pair $\{\mu_R , \overline{\mu}_S\}$; for $\longleftrightarrow$ in $\{\leftarrow, \rightarrow\}$, $\longleftrightarrow$ (e) denotes accordingly the set $\{\lambda_{\longleftrightarrow R}\}$ or the set $\{\mu_{\longleftrightarrow R} , \overline{\mu}_{\longleftrightarrow S}\}$.

The Action Rules

$$< \lambda_1, \ldots , \lambda_n >(t_1,\ldots,t_n) \xrightarrow{\lambda_i} t_i \ , \ i \in \{1\ldots n\}$$

$$\frac{t \xrightarrow{e} t'}{(t|u) \xrightarrow{\leftarrow(e)} (t'|u)} \qquad \frac{t \xrightarrow{e} t'}{(u|t) \xrightarrow{\rightarrow(e)} (u|t')}$$

$$\frac{t \xrightarrow{\lambda_R} t' \ , \ u \xrightarrow{\overline{\lambda}_S} u'}{(t|u) \xrightarrow{\lambda \leftarrow R,\ \overline{\lambda} \rightarrow S} (t'|u')}$$

$$\frac{t \xrightarrow{\lambda_R} t'}{t\ (\pi) \xrightarrow{\pi(\lambda)_R} t'\ (\pi)} \qquad \text{if } \pi(\lambda) \neq \tau$$

$$\frac{t \xrightarrow{\mu_R\ \overline{\mu}_S} t'}{t(\pi) \xrightarrow{\pi(\mu)_R\ \ \pi(\overline{\mu})_S} t'(\pi)}$$

$$t\ (\ \lambda \rhd \pi\ ) \xrightarrow{\lambda} (\ t \mid t\ (\ \lambda \rhd \pi\ )\ )\ (\pi)$$

if $t = <\lambda \Rightarrow \lambda_1 : \lambda'_1, \ldots, \lambda_n : \lambda'_n >$ then

$$t \xrightarrow{\lambda} (NIL \mid < \lambda_1, \ldots , \lambda_n > (<\lambda'_1> (t), \ldots , <\lambda'_n> (t)))$$

Now, not every computation is fair, and we have to rule out those sequences of transitions in which some process remains forever inactive although it has infinitely often the opportunity to communicate with other processes. This goal is achieved by the following statements, which make heavy use of the subscripts of actions.

definition 1 For $t \in T_\Sigma$ and $R \in ID$, the set $Act_R(t)$ of t's R-actions is the set $\{\mu \mid \exists u \in T_\Sigma, \exists S \in ID : t \xrightarrow{\mu_R \bar{\mu}_S} u\}$

definition 2 Let E_2 denote the set of pairs $\{\mu_R, \bar{\mu}_S\}$. For $p_0 \in T_\Sigma$, the associated set fair (p_0) of fair computations is the set of sequences $(p_i, e_i)_{i \in \omega}$ where $p_i \in T_\Sigma$ and $e_i \in \{\emptyset\} \cup E_2$, such that the following conditions are satisfied :

$(\forall i)(p_i \xrightarrow{e_i} p_{i+1} \vee (\forall j \geqslant i)(e_j = \emptyset \;\&\; p_j = p_{j+1}))$

$(\forall R \in ID)(\exists j)(\forall k \geqslant j)(Act_R(p_k) = \emptyset)$.

For instance, $<\alpha \Rightarrow \alpha : \alpha> \mid <\bar{\alpha} \Rightarrow \bar{\alpha} : \bar{\alpha}>$ has no fair computation of finite size. To complete our operational setting, one can assert the following...

proposition 1 For any p_0 in T_Σ, fair (p_0) is different from the empty set.

3. AN OBSERVATIONAL MODEL

In this section, we construct a model $\mathcal{N}$ of the observational preorder $\underset{\sim}{\leqslant}$ on T_Σ programs, and suggest some elements towards a proof of the full abstractness of $\mathcal{N}$. The proof, which appears with full details in (Da 4), establishes a connection between $\mathcal{N}$ and $\mathcal{M}$, an operational model of T_Σ in which a program is abstracted into a set of computation histories $<\delta, \rho, d>$.

3.1. The observational setting

First, we introduce experiments as a kind of projections of fair computations.

definition 3 Given a fair computation $\mathcal{F} = ((p_i | q_i), e_i)_{i \in \omega}$, let $\mathcal{F}' = (q_i, e'_i)_{i \in \omega}$ where $e'_i = \{\mu_R | \mu_{\rightarrow R} \in e_i\}$. Set down $|\mathcal{F}'| = \sqcup \{i + 1 | (q_i \xrightarrow{e'_i} q_{i+1})\}$. The right projection $\mathcal{F}_{\rightarrow}$ of $\mathcal{F}$ is the sequence obtained from $\mathcal{F}'$ by erasing pairs (q_i, e'_i) for every

$i < |\mathcal{F}'|$ such that $e'_i = \emptyset$. The left projection $\mathcal{F}_{\leftarrow}$ of $\mathcal{F}$ is defined in a similar way. From now on, left and right projections of fair computations are called <u>open computations</u>.

<u>definition 4</u> For p,q in T_Σ , the set $EXP_q(p)$ of the q-experiments upon p is $\{ \mathcal{F}_{\rightarrow} \mid \mathcal{F} \in \text{fair}\ (p|q)\}$ and the set EXP(p) of the experiments upon p is $\bigcup EXP_q(p),\ q \in T_\Sigma$.

The <u>observation preorder</u> $\precsim$ may now be given two equivalent definitions (as we shall prove later on) :

<u>definition 5</u> $\precsim$ is the subset of $T_\Sigma \times T_\Sigma$ such that $p \precsim q$ iff $EXP(p) \subseteq EXP(q)$.

<u>definition 5'</u> $\precsim$ is the subset of $T_\Sigma \times T_\Sigma$ such that $p \precsim q$ iff $(\forall r \in T_\Sigma)$ $(EXP_r(p) \subseteq EXP_r(q))$.

The <u>implementation preorder</u> generalizes the above to Σ-contexts, defined as 1-hole Σ-terms:

<u>definition 6</u> For $p,q \in T_\Sigma$, p implements q ($p \sqsubseteq q$) iff $\mathcal{C}[p] \precsim \mathcal{C}[q]$ for every Σ-context $\mathcal{C}$.

Thus, p implements q iff for every context $\mathcal{C}$ and for every program r, no computation of r in $(\mathcal{C}[p] \mid r)$ allows to recognize that q has been replaced by p. We shall prove later on that the implementation preorder coïncides indeed with the observational preorder.

3.2. Histories

To construct a model of the observational preorder, we need of course a domain. The objects of that domain are sets of histories. In the following definitions, we call a <u>sort</u> L any finite subset of Λ such that $L = \overline{L}$; for ρ a word in $L^\infty = L^* \cup L^\omega$, we let Ult(ρ) denote the set of actions $\lambda \in \Lambda$ which occur infinitely often in ρ.

<u>definition 7</u> $\mathcal{H}_L$, the set of L-<u>sorted histories</u>, is the collection of the triples <δ,ρ,d> which satisfy : $\delta \subseteq L$ & $\rho \in L^\infty$ & $(Ult(\rho) \subseteq d \subseteq L)$ & $(d \cap (\delta \cup \overline{\delta}) = \emptyset)$. $\mathcal{H}$, the set of histories, is the union $\bigcup \mathcal{H}_L$ for L ranging over sorts. If $\mathcal{L}$ is a language, $<\delta,\mathcal{L},d>$ denotes the subset of histories $\{<\delta,\rho,d> \mid \rho \in \mathcal{L}\}$.

<u>hint</u> : Let $\mathcal{F} = (p_i,e_i)_{i\in\omega}$ be an open computation, then $\mathcal{F}$ may be abstracted into an history abs $(\mathcal{F}) = <\delta,\rho,d>$ with components as follows :

- ρ traces the e_i but ignores communications, i.e. pairs of actions,
- δ displays the potential actions of the agents which remain unchanged

and therefore inactive throughout some subsequence $(p_i)_{i>k}$,
- $d \cup \delta$ shows those λ in Λ which are potential actions of infinitely many p_i in the sequence $(p_i)_{i\varepsilon\omega}$.

The conditions in the definition simply express that an α-action which occurs infinitely often was infinitely often possible and that an α-action which is infinitely often possible excludes any kind of infinite waiting on $\overline{\alpha}$.

We shall now provide histories with prefixing, renaming and composition operators which take their values in $\mathcal{P}(\mathcal{H})$, the powerset of $\mathcal{H}$.

<u>definition 8</u> To each name $\lambda \varepsilon \Lambda \cup \{\varepsilon\}$, we associate the operator λ : from $\mathcal{H}$ to $\mathcal{P}(\mathcal{H})$ such that $\lambda :\langle\delta,\rho,d\rangle$ is the singleton set $\langle\delta,\lambda\rho,d\rangle$

<u>hint</u> : prefixing has no effect on the infinitary properties of an open computation.

<u>definition 9</u> To each function $\pi \; \varepsilon$ Ren, we associate the function $[\![\pi]\!]$ from $\mathcal{H}$ to $\mathcal{P}(\mathcal{H})$ such that : $[\![\pi]\!]$ $(\langle\delta,\rho,d\rangle)$ is the empty subset of $\mathcal{H}$ if π is undefined for some λ in ρ , or else is the singleton set $\langle\pi\delta,\pi\rho,\pi d\rangle$ where $\pi\rho$ is the morphic image of ρ and $\pi\delta$, πd are the images of the corresponding sets δ,d intersected by π's definition domain.

<u>hint</u> : if $\pi(\lambda) = \tau$, then no λ-action may occur in an open computation of $p\,[\pi]$.

<u>definition 10</u> Given histories h' and h" in $\mathcal{H}$, let $h' = \langle\delta',\rho',d'\rangle$ and $h'' = \langle\delta'',\rho'',d''\rangle$, these histories are <u>compatible</u> ($h' \# h''$) iff

1- $\delta' \cap \mathrm{Ult}(\rho'') = \emptyset = \delta'' \cap \mathrm{Ult}(\rho')$

2- $\delta' \cap (\overline{d''} \cup \overline{\delta''}) = \emptyset = \delta'' \cap (\overline{d'} \cup \overline{\delta'})$.

The <u>parallel composition</u> $h' \| h''$ of h', h" is either the empty subset of $\mathcal{H}$ if $\neg\,(h' \# h'')$ or else is the set of histories $\langle\delta' \cup \delta'', \rho' \,\|\, \rho'', (d' \setminus \delta'') \cup (d'' \setminus \delta')\rangle$, for $\rho' \| \rho''$ the language given in definition 11.

<u>hint</u> : In an open computation of $p|q$, q cannot infinitely often communicate with the external world by some α-action while some particular process in p remains eternally waiting for α; similarly, such a case for p excludes a permanent or periodic offering of $\overline{\alpha}$ by q. An α-action which is eternally expected (resp. infinitely often offered) in an open computation of $p|q$ is eternally expected (resp. infinitely often offered) by p or by q or by both p and q.

<u>definition 11</u> Let ρ', ρ'' denote words in L^∞ , their <u>parallel composition</u> $\rho' \| \rho''$ is the set of the words $\rho = \rho_1 \rho_2 \dots \rho_i \dots$ for which there exist corresponding factorizations $\rho'_1 \rho'_2 \dots \rho'_i$ resp. $\rho''_1 \rho''_2 \dots \rho''_i \dots$

of ρ' resp. ρ'' on $(L \cup \{\varepsilon\})$ such that for every i :

- $(\rho'_i \neq \varepsilon \ \& \ \rho''_i \neq \varepsilon) \Rightarrow (\rho'_i = \overline{\rho}''_i \ \& \ \rho_i = \varepsilon)$
- $(\rho'_i = \varepsilon \vee \rho''_i = \varepsilon) \Rightarrow \rho_i = \rho'_i \rho''_i$

hint : The parallel composition of words is a variant of the classical fair shuffle or fair merge [Pa] , with additional rendez-vous which are not flagged in (the words of) the resulting language.

Finally, $\mathcal{H}$ is made into an ordered structure $(\mathcal{H}, \leqslant)$ as follows.

definition 12 $\leqslant$ is the order relation on $\mathcal{H}$ such that $\langle\delta,\rho,d\rangle \leqslant \langle\delta',\rho',d'\rangle$ iff $(\rho=\rho')$ & $(\delta \subseteq \delta')$ & $((d \cup \delta) \subseteq (d' \cup \delta'))$.

We let $\check{}$ (resp. $\hat{}$) denote the operator upon $\mathcal{P}(\mathcal{H})$ which sends parts of $\mathcal{H}$ to their greatest subsets of minimal (resp. maximal) histories.

hint : the order $\leqslant$ on histories has nothing to do with the prefix order on words.

3.3. The model

The domain of our intended model is not $\mathcal{P}(\mathcal{H})$ but a subset of it, called $\mathcal{K}$, equipped with an ordering $\sqsubset_I$ which does not even ensure the existence of limits of increasing or decreasing chains (this fact is due to the consideration of sorts). A formal statement of the structure $(\mathcal{K}, \sqsubset_I)$ needs a preliminary definition of normalized (sets of) histories .

definition 13 let $h = \langle\delta,\rho,d\rangle \in \mathcal{H}$, then h is a normalized history iff $d = \overline{d}$. A subset P of $\mathcal{H}$ is normalized iff every history in P is normalized.

definition 14 $\mathcal{K}$ is the set of the normalized subsets of $\bigcup_L \mathcal{P}(\mathcal{H}_L)$ which do not contain any two $\leqslant$ - comparable histories, and $\sqsubset_I$ is the ordering on $\mathcal{K}$ such that $P \sqsubset_I Q$ iff $(\forall h \in P)(\exists h' \in Q)(h' \leqslant h)$.

We presently start our construction of a meaning function $\mathcal{N}$: $T_\Sigma \longrightarrow \mathcal{K}$ such that $\mathcal{N}(p) \sqsubset_I \mathcal{N}(q)$ holds iff p implements q. Henceforth, we shall freely use set extensions of the operators $\lambda:$, $\|$, $[\![\pi]\!]$ with $\mathcal{K}$ or $\mathcal{P}(\mathcal{H})$ as their co-domain according to the context. For instance, $[\![\pi]\!]$ $(\{h_1,h_2\})$ stands for $[\![\pi]\!]\ (h_1) \cup [\![\pi]\!]\ (h_2)$.

In a first step, we associate sets of normalized histories to local iterators $\langle\lambda \Rightarrow \lambda_1 : \lambda'_1, \ldots, \lambda_n : \lambda'_n\rangle$. For $i \in \{1\ldots n\}$, let $u_i = \lambda\lambda_i\lambda'_i$ and $\mathcal{L} = (\Sigma\ u_i)^*$.

For $I,J \subseteq \{1\ldots n\}$, let :

$\mathcal{L}_I = \bigcap_{i \in I} (\mathcal{L}u_i)^\omega \cap (\mathcal{L}(\sum_{i \in I} u_i)^\omega)$,

$d_{I,J} = \text{sym}(\{\lambda\} \cup \{\lambda_i \mid i \in I \cup J\} \cup \{\lambda'_i \mid i \in I\})$,

$\delta_{I,J} = \{\lambda_1 \dots \lambda_n\} \setminus d_{I,J}$,

where $\text{sym}(L) = L \cup \overline{L}$.

Using an additive notation of sets of histories, we state as a definition :

$\mathcal{N}''(<\lambda \Rightarrow \lambda_1 : \lambda'_1, \dots, \lambda_n : \lambda'_n>) =$
$<\{\lambda\}, \mathcal{L}, \emptyset> + <\{\lambda_1 \dots \lambda_n\}, \mathcal{L}\lambda, \emptyset> +$
$\sum_i <\{\lambda'_i\}, \mathcal{L}\lambda\lambda_i, \emptyset> + \sum_{I,J} <\delta_{IJ}, \mathcal{L}_I, d_{IJ}>$.

- notice in passing that the $\mathcal{L}_I$ are infinitary rational languages -

In a second step, we state the defining equations of $\mathcal{N}: T_\Sigma \to \mathcal{K}$. We let $Y(G)$ denote the greatest fixpoint of $G : \mathcal{K} \to \mathcal{K}$ when such a fixpoint exists, and we use $\check{F}$ as an abbreviation for $\vee \circ F$.

<u>The equations of $\mathcal{N}$</u>

$\mathcal{N}(\text{NIL}) = <\emptyset, \varepsilon, \emptyset>$

$\mathcal{N}(<\lambda_1, \dots, \lambda_n>(t_1, \dots, t_n)) =$
$\quad <\{\lambda_1 \dots \lambda_n\}, \varepsilon, \emptyset> + \vee(\sum_{i=1}^{n} \lambda_i : \mathcal{N}(t_i))$

$\mathcal{N}(t_1 | t_2) = \vee(\mathcal{N}(t_1) \parallel \mathcal{N}(t_2))$

$\mathcal{N}(t[\pi]) = \vee([\![\pi]\!]\, \mathcal{N}(t))$

$\mathcal{N}(t[\lambda \triangleright \pi]) = Y(\check{F})$ where

$\quad F(X) = <\lambda, \varepsilon, \emptyset> + (\lambda : [\![\pi]\!]\, (\mathcal{N}(t) \parallel X)))$

$\mathcal{N}(<\lambda \Rightarrow \lambda_1 : \lambda'_1, \dots, \lambda_n : \lambda'_n>) =$
$\quad \vee(\mathcal{N}''(<\lambda \Rightarrow \lambda_1 : \lambda'_1, \dots, \lambda_n : \lambda'_n>))$

The remaining part of the section tries to give some elements towards a proof of the following...

<u>theorem</u> $\mathcal{N}$ is a <u>fully abstract</u> model of T_Σ w.r.t. the observational preorder $\lesssim$: $\mathcal{N}(p) \sqsubset_I \mathcal{N}(q)$ iff $p \sqsubseteq q$ iff $\mathcal{C}[p] \lesssim \mathcal{C}[q]$ for every Σ-context $\mathcal{C}$.

3.4. Some properties of fair computations

To prove the above theorem, we must of course analyse the basic properties of fair computations. From now on, FAIR (p) will denote the set of the open computations of program p. In clear :

$FAIR(p) = \{\mathcal{F}_{\leftarrow} \mid \mathcal{F} \in fair\ (p|q)$ for some $q\}$.

Left and right projection operators extend in a natural way to open computations of parallel programs, and will therefore be used with unchanged notation in this extended context. We shall also refine our definition of R-actions as follows :

For $t \in T_\Sigma$ and $R \in ID$, the sets of the internal resp. external R-actions of t are respectively

$\underline{Ext_R(t)} = \{\mu \mid (\exists u)(t \xrightarrow{\mu_R} u)\}$

$\underline{Int_R(t)} = \{\mu \mid (\exists u)(\exists S \in ID)(t \xrightarrow{\mu_R\ \overline{\mu}_S} u)\}$

We let $Ext(t) = \bigcup_R Ext_R(t)$.

To proceed, we need one more definition.

Let $E = E_0 \cup E_1 \cup E_2$ where $E_0 = \{\emptyset\}$,

E_1 is the set of singleton sets $\{\lambda_R\}$, and

E_2 is the set of pairs $\{\mu_R, \overline{\mu}_S\}$.

$\underline{\eta : E^\omega \to \Lambda^\infty}$ is the homomorphism determined by :

$\eta\ (e) = \varepsilon$ if $e \in E_0$

$\eta\ (e) = \lambda$ if $e = \{\lambda_R\} \in E_1$

$\eta\ (e) = \varepsilon$ if $e \in E_2$

Using the above definitions, one can state :

<u>proposition 2</u> Given p_0 in T_Σ , $FAIR(p_0)$ is equal to the set of the sequences $(p_i,e_i)_{i\in\omega}$, where $p_i \in T_\Sigma$ and $e_i \in E$, for which the following conditions 1 to 3 are satisfied :

1- $(\forall i)(p_i \xrightarrow{e_i} p_{i+1} \vee (\forall j \geqslant i)(e_j = \emptyset \ \&\ p_j = p_{j+1}))$

2- $(\forall R \in ID)(\exists j)(\forall k \geqslant j)(Int_R(p_k) = \emptyset)$

3- $(\exists R)(\exists j)(\forall k \geqslant j)(\lambda \in Ext_R(p_k))$

$\Rightarrow \lambda \notin Ult(\eta((e_i)_{i\in\omega}))$

<u>corollary</u> The set fair(p) of the (closed) fair computations of p is the subset of FAIR(p) made out of those open (fair) computations $(p_i,e_i)_{i\in\omega}$ for which $(\forall i)(e_i \in E_2 \cup E_0)$

- remark that Act_R and Int_R have an identical definition -

proposition 3 Given a pair of open (fair) computations, let $\mathcal{F}' = (p_i, e'_i)_{i\in\omega}$ and $\mathcal{F}'' = (q_i, e''_i)_{i\in\omega}$, there exists some $\mathcal{F}$ in FAIR $(p_0|q_0)$ with respective projections $\mathcal{F}'$ and $\mathcal{F}''$ iff the following implications 1 and 2 hold for every $\lambda \in \Lambda$ and $R \in ID$:

1- $\lambda \in \sqcup\{\bigcap_{k \geqslant i} Ext_R(p_k) \mid i \in \omega\} \Rightarrow$ a & b

a) $\lambda \notin Ult(\eta((e''_i)_{i\in\omega}))$

b) $\bar{\lambda} \notin \sqcap\{\bigcup_{k \geqslant i} Ext(q_k) \mid i \in \omega\}$

2- similar statement with p $\longleftrightarrow$ q and e'' $\longrightarrow$ e'.

The meaning of the above propositions may be explained as follows in terms of the function abs which sends each open (fair) computation $\mathcal{F} = (p_i, e_i)_{i\in\omega}$ to the triple abs($\mathcal{F}$) = $<\delta,\rho,d>$ given by

- $\delta = \bigcup_R (\sqcup\{\bigcap_{j \geqslant k} Ext_R(p_j) \mid k \in \omega\})$
- $\rho = \eta((e_i)_{i\in\omega})$
- $d = \sqcap\{\bigcup_{j \geqslant k} Ext(p_j) \mid k \in \omega\} \setminus \delta.$

By proposition 2, if $\mathcal{F}$ is an open fair computation, then also abs($\mathcal{F}$) = $<\delta,\rho,d>$ is an history, for conditions 2 and 3 read respectively as $\delta \cap \bar{d} = \emptyset$ and $\delta \cap Ult(\rho) = \emptyset$ (whence $Ult(\rho) \subseteq d$). By proposition 3, the conditions which a pair of open fair computations $\mathcal{F}'$, $\mathcal{F}''$ should satisfy to be the respective projections of a fair computation are reduced to the compatibility of their associated histories :
(abs($\mathcal{F}'$) # abs($\mathcal{F}''$)). This is the precise reason why the two definitions 5 and 5' of the observational preorder are equivalent. In clear :
$EXP(p) \subseteq EXP(q)$ iff $abs(EXP(p)) \subseteq abs(EXP(q))$ iff
$\forall r : abs(EXP(p)) \cap abs(FAIR(r)) \subseteq abs(EXP(q)) \cap abs(FAIR(r))$
iff $\forall r : abs(EXP_r(p)) \subseteq abs(EXP_r(q))$
iff $\forall r : EXP_r(p) \subseteq EXP_r(q)$.

3.5. An operational model

From now on, Abs(p) will denote the set of the histories associated with the open computations of p, let
$Abs(p) = \{abs(\mathcal{F}) \mid \mathcal{F} \in FAIR(p)\}$

Our demonstration of the full abstractness of $\mathcal{N}$ is based on an equational characterization of Abs. Let us consider the following definition of $\mathcal{M} : T_\Sigma \longrightarrow \mathcal{P}(\mathcal{H})$, where Y(F) denotes the greatest fixpoint of F w.r.t. the inclusion of subsets, and the $\mathcal{L}$, $\mathcal{L}_I$ are like in 3.3, then $\mathcal{M}$ and Abs may be proven identical.

The equations of $\mathcal{M}$

$\mathcal{M}(\text{NIL}) = <\emptyset,\varepsilon,\emptyset>$

$\mathcal{M}(<\lambda_1 \ldots \lambda_n> (t_1 \ldots t_n)) =$

$\quad <\{\lambda_1 \ldots \lambda_n\}, \varepsilon, \emptyset> + \sum_{i=1}^{n} \lambda_i : \mathcal{M}(t_i)$

$\mathcal{M}(t_1 | t_2) = \mathcal{M}(t_1) \parallel \mathcal{M}(t_2)$

$\mathcal{M}(t[\pi]) = [\![\pi]\!] \mathcal{M}(t)$

$\mathcal{M}(t[\lambda \rhd \pi]) = Y(F)$ where

$\quad F(X) = <\lambda,\varepsilon,\emptyset> + (\lambda : [\![\pi]\!] \ (\mathcal{M}(t) \parallel X))$

$\mathcal{M}(<\lambda \Rightarrow \lambda_1 : \lambda'_1, \ldots, \lambda_n : \lambda'_n>) =$

$\quad < \{\lambda\}, \mathcal{L}, \emptyset> + < \{\lambda_1 \ldots \lambda_n\}, \mathcal{L}\lambda, \emptyset> +$

$\quad \sum_i <\{\lambda'_i\}, \mathcal{L}\lambda\lambda_i, \emptyset> +$

$\quad \sum_{I \neq \emptyset} <\emptyset, \mathcal{L}_I, \{\lambda\} \cup \{\lambda_1 \ldots \lambda_n\} \cup \{\lambda'_i \mid i \in I\}>$

3.6. Observations

Define OBS : $T_\Sigma \longrightarrow \bigcup_L \mathcal{P}(\mathcal{H}_L)$:

$OBS(p) = abs(EXP(p))$, then

$p \lesssim q$ iff $EXP(p) \subseteq EXP(q)$ iff $OBS(p) \subseteq OBS(q)$.

OBS(p) is the large set of observations on p.
Our next task is to establish some connection between Abs and OBS. When such a connection is found, we use it to derive $\mathcal{N}$ from $\mathcal{M}$.

Clearly, OBS(p) is the collection of the histories $<\delta,\rho,d>$ which are compatible with some element $<\delta',\bar{\rho},d'>$ in Abs(p). This collection contains a lot of redundant elements and may be reduced without any loss of information into the following variant Obs(p), the small set of observations on p :

$Obs(p) = OBS(p) \cap \mathcal{H}_L$ for $L = obsort(p)$, the minimal sort L such that $\rho \in L^\infty$ for every $<\delta,\rho,d>$ in OBS(p).

$(OBS(p) = \{<\delta,\rho,d> \in \mathcal{H} \mid <\delta \cap L,\rho,d \cap L> \in Obs(p)\})$

Define the <u>inside-outside function</u>

$IO_L : \mathcal{H}_L \to \mathcal{P}(\mathcal{H}_L)$:

$IO_L(<\delta',\rho',d'>) = \{<\delta,\rho,d> \in \mathcal{H} \mid$

$(\rho = \bar{\rho}')$ & $(\delta \subseteq L \setminus (\bar{d}' \cup \bar{\delta}'))$ & $((d \cup \delta) \subseteq L \setminus \bar{\delta}')\}$.

Also let $IO_L : \mathcal{P}(\mathcal{H}_L) \to \mathcal{P}(\mathcal{H}_L)$ denote the set extension of the above, then the following relation holds if p has observable sort L :

$Obs(p) = IO_L(Abs(p))$.

Recollecting definition 12, it appears that Obs(p) is fully determined by $\widehat{Obs}(p)$, itself equal to $\widehat{IO}_L(\check{Abs}(p))$. Furthermore, $\widehat{Obs}(p) = \widehat{IO}_L(\check{norm}(Abs(p)))$ for norm the normalization operator given below.

$norm : \mathcal{P}(\mathcal{H}) \to \mathcal{P}(\mathcal{H})$

is the set extension of

$norm : \mathcal{H} \to \mathcal{P}(\mathcal{H})$:

$norm(h) = norm_{\alpha 1} \circ \cdots \circ norm_{\alpha n}(h)$

for $h \in \mathcal{H}_{\alpha 1 \ldots \alpha n}$,

where $norm_\alpha(<\delta,\rho,d>) =$

if $(Ult(\rho) \cap \{\alpha,\bar{\alpha}\} \neq \emptyset)$ then $\{<\delta,\rho,d \cup \{\alpha,\bar{\alpha}\}>\}$ else

if $(\{\alpha,\bar{\alpha}\} \subseteq d \vee \{\alpha,\bar{\alpha}\} \cap d = \emptyset)$ then $\{<\delta,\rho,d>\}$ else

if $\alpha \in d$ then $\{<\delta \cup \{\alpha\},\rho,d \setminus \{\alpha\}>, <\delta,\rho,d \cup \{\bar{\alpha}\}>\}$ else

if $\bar{\alpha} \in d$ then $\{<\delta \cup \{\bar{\alpha}\},\rho,d \setminus \{\bar{\alpha}\}>, <\delta,\rho,d \cup \{\alpha\}>\}$.

Clearly, $\check{norm}(Abs(p))$ is an element of $\mathcal{K}$. It may also be shown that the following equivalence holds :

$\check{norm} \circ Abs(p) \sqsubset_I \check{norm} \circ Abs(q)$

iff $OBS(p) \subseteq OBS(q)$.

As a consequence, let $\mathcal{N} : T_\Sigma \to \mathcal{K}$ be the function equal to $\check{norm} \circ Abs$ then :

$p \precsim q$ iff $\mathcal{N}(p) \sqsubset_I \mathcal{N}(q)$.

3.7. Relating $\mathcal{N}$ to $\mathcal{M}$

In section 3.5, $\mathcal{M}$ has been defined by six equations of the generic form :

$$\mathcal{M}(op_j(\overrightarrow{t_i})) = OP_j(\overrightarrow{\mathcal{M}(t_i)}),$$

where $op_j \in \Sigma$ and the OP_j are operators on $\mathcal{P}(\mathcal{H})$. We will show that $\mathcal{N}$ may also be characterized by six equations of the form :

$$\mathcal{N}(op_j(\overrightarrow{t_i})) = \widetilde{OP}_j(\overrightarrow{\mathcal{N}(t_i)}),$$

where the $\widetilde{OP}_j$ are the operators on $\mathcal{K}$ given by $\widetilde{OP}_j(Q) = \check{norm}(OP_j(Q))$.
- notice the identity $norm \circ \vee = \check{norm} = \vee \circ norm$ -
The main propositions follow.

<u>proposition 4</u> $\check{OP}_j(Q_1 \ldots Q_n) = \check{OP}_j(\check{Q}_1 \ldots \check{Q}_n)$
for every $Q_i \in \bigcup_L \mathcal{P}(\mathcal{H}_L)$ and $op_j \in \Sigma_n$, $n > 0$.

<u>proposition 5</u> Under similar assumptions,
$norm \circ OP_j(Q_1 \ldots Q_n) = OP_j(norm(Q_1), \ldots, norm(Q_n))$.

<u>proposition 6</u> For any $op_j \in \Sigma_n$, $n > 0$, the associated operator $\check{OP}_j$: $\mathcal{K}^n \to \mathcal{K}$ is monotonic w.r.t. $\sqsubset_I$.

Essential to the proof of proposition 5 is the following
<u>lemma</u> $norm_\alpha(h' \| h'') = norm_\alpha(h') \| norm_\alpha(h'')$.

For $op_j \in \Sigma_n$, $n > 0$, let us state easy consequences of propositions 4 and 5 :

<u>fact 1</u> $\check{norm} \circ OP_j(Q_1, \ldots, Q_n) = \check{OP}_j(\check{norm}(Q_1), \ldots, \check{norm}(Q_n))$

<u>fact 2</u> $\mathcal{N}(op_j(\overrightarrow{t_i})) = \check{OP}_j(\overrightarrow{\mathcal{N}(t_i)})$
- recall $\mathcal{N} = \check{norm} \circ Abs = \check{norm} \circ \mathcal{M}$ -

<u>fact 3</u> $\mathcal{N}$ is a fully abstract model of T_Σ w.r.t. the observational preorder $\lesssim$: $\mathcal{N}(t) \sqsubset_I \mathcal{N}(t')$ iff $OBS(\mathcal{C}(t)) \subseteq OBS(\mathcal{C}(t'))$ holds for every Σ-context $\mathcal{C}$. Furthermore, $\mathcal{N}(t) \sqsubset_I \mathcal{N}(t')$ iff $OBS(t) \subseteq OBS(t')$.

<u>proof</u> The latter equivalence has been stated with the definition of $\mathcal{N}$. Owing to the induction on Σ-contexts, the former equivalence follows from the latter by fact 2 and proposition 6.

corollary The observational preorder $\precsim$ and the implementation preorder $\sqsubseteq$ are identical.

The full abstractness of $\mathcal{N}$ w.r.t. $\precsim$ follows from fact 3 by the identity $\mathcal{K} = \mathcal{N}$, half proven by fact 2. The remaining elements of the proof are given below.

fact 4 $\mathcal{N}''(<\lambda \Rightarrow \lambda_1 : \lambda'_1, \ldots, \lambda_n : \lambda'_n>) =$
$\mathrm{norm} \circ \mathcal{M}(<\lambda \Rightarrow \lambda_1 : \lambda'_1, \ldots, \lambda_n : \lambda'_n>)$.

fact 5 $\mathcal{K}(t[\lambda \triangleright \pi]) = Y(\check{F})$, the greatest fixpoint w.r.t. $\sqsubset_I$ of $\check{F} : \mathcal{K} \to \mathcal{K}$ where $F : \mathcal{P}(\mathcal{H}) \to \mathcal{P}(\mathcal{H})$ is the function given by $F(X) = <\lambda, \varepsilon, \emptyset> + \lambda : [\![\pi]\!] (\mathcal{K}(t) \| X)$.

proof By fact 2, $\mathcal{K}(t[\lambda \triangleright \pi]) = \check{} (Y(F))$, where $Y(F)$ is the greatest fixpoint of F w.r.t. the inclusion of subsets. Now, $Y(F) = F^{\alpha}(\mathcal{H})$ for any sufficiently high ordinal α. By proposition 4, $\check{F}(F^{\alpha}(\mathcal{H})) = \check{F}(\check{F}(F^{\alpha}(\mathcal{H})))$. Therefore, $\mathcal{K}(t[\lambda \triangleright \pi])$ is a fixpoint of $\check{F} : \mathcal{K} \to \mathcal{K}$. To show that it is the greatest fixpoint, consider Q in $\mathcal{K}$ and suppose $Q = \check{F}(Q)$. Since $F(Q) \subseteq F(F(Q))$, F(Q) is a subset of Y(F), and hence it comes $\check{F}(Q) \sqsubset_I \check{} (Y(F)) = \mathcal{K}(t[\lambda \triangleright \pi])$.

So, under the assumption of fair asynchrony, $\mathcal{N}$ is a fully abstract model of T_{Σ} w.r.t. the observational preorder $\precsim$. Unfortunately, no complete proof system with practical interest is associated with that model.

4. THE CASE OF BOUNDED PARALLELISM

We aim presently to show that the issue of proof systems is not so desperate as it has just been told, for the hindrance inherent to the lack of ω-continuity collapses in the restricted case of programs with bounded parallelism, called rational programs in the sequel. The reason is that, for these simplified programs, the semantic calculus shown in section 3 keeps within the bounds of infinitary rational languages and their operations [Da 1]. Decision procedures may therefore be constructed for the implementation preorder, and also for a lot of observationally meaningful properties of programs. Applications may be found in studies on communication protocols and synchronization skeletons.

For such applications, what we suggest here is :

- a syntax in recursive style to define static systems of communicating agents

- a syntax to specify the observational properties to be met by such systems of agents, including comparisons w.r.t. the implementation ordering
- a general method for the verification (or decision) of properties of systems of agents under the assumption of fair asynchrony.

What more could afford the various temporal logics ?

The very fact that our model $\mathcal{N}$ has been proven fully abstract w.r.t. the most discriminative observational congruence indicates without any doubt that branching time logics [Be] are inadequate to reason about observable behaviour. And it is our feeling that linear time logics [Ga] are only a different vision of infinitary rational expressions and languages.

The three points above are now addressed in separate subsections.

4.1. A recursive style syntax

To start with, we suggest an attractive syntax in recursive style for the new subset of CCS which we consider, call it RCCS. The parameters of the syntax are Λ and Ren as previously, together with a new set X whose elements are the variables used in the recursive statements. The syntax shows terms which may have free variables, but only the closed terms are programs. We let FV(t) denote the set of the free variables of term t. Here is the syntax.

- NIL is a term, and $FV(NIL) = \emptyset$
- x is a term, and $FV(x) = \{x\}$
- $<\lambda_1 \ldots \lambda_n> (t_1 \ldots t_n)$ is a term, let t, and $FV(t) = \bigcup_i FV(t_i)$
- $rec(x_1 = t_1, \ldots, x_n = t_n)$ is a program iff $\bigcup_i FV(t_i) \subseteq \{x_1 \ldots x_n\}$
- $t_1 | t_2$ is a program iff t_1 and t_2 are programs
- $t\ [\pi]$ is a program iff t is a program.

Clearly, flow operations have been restricted here to act upon programs instead of general terms. Given $p \in$ RCCS, we suggest to translate it into $\mathcal{G}(p) \in T_\Sigma$ by performing the following transformations a then b :

- a : as long as there occurs in p some term $t \equiv rec(x_1 = t_1 \ldots x_n = t_n)$ in which some t_i, say t_1, has form $<\lambda_1 \ldots \lambda_m>(u_1 \ldots u_m)$ where some u_j is neither a variable nor a closed term, replace t by :

$rec\ (x_1 = <\lambda_1 \ldots \lambda_m>\ (x_{n+1} \ldots x_{n+m}),$
$x_2 = t_2, \ldots, x_n = t_n,\ x_{n+1} = u_1, \ldots, x_{n+m} = u_m)$;

- b : as long as there occurs in p some recursive definition $D \equiv rec(x_1 = t_1 \ldots x_n = t_n)$, choose fresh names $\alpha_1 \ldots \alpha_n$ in Λ and replace D by : $((<\bar{\alpha}_1>(NIL) \mid P) [\varphi]) [\psi]$ where

- φ is undefined on the α_i and $\psi \circ \varphi$ acts as an identity on $\bigcup_i sort(t_i)$
- $P = (P_1 \mid (P_2 \mid \ldots P_n))$ and either

$P_i = <\alpha_i>(t_i)$ if t_i is a closed term, or else

$P_i = <\alpha_i \Rightarrow \lambda_{i_1} : \bar{\alpha}_{j_1}, \ldots, \lambda_{i_n} : \bar{\alpha}_{j_n}>$ for t_i equal to $<\lambda_{i_1} \ldots \lambda_{i_n}>$ $(x_{j_1} \ldots x_{j_n})$.

Owing to the above translation, the study of recursively defined programs with bounded parallelism may be led simply by considering the restriction $\mathcal{N}'$ of $\mathcal{N}$ to $T_{\Sigma'}$, the term algebra introduced by the following...

definition Σ' is the signature obtained from Σ by deleting network iterators $[\lambda \triangleright \pi]$.

Remark that for any pair of programs $\{p,q\}$ in $T_{\Sigma'}$, p and q are distinguished by some observer in T_Σ iff they are distinguished by some observer in $T_{\Sigma'}$. Also remark that for any program p in $T_{\Sigma'}$, there exists some corresponding q in RCCS such that $\mathcal{N}'(p) = \mathcal{N}'(\mathcal{T}(q))$. For those reasons, the restriction $\mathcal{N}'$ of $\mathcal{N}$ to $T_{\Sigma'}$ may be considered as a fully abstract model of $T_{\Sigma'}$ and also of RCCS.

4.2. Semantics and regularity

Recollecting the definition of operators λ : , $\|$, $[\![\pi]\!]$ and $\vee$ on sets of histories, we will prove by induction on terms $t \in T_{\Sigma'}$ that $\mathcal{N}'(t)$ may be computed as a finite union $\sum_i < \delta_i, \mathcal{L}_i, d_i>$ where the $\mathcal{L}_i$ are infinitary rational languages on finite subsets Λ_i of Λ. We say that a set of histories has property R when it may be written in that form.

For L a finite subset of Λ , let $Rat(L^\infty)$ denote the family of the infinitary rational languages over L. By definition, $Rat(L^\infty)$ is the least family of subsets of $L^\infty = L^* \cup L^\omega$ which contains the finite subsets of L^* and is closed under concatenation, set union, star and ω-star operations [Ei]. Rat (L^∞) is closed under complementation w.r.t. L^∞, and thus also under set intersection. Languages in $Rat(L^\infty)$ have the characteristic property to be denoted by finite unions $B + \sum_i B_i C_i^{\omega}$ where B, B_i, C_i are finitary rational expressions.

If set Q has property R, then so has $\check{Q}$ by the properties of Rat(L^{∞}) : indeed, for $\delta \subseteq \delta'$ and $d \cup \delta \subseteq d' \cup \delta'$,
$\vee(<\delta,\mathcal{L},d> + <\delta',\mathcal{L}',d'>) =$
$<\delta,\mathcal{L},d> + <\delta',\mathcal{L}' \cap \sim \mathcal{L},d'>$
where $\sim$ denotes complementation.
So, to prove by induction that $\mathcal{N}'(t)$ satisfies R for every $t \in T_{\Sigma'}$, the only non trivial step is to establish the following...

<u>lemma</u> If $\mathcal{L}_1$, $\mathcal{L}_2$ are languages in Rat(L^{∞}), then so is their **parallel** composition $\mathcal{L}_1 \| \mathcal{L}_2 = \bigcup (\rho' \| \rho'')$, $\rho' \in \mathcal{L}_1$ and $\rho'' \in \mathcal{L}_2$.

A constructive proof of that lemma was given in [Da 2], which shows how to compute $\mathcal{L}_1 \| \mathcal{L}_2$ by purely syntactic means. Indeed, the problem may be simplified by considering instead of the parallel composition $\|$ the <u>quasi-parallel composition</u> $\wr$ which differs from the former as regards the first implication in definition 11. In the definition of $\rho' \wr \rho''$, this implication becomes simply :
$(\rho'_i \neq \varepsilon \ \& \ \rho''_i \neq \varepsilon) \Rightarrow \rho'_i = \bar{\rho}''_i \ \& \ \rho_i = \sigma$, for σ some new symbol not in Λ.

For $\mathcal{L}_1$, $\mathcal{L}_2$ in Rat(L^{∞}), $\mathcal{L}_1 \wr \mathcal{L}_2$ is the **solution** of a particular system of linear equations which depend on the residual normal forms of $\mathcal{L}_1$ and $\mathcal{L}_2$. We call a <u>residual normal form</u> of $\mathcal{L} \in$ Rat(L^{∞}) any finite union $\sum_{i=1}^{m} E_i F_i$ with $E_i \in$ Rat(L^{*}) and $F_i \in$ Rat(L^{∞}) , such that :

- $\{F_1 \dots F_n\} = \{\mathcal{L} \backslash f \mid f \in L^{\infty}\}$
- $E_i = \{f \mid f \in L^{\infty} \ \& \ \mathcal{L} \backslash f = F_i\}$

where $\mathcal{L} \backslash f = \{g \mid g \in L^{\infty} \ \& \ fg \in \mathcal{L}\}$
($\varepsilon \in K_1$ will henceforth be assumed).

Clearly, it is enough to give a constructive characterization of $\mathcal{L}_1 \wr \mathcal{L}_2$ for cases i and ii below.

i) $\mathcal{L}_1 = BC^{\omega}$, $\mathcal{L}_2 = B'C'^{\omega}$ where
C and C' are ε-free.

Let C and C' be associated with residual normal forms $\sum_i D_i C_i$ resp. $\sum_j D'_j C'_j$, then :

$$\mathcal{L}_1 \wr \mathcal{L}_2 = \sum_{i,j} (BC^{*} D_i \wr B'C'^{*} D'_j) X_{ij}$$

for $\overrightarrow{X_{ij}}$ the greatest solution of the system of linear equations

$$\{ X_{ij} = \sum_{k,l} (C_i\ C^+\ D_k \between C'_j\ C'^+\ D'_l)\ X_{kl} \}$$

ii) $\mathcal{L}_1$ is finitary ,i.e. $\mathcal{L}_1 \varepsilon \mathrm{Rat}(L^*)$

Let $\mathcal{L}_1$ and $\mathcal{L}_2$ be associated with residual normal forms $\sum_{i=1}^{n_1} E_i\ F_i$ resp. $\sum_{i=1}^{n_2} E'_i\ F'_i$. Let $n = n_1 \times n_2$ and define $(n \times n)$ matrices A, B, C as follows :

$$A_{(i_1 i_2)(j_1 j_2)} = \{ \sigma \} \text{ if } \exists \lambda \ \varepsilon\ L \quad \text{s.t.} \quad C_{j_1} = C_{i_1} \setminus \lambda \ \text{ and } C'_{j_2} = C'_{i_2} \setminus \overline{\lambda}$$

otherwise $\emptyset$

$$B_{(i_1 i_2)(j_1 j_2)} = \{ \lambda \ \varepsilon\ L | \ C_{j_1} = C_{i_1} \setminus \lambda \text{ and } i_2 = j_2 \}$$

$$C_{(i_1 i_2)(j_1 j_2)} = \{ \lambda \ \varepsilon\ L \mid C'_{j_2} = C'_{i_2} \setminus \lambda \text{ and } i_1 = j_1 \}.$$

Also define the n-vector D :

$$D_{i_1 i_2} = \begin{cases} C_{i_1} + C'_{i_2} & \text{if } \mathcal{E} \ \varepsilon\ C_{i_1} \cap C'_{i_2} \\ C'_{i_2} & \text{if } \mathcal{E} \ \varepsilon\ C_{i_1},\ \mathcal{E} \notin C'_{i_2} \\ C_{i_1} & \text{if } \mathcal{E} \notin C_{i_1},\ \mathcal{E} \ \varepsilon\ C'_{i_2} \\ \emptyset & \text{if } \mathcal{E} \notin C_{i_1},\ \mathcal{E} \notin C'_{i_2} \end{cases}$$

If X denotes the n-vector with elements $X_{i_1 i_2} = C_{i_1} \between C'_{i_2}$ then X is the least solution of the following system of linear equations :

$$X = ((B^* + C^*)\ A + B^+C + C^+B)X + (B^* + C^*)\ D$$

- thus $\mathcal{L}_1 \between \mathcal{L}_2 = C_1 \between C'_1 = X_{1\,1}$ -

The lemma follows by a simple fact :
Systems of linear equations on $\mathcal{P}(L^\infty)$ with rational coefficients and constants admit extremal solutions which are rational languages, and which may be computed by stepwise resolution of the equations - see (Da 2)-.

4.3. Observable properties of programs

The language of formulae which we suggest for specifying the expected properties of programs is constructed with the usual connectives from atomic formulae of the following types :

$(p \underset{\sim}{\sqsubseteq} q)$ where $p,q \in T_{\Sigma'}$,

$(p \subseteq Q)$ where $p \in T_{\Sigma'}$, Q is a finite sum $\sum_i < \delta_i, \mathcal{L}_i, d_i >$, and the $\mathcal{L}_i$ are infinitary rational expressions,

$(p \oplus Q)$ with p and Q as above.

The semantics of this simple minded logic may be characterized as follows :

- the formula $(p \underset{\sim}{\sqsubseteq} q)$ is true iff $\mathcal{N}'(p) \sqsubset_I \mathcal{N}'(q)$,
- the formula $(p \subseteq Q)$ is true iff $\mathcal{N}'(p) \subseteq Q$,
- the formula $(p \oplus Q)$ is true iff $\mathcal{N}'(p)$ is disjoint from Q.

It is not difficult to see that all and only the observationally meaningful properties of $T_{\Sigma'}$ programs may be expressed in the above language, on account of the following connection between OBS and $\mathcal{N}'$(cf. § 3.6) :

$OBS(p) = \{<\delta,\rho,d> \in \mathcal{H} \mid \exists \delta',d'$ s.t.
$(<\delta',\bar{\rho},d'> \in \mathcal{N}'(p)\ \&\ \delta \cap (\bar{d}' \cup \bar{\delta}') = \emptyset\ \&\ d \cap \bar{\delta}' = \emptyset)\}$

Consider for instance the assertion :
" p may permanently ignore some external communication attempt λ_1 while it interacts with external observers by a sequence of communications in which they perform an infinite number of action λ_n".

For p a program with sort $L = \bar{L} = \{\lambda_1 \ldots \lambda_n\}$, this property is expressed by the formula

$\neg\,(p \oplus \sum_{Ij} <\delta_{Ij}, \mathcal{L}_I, d_{Ij}>)$ where :

I ranges over the non-empty subsets of $\{\lambda_1 \ldots \lambda_n\}$ such that $\bar{\lambda}_n \in I$ and $\lambda_1 \notin I$,

$$\mathcal{L}_I = \bigcap_{i \in I} ((\sum_{j=1}^{n} \lambda_j)^* \lambda_i)^\omega \cap (\sum_{j=1}^{n} \lambda_j)^* (\sum_{i \in I} \lambda_i)^\omega,$$

and for each I, $<\delta_{Ij}, d_{Ij}>$ ranges over the disjoint pairs of subsets of L for which :

$\bar{\lambda}_1 \notin (d_{Ij} \cup \delta_{Ij})$ and $I \subseteq d_{Ij} = \bar{d}_{Ij}$.

4.4. Decision and proof of properties

We are in a position where we can make some conclusive claims.

First claim. An effective procedure can be found for deciding properties expressed by formulae of our simple assertion language. Evidence of this fact is given by the folllowing remarks :

- for t ranging over $T_{\Sigma'}$, $\mathcal{N}'(t)$ may be computed by purely syntactic means,
- for each particular pair of elements of $\mathcal{K}$, let $P = \sum_{i\in I} \langle\delta_i, \mathcal{L}_i, d_i\rangle$ and $Q = \sum_{i\in I} \langle\delta_i, \mathcal{L}'_i, d_i\rangle$, $P \sqsubset_I Q$ may be expressed by the conjunction of the inclusion relations
$\mathcal{L}_i \subseteq \bigcup_j \mathcal{L}'_j \mid (\delta_j \subseteq \delta_i)\ \&\ (d_j \cup \delta_j \subseteq d_i \cup \delta_i)$,
- for infinitary rational languages, there exist effective procedures which decide the relations of inclusion and disjointness.

Second claim. One can go a step further by providing a proof system without induction for $(\mathrm{Rat}(L^{\infty}), \{\subseteq, \oplus\})$. This work has been done in [Da 3]. The underlying principle is to reduce relations between infinitary rational expressions to equivalent relations between finitary rational expressions.

REFERENCES

[Be] Ben-Ari M., Manna Z., Pnueli A.
"The Temporal Logic of Branching Time"
8th Ann. ACM Symp. on POPL (1981)

[Br] Brookes S.D., Hoare C.A.R., Roscoe A.W.
"A theory of Communicating Sequential Processes"
JACM. Vol 31 n° 3, July 84, pp. 560-599

[Co] Costa G., Stirling C.
"A fair Calculus of Communicating Systems"
Proc. FCT 83, Springer-Verlag LNCS Vol. 158

[Da 1] Darondeau Ph., Kott L.
"On the Observational Semantics of Fair Parallelism"
Proc. ICALP 83, Springer-Verlag LNCS Vol. 154

[Da 2] - Full Version of the above -
INRIA Report 262 (1983)

[Da 3] Darondeau Ph., Kott L.
"A Formal Proof System for Infinitary Rational Expressions"
INRIA Report 218 (1983)

[Da 4] Darondeau Ph.
"Infinitary Languages and Fully Abstract Models of Fair Asynchrony"
INRIA Report 330 (1984)

[Ei] Eilenberg S.
"Automata, Languages and Machines", Vol. A.
Academic Press, New York (1974)

[Ga] Gabbay D., Pnueli A., Shelah S., Stavi J.
"On the Temporal Analysis of Fairness"
Proc. 7th Ann. ACM Symp. on POPL (1980)

[He] Hennessy M.
"Synchronous and Asynchronous Experiments on Processes"
Internal Report CSR -125-82,
University of Edinburgh (1982)

[Jo] Jorrand Ph.
"Specification of Communicating Processes and Process Implementation Correctness"
Proc. 5th Int. Symp. on Programming
Springer-Verlag LNCS Vol 137 (1982)

[Mi 1] Milner R.
"Fully Abstract Models of Typed λ-Calculi"
TCS Vol 4 n°1, 1977, pp. 1-23

[Mi 2] Milner R.
"A Calculus of Communicating Systems"
Springer-Verlag LNCS Vol.92 (1980)

[Mi 3] Milner R.
"Calculi for Synchrony and Asynchrony"
TCS Vol. 25 n°3, 1983, pp. 267-310

[Mi 4] Milner R.
"A finite Delay Operator for Synchronous CCS"
Internal Report CSR 116-82
University of Edinburgh (1982)

[Pa] Park D.
"On the Semantics of Fair Parallelism"
in Abstract Software Specifications
Springer-Verlag LNCS Vol.86 (1980)

[Pl] Plotkin G.
"A Structural Approach to Operational Semantics"
DAIMI FN-19, Computer Science Dept.
Aarhus University (1981)

Acknowledgements Part of the ideas which have been presented in the paper, specially in the last section, come from joint work with Laurent Kott.

A LOGIC FOR THE SPECIFICATION AND PROOF OF CONTROLLABLE PROCESSES OF CCS

Susanne Graf and Joseph Sifakis
IMAG
BP68
F-38402 St.Martin d'Hères

1. INTRODUCTION

This work has been motivated by the following general problem: find logics for the specification and proof of non deterministic programs. We suppose that programs belong to the set of terms T of an algebra with a congruence relation ~. The operators of the algebra correspond to program constructors and the relation ~ defines a concept of equivalence which is supposed to be adequate for the comparison of programs. A requirement for a logic with set of formulas F, to be a satisfactory tool for the specification and proof of such programs is,

$\forall t_1, t_2 \in T \; (t_1 \sim t_2 \text{ iff } \forall f \in F \; (t_1 \models f \text{ iff } t_2 \models f)),$

i.e. the congruence ~ and the equivalence relation induced by the logic on programs, agree [GS]. Furthermore, the use of a logic as a tool for syntax directed proofs, requires that for any n-ary operator * of the algebra there exists an operator ⊛ on the logic such that

$\forall t_i \in T, \; \forall f_i \in F \;\; t_i \models f_i \;\; i=1,..n \text{ implies } *(t_1,..t_n) \models \circledast(f_1,..f_n)$

and this is the strongest assertion one can deduce from the validity of $t_i \models f_i$ for $i=1,..n$.

In this paper we present a logic for the specification and proof of a sub-class of processes of CCS [Mi] called <u>controllable</u> processes. A controllable process is any term t for which there exists t' without occurrences of τ, t' observationnally congruent to t ($t \stackrel{c}{\approx} t'$). This paper is a continuation of [GS]; its results have been published in [Gr].

In section 2 we propose a simple modal language with next-time and least fixpoint operator, for which labelled trees (CCS-terms) constitute a class of models. To obtain

NATO ASI Series, Vol. F13
Logics and Models of Concurrent Systems
Edited by K. R. Apt

a modal characterization of the observational congruence on finite CCS-terms, we define a function | | associating with any term t a formula |t| of this language such that, $\forall t,t' \in T$ $t' \models |t|$ iff $t' \approx t$.
The function | | is defined by induction on the structure of CCS-terms by associating with Nil, + and the set of actions $\{a\}_{a\in A}$ respectively, a constant |Nil| and operators $\oplus$, $\{\circledast\}_{a\in A}$. The characterization thus obtained, is extended to recursive CCS terms by introducing an appropriate order for their approximation by sequences of classes of finite terms.

The language of the formulas of the logic proposed is the set of the formulas built by using constants true and |Nil|, logical operators, the operators $\oplus$ and $\{\circledast\}_{a\in A}$ and the least fixpoint operator.

2. DEFINITION OF THE MODAL LANGUAGE

We introduce as in [Ko] the modal language F(A) as the sublanguage of the closed formulas of F'(A), defined on the logical constants true, false, a set of constants A and a set of variables X as follows:

- true, false $\in$ F'(A),
- AUX $\subseteq$ F'(A),
- $f, f' \in F'(A)$ implies $\neg f$, $f \vee f' \in F'(A)$,
- $x \in X$ and $f(x) \in F'(A)$ is a functional positive in the variable x, implies $\mu x.f(x) \in F'(A)$.

Semantics : The class of models of F(A) is the class M(A) of the labelled trees on A. A labelled tree is defined as $T = (Q_T, q_0, \{\xrightarrow{a}\}_{a\in A})$ where,

- Q_T is a set of states, the nodes of T,
- $q_0 \in Q_T$ is the initial state, the root of T,
- $\{\xrightarrow{a}\}_{a\in A}$ is a set of transition relations, $\xrightarrow{a} \subseteq Q_T \times Q_T$; as T is a tree, we have $\nexists q \in Q_T$ $\nexists a \in A$ $q \xrightarrow{a} q_0$ and $\forall q \in Q_T$ $q \neq q_0$, q has exactly one predecessor.

We define in the usual manner a satisfaction relation

$$\models \subseteq (\bigcup_{T\in M(A)} \{T\} \times Q_T) \times F(A).$$

For a formula $f \in F(A)$ we write,

- $T,q \models f$ iff $(T,q,f) \in \models$

- $T \models f$ iff $T, q_0 \models f$ where q_0 is the root of T,
- $\models f$ iff $T \models f$ $\forall T \in M(A)$.

For $T \in M(A)$, $q \in Q_T$, $f, f' \in F(A)$, $g \in F'(A)$ and $a \in A$,

- $T, q \models true$,
- $T, q \models \neg f$ iff $T, q \not\models f$,
- $T, q \models f \vee f'$ iff $T, q \models f$ or $T, q \models f'$,
- $T, q \models a$ iff $\exists q' \in Q_T$ $q' \xrightarrow{a} q$,
- $T, q \models \langle f \rangle$ iff $\exists q' \in Q_T$ $\exists a \in A$ $(q \xrightarrow{a} q'$ and $T, q' \models f)$,
- $T, q \models \mu x.g(x)$ iff $\forall f \in F(A)$ $(\models g(f) \supset f$ implies $T, q \models f)$.

The notations false, $\wedge$, $\supset$, $\equiv$ are used in the standard manner.

We use the abbreviations

- $[f] = \neg \langle \neg f \rangle$, i.e. $T, q \models [f]$ iff $\forall q' \in Q_T$ $\forall a \in A$ $(q \xrightarrow{a} q'$ implies $T, q' \models f)$.
- $\nu x.g(x) = \mu x. \neg g(\neg x)$, i.e. $T, q \models \nu x.g(x)$ iff $\forall f \in F(A)$ $(\models f \supset \neg g(\neg f)$ implies $T, q \models f)$.

Notice that each state $q \in Q$ in $T = (Q, q_0, \{\xrightarrow{a}\}_{a \in A})$ defines a subtree T_q of T, with root q and set of states the set of the states reachable from q in T. Thus, the transition relations $\xrightarrow{a}$ can be considered as relations on M(A) and one can write $T_q \xrightarrow{a} T_{q'}$, instead of $q \xrightarrow{a} q'$.
In the sequel we consider the class FF(A) of the formulas where any element of A is written within the scope of one of the operators $\langle\rangle$ or $[\,]$. For such formulas f we have $T, q \models f$ iff $T_q \models f$, i.e. f is true at a state q of a tree T iff f is true for the subtree T_q of T. So, we consider only the satisfaction relation subset of $M(A) \times FF(A)$.

<u>Properties 1</u>

For $T \in M(A)$ and f, f_i, $i \in I$, elements of FF(A),

a) $T \models \langle a \wedge f \rangle$ iff $\exists T' \in M(A)$ $(T \xrightarrow{a} T'$ and $T' \models f)$,

b) $T \models [\bigvee_{i \in I} a_i \wedge f_i]$ iff $\forall T' \in M(A)$ $(T \xrightarrow{a} T'$ implies $\exists i \in I$ $(a = a_i$ and $T' \models f_i))$,

c) $\models \langle f \vee f' \rangle \equiv \langle f \rangle \vee \langle f' \rangle$,

d) $\models \langle f \wedge f' \rangle \supset \langle f \rangle \wedge \langle f \rangle$.

Other properties of F(A) can be found in [Ko] where a complete axiomatization is given for a similar logic.
In the sequel, we often simply write f instead of $\models f$.

Definition 1

a) Represent by $T[\Sigma]$ the term algebra with signature $\Sigma = \{Nil,+\} \cup A$ where Nil is a constant, A a family of unary operators and + a binary operator.

b) For $a \in A$ the relation $\xrightarrow{a} \subseteq T[\Sigma] \times T[\Sigma]$ is defined as the smallest relation satisfying,

- $at \xrightarrow{a} t$,
- $t_1 \xrightarrow{a} t$ implies $t_1+t_2 \xrightarrow{a} t$ and $t_2+t_1 \xrightarrow{a} t$.

With a term t can be associated a labelled tree $T_t=(Q,t,\{\xrightarrow{a}\}_{a\in A}) \in M(A)$ where Q is a set of subterms of t and $\xrightarrow{a}$ is the relation defined above. Thus, t can be considered as a transition system with set of actions (transitions) A. In the sequel we identify a term $t \in T[\Sigma]$ with the tree T_t representing it. So, if f is any formula of FF(A'), where A' is isomorphic to A, then we can write $t \models f$ instead of $T_t \models f$. As there is no risk of confusion, we shall not distinguish between a unary operator a and the corresponding constant of the modal language.

Properties 2

a) $Nil \models [false]$,

b) $t \models f$ implies $at \models \langle a \wedge f \rangle \wedge [a \wedge f]$,

c) $t \models \langle a \wedge f \rangle$ implies $t+t' \models \langle a \wedge f \rangle$ and $t'+t \models \langle a \wedge f \rangle$,

d) $t_1 \models [f_1]$ and $t_2 \models [f_2]$ implies $t_1+t_2 \models [f_1 \vee f_2]$,

e) $t+Nil \models f$ iff $t \models f$,

f) $t+t' \models [f]$ iff $t \models [f]$ and $t' \models [f]$.

In the sequel we often omit conjunction operators in order to simplify formulas.

3. MODAL CHARACTERIZATION OF OBSERVATIONAL CONGRUENCE ON FINITE TERMS

In this section we recall briefly results presented in [GS]. The following definition and properties are given in [HM], [Mi] where a Calculus for Communicating Systems (CCS) is defined on term algebras $T[\Sigma]$ such that A contains a special symbol τ; τ represents a hidden or unobservable action. Following standard terminology, we call terms of such algebras processes.

Definition 4

a) For $s=s_0...s_n$ a sequence of A^*, $t,t' \in T[\Sigma]$, write,

$t\overset{s}{\rightarrow}t'$ iff $\exists t_1...t_n \in T[\Sigma]$ $t\overset{s_0}{\rightarrow}t_1...t_n\overset{s_n}{\rightarrow}t'$.

b) For a sequence s of $(A-\{\tau\})^*$, $t,t' \in T[\Sigma]$, write,

$$t\overset{s}{\Rightarrow}t' \text{ iff } \begin{cases} t\xrightarrow{\tau^* s_0 \tau^* ... s_n \tau^*}t' \text{ if } s=s_0...s_n, \\ t\xrightarrow{\tau^*}t' \text{ if } s=\epsilon, \text{ the empty word of } A^*. \end{cases}$$

c) The relation $\approx$, called observational equivalence, is defined by $\approx \; = \bigcap_{k \in N} \approx_k$, where,

- $t \approx_0 t'$ for any $t,t' \in T[\Sigma]$,
- $t \approx_{k+1} t'$ if $\forall s \in (A-\{\tau\})^*$ $[(t\overset{s}{\Rightarrow}t_1$ implies $\exists t_1'$ $(t'\overset{s}{\Rightarrow}t_1'$ and $t_1 \approx_k t_1'))$ and $(t'\overset{s}{\Rightarrow}t_1'$ implies $\exists t_1$ $(t\overset{s}{\Rightarrow}t_1$ and $t_1 \approx_k t_1'))]$.

It has been shown that $\approx$ is an equivalence relation. Denote by $\overset{c}{\approx}$ the greatest congruence on $T[\Sigma]$ such that $\overset{c}{\approx} \subseteq \approx$, called observational congruence. The following is a complete axiomatization of $\overset{c}{\approx}$ on $T[\Sigma]$ [HM]:

(A1) $(t_1+t_2)+t_3 \;=\; t_1+(t_2+t_3)$

(A2) $t_1+t_2 \;= t_2+t_1$

(A3) $t+t \;=\; t$

(A4) $t+Nil \;=\; t$

(A5) $a\tau t \;=\; at$

(A6) $\tau t+t \;=\; \tau t$

(A7) $a(t_1+\tau t_2)+at_2 \;=\; a(t_1+\tau t_2)$

Properties 3 [HM]

a) $\tau(t_1+t_2)+t_1 \;=\; \tau(t_1+t_2)$ (A8)

b) $t \approx t'$ iff $t \overset{c}{\approx} t'$ or $t \overset{c}{\approx} \tau t'$ or $\tau t \overset{c}{\approx} t'$.

Definition 5

We call controllable a process (term) t of $T[\Sigma]$ such that there exists t', $t' \overset{c}{\approx} t$ and t' has no occurrences of τ. We represent by $CT[\Sigma]$ the set of the controllable terms.

We give hereafter the definition of the function $|\ |$ associating with a term of $CT[\Sigma]$ a formula of FF(A) representing its observational congruence class.

Definition 6

For the class of the formulas of the form $f = \bigwedge_{i \in I} \langle a_i \wedge f_i \rangle \wedge [\bigvee_{i \in K} a_i \wedge f_i]$ such that the f_i's belong to FF(A) and $\not\models f \equiv false$, define $\hat{f}$ as the formula $\hat{f} = \bigvee_{i \in K} a_i \wedge f_i$.

Proposition 1

$\wedge$ is a partial function from FF(A) into F(A).

Proof: Given in [GS].

Definition 7

Let f be a formula such that $\hat{f}$ is defined. Denote by E(f) the formula,

$$E(f) = \mu x.(f \vee \langle \tau \wedge x \rangle \wedge [\tau \wedge x \vee \hat{f}]).$$

Proposition 2

If f is a formula representing an observational congruence class then,

$$t \models E(f) \text{ iff } t \models f \text{ or } \exists t' (\tau t' \approx^{\mathcal{S}} t \text{ and } t' \models f). \ \square$$

Definition 8

Let $|\ |$ be the function from $CT[\Sigma]$ into FF(A) defined as follows:

- $|Nil| = [false]$
- $|at| = \langle a \wedge E|t| \rangle [a \wedge E|t|]$ for $a \in A - \{\tau\}$
- $|\tau t| = |t|$
- $|t_1 + t_2| = A_1 \wedge A_2 \wedge [B_1 \vee B_2]$ where,
    - $|t_i|$ is of the form $|t_i| = A_i \wedge [B_i]$ for $i=1,2$ and
    - A_i is true or of the form $\bigwedge_{i \in I} \langle f_i \rangle$.

Proposition 3

For any $t, t' \in CT[\Sigma]$, $t' \approx^{\mathcal{S}} t$ iff $t' \models |t|$. $\square$

This proposition is an application of a more general result given in [GS].

4. SEMANTICS OF RECURSIVE CONTROLLABLE TERMS

4.1 Controllable recursive terms

Consider the term language built on the signature Σ and a set of variables X, in the following manner:

- Nil, $x \in X$ are terms,
- if t,t' are terms and $x \in X$ then at, t+t' and recx.t are terms.

We represent by $T[\Sigma,X]$ the set of the closed and well-guarded terms of this language. A term t is well-guarded if any occurrence of a variable x in t is under the scope of an operator $a \in A-\{\tau\}$; for example recx.a(x+recy.by) is well-guarded but not recx.(ax+x). The terms of $T[\Sigma,X]$ are considered as processes with transition relations $\xrightarrow{a} \subseteq T[\Sigma,X] \times T[\Sigma,X]$. For any $a \in A$, $\xrightarrow{a}$ is defined as the least relation satisfying,

- $at \xrightarrow{a} t$,
- $t_1 \xrightarrow{a} t$ implies $t_1+t_2 \xrightarrow{a} t$ and $t_2+t_1 \xrightarrow{a} t$,
- $t[recx.t/x] \xrightarrow{a} t'$ implies $recx.t \xrightarrow{a} t'$ if x is free in t.

Definition 4 can also be applied to extend observational congruence $\overset{\mathcal{S}}{\approx}$ on $T[\Sigma,X]$.

Obviously, recx.t(x) is a solution of the equation x=t(x). We study the problem of the solution of recursive equations of this type. Following the standard approach we define the solutions as limits of ordered sequences. To this end, we extend $T[\Sigma]$ by adjoining to it a constant Ω representing the "less defined" process. On this extension, we define a preorder $\ll$ such that $\underset{\sim}{\Omega} = \ll \cap \ll^{-1}$ is a congruence relation whose restriction to $T[\Sigma]$ is the observational congruence $\overset{\mathcal{S}}{\approx}$. We put,

$$CT[\Sigma,X] = \{t \in T[\Sigma,X] \mid \exists t' \in T[\Sigma-\{\tau\},X] \;\; t \overset{\mathcal{S}}{\approx} t'\}.$$

4.2 The extension $CT_\Omega[\Sigma]$ of $CT[\Sigma]$

Consider the term language $T_\Omega[\Sigma]$ defined on the signature $\Sigma \cup \{\Omega\}$ where Ω is a constant.

Represent by $\underset{\approx}{\Omega}$ the congruence induced by the axioms (A1) to (A7) on $T_\Omega[\Sigma]$.

Obviously, the restriction of $\underset{\approx}{\Omega}$ to $T[\Sigma]$ is $\overset{\mathcal{S}}{\approx}$.

The set of controllable terms $CT_\Omega[\Sigma]$ of $T_\Omega[\Sigma]$ is defined by,

$$CT_\Omega[\Sigma] = \{t \in T_\Omega[\Sigma] \mid \exists t' \in T_\Omega[\Sigma-\{\tau\}] \;\; t \underset{\approx}{\Omega} t'\}.$$

The terms of $CT_\Omega[\Sigma]$ will be interpreted as sets of terms of $CT[\Sigma]$ which correspond to unions of classes of $\stackrel{\mathcal{S}}{\approx}$.

The following properties can be proved [Gr].

Property 4

$\forall t \in CT_\Omega[\Sigma]$ $t \lesssim at'$ iff t is of the form $t = \sum_{i \in I} at_i$ where $at_i \lesssim at'$. □

Property 5

$\forall t \in CT_\Omega[\Sigma]$ $t \lesssim t_1+t_2$ implies $\exists t_1', t_2'$ such that t and $t_1'+t_2'$ are congruent by application of axioms (A1) to (A4), $t_1' \lesssim t_1$ and $t_2' \lesssim t_2$. □

Definition 9

Let $t \in T_\Omega[\Sigma]$ and $\vec{p}=(p_1,\ldots p_n)$ a tuple of terms of $T[\Sigma]$. If t has $n \geqslant 0$ occurrences of Ω then $t*\vec{p}$ denotes the term of $T[\Sigma]$ obtained from t by substituting in the order the Ω's by the p_i's. If t has no occurrences of Ω then $t*\vec{p}$ is equal to t.

Definition 10

Define the function $prol \in CT_\Omega[\Sigma] \rightarrow 2^{CT[\Sigma]}$ such that for $t \in CT_\Omega[\Sigma]$,

$$prol(t) = \{t' \in CT[\Sigma] \mid \exists t_c \; t_c \lesssim t \; \exists \vec{p} \; t' \stackrel{\mathcal{S}}{\approx} t_c * \vec{p}\}.$$

We call prol(t) the prolongation of t.

Property 6

$prol(\Omega)=CT[\Sigma]$. □

Property 7

For $t \in CT_\Omega[\Sigma]$, $prol(at) = \{t' \mid t' \stackrel{\mathcal{S}}{\approx} \sum_{i \in I} at_i$ where $t_i \in prol(t)\}$. □

Property 8

For $t_1, t_2 \in CT_\Omega[\Sigma]$, $prol(t_1+t_2) = \{t \mid t \stackrel{\mathcal{S}}{\approx} t_1'+t_2',\ t_i' \in prol(t_i)$ for $i=1,2\}$. □

<u>Property 9</u>

For $t \in CT_{\Omega}[\Sigma]$, prol(t) represents a union of classes of $\mathcal{S}$ on $CT[\Sigma]$. □

<u>Definition 11</u>

We define the binary relations $\ll$ and $\underset{\sim}{\Omega}$ on $CT_{\Omega}[\Sigma]$ as follows:

a) $t \ll t'$ iff $prol(t) \subseteq prol(t')$

b) $\underset{\sim}{\Omega} = \ll \cap \ll^{-1}$

Obviously, $\ll$ is a preorder relation on $CT_{\Omega}[\Sigma]$ and $\underset{\sim}{\Omega}$ an equivalence relation. Notice that the restrictions of $\underset{\sim}{\Omega}$, $\ll$ and $\mathcal{S}$ on $CT[\Sigma]$ agree.

<u>Property 10</u>

For $t_i, t_i' \in CT[\Sigma]$, $i=1,2$, we have,

a) $t_1 \ll t_1'$ implies $at_1 \ll at_1'$,

b) $t_1 \ll t_1'$ and $t_2 \ll t_2'$ implies $t_1+t_2 \ll t_1'+t_2'$. □

A consequence of this property is that $\underset{\sim}{\Omega}$ is a congruence.

Notice that $\mathbf{\Omega} \subseteq \underset{\sim}{\Omega}$ and this inclusion is strict. Obviously, two terms t_1, t_2 such that $t_1 \mathbf{\Omega} t_2$, have the same prolongations according to definition 10. The following example shows that $\underset{\sim}{\Omega} \subseteq \mathbf{\Omega}$ is not true.

For $t_1 = a\Omega + aa\Omega + aaa\Omega$ and $t_2 = a\Omega + aaa\Omega$, we have not $t_1 \mathbf{\Omega} t_2$. On the other hand, we have $a\Omega \ll a\Omega$, $aa\Omega \ll a\Omega$ and $aaa\Omega \ll aaa\Omega$ from which we deduce $t_1 \ll t_2$. Also, $a\Omega \ll a\Omega$, $aaa\Omega \ll aa\Omega$ and $aaa\Omega \ll aaa\Omega$ from which we deduce $t_2 \ll t_1$.

4.3 <u>Operational properties of $\ll$ on $CT_{\Omega}[\Sigma]$</u>

In this section we give operational properties of $\ll$ on $CT_{\Omega}[\Sigma]$ which are used in the sequel. To this end, we define for $a \in A$ a relation $\xrightarrow{a} \subseteq T_{\Omega}[\Sigma] \times T_{\Omega}[\Sigma]$ exactly as in definition 1. (This implies that Ω has no $\xrightarrow{a}$ derivation.) Also, we define for $a \in A-\{\tau\}$ the relation $\overset{a}{\Rightarrow}$ as the restriction of $\xrightarrow{a}(\xrightarrow{\tau})^*$ on $CT_{\Omega}[\Sigma]$.

<u>Notation</u>

For $t \in CT_{\Omega}[\Sigma]$ we denote by,

$\ell(t) = \max\{s \in (A-\{\tau\})^* \mid \exists t' \ t \overset{s}{\Rightarrow} t'\}$

$\Omega\text{-}d(t) = \min\{s \in (A-\{\tau\})^* \mid t \overset{s}{\Rightarrow} \Omega\}$

We call $\ell(t)$ the <u>length</u> of t and Ω-d(t) the <u>Ω-depth</u> of t. For $t \in CT[\Sigma]$ we put $\Omega\text{-}d(t)=\infty$.

<u>Definition 12</u>

Define the relation $\overset{w}{\approx} = \bigcap_{k \in \mathbf{N}} \overset{w}{\approx}_k \subseteq CT_\Omega[\Sigma] \times CT_\Omega[\Sigma]$ where the relations $\overset{w}{\approx}_k$ for $k \in \mathbf{N}$ are defind by,

$t_1 \overset{w}{\approx}_0 t_2$ iff $\Omega\text{-}d(t_i)>0$ for i=1,2.

$t_1 \overset{w}{\approx}_{k+1} t_2$ iff $\forall a \in A-\{\tau\}$ $(t_1 \overset{a}{\Rightarrow} t_1'$ implies $\exists t_2' (t_2 \overset{a}{\Rightarrow} t_2'$ and $t_1' \overset{w}{\approx}_k t_2')$ and

$(t_2 \overset{a}{\Rightarrow} t_2'$ implies $\exists t_1' (t_1 \overset{a}{\Rightarrow} t_1'$ and $t_1' \overset{w}{\approx}_k t_2')$.

The relations $\overset{w}{\approx}_k$ are equivalence relations for any $k \in \mathbf{N}$. Notice that, as $\overset{w}{\approx} \subseteq CT[\Sigma] \times CT[\Sigma]$, $\overset{w}{\approx}$ is the restriction on $CT[\Sigma]$ of the weak equivalence of CCS [BR].

<u>Proposition 4</u>

$\forall t \in CT_\Omega[\Sigma]$ $\Omega\text{-}d(t)>k$ implies $\forall t', t'' \in prol(t)$ $t' \overset{w}{\approx}_k t''$ □

<u>Proposition 5</u>

$\forall t_1, t_2 \in CT_\Omega[\Sigma]$ such that $\Omega\text{-}d(t_i)>k$ for i=1,2, we have,

$(\forall t_i' \in prol(t_i)$ for i=1,2 $t_1' \overset{w}{\approx}_k t_2')$ implies $t_1 \overset{w}{\approx}_k t_2$. □

<u>Proposition 6</u>

$\forall t_1, t_2 \in CT_\Omega[\Sigma]$ such that $\Omega\text{-}d(t_i)>k$ for i=1,2, we have,

$t_1 \ll t_2$ implies $t_1 \overset{w}{\approx}_k t_2$. □

<u>Proposition 7</u>

$\forall t_1, t_2 \in CT_\Omega[\Sigma]$ we have,

$t_1 \ll t_2$ implies $(t_2 \overset{a}{\Rightarrow} t_2'$ implies $\exists t_1' (t_1 \overset{a}{\Rightarrow} t_1'$ and $t_1' \ll t_2'))$. □

<u>Proposition 8</u>

$\forall t_1, t_2 \in CT_\Omega[\Sigma]$ such that $\Omega\text{-}d(t_1)>k$ and $\ell(t_2)<k$ we have,

$(\forall t_1' \in prol(t_1)$ $\exists t_2' \in prol(t_2)$ $t_1' \overset{w}{\approx}_k t_2')$ implies $t_1 \ll t_2$. □

4.4 Completion $CT^{\infty}_{\Omega}[\Sigma]$ of $CT_{\Omega}[\Sigma]$

We define a completion of $CT_{\Omega}[\Sigma]$ by adjunction of the limits of decreasing sequences of $CT_{\Omega}[\Sigma]$ which will be used to represent solutions of recursive equations on $CT[\Sigma,X]$.

- Let S be the set of sequences of the form $\{t_i\}_{i\in\mathbf{N}}$ with $t_i\in CT_{\Omega}[\Sigma]$ and such that,
  - $\forall i\in\mathbf{N}$ $t_{i+1}\ll t_i$, i.e. the sequence $\{t_i\}$ is decreasing,
  - $\forall k\in\mathbf{N}$ $\exists i(k)$ $\forall m>i(k)$ $\Omega\text{-}d(t_m)\geqslant k$, i.e. the occurrences of Ω are in an increasing depth.
- Let $B=\{\bigcap_{i\in\mathbf{N}} t_i \mid \{t_i\}\in S\}$ a set of constants where $\bigcap_{i\in\mathbf{N}}$ is interpreted as a greatest lower bound operation.

Consider the term algebra $T^{\infty}_{\Omega}[\Sigma]$ on the signature $\Sigma\cup\{\Omega\}\cup B$. As in 4.2 we represent by $\underset{\approx}{\Omega}$ the congruence induced by the axioms (A1) to (A7) on $T^{\infty}_{\Omega}[\Sigma]$. We define the set of controllable terms $CT^{\infty}_{\Omega}[\Sigma]$ of $T^{\infty}_{\Omega}[\Sigma]$ by

$$CT^{\infty}_{\Omega}[\Sigma]=\{t\in T^{\infty}_{\Omega}[\Sigma] \mid \exists t'\in T^{\infty}_{\Omega}[\Sigma-\{\tau\}] \ \ t'\underset{\approx}{\Omega}t\}.$$

For any $a\in A$ a relation $\xrightarrow{a}\subseteq T^{\infty}_{\Omega}[\Sigma]\times T^{\infty}_{\Omega}[\Sigma]$ is defined as the least relation such that

- $at\xrightarrow{a}t$
- $t_1\xrightarrow{s}t$ implies $t_1+t_2\xrightarrow{a}t$ and $t_2+t_1\xrightarrow{a}t$

For any $a\in A-\{\tau\}$ a relation $\overset{a}{\Rightarrow}\subseteq CT^{\infty}_{\Omega}[\Sigma]\times CT^{\infty}_{\Omega}[\Sigma]$ is defined as the least relation such that,

- for $t,t'\in CT^{\infty}_{\Omega}[\Sigma]$ $t\xrightarrow{a}(\xrightarrow{\tau})^{*}t'$ implies $t\overset{a}{\Rightarrow}t'$
- $[\{t_i\}\in S$ and $\forall i\in\mathbf{N}$ ($t_i\neq\Omega$ implies $t_i\overset{a}{\Rightarrow}t_i'$) and $\{t_i'\}\in S]$ implies $\cap t_i\overset{a}{\Rightarrow}\cap t_i'$.

For $\cap t_i\in B$ we put $\Omega\text{-}d(\cap t_i)=\infty$. The relations $\underset{\approx}{W}_k\subseteq CT^{\infty}_{\Omega}[\Sigma]\times CT^{\infty}_{\Omega}[\Sigma]$ and $\underset{\approx}{W}=\bigcap_{k\in\mathbf{N}}\underset{\approx}{W}_k$ are defined exactly as on $CT_{\Omega}[\Sigma]$.

Remarks:

- If $\{t_i\}\in S$ becomes stationary after some index k, for example $\{t_i\}=t_0,t_1,\ldots t_k,t_k,\ldots$, then $\cap t_i\underset{\approx}{W}t_k$.
- For $\cap t_i\in B$, we have taken $\Omega\text{-}d(\cap t_i)=\infty$ because there exists no sequence $s\in(A-\{\tau\})^{*}$ such that there exists an index n for which $\forall i\geqslant n$ $t_i\overset{s}{\Rightarrow}\Omega$, i.e. there exists no s such that $\cap t_i\overset{s}{\Rightarrow}\Omega$.

- The relation $\approx^{w}$ on $CT^{\infty}_{\Omega}[\Sigma]$ is defined only for the terms t such that Ω-d(t)=∞ i.e. terms constructed from elements of B and Nil.
- The relations $\approx^{w}$ and $\approx^{w}_{k}$ are extensions of the relations $\approx^{w}$ and $\approx^{w}_{k}$ defined in 4.3.

We extend the relation $\ll$ on $CT^{\infty}_{\Omega}[\Sigma]$ in the following manner.

<u>Definition 13</u>

For $\{t_i\},\{t_i'\}\in S$, $\cap t_i \ll \cap t_i'$ iff $\forall m\in \mathbf{N}\ \exists n\ t_n \ll t_m'$.
We represent by $\underset{\sim}{\Omega} \subseteq CT^{\infty}_{\Omega}[\Sigma]\times CT^{\infty}_{\Omega}[\Sigma]$ the relation $\underset{\sim}{\Omega} = \ll\cap\ll^{-1}$.

<u>Proposition 9</u>

For $\{t_i\}\in S\ \forall k\in \mathbf{N}\ \exists i(k)\ \forall n\geq i(k)\ \cap t_i \approx^{w}_{k} t_n$. □

<u>Proposition 10</u>

For $\{t_i\},\{t_i'\}\in S$ we have, $\cap t_i \ll \cap t_i'$ iff $\cap t_i \approx^{w} \cap t_i'$. □

<u>Remark</u>: As a consequence of proposition 10, the relations $\underset{\sim}{\Omega}$, $\ll$ and $\approx^{w}$ coincide on $CT[\Sigma]\cup B$.

The function prol can be extended on $CT^{\infty}_{\Omega}[\Sigma]$ in the following manner.

<u>Definition 14</u>

- For $\cap t_i \in B$ $\quad prol(\cap t_i) = \{t'\in CT^{\infty}_{\Omega}[\Sigma] \mid t' \approx^{w} \cap t_i\}$.
- For $t\in CT^{\infty}_{\Omega}[\Sigma]-B$ $\quad prol(t) = \bigcup_{t'\ll t} prol(t')$.

<u>Property 11</u>

For $t,t',t_1,t_1'\in CT^{\infty}_{\Omega}[\Sigma]$

a) $t\ll t'$ iff $prol(t)\subseteq prol(t')$

b) $t\ll t'$ implies $at\ll at'$

c) $t\ll t'$ and $t_1\ll t_1'$ implies $t+t_1\ll t'+t_1'$. □

<u>Property 12</u>

- $t_1\approx^{w} t_2$ implies $at_1\approx^{w} at_2$ $\forall a\in A-\{\tau\}$.

- $t_1 \overset{w}{\approx} t_2$ implies $t_1+t \overset{w}{\approx} t_2+t$ $\forall t \in CT_\Omega^\infty[\Sigma]$ with Ω-d(t)=∞. □

Proposition 11

For $\{t_i\},\{t_i'\} \in \mathbf{S}$

- $a(\cap t_i) \overset{w}{\approx} \cap(at_i)$
- $\cap t_i + \cap t_i' \overset{w}{\approx} \cap(t_i+t_i')$. □

A consequence of this proposition is that with each term t of $CT_\Omega^\infty[\Sigma]$ a term t' of $CT_\Omega[\Sigma] \cup B$ can be associated, such that $t \overset{w}{\approx} t'$.

4.5 Interpretation of $CT[\Sigma,X]/\mathcal{S}$ in $CT_\Omega^\infty[\Sigma]/\overset{\Omega}{\sim}$

We show that for a system of equations of the form,

(S) $x_i = f_i(x_1,...x_n)$ i=1,..n

where the f_i's are well-guarded functionals of $CT[\Sigma,X]$ without occurrences of rec and $X=\{x_1,..x_n\}$, the set $\{z_i\}_{1..n}$ defines a solution of (S) where,

- $z_i = \bigcap_{k \in \mathbf{N}} z_{i,k}$
- $z_{i,0} = \Omega$ and $z_{i,k+1} = f_i(z_{1,k},...,z_{n,k})$ for i=1..n.

For i=1..n, $f_i(\bigcap_{k\in\mathbf{N}} z_{1,k},...\bigcap_{k\in\mathbf{N}} z_{n,k}) \overset{\Omega}{\sim} \bigcap_{k\in\mathbf{N}} f_i(z_{1,k},...,z_{n,k})$ due to proposition 11. We have $\bigcap_{k\in\mathbf{N}} f_i(z_{1,k},...,z_{n,k}) \overset{\Omega}{\sim} \bigcap_{k\in\mathbf{N}} z_{i,k+1} \overset{\Omega}{\sim} \bigcap_{k\geq 1} z_{i,k}$ and as the functional f_i is well-guarded $\bigcap_{k\geq 1} z_{i,k} \overset{\Omega}{\sim} \bigcap_{k\in\mathbf{N}} z_{i,k}$. Obviously, $\{z_i = \bigcap_{k\in\mathbf{N}} z_{i,k}\}_{1..n}$ is the greatest solution of (S) in $(CT_\Omega[\Sigma]/\overset{\Omega}{\sim})^n$. If $\{z_i'\}_{1..n}$ is a solution then $z_i' \ll z_i$ for i=1..n, from properties 11 (b) and (c). From proposition 10 it follows that $z_i' \overset{w}{\approx} z_i$ and from a preceding remark $z_i' \overset{\Omega}{\sim} z_i$. Thus, we get the following proposition.

Proposition 12

The system of equations $\{x_i=f_i(z_1,..z_n)\}_{1..n}$, where the f_i's are well-guarded functionals, has a unique solution

$\{z_i = \bigcap_{k\in\mathbf{N}} f^k(\Omega,...,\Omega)\}_{1..n}$ in $(CT_\Omega^\infty[\Sigma]/\overset{\Omega}{\sim})^n$. □

We define a function $h \in CT[\Sigma,X] \to CT^{\infty}_{\Omega}[\Sigma]$ such that

$\forall t_1,t_2 \in CT[\Sigma,X]$ $t_1 \approx^{\mathcal{S}} t_2$ iff $h(t_1) \overset{\Omega}{\sim} h(t_2)$.

This function associates with recursive terms of $CT[\Sigma,X]$ elements of B.

Notice that the terms of $CT[\Sigma,X]/\approx^{\mathcal{S}}$ without occurences of rec are also terms of $CT^{\infty}_{\Omega}[\Sigma]/\overset{\Omega}{\sim}$ as $\approx^{\mathcal{S}}$ and $\overset{\Omega}{\sim}$ coincide.

Recursive terms are of the form,

$$t = recx_1.f_1(x_1,recx_2.f_2(x_1,x_2,recx_3(\ ),\ldots recx_n.f_n(\ )),\ recx_3.f_3(x_1.recx_2.f_2(\ ),x_3,\ldots recx_n.f_n(\ )), \ldots recx_n.f_n(x_1,recx_2.f_2(\ ),\ldots x_n)\ ) \qquad (1)$$

where it can be supposed without loss of generality, that the f_i's are functionals constructed from Nil,+ and $a \in A$.

Definition 15

Define $h \in CT[\Sigma,X] \to CT^{\infty}_{\Omega}[\Sigma]$ such that,

- $h(Nil) = Nil$
- $h(t_1+t_2) = h(t_1)+h(t_2)$
- $h(at) = ah(t)$
- For recursive terms t of the form (1) $h(t)=z_1$ where $\{z_i\}_{1..n}$ is the solution of $\{x_i=f_i(x_1,..x_n)\}_{1..n}$.

Definition 16

We define the relation $\overset{W}{\approx} = \bigcap_{k \in \mathbf{N}} \overset{W}{\approx}_k \subseteq CT[\Sigma,X] \times CT[\Sigma,X]$ where $\overset{W}{\approx}_k$ for $k \in \mathbf{N}$, is given by,

- $t_1 \overset{W}{\approx}_0 t_2$ always
- $t_1 \overset{W}{\approx}_{k+1} t_2$ iff $\forall a \in A-\{\tau\}$ $(t_1 \overset{a}{\Rightarrow} t_1'$ implies $\exists t_2' (t_2 \overset{a}{\Rightarrow} t_2'$ and $t_1' \overset{W}{\approx}_k t_2'))$ and $(t_2 \overset{a}{\Rightarrow} t_2'$ implies $\exists t_1' (t_1 \overset{a}{\Rightarrow} t_1'$ and $t_1' \overset{W}{\approx}_k t_2'))$.

<u>Remark</u>: To simplify notations, we use $\overset{W}{\approx}$ and $\overset{W}{\approx}_k$ in both definitions 12 and 16 as their restrictions to $CT[\Sigma]$ agree.

Proposition 13

For any $t \in CT[\Sigma,X]$ $t \approx^{\mathcal{S}} h(t)$.

<u>Proof</u>: The relations $\approx^{\mathcal{S}}$ and $\overset{W}{\approx}$ agree on $CT[\Sigma,X]$ [BR]. We prove the proposition

by induction on the structure of the terms of $CT[\Sigma,X]$.

- $h(Nil) \overset{\mathcal{S}}{\approx} Nil$
- If $h(t_i) \overset{\mathcal{S}}{\approx} t_i$ for i=1,2 then $h(t_1+t_2)=h(t_1)+h(t_2) \overset{\mathcal{S}}{\approx} t_1+t_2$.
- If $h(t) \overset{\mathcal{S}}{\approx} t$ then $h(at)=ah(t) \overset{\mathcal{S}}{\approx} at$.
- If t_1 is a recursive term of the form (1), i.e.

  $t_1=recx_1.f_1(x_1,t_2,..t_n)$ where $t_i(x_1,..x_n)=recx_i.(f_i(x_1,t_2,..x_i..t_n)$ for i=2..n,

  we have $t_1 \overset{\mathcal{S}}{\approx} t_1[t_i(x_1,..x_n)/x_i] \overset{W}{\approx}_0 z_{1,1}$, because t_1 is well-guarded $(z_{1,1}=f_1[\Omega/x_i]$ as in the beginning of this section).

  Put $t_{1,0}=t_1$ and $t_{1,k+1}=t_{1,k}[t_i/x_i]$. We obtain,

  $t_1 \overset{\mathcal{S}}{\approx} t_{1,2} \overset{W}{\approx}_1 z_{1,2}$ and by successive substitution,

  $t_1 \overset{\mathcal{S}}{\approx} t_{1,k+1} \overset{W}{\approx}_k z_{1,k+1}$. This implies,

  $t_1 \overset{W}{\approx}_k z_{1,k+1}$ $\forall k\in\mathbf{N}$, from which we deduce by proposition 9, $z_{1,k+1} \overset{W}{\approx} \bigcap_{i\in\mathbf{N}} z_{1,j}$ $\forall k\in\mathbf{N}$.

  Thus, $t_1 \overset{W}{\approx}_k \bigcap_{i\in\mathbf{N}} z_{1,j}$ $\forall k\in\mathbf{N}$, which is equivalent to $t_1 \overset{W}{\approx} \bigcap_{i\in\mathbf{N}} z_{1,j}$. □

<u>Corollary</u>

For $t_1,t_2\in CT^{\infty}_{\Omega}[\Sigma]$ $\quad t_1 \overset{\mathcal{S}}{\approx} t_2$ iff $h(t_1) \overset{\mathcal{S}}{\approx} h(t_2)$. □

5. MODAL CHARACTERIZATION OF $\overset{\Omega}{\sim}$ ON $CT[\Sigma]$

The aim of this section is to define a function $\| \; \| \in CT_{\Omega}[\Sigma] \to FF(A)$ such that,

$t' \models \|t\|$ iff $t' \in prol(t)$ $\forall t,t' \in CT_{\Omega}[\Sigma]$.

Obviously, $t \overset{\Omega}{\sim} t'$ iff $\|t\| \equiv \|t'\|$.

The function $\| \; \|$ is defined by,

- $\|Nil\| = [false]$
- $\|\Omega\| = true$
- $\|at\| = \langle a \wedge E\|t\|\rangle[a \wedge E\|t\|]$ for $a\in A-\{\tau\}$
- $\|\tau t\| = \|t\|$
- $\|t_1+t_2\| = A_1 \wedge A_2 \wedge [B_1 \vee B_2]$ where,
  - $\|t_i\|$ is of the form $\|t_i\| = A_i \wedge [B_i]$ for i=1,2 and
  - A_i is true or of the form $\bigwedge_{i\in I} \langle f_i \rangle$.

Notice that the restriction of $\| \; \|$ on $CT[\Sigma]$ agrees with $| \; |$. We define on the image of $\| \; \|$ the operators $\oplus$ and $\circledast$ by,

- $ⓐ \| t \| = \| at \|$
- $\| t_1 \| \oplus \| t_2 \| = \| t_1 + t_2 \|$.

Represent by $FF_\Omega(A)$ the language of the formulas generated from [false] and true by application of $\oplus$ and ⓐ for $a \in A - \{\tau\}$, i.e. $FF_\Omega(A)$ is the image of $\| \; \|$.

Property 13

For $f_1, f_1', f_2, f_2' \in FF_\Omega(A)$,
- $f_1 \supset f_1'$ implies $ⓐ f_1 \supset ⓐ f_1'$
- $f_1 \supset f_1'$ and $f_2 \supset f_2'$ implies $f_1 \oplus f_2 \supset f_1' \oplus f_2'$

Proposition 14

Let f be a formula of $FF_\Omega(A)$ representing a union of classes of $\approx$. Then, for any $t' \in T[\Sigma]$ such that $\exists t'' \in CT[\Sigma]$ $t' \approx \tau t''$ or $t' \approx t''$ we have,

$$t' \models E(f) \text{ iff } t' \models \bigvee_{|t| \supset f} E|t|.$$

Proof: As E is a monotonic operator, we have $(\bigvee_{|t| \supset f} E|t|) \supset E(f)$.
If $t' \models E(f)$ then $\exists t''$ $t' \overset{\epsilon}{\Rightarrow} t''$ and $t'' \models f$, i.e. $t'' \models \bigvee_{|t| \supset f} |t|$. Thus, $\exists t(|t| \supset f$ and $t'' \models |t|)$, $t' \overset{\epsilon}{\Rightarrow} t''$ implies $t' \approx t''$ or $t' \approx \tau t''$ (cf. [Mi] chap.9). Thus, $t' \models E|t|$ which implies $t' \models \bigvee_{|t| \supset f} E|t|$.

Proposition 15

Let f be a formula of $FF_\Omega(A)$ representing a union of classes of $\approx$, i.e. $f = \bigvee_{|t| \supset f} |t|$. Then,

$$ⓐ f = \bigvee_{F \in H} | \sum_{t \in F} at | \text{ where } H = \{\{t_1, \ldots t_n\} \mid |t_i| \supset f \; \forall i \; 1 \leqslant i \leqslant n\}$$

Proof: As for $t \in CT[\Sigma]$ $\|t\| = |t|$, we have $|at| = ⓐ \|t\|$. Thus, $|t| \supset f$ implies $|at| \supset ⓐ f$. Also, $|t| \supset f$ and $|t'| \supset f$ implies $|at + at'| \equiv \|at\| \oplus \|at'\|$ and $\|at\| \oplus \|at'\| \supset ⓐ f \oplus ⓐ f$. Thus, by $ⓐ f \oplus ⓐ f \equiv ⓐ f$ we obtain $(\bigvee_{F \in H} | \sum_{|t| \supset f} at |) \supset ⓐ f$.
To prove the converse we show that,
$t' \models ⓐ f$ implies $\exists \{t_i\}_{i \in I}$ $t' \models | \sum_{i \in I} at_i |$ where I is finite and $|t_i| \supset f$.
$t' \models ⓐ f$ is equivalent to $t' \models \langle a \wedge E(f) \rangle [a \wedge E(f)]$ which implies $t' = \sum_{i \in I} at_i$ where I is finite and $\forall i \in I$ $t_i \models E(f)$.
From proposition 14 we obtain $t_i \models E(f)$ implies $\exists t_i'$ $|t_i'| \supset f$ and $t_i \models E|t_i'|$. This

implies $at_i \models |at_i'|$ and consequently, $\sum_{i\in I} at_i \models |\sum_{i\in I} at_i'|$. □

Proposition 16

Let f,f′ be formulas of $FF_\Omega(A)$ representing unions of classes of $\approx^{\mathcal{S}}$, i.e. $f = \bigvee_{|t|\supset f} |t|$ and $f' = \bigvee_{|t|\supset f'} |t|$. Then,

$$f\oplus f' = \bigvee_{|t|\supset f,\, |t'|\supset f'} |t+t'|.$$

Proof: Notice that for $t,t'\in CT[\Sigma]$ $\|t\|\oplus\|t'\| \equiv |t+t'|$. As the operator ⊕ is monotonic we have $\|t\|\supset f$ and $\|t'\|\supset f'$ implies $\|t\|\oplus\|t'\|\supset f\oplus f'$ equivalent to $|t+t'|\supset f\oplus f'$. Thus, we obtain $(\bigvee_{|t|\supset f,\, |t'|\supset f'} |t+t'|)\supset f\oplus f'$.

To prove the converse, we show that $t''\models f\oplus f'$ implies $t''\models |t+t'|$ for $t,t'\in CT[\Sigma]$ such that $|t|\supset f$ and $|t'|\supset f'$.

If $f=[false]$ and $t'\models f'$ we have $t'+Nil \approx^{\mathcal{S}} t'$ and $f\oplus f' \equiv f'$, thus $t'+Nil \models f\oplus f'$.

If $f\equiv true \equiv \bigvee_{t\in CT[\Sigma]} |t|$ and $f' = A\wedge[\hat{f}]$ then $f\oplus f' = A = \bigvee_{|t'|\supset f',\, |t|\supset true} |t+t'|$.

Otherwise $f = \bigwedge_{i\in I} \langle x_i\rangle[\hat{f}]$ and $f' = \bigwedge_{i\in J} \langle y_i\rangle[\hat{f}']$ where x_i, y_i are of the form $a\wedge E(f_i)$. This implies $f\oplus f' = \bigwedge_{i\in I} \langle x_i\rangle \bigwedge_{i\in J} \langle y_i\rangle[\hat{f}\vee\hat{f}']$. From $t''\models f\oplus f'$ we deduce that t" is of the form $t'' = \sum_{i\in K} a_i t_i$ where $\forall k\in K$ $a_k t_k \models [\hat{f}]$ (α) or $a_k t_k \models [\hat{f}']$ (β).

Let K′,K" be the subsets of K for which (α) respectively (β) are verified. We have, $\forall i\in I$ $\exists k\in K'$ $a_k t_k \models \langle x_i\rangle$ and $\forall i\in J$ $\exists k\in K''$ $a_k t_k \models \langle y_i\rangle$.

So, by taking $t = \sum_{k\in K'} a_k t_k$ and $t' = \sum_{k\in K''} a_k t_k$ we get the result. □

Proposition 17

For $t\in CT_\Omega[\Sigma]$, $t'\in CT[\Sigma]$, $t'\models \|t\|$ iff $t'\in prol(t)$.

Proof: By induction on the structure of $FF_\Omega(A)$.

- $t'\models true$ iff $t'\in prol(\Omega) = CT[\Sigma]$.
- $t'\models [false]$ iff $t'\in prol(Nil) = \{t' \mid t' \approx^{\mathcal{S}} Nil\}$.
- Let $\|t\|$ be a formula such that $t'\models \|t\|$ iff $t'\in prol(t)$. Then, $t'\models ⓐ\|t\|$ iff $\exists t_i\in CT[\Sigma]$ for $i\in I$ finite $t' \approx^{\mathcal{S}} \Sigma a t_i$ and $t_i\models \|t\|$ by proposition 15. By induction hypothesis, we deduce $t_i\in prol(t)$. By property 7 we get $t'\in prol(at)$.
- Let $\|t_1\|, \|t_2\|$ be formulas such that $t'\models \|t_i\|$ iff $t'\in prol(t_i)$ for i=1,2. Then, $t'\models \|t_1\|\oplus\|t_2\|$ iff $t' \approx^{\mathcal{S}} t_1'+t_2'$ where $t_i'\models \|t_i\|$ by proposition 16. By induction hypothesis we get $t_i'\in prol(t_i)$ for i=1,2. By property 8 we deduce $t' = t_1'+t_2' \in prol(t_1+t_2)$. □

6. PROPOSITION OF A LOGIC FOR THE PROOF OF CONTROLLABLE PROCESSES

6.1 Definition of the basic language $FF_B(A)$

The formulas of $FF_\Omega(A)$ characterize unions of particular classes of $\approx^{\mathcal{S}}$ on $CT[\Sigma]$ (these which are prolongations of the terms of $CT_\Omega[\Sigma]$). We want to enrich the language $FF_\Omega(A)$ so as to obtain a logic by extending the operators ⓑ and ⊕ for disjunctions and conjunctions of formulas of $FF_\Omega(A)$.

Consider the language of formulas $FF_B(A)$ defined by

- true, false, [false] $\in FF_B(A)$
- If $f, f' \in FF_B(A)$ then $f \vee f', f \wedge f' \in FF_B(A)$
- If $f \in FF_B(A)$ and b is a subset of $A-\{\tau\}$ then ⓑ$f \in FF_B(A)$
- If $f, f' \in FF_B(A)$ then $f \oplus f' \in FF_B(A)$

The semantics of the operators is defined in the following manner.

- true, false, [false], $f \vee f'$, $f \wedge f'$ as in FF(A),
- $t \models$ ⓑf iff $\exists t_i \in CT[\Sigma]$ $\exists a_i \in A$ $(t \approx^{\mathcal{S}} \Sigma a_i t_i$ and $a_i \in b$ and $t_i \models f)$.
- $t \models f \oplus f'$ iff $\exists t', t'' \in CT[\Sigma]$ $(t \approx^{\mathcal{S}} t'+t''$ and $t' \models f$ and $t'' \models f')$.

Property 14

1) ⓑfalse ≡ false
2) false⊕f ≡ false
3) ∅f ≡ false, where ∅ is the empty set. □

The following property shows that formulas of $FF_B(A)$ represent disjunctions of formulas of $FF_\Omega(A)$ and consequently, unions of classes of $\approx^{\mathcal{S}}$ on $CT[\Sigma]$.

Property 15

1) $f \oplus (f' \vee f'') \equiv f \oplus f' \vee f \oplus f''$
2) ⓑ$(f \vee f')$ ≡ ⓑf v ⓑf' v ⓑ$f \oplus$ⓑf'
3) (aUb) f ≡ ⓐf v ⓑf v ⓐ$f \oplus$ⓑf

Proof:

1) $t \models f \oplus (f' \vee f'')$ iff

$\exists t', t''$ $t \approx^{\mathcal{S}} t' \oplus t''$ and $t' \models f$ and $t'' \models f' \vee f''$ iff

$\exists t', t'' (t \approx^{\mathcal{S}} t'+t''$ and $t' \models f$ and $t'' \models f')$ or $\exists t', t'' (t \approx^{\mathcal{S}} t'+t''$ and $t' \models f$ and $t'' \models f'')$ iff

$t \models f \oplus f' \vee f \oplus f''$

2) $t \models \circledB (f \vee f')$ iff

t is of the form $t \approx^{\mathcal{S}} \sum_{i \in I} a_i t_i$ for $a_i \in b$ and $t_i \models f \vee f'$ for $t_i \in CT[\Sigma]$ iff

$t \approx^{\mathcal{S}} \sum_{i \in I} a_i t_i$ $a_i \in b$ and $(\forall i \in I\ t_i \models f$ or $\forall i \in I\ t_i \models f'$ or $\exists I', I'' \neq \emptyset\ I' \cup I'' = I$ and $\forall i \in I'\ t_i \models f$ and $\forall i \in I''\ t_i \models f')$ iff

$t \models \circledB f$ or $t \models \circledB f'$ or $(\sum_{i \in I'} a_i t_i \models \circledB f$ and $\sum_{i \in I''} a_i t_i \models \circledB f')$ iff

$t \models \circledB f \vee \circledB f' \vee \circledB f \oplus \circledB f'$.

3) similar to the proof of (2). □

Proposition 18

For any formula f of $FF_B(A)$ either $f \equiv$ false or f is a disjunction of formulas of $FF_\Omega(A)$.

Proof:

- We have false$\wedge f \equiv$false, $\circledB$false$\equiv$false, false$\oplus f \equiv$false et false$\vee f \equiv f$.
- [false] and true are formulas of $FF_\Omega(A)$.
- if f, f' are disjunctions of formulas of $FF_\Omega(A)$ (representing unions of classes of $\approx^{\mathcal{S}}$ on $CT[\Sigma]$) then this is the case for $f \vee f'$ and $f \wedge f'$.
- If $f = \vee f_i$ for $f_i \in FF_\Omega(A)$, then

  $$\circledB f = \begin{cases} \text{false} & \text{if } b = \emptyset \\ \circled{\{a_1\} \cup \ldots \cup \{a_n\}}\ f & \text{if } b = \{a_1, \ldots a_n\} \subseteq A - \{\tau\} \end{cases}$$

  In the second case, by using properties 15.2 and 15.3, $\circledB f$ can be decomposed into a disjunction of formulas of the form $\circled{a_{i_1}} f_{i_1} \oplus \ldots \oplus \circled{a_{i_k}} f_{i_k}$ where the $\circled{a_{i_j}} f_{i_j}$ are formulas of $FF_\Omega(A)$.

- If $f = \bigvee_{i \in I} f_i$ and $f' = \bigvee_{i \in I'} f_i'$ where $f_i, f_i' \in FF_\Omega(A)$, then $f \oplus f' = (\bigvee_{i \in I} f_i) \oplus (\bigvee_{i \in I'} f_i') = \bigvee_{(i,j) \in I \times I'} f_i \oplus f_j'$ and according to property 15.1 this is a disjunction of formulas of $FF_\Omega(A)$.

We show that $\circledB f$ and $f \oplus f'$ can be represented by formulas of FF(A) by following a method similar to this one given in 5 for formulas of $FF_\Omega(A)$. To this end we define an operator E such that for any $f \in FF_B(A)$,

$f \models E(f)$ iff $(t \in CT[\Sigma]$ and $t \models f)$ or $(\exists t' \in CT[\Sigma]\ t \approx^{\mathcal{S}} \tau t'$ and $t' \models f)$.

This operator E is shown to be an extension of the operator defined in 2.

Property 16

For $f, f' \in FF_B(A)$

1) $E(f \vee f') = E(f) \vee E(f')$

2) $E(f \wedge f') = E(f) \wedge E(f')$

Proof: Consider $t', t'' \in CT[\Sigma]$ $t \overset{\mathcal{S}}{\approx} \tau t'$ and $t \overset{\mathcal{S}}{\approx} \tau t''$. This implies $t' \overset{\mathcal{S}}{\approx} t''$. As the formulas $f \in FF_\Omega(A)$ represent unions of classes of $\overset{\mathcal{S}}{\approx}$, we have $t' \models f$ iff $t'' \models f$.

1) $t \models E(f \vee f')$ iff

$t \in CT[\Sigma]$ and ($t \models f$ or $t \models f'$) or $\exists t' \in CT[\Sigma]$ $t \overset{\mathcal{S}}{\approx} \tau t'$ and ($t' \models f$ or $t' \models f'$) iff

$t \models E(f)$ or $t \models E(f')$.

2) $t \models E(f) \wedge E(f')$ iff

($t \in CT[\Sigma]$ and $t \models f$ or $\exists t' \in CT[\Sigma]$ $t \overset{\mathcal{S}}{\approx} \tau t'$ and $t' \models f$) and

($t \in CT[\Sigma]$ and $t \models f'$ or $\exists t'' \in CT[\Sigma]$ $t \overset{\mathcal{S}}{\approx} \tau t''$ and $t'' \models f'$) iff

$t \in CT[\Sigma]$ and $t \models f \wedge f'$ or $\exists t' \in CT[\Sigma]$ $t \overset{\mathcal{S}}{\approx} \tau t'$ and $t' \models f \wedge f'$ iff

$t \models E(f \wedge f')$ □

Thus, for any formula $f \in FF_B(A)$, $E(f)$ can be expressed in terms of formulas of $FF(A)$: if $f = \vee f_i$ where $f_i \in FF_\Omega(A)$ then $E(f) = \vee E(f_i)$.

We define for any subset b of $A - \{\tau\}$ a formula b' of $F(A)$ by using the following rules

- $\emptyset' = \text{false}$
- $A' = \text{true}$
- $\{a\}' = a$ for $a \in A$
- $(b_1 \cup b_2)' = b_1' \vee b_2'$
- $(b_1 \cap b_2)' = b_1' \wedge b_2'$

i.e. $'$ associates with a set $b = \{a_1, \ldots a_n\} \subseteq A - \{\tau\}$ the formula $b' = a_1 \vee \ldots \vee a_n$. In the sequel we do not distinguish between b and b'.

Proposition 19

1) $\textcircled{b} f = \langle b \wedge E(f) \rangle [b \wedge E(f)]$

2) For $g = \bigwedge_{i \in I} \langle f_i \rangle [\hat{g}]$ and $g' = \bigwedge_{i \in J} \langle f_i' \rangle [\hat{g}']$ or $g' \equiv \text{true}$ we have,

$$g \oplus g' = \begin{cases} \bigwedge_{i \in I} \langle f_i \wedge \hat{g} \rangle & \text{if } g' \equiv \text{true} \\ \bigwedge_{i \in I} \langle f_i \wedge \hat{g} \rangle \bigwedge_{i \in J} \langle f_i' \wedge \hat{g}' \rangle [\hat{g} \vee \hat{g}'] & \text{otherwise.} \end{cases}$$

Proof:

1) $t \models \textcircled{b} f$ iff

t is of the form $t=\Sigma a_j t_j'$ $a_j \in b$ and $\exists t_j \in CT[\Sigma]$ $(t_j' \approx^{\mathcal{S}} t_j$ or $t_j' \approx^{\mathcal{S}} \tau t_j)$ and $t_j \models f$ iff

$t=\Sigma a_j t_j'$ and $t_j' \models E(f)$ iff

$t \models \langle b \wedge E(f) \rangle [b \wedge E(f)]$.

2) Proof given in [Gr]. □

Property 17

1) $\textcircled{a \cap b} f \equiv \textcircled{a} f \wedge \textcircled{b} f$

2) $\textcircled{b}(f \wedge f') \equiv \textcircled{b} f \wedge \textcircled{b} f'$

Proof:

1) $\textcircled{a \cap b} f \equiv \langle a \wedge b \wedge E(f) \rangle [a \wedge b \wedge E(f)]$

$\equiv \langle a \wedge E(f) \rangle \langle b \wedge E(f) \rangle [a \wedge E(f)][b \wedge E(f)]$

$\equiv \textcircled{a} f \wedge \textcircled{b} f.$

2) $\textcircled{b}(f \wedge f') \equiv \langle b \wedge E(f \wedge f') \rangle [b \wedge E(f \wedge f')]$

$\equiv \langle b \wedge E(f) \wedge b \wedge E(f') \rangle [b \wedge E(f) \wedge b \wedge E(f')]$

$\equiv \textcircled{b} f \wedge \textcircled{b} f'.$

Property 18

Let $f, f', f'' \in FF_{\Omega}(A)$ such that $g \oplus g \equiv g$ for $g=f, f', f''$. Then, $f \supset f'$ and $f' \supset f''$ implies $f \oplus f' \oplus f'' \equiv f \oplus f''$.

Proof: Notice that $g \oplus g \equiv g$ iff $\forall t, t' \in CT[\Sigma]$ ($t \models g$ and $t' \models g$ implies $t+t' \models g$). This is the case iff g has the form $g \equiv \Lambda \langle g_i \rangle \wedge [\hat{g}]$ or $g \equiv [\hat{g}]$ or $g \equiv true$.
Let $f', f', f'' \in FF_{\Omega}(A)$ such that $g \oplus g \equiv g$ for $g=f, f', f''$, $f \supset f'$ and $f' \supset f''$.
$f \supset f'$ implies $f \oplus f \supset f \oplus f'$ $\equiv$ $f \supset f \oplus f'$ implies $f \oplus f'' \supset f \oplus f' \oplus f''$,
$f' \supset f''$ implies $f' \oplus f'' \supset f'' \oplus f''$ $\equiv$ $f' \oplus f'' \supset f''$ implies $f \oplus f' \oplus f'' \supset f \oplus f''$. □

Proposition 20

$$\left(\bigoplus_{i \in I} \textcircled{b_i} f_i\right) \wedge \left(\bigoplus_{i \in J} \textcircled{c_i} g_i\right) \equiv \bigoplus_{i \in I}\left(\textcircled{b_i} f_i \wedge \left(\bigvee_{i \in J} \textcircled{c_i} g_i\right)\right) \oplus \bigoplus_{i \in J}\left(\textcircled{c_i} g_i \wedge \left(\bigvee_{i \in I} \textcircled{b_i} f_i\right)\right)$$

Proof:

$$\left(\bigoplus_{i \in I} \textcircled{b_i} f_i\right) \wedge \left(\bigoplus_{i \in J} \textcircled{c_i} g_i\right) =$$

$$\bigwedge_{i\in I} \langle b_i E(f_i)\rangle \bigwedge_{i\in J} \langle c_i E(g_i)\rangle \;\left[\bigvee_{i\in I} b_i E(f_i) \wedge \bigvee_{i\in J} c_i E(g_i) \right] =$$

$$\bigwedge_{i\in I} \langle b_i E(f_i) \wedge (\bigvee_{i\in J} c_i E(g_i))\rangle \bigwedge_{i\in J} \langle c_i E(g_i) \wedge (\bigvee_{i\in I} b_i E(f_i))\rangle \;\left[\bigvee_{(i,j)\in I\times J} b_i c_j E(f_i g_j) \right] =$$

$$\bigwedge_{i\in I} (\bigvee_{j\in J} \langle b_i c_j E(f_i g_j)\rangle) \wedge \bigwedge_{j\in J} (\bigvee_{i\in I} \langle c_j b_i E(g_j f_i)\rangle) \;[\;.\;.\;.\;] =$$

$$\bigvee_{\bar{i}_k\in J^n} (\bigwedge_{i\in I} \langle c_{i_k} b_i E(g_{i_k} f_i)\rangle) \wedge \bigvee_{\bar{i}_l\in I^m} (\bigwedge_{j\in J} \langle c_j b_{i_l} E(g_j f_{i_l})\rangle) \;[\;.\;.\;.\;] =$$

where $n=|I|$ and $m=|J|$

$$\bigvee_{\bar{i}_k\in J^n} \bigvee_{\bar{i}_l\in I^m} (\bigwedge_{i\in I} \langle c_{i_k} b_i E(g_{i_k} f_i)\rangle \wedge \bigwedge_{j\in J} \langle c_j b_{i_l} E(g_j f_{i_l})\rangle \;[\;.\;.\;.\;] =$$

$$\bigvee_{\bar{i}_k\in J^n} \bigvee_{\bar{i}_l\in I^m} (\bigoplus_{i\in I} \textcircled{$c_{i_k} b_i$} (g_{i_k} \wedge f_i) \oplus \bigoplus_{j\in J} \textcircled{$c_j b_{i_l}$} (g_j \wedge f_{i_l}) =$$

$$\bigoplus_{i\in I} (\textcircled{b_i} f_i \wedge (\bigvee_{i\in J} \textcircled{c_i} g_i)) \oplus \bigoplus_{i\in J} (\textcircled{c_i} g_i \wedge (\bigvee_{i\in I} \textcircled{b_i} f_i)) \qquad \square$$

Notice that by using this proposition and the following rules, any term of the form $(\bigoplus_{i\in I} \textcircled{b_i} f_i) \wedge (\bigoplus_{i\in J} \textcircled{c_i} g_i)$ can be transformed into a term where conjunction is "pushed" into a lower level.

- $\textcircled{$a \cup b$}\, f \equiv \textcircled{\textbf{a}} f \vee \textcircled{\textbf{b}} f \vee \textcircled{\textbf{a}} f \oplus \textcircled{\textbf{b}} f$,
- $\textcircled{\textbf{a}} f \wedge \textcircled{\textbf{b}} f \equiv \textcircled{$a \cap b$}\, f$,
- $(\bigvee_{i\in I} f_i) \wedge g \equiv \bigvee_{i\in I} (f_i \wedge g)$,
- $f \wedge [\text{false}] \equiv \begin{cases} [\text{false}] & \text{if } f \equiv [\text{false}] \text{ or } f \equiv \text{true}, \\ \text{false} & \text{otherwise}. \end{cases}$

Thus, one can obtain from a formula g an equivalent formula g' without occurrence of conjunction.

The following example illustrates this idea in the case where $I=J=\{1,2\}$.

<u>Example</u>

Denote by $\alpha := \textcircled{$a_1$} f_1$, $\alpha' := \textcircled{$a_2$} f_2$, $\beta := \textcircled{$b_1$} g_1$, $\beta' := \textcircled{$b_2$} g_2$. We obtain,

$$(\alpha\oplus\alpha')\wedge(\beta\oplus\beta') \equiv (\alpha\wedge(\beta\vee\beta'))\oplus(\alpha'\wedge(\beta\vee\beta')) \oplus (\beta\wedge(\alpha\vee\alpha'))\oplus(\beta'\wedge(\alpha\vee\alpha'))$$
$$\equiv \alpha\beta\oplus\alpha'\beta' \vee \alpha\beta'\oplus\alpha'\beta \vee \alpha\beta\oplus\alpha'\beta\oplus\alpha'\beta' \vee \alpha\beta\oplus\alpha\beta'\oplus\alpha'\beta' \vee \alpha\beta\oplus\alpha\beta'\oplus\alpha'\beta$$
$$\vee\ \alpha\beta'\oplus\alpha'\beta\oplus\alpha'\beta' \vee \alpha\beta\oplus\alpha\beta'\oplus\alpha'\beta\oplus\alpha'\beta'.$$

The sub-formulas of the form $\alpha\beta$ occuring in this formula can be put into the form $\alpha\wedge\beta \equiv \textcircled{$a \cap b$} (f\wedge g)$. The rules given and the proposition 20 can be applied again to $f\wedge g$.

The operators $\textcircled{\textbf{b}}$ of $FF_B(A)$ express eventual reachability by executing an observable transition belonging to b. In $FF_B(A)$ one can also define operators $\Diamond_b$ expressing possible reachability by executing one observable transition of b. These operators are defined by,

$$\Diamond_b f = \textcircled{b} f \oplus true.$$

We have the following properties.

Properties 19

1) $t \models \Diamond_b f$ iff $\exists t'$ $\exists a \in b$ $t \overset{a}{\Rightarrow} t'$ and $t' \models f$
2) $\Diamond_b f \equiv \langle b \wedge E(f) \rangle$
3) $\Diamond_{b \cup c} f \equiv \Diamond_b f \vee \Diamond_c f$
4) $\Diamond_b (f \vee f') \equiv \Diamond_b f \vee \Diamond_b f'$
5) $\Diamond_b f \wedge \Diamond_b f' \equiv \Diamond_b f \oplus \Diamond_b f'$. □

6.2 The Extension $FF_\mu(A)$ of $FF_B(A)$

The modalities $\textcircled{b}$ and $\Diamond_b$ of $FF_B(A)$ express eventual and possible reachability under a condition b by executing one observable transition. In this section, we extend $FF_B(A)$ by adjunction of fixpoint operators to obtain modalities expressing eventual and possible reachability for an arbitrary number of observable transitions. In this extension we also give a characterization of $CT[\Sigma,X]/\approx^{\mathcal{S}}$.

Consider the language of formulas, defined by,

- false, true, [false], $x \in X$ are formulas, where X is a set of variables,
- If f, f' are formulas then, $f \vee f'$ and $f \wedge f'$ are formulas too,
- If f, f' are formulas then
  - $\textcircled{b} f$ is a formula for $b \subseteq A-\{\tau\}$
  - $f \oplus f'$ is a formula
  - $\mu x.f$ and $\nu x.f$ are formulas.

We denote by $FF_\mu(A)$ the set of the closed formulas of this language.
The semantics of $FF_\mu(A)$ are defined as for $FF_B(A)$ and $FF(A)$ on the set of the terms $CT[\Sigma,X]$. We show that the formulas of $FF_\mu(A)$ represent unions of classes of $\approx^{\mathcal{S}}$.

Proposition 21

A functional F of $FF_{\mu}(A)$ is $\vee$-continuous, i.e. for any sequence $\{f_i\}$ on $FF_{\mu}(A)$ such that $f_i \supset f_{i+1}$,

$$F(\bigvee_{i \in \mathbf{N}} f_i) \equiv \bigvee_{i \in \mathbf{N}} F(f_i).$$

Proof: It is sufficient to show that the operators of $FF_{\mu}(A)$ are $\vee$-continuous. For $\vee$ and $\wedge$ this is obvious.

Let $\{f_i\}$ and $\{g_i\}$ two sequences of formulas of $FF_{\mu}(A)$ such that $f_i \supset f_{i+1}$ and $g_i \supset g_{i+1}$ $\forall i \in \mathbf{N}$.

- We show that $\vee \textcircled{b} f_i = \textcircled{b}(\vee f_i)$:

  $\vee \textcircled{b} f_i \supset \textcircled{b}(\vee f_i)$ as $\textcircled{b}$ is a monotonic operator. Let $t = \Sigma a_i t_i$ and $t \models \textcircled{b}(\vee f_i)$. This implies that $\forall i$ $a_i \in b$ and $t_i \models E(\vee f_i)$. Thus, $\forall i$ $\exists j(i)$ $a_i t_i \models \textcircled{b} f_{j(i)}$. Let $n = \max\{j(i)\}$. As $\{f_i\}$ is such that $f_i \supset f_{i+1}$, we have $\forall i$ $a_i t_i \models \textcircled{b} f_n$ which implies $t \models \textcircled{b} f_n$.

- We show that $(\vee f_i) \oplus (\vee g_i) \equiv \vee(f_i \oplus g_i)$.

  As $\oplus$ is monotonic, we have $\vee(f_i \oplus g_i) \supset (\vee f_i) \oplus (\vee g_i)$. Let $t \in CT[\Sigma, X]$ and $t \models (\vee f_i) \oplus (\vee g_i)$. This implies $\exists t_1, t_2$ $t \overset{\mathcal{S}}{\approx} t_1 + t_2$ and $t_1 \models \vee f_i$ and $t_2 \models \vee g_i$, i.e. $\exists i, j$ $t_1 \models f_i$ and $t_2 \models g_j$. For $n = \max\{i, j\}$ we have $t_1 \models f_n$ and $t_2 \models g_n$, which implies $t_1 + t_2 \models f_n \oplus g_n$. Thus, $t \models \vee(f_i \oplus g_i)$.

  □

Proposition 22

Any functional F of $FF_{\mu}(A)$ is $\wedge$-continuous, i.e. for any sequence $\{f_i\}$ on $FF_{\mu}(A)$ such that $f_{i+1} \supset f_i$,

$$F(\bigwedge_{i \in \mathbf{N}} f_i) \equiv \bigwedge_{i \in \mathbf{N}} F(f_i).$$

Proof: As in the preceding proof, it is sufficient to show that $\textcircled{b}$ and $\oplus$ are $\wedge$-continuous.

Let $\{f_i\}, \{g_i\}$ be sequences on $FF_{\mu}(A)$ such that $f_{i+1} \supset f_i$ and $g_{i+1} \supset g_i$ $\forall i \in \mathbf{N}$.

- We show that $\textcircled{b}(\wedge f_i) \equiv \wedge \textcircled{b} f_i$.

  $\textcircled{b}(\wedge f_i) \supset \wedge \textcircled{b} f_i$ as $\textcircled{b}$ is monotonic. Let $t = \Sigma a_j t_j$ where, $t_j \overset{\mathcal{S}}{\approx} t_j'$ or $t_j \overset{\mathcal{S}}{\approx} \tau t_j'$ for $t_j' \in CT[\Sigma, X]$ and $t \models \wedge \textcircled{b} f_i$. This implies $\forall i \in \mathbf{N}$ $t \models \textcircled{b} f_i$, i.e. $\forall i \in \mathbf{N}$ $\forall j$ $a_j \in b$ and $t_j' \models f_i$. We obtain $\forall j$ $t_j' \models \wedge f_i$. This implies $\forall j$ $a_j t_j \models \textcircled{b}(\wedge f_i)$ and consequently, $t \models \textcircled{b}(\wedge f_i)$.

- We show that $(\wedge f_i) \oplus (\wedge g_i) \equiv \wedge(f_i \oplus g_i)$.

  As $\oplus$ is monotonic, $(\wedge f_i) \oplus (\wedge g_i) \supset \wedge(f_i \oplus g_i)$. Let $t \in CT[\Sigma, X]$ and $\forall i \in \mathbf{N}$ $t \models f_i \oplus g_i$. As t represents a tree of finite degree, there exists a finite number of t_1', t_2' and t_1'', t_2'' such that $t \overset{\mathcal{S}}{\approx} t_1' + t_2'$ and $t \overset{\mathcal{S}}{\approx} t_1'' + t_2''$ and ($t_i' \overset{\mathcal{S}}{\approx} t_i''$ or $t_2' \overset{\mathcal{S}}{\approx} t_2''$ for $i=1,2$). Thus, there exists t_1', t_2' such that $t \lesssim t_1'+t_2'$ and $t_1' \models f_i$ and $t_2' \models g_i$ for an infinite number of indices $i \in \mathbf{N}$. By hypothesis, $t_1' \models f_i$ and $t_2' \models g_i$ implies $t_1' \models \bigwedge_{j \leq i} f_i$ and $t_2' \models \bigwedge_{j \leq i} f_i$ for an infinite number of indices $i \in \mathbf{N}$, equivalent to $t_1' \models \bigwedge_{i \in \mathbf{N}} f_i$ and $t_2' \models \bigwedge_{i \in \mathbf{N}} g_i$. Thus, $t \models (\wedge f_i) \oplus (\wedge g_i)$.

From the propositions 21 and 22 we obtain easily.

Proposition 23

a) If F is a functional of $FF_\mu(A)$ then,

$\mu x.F(x) = \vee f_i$ where, f_0=false and $f_{i+1}=F(f_i)$

$\nu x.F(x) = \wedge f_i$ where, f_0=true and $f_{i+1}=F(f_i)$

b) The formulas of $FF_\mu(A)$ represent unions of classes of $CT[\Sigma,X]$. □

Proposition 23 shows that it is possible to associate with terms of the form recx.t of $CT[\Sigma,X]$ formulas of $FF_\mu(A)$. According to the results of 4.5, for a recursive term recx.t we have, $t' \lesssim$ recx.t iff $t' \models \bigwedge_{i \in \mathbf{N}} \| z_{i,i} \|$ where the $z_{i,j}$'s are defined as in 4.5. Thus, we obtain the result $t' \lesssim$ recx.t iff $t' \models \nu x. \| t \|$ where the functional $\| t \|$ of $FF_\mu(A)$ is obtained as the image of a function $\| \; \| \in CT[\Sigma,X] \to FF_\mu(A)$ defined by,

- $\|$Nil$\|$ = [false]
- $\| x \| = x$
- $\|$at$\| = ⓐ \| t \|$
- $\| \tau t \| = \| t \|$
- $\| t+t' \| = \| t \| \oplus \| t' \|$
- $\|$recx.t$\| = \nu x. \| t \|$

The following proposition is a direct consequence of the results given in 4.5, 4.6 and 5.

Proposition 24

$\forall t,t' \in CT[\Sigma,X]$ $t' \lesssim t$ iff $t' \models \| t \|$. □

7. DISCUSSION

This paper proposes a logic for the specification and proof of a sub-class of processes of CCS. This logic has been obtained by searching for a modal characterization of observational congruence. Such characterizations have already been proposed in [HM],[BR],[St] where the class of a term t can be represented by $\bigwedge_{t\models f} f$ (as the infinite conjunction of the formulas satisfied by t). Following a different approach, we have defined in a constructive manner a function $|\ |$ associating with t a formula $|t|$ which represents its congruence class. We have thus obtained operators ⓐ and ⊕ such that $|at| \equiv$ ⓐ$|t|$ and $|t+t'| \equiv |t| \oplus |t'|$. These operators have been extended to formulas representing unions of congruence classes by defining an Ω-extension of CCS. However, we failed to do this work for non controllable processes. The cause of this limitation - not discussed in the paper - is the "non-linearity" of the axioms (A6) and (A7).

The logic proposed is a kind of propositional μ-calculus with a binary operator ⊕ corresponding to non-deterministic choice. The underlying algebraic structure seems to be original and has many interesting features (for example expression of finite conjunction in terms of disjunction and ⊕).

Finally, it is important to notice that although this study is specific to CCS, the results obtained are of much more general application as most of them depend essentially on axioms (A1) to (A4). As a continuation of this work we define - in a forthcoming paper - a very general logic for the specification of non-deterministic programs modelled by labelled trees.

REFERENCES

[BR] Brooks S.D., Rounds W.C. *Behavioural equivalence relations induced by programming logics* Proceedings 10th ICALP 83, LNCS 154.

[Gr] Graf S. *Logiques du temps arborescent pour la spécification et la preuve de programmes.* Thèse 3ème Cycle, IMAG, Grenoble, February 84.

[GS] Graf S., Sifakis J. *A modal characterisation on finite terms of CCS* ICALP 84, LNCS 172.

[HM] Hennessy M., Milner R. *On observing non determinism and concurrency* 7th ICALP,80 LNCS 85.

[Ko] Kozen D. *Results on the propositional μ-Calculus* ICALP 82.

[Mi] Milner R. *A calculus for communicating systems* LNCS 92.

[St] Stirling C. *A proof theoretic characterization of observational equivalence.* University of Edinburgh, Internal Report CSR-123-83.

SPECIFICATION-ORIENTED PROGRAMMING IN TCSP

- Preliminary Version -

by

Ernst-Rüdiger Olderog
Institut für Informatik und Praktische Mathematik
Christian-Albrechts-Universität Kiel
Olshausenstr. 40-60
2300 Kiel 1, Fed. Rep. Germany

1. Introduction

We wish to study computational systems at two levels of abstraction: the level of specification and the level of program. A specification describes what one wishes to achieve, i.e. the properties or semantics of the desired system. A program describes how this system can be constructed, i.e. expressed or implemented in the restricted syntax of a specific programming language.

The idea of specification-oriented programming is to bridge the gap between these two levels systematically. More specifically, its task is to develop methods both for gradually transforming a given specification into a program which satisfies that specification and for proving that a given program satisfies some desired specification. Such methods have been advocated, developed and successfully applied in the area of sequential programming (e.g. /Bac, Bau, BD, KS, MWa, SSc/).

For concurrent programming, however, things are much more in a beginning state. Here even the basic concepts of specification and correctness are still a topic of ongoing research (e.g. /La, NH, Wi/). This is because a number of new, exciting features create difficulties: concurrent programs

- may not terminate,
- may not use conventional states,
- exhibit a delicate interaction of
  nondeterminism, parallelism and recursion.

NATO ASI Series, Vol. F13
Logics and Models of Concurrent Systems
Edited by K. R. Apt

This paper now presents an approach to specification-oriented programming for a simple kernel language of concurrency, called Theoretical CSP or simply TCSP. It is taken from /BHR/ and somewhat resembles Milner's CCS /Mi/. Our interest in specification-oriented programming originates from recent ideas of Hehner and Hoare who advocate that programs should be equated with the predicates describing their observable behaviour /He, Ho2/. We first present our interpretation of these ideas, we then base a method of specification-oriented programming on them, and we finally apply the method to a larger example.

2. Programs, Specifications and Correctness: The Concepts

We start with the description of TCSP, our kernel language for concurrent programming.

TCSP Syntax

Let Rec be the set of recursive terms P, Q generated by the following production system /BHR , OH/:

$$P ::= \underline{stop} \mid \underline{div} \mid a \rightarrow P \mid P \;\underline{or}\; Q \mid P \;\square\; Q \mid$$
$$P \parallel_A Q \mid P[\Phi] \mid \Phi^{-1}(P) \mid P \setminus b \mid$$
$$\xi \mid \mu \xi . P$$

Here a,b range over a finite set Comm of communications, A over the subsets of Comm, Φ over the functions Comm $\rightarrow$ Comm, and ξ over a set of identifiers. In particular $\Phi = [b/a]$ denotes the identity function except for a where $\Phi(a) = b$ holds. This notation extends to lists of distinct communications: $\Phi = [b_1,\dots,b_n/a_1,\dots,a_n]$. The recursive construct $\mu \xi .\_$ defines a binding occurrence of ξ and thus induces the usual notions of free and bound identifiers.

By a process we mean a recursive term without free identifiers. TCSP is now the set of all such processes. What is the intuition behind the TCSP operators ? stop denotes the inactive process which never engages in any communication nor any internal action. div is the diverging process which pursues an infinite sequence of internal actions. $a \rightarrow P$ first communicates a and then behaves like P. This concept of prefixing is a restricted form of sequential composition. P or Q models internal nondeterminism: it behaves like P or like Q, but the choice between them is not controllable from outside. In contrast P $\square$ Q models external nondeterminism: here the user can control whether P $\square$ Q behaves like P or like Q by choosing in the first step either to communicate with P or with Q.

$P \parallel_A Q$ introduces parallelism: it behaves as if P and Q are working independently (asynchronously) except that all communications in the set A have to be synchronized. By varying its synchronization set A parallel composition $\parallel_A$ reaches from arbitrary asynchrony ($\parallel_\emptyset$) to full synchrony ($\parallel_{Comm}$). We remark that semantically asynchronous parallelism will be modelled by interleaving. $P[\Phi]$ and $\Phi^{-1}(P)$ are renaming operators: $P[\Phi]$ behaves like P but with all communications a renamed to $\Phi(a)$. $\Phi^{-1}(P)$ is the inverse image of P under Φ; it communicates a whenever P communicates $\Phi(a)$. Quite different is the hiding operator: $P \setminus b$ behaves like P but with all communications b hidden or unobservable from outside. This idea of hiding or abstraction will be useful for hierarchical constructions of large processes as networks of smaller ones.

The operators discussed so far allow only the construction of processes with a finite observable behaviour. Infinite observable behaviours require the use of recursion $\mu \xi.P$.

Usually communications are atomic but sometimes it is advantageous to assume a structure

$$Comm = Cha \times \mathcal{M}$$

for communications. Here Cha is a finite set of channel names c,d,ch and $\mathcal{M}$ is a finite set of messages m. We write c!m instead of (c,m) for structured communications, and use the following abbreviations:

$$c!\mathcal{M} = \{ c!m \mid m \in \mathcal{M} \} ,$$

$$P \parallel_{\{c\}} Q \equiv P \parallel_{c!\mathcal{M}} Q ,$$

$$P[d/c] \equiv P[d!m_1,\dots,d!m_n / c!m_1,\dots,c!m_n] ,$$

$$P \setminus c \equiv (P \setminus c!m_1) \dots \setminus c!m_n ,$$

$$c?x \rightarrow P(x) \;=\; \underset{m \in \mathcal{M}}{\Box} \; c!m \rightarrow P(m)$$

where $\mathcal{M} = \{m_1,\dots,m_n\}$.

For substitutions we use the following notation: $P[Q/\xi]$ denotes the result of substituting Q for every free occurrence of ξ in P. $P(\xi)$ indicates that ξ occurs freely in P; then P(Q) abbreviates $P[Q/\xi]$.

Semantic Domain

In this subsection we prepare ourselves for defining a denotational semantics for TCSP, called the Readiness Model /OH/.

First some conventions. Let h range over $Comm^*$, the set of finite traces or histories over Comm. ε denotes the empty history, $h_1 \cdot h_2$ or just h_1h_2 the concatenation of histories h_1 and h_2. Further on, X,Y range over $\mathcal{P}(Comm)$ and Δ over $\mathcal{P}(Comm) \cup \{\uparrow\}$ where $\uparrow$ is a special symbol not mentioned in Comm and $\mathcal{P}(M)$ is the usual powerset of a set M: $\mathcal{P}(M) = \{ N \mid N \subseteq M \}$.

Operationally, processes in TCSP can exhibit a rather complex behaviour of communications and internal actions. But we wish to abstract from many of these details and consider the following set Obs of observations:

$$Obs = \left\{ \begin{array}{c} h, \\ (h,X), \\ (h,\uparrow) \end{array} \;\middle|\; \begin{array}{c} h \in Comm^*, \\ X \in \mathcal{P}(Comm) \end{array} \right\}$$

Intuitively, an observation (h,X) says that after having engaged in a history h of communications, the process has come to a stable state where all internal activity has ceased and is now ready to engage in all communications $a \in X$ in its next step. Therefore X is called a ready set /Ho1/. An observation $(h,\uparrow)$ says that after h the process may diverge, i.e. engage in an infinite sequence of internal actions.

As semantic domain we take now simply

$$\mathcal{P}(Obs)$$

with $\mathbf{S},\mathbf{T}$ as typical elements. An element $\mathbf{S} \subseteq Obs$ describes a set of nondeterministic possibilities of observations, and the idea is that another element $\mathbb{T} \subseteq Obs$ is "better" than $\mathbb{S}$ if $\mathbb{T}$ is <u>more deterministic</u> than $\mathbb{S}$. This leads to the following very simple <u>nondeterminism ordering</u> $\sqsubseteq$ on $\mathcal{P}(Obs)$:

$$\mathbb{S} \sqsubseteq \mathbb{T} \quad \text{iff} \quad \mathbb{S} \supseteq \mathbb{T} \ .$$

<u>Proposition 2.1</u> $\mathcal{P}(Obs)$ is a complete lattice under $\sqsubseteq$. //

<u>Semantic Operators</u>

Next we define for every syntactic operator op of TCSP a corresponding semantic operator

$$op^{\mathcal{R}} : \mathcal{P}(Obs) \times \ldots \times \mathcal{P}(Obs) \longrightarrow \mathcal{P}(Obs) \ .$$

The superscript $\mathcal{R}$ hints at the Readiness Model to be defined in the subsequent subsection.

(1) $\underline{stop}^{\mathcal{R}} = \{\varepsilon, (\varepsilon, \emptyset)\}$

(2) $\underline{div}^{\mathcal{R}} = Obs$

(3) $a \rightarrow^{\mathcal{R}} \mathbb{S} = \{\varepsilon, (\varepsilon, \{a\})\} \cup \{ah \mid h \in \mathbb{S}\} \cup \{(ah, \Delta) \mid (h, \Delta) \in \mathbb{S}\}$

(4) $\mathbb{S}\ \underline{or}^{\mathcal{R}}\ \mathbb{T} = \mathbb{S} \cup \mathbb{T}$

(5)
$$\begin{aligned} \mathbb{S}\ \Box^{\mathcal{R}}\ \mathbb{T} = \ & \{\varepsilon\} \cup \{(\varepsilon, X \cup Y) \mid (\varepsilon, X) \in \mathbb{S} \wedge (\varepsilon, Y) \in \mathbb{T}\} \\ & \cup \{(\varepsilon, \Delta) \mid (\varepsilon, \uparrow) \in \mathbb{S} \cup \mathbb{T}\} \\ & \cup \{h \mid h \neq \varepsilon \wedge h \in \mathbb{S} \cup \mathbb{T}\} \\ & \cup \{(h, \Delta) \mid h \neq \varepsilon \wedge (h, \Delta) \in \mathbb{S} \cup \mathbb{T}\} \end{aligned}$$

(6)
$$\begin{aligned} \mathbb{S}\ \|_A^{\mathcal{R}}\ \mathbb{T} = \ & \{h \mid \exists h_1 \in \mathbb{S}, h_2 \in \mathbb{T}: h \in h_1 \|_A h_2\} \\ & \cup \left\{(h, X) \ \middle|\ \begin{array}{l} \exists (h_1, X_1) \in \mathbb{S}, (h_2, X_2) \in \mathbb{T}: \\ \qquad h \in h_1 \|_A h_2 \wedge X = X_1 \|_A X_2 \end{array} \right\} \\ & \cup \left\{ \begin{array}{l} hh', \\ (hh', \Delta) \end{array} \ \middle|\ \begin{array}{l} \exists h_1 \in \mathbb{S}, h_2 \in \mathbb{T}: h \in h_1 \|_A h_2 \\ \wedge ((h_1, \uparrow) \in \mathbb{S} \vee (h_2, \uparrow) \in \mathbb{T}) \end{array} \right\} \end{aligned}$$

Here $h_1 \|_A h_2$ denotes the set of all successful interleavings of h_1 and h_2 with synchronizing communications in A. This set is defined inductively:

$$\begin{aligned} \varepsilon \|_A \varepsilon &= \{\varepsilon\}, \\ \varepsilon \|_A bh &= bh \|_A \varepsilon = (\{b\} \cap A) \cdot (\varepsilon \|_A h) \ , \end{aligned}$$

$$ah_1 \parallel_A bh_2 \;=\; [\{a\},\{b\},\bar{A}]\cdot(h_1 \parallel_A h_2) \;.$$

where $\bar{A}$ = Comm - A and [X,Y,Z] is the ternary majority operator on sets X,Y,Z defined by

$$[X,Y,Z] \;=\; (X\cap Y)\cup(Y\cap Z)\cup(X\cap Z) \;.$$

Thus [X,Y,Z] is the set of all elements contained in at least two of the three sets X,Y and Z. Correspondingly,

$$X_1 \parallel_A X_2 \;=\; [X_1,X_2,\bar{A}]$$

is the set of all communications contained in at least two of the three sets X_1,X_2 and $\bar{A}$.

(7) $$\$[\Phi]^{\mathcal{R}} \;=\; \{\Phi(h) \mid h\in\$\}\cup\{(\Phi(h),\,\Phi(\Delta)) \mid (h,\Delta)\in\$\}$$

where Φ : Comm $\rightarrow$ Comm is extended pointwise to histories h and ready sets X. (For $\uparrow$ we put $\Phi(\uparrow) = \uparrow$.)

(8) $$\Phi^{-1}(\$)^{\mathcal{R}} \;=\; \{\, h \mid \Phi(h)\in\$\,\}\cup\{(h,\Delta) \mid (\Phi(h),\Phi(\Delta))\in\$\}$$

(9) $$\begin{aligned}\$\setminus b^{\mathcal{R}} \;=\; & \{\; h\setminus b \mid h\in\$ \;\}\\ \cup & \{\; (h\setminus b,X) \mid (h,X)\in\$\wedge b\notin X \;\}\\ \cup & \left\{ \begin{matrix}(h\setminus b)h',\\ ((h\setminus b)h',\Delta)\end{matrix} \;\middle|\; \forall n\geq 0:\; h\cdot b^n\in\$ \right\}\end{aligned}$$

where the definition

$$a\setminus b \;=\; \begin{cases}\varepsilon & \text{if } a=b\\ a & \text{otherwise}\end{cases}$$

for communications is extended pointwise to histories h.

<u>Proposition 2.2</u> All operators $op^{\mathcal{R}}$ defined above are monotonic under the nondeterminism ordering $\sqsubseteq$.

TCSP Semantics

Using the previous operators $op^{\mathcal{R}}$ we now define a <u>denotational semantics</u> $[\![\cdot]\!]$ for TCSP, in fact for all recursive terms in Rec. Let Val be the set of <u>valuations</u>, i.e. of mappings $\mathcal{V}$ assigning sets $\$\subseteq$ Obs to identifiers ξ. Then

$$[\![\cdot]\!] \;:\; \text{Rec}\rightarrow(\text{Val}\rightarrow\mathcal{P}(\text{Obs}))$$

is given in the usual way:

$$[\![op(P_1,\dots,P_n)]\!] (\mathcal{V}) = op^{\mathcal{R}} ([\![P_1]\!] (\mathcal{V}),\dots, [\![P_n]\!] (\mathcal{V}))$$

$$[\![\xi]\!] (\mathcal{V}) = \mathcal{V}(\xi)$$

$$[\![\mu\xi . P]\!] (\mathcal{V}) = LFP(\lambda \mathbb{S}. [\![P]\!] (\mathcal{V}[\mathbb{S}/\xi]))$$

Here $\mathcal{V}[\mathbb{S}/\xi]$ is the valuation identical with $\mathcal{V}$ except for ξ where its value is $\mathbb{S}$. LFP is the <u>least fixed point operator</u> on the set of monotonic mappings from $\mathcal{P}$(Obs) to $\mathcal{P}$(Obs). Here LFP is applied to the mapping (written in λ-notation) which assigns $[\![P]\!](\mathcal{V}[\mathbb{S}/\xi])$ to $\mathbb{S}$; this application is well-defined since $\mathcal{P}$(Obs) is a complete lattice (Proposition 2.1) and all operators $op^{\mathcal{R}}$ are monotonic (Proposition 2.2). For processes $P \in$ TCSP (without free identifiers ξ) we write $[\![P]\!]$ instead of $[\![P]\!] (\mathcal{V})$.

Let us investigate the semantic structure of processes more deeply. Call a subset $\mathbb{S} \subseteq$ Obs <u>saturated</u> if the following holds:

(1) $\varepsilon \in \mathbb{S}$

(2) $ha \in \mathbb{S}$ implies $h \in \mathbb{S}$

(3) $(h,\Delta) \in \mathbb{S}$ implies $h \in \mathbb{S}$

(4) $h \in \mathbb{S}$ implies $\exists \Delta : (h,\Delta) \in \mathbb{S}$

(5) $(h, X) \in \mathbb{S}$ implies $\forall a \in X: ha \in \mathbb{S}$

(6) $(h,\uparrow) \in \mathbb{S}$ implies $\forall h',\Delta: hh' \in \mathbb{S} \wedge (hh',\Delta) \in \mathbb{S}$

Let $\mathcal{P}_{sat}$(Obs) denote the set of all saturated subsets $\mathbb{S} \subseteq$ Obs.

<u>Theorem 2.3</u> The operators $op^{\mathcal{R}}$, considered as mappings

$$op^{\mathcal{R}} : \mathcal{P}_{sat}(Obs) \times \dots \times \mathcal{P}_{sat}(Obs) \longrightarrow \mathcal{P}_{sat}(Obs),$$

are well-defined, i.e. preserve the saturation properties, and they are all continuous under $\sqsubseteq$. Thus in particular for every process P the set $[\![P]\!] \subseteq$ Obs is saturated, and the least fixed point can be approximated in the usual way:

$$[\![\mu\xi.P]\!] (\mathcal{V}) = \bigsqcup_{n \geq 0} [\![P^n(\underline{div})]\!] (\mathcal{V}).$$

Here $P^n(\underline{div})$ denotes the n-fold syntactic substitution defined inductively by $P^0(\underline{div}) \equiv \underline{div}$ and $P^{n+1}(\underline{div}) \equiv P(P^n(\underline{div}))$. //

We summarize the most important properties of the semantics $[\![\cdot]\!]$ for TCSP.

- Readiness:

  $(h,X) \in [\![P]\!]$ implies $\forall a \in X: ha \in [\![P]\!]$

- Nondeterminism:

  $[\![P \underline{or} Q]\!] = [\![P]\!] \cup [\![Q]\!]$

- Divergence:

  $(h,\uparrow) \notin [\![P]\!]$ iff P is divergence free.

Intuitively, divergence freedom means the absence of infinite sequences of internal actions. (A precise definition of this operational concept can be found in /OH/.) Because of the readiness property the semantics $[\![\cdot]\!]$ is called the <u>Readiness Model</u> for TCSP. It is due to /OH/ where also its consistency with an underlying operational semantics and its relationship to the (slightly more sophisticated) Failure Model of TCSP /BHR/ is established.

<u>Specifications</u>

To describe the properties of processes we take predicates in two specially typed free variables:

h ranging over $Comm^*$, and

X ranging over $\mathcal{P}(Comm)$.

Such predicates are called <u>specifications</u>. Let Spec be the set of all specifications and S,T range over Spec.

Specifications may use all standard operators of the predicate calculus, e.g. $\wedge$, $\vee$, <u>if</u> · <u>then</u> · (for implication), <u>true</u>, <u>false</u>, $\exists$, $\forall$ (quantification over h and X), and all the constants and operators associated with the basic types Comm and $\mathcal{P}(Comm)$. Additionally, we use the following notation:

$\alpha.h$ is the set of communications occurring in h, called the <u>alphabet</u> of h,

a.h is the number of communications a in h, called the <u>counter</u> of h,

ch.h	is the sequence of messages $m_1,\ldots,m_n$ sent along a channel ch in h in the case of structured communications; ch.h is called the <u>channel history</u> of ch,
$\|h\|$	is the length of h,
$h_1 \leq h_2$	states that h_1 is a prefix of h_2,
$h_2 - h_1$	results from h_2 by removing a prefix h_1,
<u>first</u>.h	is the first (leftmost) symbol in h if $h \neq \varepsilon$,
<u>rest</u>.h	abbreviates h - first.h,
<u>last</u>.h	is the last (rightmost) symbol in h if $h \neq \varepsilon$,
B <u>in</u> h	states that the Boolean condition B holds if every occurrence of $a \in \text{Comm}$ in B is replaced by a.h,
S[h'/h]	denotes the result of substituting h' for h in S.

We now extend the previous semantics $[\![\cdot]\!]$ to specifications $S \in \text{Spec}$:

$$[\![S]\!] = \{ h \mid \exists X: S \} \cup \{(h,X) \mid S \} .$$

<u>Correctness</u>

Given a specification S we wish to construct a process P which realizes S. Or the other way round: given a process P we wish to prove P satisfies some desired specification S. For both purposes we need a precisely defined relationship

P <u>sat</u> S

between processes P and specifications S which determines when P <u>satisfies</u> S or is <u>correct</u> w.r.t. S. We give here a very simple definition of this relationship due to Hoare /Ho1/:

P <u>sat</u> S iff $[\![P]\!] \subseteq [\![S]\!]$.

By the saturation properties of processes (Theorem 2.3), a process P satisfies a specification S if P is divergence free (because S does not allow the symbol $\uparrow$ to occur) and if P is more deterministic than S in the sense of the nondeterminism ordering $\sqsubseteq$.

Now, having discussed the notions of process, specification and correctness, we seem prepared for developing a discipline of specification-oriented programming. However, one important idea is still missing. To make the whole task of specification-oriented programming practically feasible, we better develop the processes stepwise from their specifications. Such a stepwise approach is eased very much if we allow - as intermediate steps - mixed terms of specifications (describing the semantic parts still to be developed in the following steps) and of TCSP operators (describing the syntactic parts already fixed in the previous steps). We thus extend TCSP by arbitrary predicates in the variables h and X.

Mixed Terms

The set Rec+Spec of mixed terms is the set of all recursive terms P,Q generated by the following extended production system

$$
\begin{aligned}
P ::= \; & S \quad \text{where} \quad S \in \text{Spec} \mid \\
& \underline{\text{stop}} \mid \underline{\text{div}} \mid a \rightarrow P \mid P \; \underline{\text{or}} \; Q \mid P \;\Box\; Q \mid \\
& P \parallel_A Q \mid P[\Phi] \mid \Phi^{-1}(P) \mid P \setminus b \mid \\
& \xi \mid \mu \xi . P
\end{aligned}
$$

where we apply the TCSP operators to specifications (predicates) as well. Since specifications S have a semantics $[\![S]\!] \in \mathcal{P}(\text{Obs})$ and the TCSP operators $op^{\mathcal{R}}$ are defined on $\mathcal{P}(\text{Obs})$, we immediately obtain a denotational semantics

$$[\![\cdot]\!] : \quad \text{Rec+Spec} \rightarrow (\text{Val} \rightarrow \mathcal{P}(\text{Obs}))$$

defined in just the same way as for Rec. Let TCSP+Spec denote the set of all mixed terms without free identifiers. Again we drop the valuation $\mathcal{V}$ and write $[\![P]\!]$ instead of $[\![P]\!](\mathcal{V})$ for $P \in$ TCSP+Spec. Note that in general $[\![P]\!] \in \mathcal{P}(\text{Obs})$ is not saturated any more.

The advantage of TCSP+Spec is that processes, specifications and mixed terms are now on the same semantic level and thus easy to compare. To do so, we use the following notation for $P,Q \in$ TCSP+Spec:

$P \Rightarrow Q$ iff $[\![P]\!] \subseteq [\![Q]\!]$

$P \Leftarrow Q$ iff $Q \Rightarrow P$

$P \equiv Q$ iff $[\![P]\!] = [\![Q]\!]$

$P \equiv_{df} Q$ iff by definition $P \equiv Q$

Thus $\Rightarrow$ asserts the validity of a <u>semantic implication</u> and $\equiv$ that of a <u>semantic equation</u>. In particular

P <u>sat</u> S iff $P \Rightarrow S$

holds now for processes P and specifications S. Some examples of semantic equations are given in:

<u>Proposition 2.4</u>

$$\underline{stop} \equiv h = \varepsilon \wedge X = \emptyset$$

$$a \rightarrow S \equiv (h = \varepsilon \wedge X = \{ a \}) \wedge (\underline{first}.h = a \wedge S[\underline{rest}.h/h])$$

$$S \ \underline{or}\ T \equiv S \vee T$$

//

<u>Remarks</u>

1) We believe that the idea of a free mixture of specifications with programming operators is essential for obtaining an elegant discipline of specification-oriented programming. In the area of sequential programming we first met this idea in Back's thesis /Bac/; for concurrent programming we first saw it in the work of Hehner and Hoare /He, Ho2/. The following two points mark essential differences between our approach and Hehner's work.

2) In /He/ semantic equations akin to those in Proposition 2.4 are used to define the semantics of programming language constructs in sequential and concurrent programming. However, these definitions are stated without supporting semantic model. This omission is responsible for some inconsistencies, e.g. a missing associativity property of the definition for sequential composition (cf. /He/).

   In our approach we avoid such inconsistencies by first defining a sound semantic model, the Readiness Model, and then stating all semantic equations as theorems about this model.

3) Moreover, semantic equations as in /He/ or Proposition 2.4 are not sufficient for the purposes of specification-oriented programming. There we do not wish to (and often cannot) show that a program P is equal to a given specification S, only that P satisfies, i.e. implies S. Thus in our approach theorems about semantic implications are more important.

3. Specification-oriented Programming: A Strategy

Suppose we wish to construct a process P which behaves like a buffer that can input messages along an input channel, and after some time is prepared to output them in the same order along an output channel. Schematically:

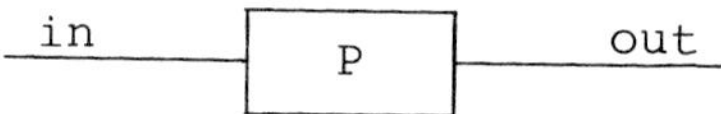

We make no assumption about the capacity of the buffer. But for simplicity we abstract away from the actual messages input or output, and assume here that we can only observe the event of an input via a communication "in" and the event of an output via a communication "out".

Thus P should satisfy the following specification BUFF of an <u>(abstract) buffer</u>:

$$\begin{aligned} \mathrm{BUFF} \equiv_{df} \quad & \alpha.h \subseteq \{in, out\} & (1) \\ \wedge \quad & out.h \leq in.h & (2) \\ \wedge \quad & \underline{if}\ out.h = in.h\ \underline{then}\ in \in X & (3) \\ \wedge \quad & \underline{if}\ out.h < in.h\ \underline{then}\ out \in X & (4) \end{aligned}$$

Lines (1) and (2) specify the <u>safety aspect</u> of a buffer. In particular, line (1) determines the alphabet: a buffer can only engage in the communications "in" and "out", and line (2) requires that the number of outputs is always less or equal the number of inputs. Clearly, every buffer should satisfy (1) and (2).

But these conditions alone are also satisfied by many processes P which we don't regard as a buffer - even the inactive process P ≡ <u>stop</u>. To rule out such idle processes we add lines (3) and (4) specifying the <u>local liveness aspect</u> of a buffer. Line (3) says an empty buffer, i.e. one where all inputs have been output, should eventually be ready for another input, and line (4) says a non-empty buffer should eventually be ready for another output. "Eventually" refers here to the fact that the buffer may need some time until it has reached a stable state where all internal activity has ceased and it is ready for the required (external) communication. Clearly, $P \equiv$ stop does not satisfy (3) or (4).

The construction of P should proceed systematically in a top-down fashion from BUFF:

$$\begin{array}{c} BUFF \equiv S_1 \\ \Uparrow \\ S_2 \\ \Uparrow \\ \vdots \\ \Uparrow \\ S_n \equiv P \end{array}$$

Whereas $S_1 \equiv BUFF$ is the original specification and S_n is the desired process P, the intermediate steps $S_2,\ldots,S_{n-1}$ can be mixed terms involving both specification parts and operator parts already constructed in TCSP. The transitivity of $\Longrightarrow$ ensures $P \Longrightarrow BUFF$.

Systematic construction of P means that every step $S_i \Longleftarrow S_{i+1}$ should correspond to an application of a theorem about the underlying Readiness Model for specifications and processes. Most of these theorems deal with the individual language operators op in TCSP and have the following form:

(*) If S and $T_1,\ldots,T_n$ are such and such, then

$$S \Longleftarrow op(T_1,\ldots,T_n)$$

holds.

Our strategy will be to apply theorems of type (*) in order to obtain a system of recursive implications (rather than recursive equations) from which we can read off a recursive process P satisfying S_1. This idea will become precise in the following subsection where we explain the basic principles of specification-oriented programming in TCSP:

Initial Communication, Substitution and Guarded Recursion

A first, very simple theorem of type (*) is:

Theorem 3.1 (Initial Communication)

Consider some $S \in Spec$ with $(\varepsilon, \{a_1, \ldots, a_n\}) \in [\![S]\!]$. Then

$$S \Leftarrow a_1 \rightarrow S[a_1 h/h] \,\Box\, \ldots \,\Box\, a_n \rightarrow S[a_n h/h]$$

holds. //

Thus S is satisfied or realized by a mixed term consisting of n alternatives $a_i \rightarrow S[a_i h/h]$, $i=1,\ldots,n$, where $S[a_i h/h]$ results from S by substituting $a_i h$ for h. The order of the alternatives is irrelevant as the operator $\Box$ is commutative and associative. Note that we cannot claim more than implication in Theorem 3.1; the semantic equation

$$S \equiv a_1 \rightarrow S[a_1 h/h] \,\Box\, \ldots \,\Box\, a_n \rightarrow S[a_n h/h]$$

is false in general.

Let us apply the Initial Communication Theorem to $S \equiv$ BUFF. Since $(\varepsilon, \{in\}) \in [\![BUFF]\!]$ holds, we obtain:

(A)

$$\begin{array}{c} BUFF \\ \Uparrow \\ in \rightarrow BUFF_{in} \end{array}$$

where

$$\begin{aligned} BUFF_{in} \equiv_{df} BUFF[in \cdot h/h] \equiv \; & \alpha.h \subseteq \{in, out\} \\ \wedge \; & out.h \leqslant 1+in.h \\ \wedge \; & \underline{if}\ out.h = 1+in.h\ \underline{then}\ in \in X \\ \wedge \; & \underline{if}\ out.h < 1+in.h\ \underline{then}\ out \in X \end{aligned}$$

Next, we apply the Initial Communication Theorem to the remaining specification $BUFF_{in}$. Since $(\varepsilon, \{out\}) \in [\![BUFF_{in}]\!]$ holds, we obtain:

(B)
$$\begin{array}{c} BUFF_{in} \\ \Uparrow \\ out \rightarrow BUFF_{in \cdot out} \end{array}$$

where

$$BUFF_{in \cdot out} \equiv_{df} BUFF_{in}[out \cdot h/h] \equiv$$

$$\begin{array}{ll} & \alpha.h \subseteq \{in, out\} \\ \wedge & 1+out.h \leqslant 1+in.h \\ \wedge & \underline{if}\ 1+out.h = 1+in.h\ \underline{then}\ in \in X \\ \wedge & \underline{if}\ 1+out.h < 1+in.h\ \underline{then}\ out \in X \quad . \end{array}$$

Note that in fact

$$BUFF_{in \cdot out} \equiv BUFF$$

holds. To connect the implications (A) and (B), we need:

Theorem 3.2 (Substitution)

With $S \Leftarrow T$ also $Q(S) \Leftarrow Q(T)$ holds for arbitrary mixed terms $Q(\xi)$.

Proof. By Proposition 2.2 all TCSP operators in Q are monotonic under the nondeterminism ordering. //

Though simple, the Substitution Theorem is essential in any top-down design

$$S \equiv S_1 \Leftarrow S_2 \Leftarrow \ldots. \Leftarrow S_n \equiv P \ .$$

It allows us to apply the Initial Communication Theorem or any other theorem yielding an implication $S \Leftarrow T$ not only at the beginning of the design where S coincides with S_1 but also in every step $S_i \Leftarrow S_{i+1}$ where S may occur inside S_i.

In our example we thus obtain from (A) and (B):

(C)
$$\begin{array}{c} BUFF \\ \Uparrow \\ in \rightarrow BUFF_{in} \\ \Uparrow \\ in \rightarrow out \rightarrow BUFF \quad . \end{array}$$

Usually, we will apply the Substitution Theorem tacitly and, for example, deduce (C) by the Initial Communication Theorem directly from (A) - without mentioning (B).

Now, in (C) we see a recursive implication of the form

$$\text{BUFF} \Leftarrow \text{in} \rightarrow \text{out} \rightarrow \text{BUFF}$$

which can be dealt with by the next theorem.

Theorem 3.3 (Guarded Recursion)

Consider a mixed term $P(\xi)$ with one free identifier ξ such that every occurrence of ξ in $P(\xi)$ is guarded, i.e. $P(\xi)$ is of the form

$$P(\xi) \equiv Q(b_1 \rightarrow R_1(\xi), \ldots, b_n \rightarrow R_n(\xi))$$

where Q does not contain any free occurrence of ξ and where the "guards" $b_i \in \text{Comm}$ are not within the scope of a hiding operator $\setminus b_i$ in Q. Assume now that

$$S \Leftarrow P(S)$$

holds for some specification $S \in \text{Spec}$. Then also

$$P(S) \Leftarrow \mu\xi.P(\xi)$$

holds. //

Note that in general Theorem 3.3 is false for terms $P(\xi)$ with unguarded occurrences of ξ. For example, with $P(\xi) \equiv \xi$ the implication $S \Leftarrow S$ trivially holds for arbitrary $S \in \text{Spec}$ but $S \Leftarrow \mu\xi.\xi$ is false. Fortunately, in the case of BUFF the identifier ξ is guarded in $P(\xi) \equiv \text{in} \rightarrow \text{out} \rightarrow \xi$. Thus the Guarded Recursion Theorem finally yields:

(D)

$$\begin{array}{c} \text{BUFF} \\ \Uparrow \\ \text{in} \rightarrow \text{BUFF}_{\text{in}} \\ \Uparrow \\ \text{in} \rightarrow \text{out} \rightarrow \text{BUFF} \\ \Uparrow \\ \mu\xi.\text{in} \rightarrow \text{out} \rightarrow \xi \end{array}$$

Summarizing, we have constructed a 1-place buffer

$$P(1) \equiv_{df} \mu \xi . in \rightarrow out \rightarrow \xi \Rightarrow BUFF$$

which holds at most one input at a time.

Remarks

1) Let us call a specification S consistent or satisfiable if there exists a process P with P $\Rightarrow$ S. Then S $\equiv$ BUFF is satisfiable as our construction of P(1) $\Rightarrow$ BUFF shows. But in general specifications S need not be satisfiable. The simplest example of such a specification is S $\equiv$ false.

2) Our strategy of unwinding the original specification BUFF into a recursive implication

$$BUFF \Leftarrow in \rightarrow out \rightarrow BUFF$$

resembles somewhat the induction strategy applied in /MWa/ to derive sequential programs from specifications. But we will soon add a technique of parallel decomposition to our approach.

3) Note that we cannot claim more than a recursive implication

$$BUFF \Leftarrow in \rightarrow out \rightarrow BUFF$$

since the recursive equation

$$BUFF \equiv in \rightarrow out \rightarrow BUFF$$

is wrong. Thus P(1) implies (satisfies) BUFF but is not equal to BUFF. This is because BUFF leaves unspecified the capacity of the buffer. Hence there are infinitely many (semantically different) processes satisfying BUFF.

These processes can be constructed by changing the above top-down design of P(1). For example, to construct a 2-place buffer P(2) we would realize that also

$$(\varepsilon, \{in, out\}) \in [\![BUFF_{in}]\!]$$

holds, and apply the Initial Communication Theorem appropriately. This would finally lead to

$$P(2) =_{df} in \rightarrow \mu \xi . (\; in \rightarrow out \rightarrow \xi \; \Box \; out \rightarrow in \rightarrow \xi) \Rightarrow BUFF \, .$$

Similarly, we can construct n-place buffers P(n) for arbitrary

$n \geq 1$. However, instead of such a direct construction we will present a systematic, hierarchical construction, first of P(n) and later of an infinite buffer $P(\infty)$.

Compactification

As indicated above, the previous specification BUFF is satisfied by (infinitely) many semantically different processes:

$$P(1), P(2), \ldots, P(n), \ldots, P(\infty) \Longrightarrow \text{BUFF} .$$

This is due to the gap between the safety condition

$$\text{out.h} \leq \text{in.h} \tag{2}$$

and the local liveness condition

$$\underline{\text{if}}\ \text{out.h} = \text{in.h}\ \underline{\text{then}}\ \text{in} \in X \tag{3}$$

of BUFF. Whereas condition (2) imposes no bound on the number of inputs which may happen, condition (3) requires readiness for another input only if the buffer is empty. Thus the 1-place buffer P(1) represents minimal readiness and the infinite buffer $P(\infty)$ maximal readiness for input.

The picture changes completely if we now consider the specification BUFF(n) of an (abstract) n-place buffer:

$$\begin{array}{llr} \text{BUFF(n)} =_{df} & \alpha.\text{h} \subseteq \{\text{in, out}\} & (1') \\ & \wedge\ \ \text{out.h} \leq \text{in.h} \leq \text{n+out.h} & (2') \\ & \wedge\ \underline{\text{if}}\ \text{in.h} < \text{n+out.h}\ \underline{\text{then}}\ \text{in} \in X & (3') \\ & \wedge\ \underline{\text{if}}\ \text{out.h} < \text{in.h}\ \ \underline{\text{then}}\ \text{out} \in X & (4') \end{array}$$

By the safety condition (2'), at most n more inputs than outputs are allowed to happen. Moreover, as long as this bound of n is not exhausted, another input is eventually ready to occur due to the local liveness condition (3'). In fact, every communication which is allowed to happen by (1') and (2') is also ready to occur due to (3') and (4'). Thus the safety conditions (1') and (2') completely determine the local liveness conditions (3') and (4'), and hence the semantics of processes P satisfying BUFF(n).

To capture this situation formally, we introduce a special notation. Let $S(h) \in$ Spec contain only h as free variable, and no angle brackets. Then we let

$\langle S(h) \rangle$

denote a new specification in Spec with the following semantics:

$$[\![\langle S(h) \rangle]\!] = \begin{array}{l} \{ h \mid S(h) \} \\ \{ (h,X) \mid S(h) \wedge X = \{ a \mid S(ha) \} \} \end{array}$$

Regard S(h) as describing the safety conditions of a process. Then $\langle S(h) \rangle$ (semantically) adds the maximal ready sets to S(h). More precisely, since S(ha) results from S(h) by substituting ha for h, the ready set $X = \{ a \mid S(ha) \}$ is the set of all communications a which stay within S(h) after the history h has happened.

Example

$$\begin{array}{rl} BUFF(n) \equiv \langle & \alpha.h \subseteq \{in, out\} \\ & \wedge\ out.h \leqslant in.h \leqslant n{+}out.h \rangle \end{array}$$

Since we have reduced the size of BUFF(n), we say that BUFF(n) has been compactified.

All the examples studied in remainder of this paper deal with compactified specifications. This will simplify our presentation considerably.

Parallel Decomposition and Hiding

We now discuss the idea of hierarchical construction of processes based on parallel decomposition and hiding. As example we use the previous specification of an (abstract) n-place buffer:

$$\begin{array}{rl} BUFF(n) \equiv \langle & \alpha.h \subseteq \{in, out\} \\ & \wedge\ out.h \leqslant in.h \leqslant n{+}out.h \rangle \ . \end{array}$$

Note that every n-place buffer is a buffer and that P(1) is a 1-place buffer:

$$\begin{array}{l} BUFF(n) \Longrightarrow BUFF \ , \\ P(1) \Longrightarrow BUFF(1) \ . \end{array}$$

The basic idea of constructing a large (m+n)-place buffer is to link two smaller buffers with m and n places as indicated by the following diagram:

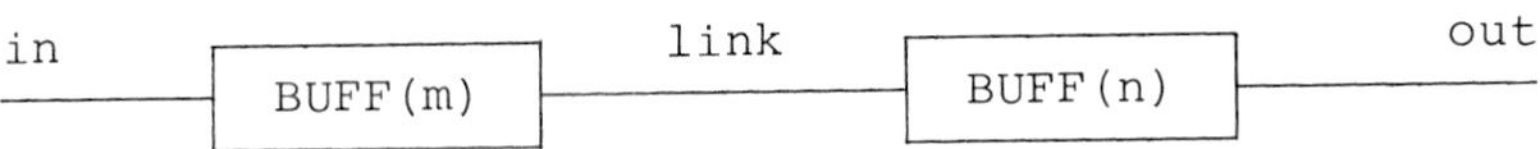

More formally, we construct

$$\text{BUFF(m)[link/out]} \parallel_{\{link\}} \text{BUFF(n)[link/in]} .$$

But does this construction work, does it satisfy the specification BUFF(m+n) ? To answer this question we need theorems about renaming and parallel (de)composition.

Theorem 3.4 (Renaming)

S[Φ] results from S by textually replacing every occurrence of a communication $a \in$ Comm in S by $\Phi(a)$. //

For example, with Φ = [link/out]

$$\text{BUFF(m)[link/out]} \equiv \langle \quad \alpha.h \subseteq \{in, link\} \\ \wedge \ link.h \leqslant in.h \leqslant m+link.h \rangle$$

and analogously

$$\text{BUFF(n)[link/in]} \equiv \langle \quad \alpha.h \subseteq \{link, out\} \\ \wedge \ out.h \leqslant link.h \leqslant n+out.h \rangle .$$

To formulate the theorem about parallel decomposition we need more information about the specific structure of the specifications. We say a specification S is in compact normal form if

$$S \equiv \langle \ \alpha.h \subseteq A_S \wedge safe_S(h) \ \rangle$$

where A_S is a set of communications, the alphabet of S, and $safe_S(h)$ is a condition with h as its only free variable such that for all histories h_1 and h_2

(+) $\qquad h_1 \upharpoonright A_S = h_2 \upharpoonright A_S$ implies $safe_S(h_1) = safe_S(h_2)$.

Here $h_i \upharpoonright A_S$ denotes the history h_i restricted to the communications in A_S. Informally (+) says that $safe_S(h)$ can access the history h only through the alphabet A_S. Note that (+) is formulated as a semantic criterion. The following proposition provides a sufficient (but not necessary) syntactic criterion for (+).

Proposition 3.5 A specification $S \equiv \langle \ \alpha.h \subseteq A_S \wedge safe_S(h) \ \rangle$ is in compact normal form if $safe_S(h)$ references the variable h only via

- counters $a.h$ with $a \in A_S$ or
- channel histories ch.h with $ch!\mathcal{M} \subseteq A_S$. //

By this proposition, BUFF(n) is in compact normal form. Note that specifications in compact normal form are completely determined by their components A_S and $safe_S(h)$. This fact is utilized in the following theorem:

Theorem 3.6 (Parallel Decomposition)

Let S,T,U be specifications in compact normal form such that

$$A_S = A_T \cup A_U ,$$
$$safe_S(h) \equiv safe_T(h) \wedge safe_U(h) .$$

Then S can be decomposed in T and U as follows:

$$S \Leftarrow T \parallel_{A_T \cap A_U} U .$$

//

The point of this theorem is that we can (essentially) use the logical operator $\wedge$ to reason syntactically about the parallel operator $\parallel_{A_T \cap A_U}$ which enforces synchronization for all communications common to A_T and A_U. Syntactic reasoning about the general operator $\parallel_A$ is not so simple. We remark that even under the assumptions of Theorem 3.6 we cannot prove more than implication; the semantic equation $S \equiv T \parallel_{A_T \cap A_U} U$ is false in general.

It is interesting to remark that the formulation of Theorem 3.6 somewhat resembles an approach to the decomposition of relational data base queries described in /WY/.

We apply Theorem 3.6 to our specific problem of n-place buffers. Let

$$\begin{aligned} B \equiv_{df} \langle\ & \alpha.h \subseteq \{in, link, out\} \\ & \wedge\ link.h \leqslant in.h \leqslant m{+}link.h \\ & \wedge\ out.h \leqslant link.h \leqslant n{+}out.h \ \rangle . \end{aligned}$$

Then

$$B \Leftarrow BUFF(m)[link/out] \parallel_{\{link\}} BUFF(n)[link/in] .$$

Unfortunately, B looks quite different from the specification BUFF(m+n) we wished to satisfy by linking BUFF(m) and BUFF(n). The problem with B is that we can observe the communication "link" which is not mentioned in BUFF(m+n). We say that B has a different <u>grain of atomicity</u> in its communications than BUFF(m+n). To overcome this difference we will hide the communication "link" by applying the hiding operator \ link to B. But this requires an additional theorem.

<u>Theorem 3.7 (Hiding)</u>

Let S,T be specifications in compact normal form such that

(1) $A_S = A_T - \{b\}$

(2) $safe_T(h) \Longrightarrow safe_S(h)$

(3) $\neg \exists h \in A_T^* \; \forall n \geq 0 \colon \; safe_T(h \cdot b^n)$

(4) $safe_S(h) \Longrightarrow (\exists h' \colon \; h = h' \setminus b \wedge safe_T(h'))$

(5) $(h_1 \setminus b = h_2 \setminus b \wedge b \notin X_T(h_1) \wedge b \notin X_T(h_2)) \Longrightarrow$

$X_T(h_1) = X_T(h_2)$.

Then

$$S \Leftarrow T \setminus b$$

holds. //

Conditions (1) and (2) are easy to understand. Conditions (3) - (5) are more subtle. They guarantee that independently of all, now hidden communications b, the specification T will always realize the requirements of S. This in particular requires in (3) that no infinite sequence of hidden b's is possible in T. In (5) we use the abbreviation

$$X_T(h) = \{ a \mid safe_T(ha) \} .$$

This is the maximal ready set after h generated by (the semantics of)

$$T \equiv \langle \alpha . h \subseteq A_T \wedge safe_T(h) \rangle \; .$$

Applying the Hiding Theorem to B we see that

$$BUFF(m+n) \Leftarrow B \setminus link$$

and hence by the Substitution Theorem

(*)

$$\begin{array}{c} BUFF(m+n) \\ \Uparrow \\ (BUFF(m)[link/out] \;\|_{\{link\}}\; BUFF(n)[link/in]) \setminus link \; . \end{array}$$

This solution to BUFF(m+n) is depicted in the following diagram:

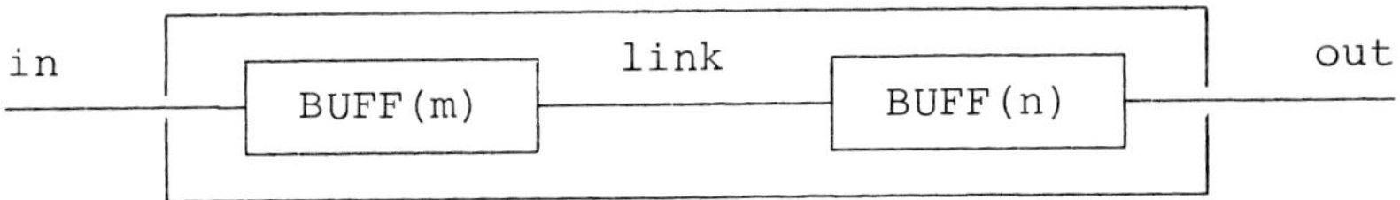

The box indicates a <u>hierarchical construction</u> where first BUFF(m) and BUFF(n) are linked and then the link is internalized or hidden so that no other process can interact with this link from outside. Let us abbreviate this construction by a special linking operator $\gg$ /BHR/:

$$P \gg Q =_{df} (P[\text{link/out}] \parallel_{\{\text{link}\}} Q[\text{link/in}]) \setminus \text{link}$$

for arbitrary mixed terms P and Q.

Using the recursive implication (*) above it is now easy to construct an arbitrary n-place buffer P(n) hierarchically from the 1-place buffer P(1) developed earlier. Indeed, with

$$P(n) \equiv_{df} \underbrace{P(1) \gg (P(1) \gg \ \ldots \ P(1))}_{\text{n times}}$$

we obtain

$$P(n) \Longrightarrow \text{BUFF}(n) \ .$$

So far all our processes P constructed from specifications S are simple in that their observable operational behaviour can be described by <u>finite state transition diagrams</u>. For example, P(1) and P(n) have the following diagrams:

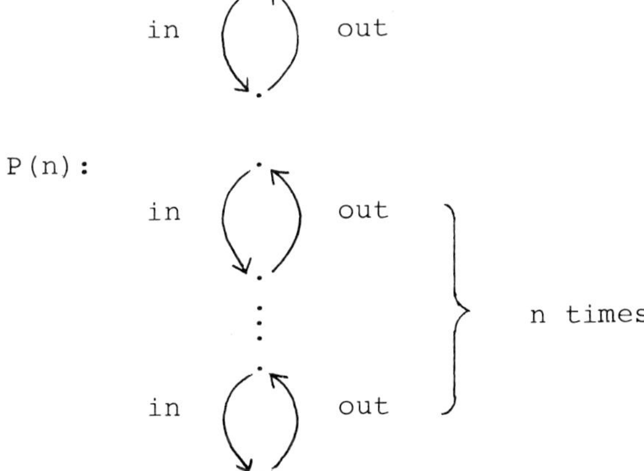

It is interesting to remark that the work on automatic program synthesis from temporal logic specifications by /EC, MWo/ explicitly aims at solutions corresponding to finite state transition diagrams. These solutions are called synchronization skeletons in /EC/. The next example will show that we can do more.

Infinite State Solutions

We now consider a specification which has no finite state solution, an (abstract) infinite buffer:

$$\begin{aligned} \mathrm{BUFF}(\infty) \equiv_{df}\ & \alpha.h \subseteq \{in, out\} && (1)\\ \wedge\ & out.h \leqslant in.h && (2)\\ \wedge\ & in \in X && (3)\\ \wedge\ & \underline{if}\ out.h < in.h\ \underline{then}\ out \in X && (4) \end{aligned}$$

This specification is like BUFF except for line (3) where we now require that an additional input is always possible. BUFF(∞ can be compactified:

$$\mathrm{BUFF}(\infty) \equiv_{df} \left\langle \begin{array}{l} \alpha.h \subseteq \{in, out\} \\ \wedge\ out.h \leqslant in.h \end{array} \right\rangle .$$

Of course

$$\mathrm{BUFF}(\infty) \Longrightarrow \mathrm{BUFF}$$

holds.

Our aim is to construct a process P(∞) with P(∞) $\Longrightarrow$ BUFF(∞). The first step in this construction consists of an application of the Initial Communication Theorem. Similarly to BUFF we get

$$\begin{array}{c} \mathrm{BUFF}(\infty) \\ \Uparrow \\ in \rightarrow \mathrm{BUFF}(\infty)_{in} \end{array}$$

where

$$\mathrm{BUFF}(\infty)_{in} \equiv_{df} \mathrm{BUFF}(\infty)[in.h/h] = \left\langle \begin{array}{l} \alpha.h \subseteq \{in, out\} \\ \wedge\ out.h \leqslant 1 + in.h \end{array} \right\rangle .$$

Note that BUFF(∞)$_{in}$ can behave like BUFF(∞), i.e.

$$\mathrm{BUFF}(\infty) \Longrightarrow \mathrm{BUFF}(\infty)_{in} ,$$

but additionally it can engage in one more output. Following an idea of /BHR/, we will present a solution to $BUFF(\infty)_{in}$ where this additional output operationally happens _before_ all the outputs of $BUFF(\infty)$. Strictly speaking, this degree of sophistication is not needed in the case of our abstract infinite buffer where we cannot observe the message structure of inputs or outputs. But it will enable us to treat the case of a "real" buffer where messages are observable as an immediate generalization.

Formally, the idea is to show

$$\begin{array}{c} BUFF(\infty)_{in} \\ \Uparrow \\ BUFF(\infty) \gg out \rightarrow P(1) \end{array}$$

where $\gg$ is the linking operator and P(1) is the 1-place buffer constructed earlier. Let

$$\begin{aligned} B(1) &\equiv_{df} BUFF(1)[out, in / in, out] \\ &\equiv \langle \quad \alpha.h \subseteq \{out, in\} \\ &\qquad \wedge in.h \leqslant out.h \leqslant 1+in.h \rangle \ . \end{aligned}$$

Similarly to $P(1) \Longrightarrow BUFF$ we can show

$$out \rightarrow P(1) \Longrightarrow B(1) \ .$$

Applying the theorems for Parallel Decomposition, Renaming and Substitution, we obtain

$$\begin{array}{c} \langle \quad \alpha.h \subset \{in, link, out\} \\ \wedge link.h \leqslant in.h \wedge link.h \leqslant out.h \leqslant 1+link.k \rangle \\ \Uparrow \\ BUFF(\infty)[link/out] \parallel_{\{link\}} (out \rightarrow P(1))[link/in]) \ . \end{array}$$

Next, the theorems for Hiding and Substitution yield

$$\begin{array}{c} BUFF(\infty)_{in} \\ \Uparrow \\ (BUFF(\infty)[link/out] \parallel_{\{link\}} (out \rightarrow P(1))[link/in]) \setminus link \ . \end{array}$$

Now we have derived a recursive implication from $BUFF(\infty)$; the Guarded Recursion Theorem finally yields:

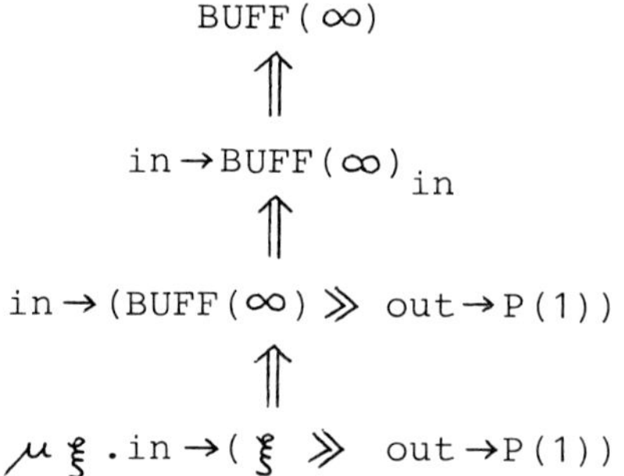

The last line is the desired process $P(\infty)$ with $P(\infty) \Rightarrow BUFF(\infty)$. Its infinite state transition diagram is:

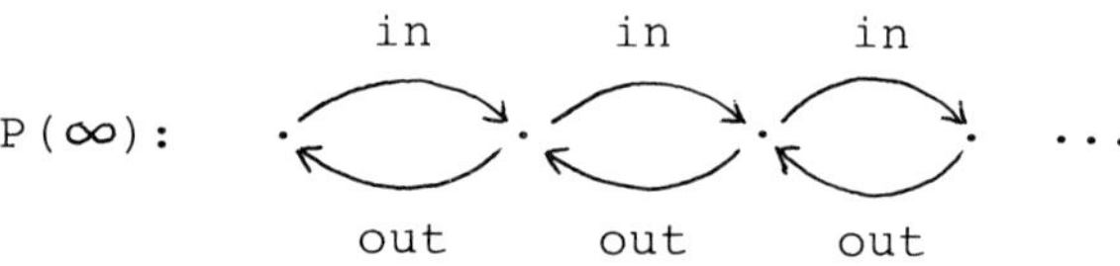

Remarks

Our hierarchical constructions of P(n) and $P(\infty)$ were not in the same way "mechanical" as the construction of P(1) which simply consisted of unwinding the specification BUFF into a recursive implication. This indicates that in general specification-oriented programming will be "intuition-guided" in the sense of /Bau/ rather than fully automatic. Of course, it is a very interesting task to discover classes of problems which can be solved automatically as in /EC, MWo/.

Finally, we briefly discuss three specifications which are closely related to the abstract infinite buffer $BUFF(\infty)$. They will be important in Section 4.

Real Infinite Buffer

By a real buffer we mean a buffer where "in" and "out" are not only abstract atomic communications but channels along which one can observe the passage of messages. For a given finite message set $\mathcal{M}$ we specify a real infinite buffer by:

$$\begin{aligned}
\mathcal{M}_BUFF(\infty) \equiv_{df} \quad & \alpha.h \subseteq in!\mathcal{M} \cup out!\mathcal{M} && (1)\\
\wedge\ & out.h \leqslant in.h && (2)\\
\wedge\ & in!\mathcal{M} \subseteq X && (3)\\
\wedge\ & \underline{if}\ out.h < in.h \\
& \quad \underline{then}\ out!\underline{first}.(in.h - out.h) \in X && (4)
\end{aligned}$$

Recall that since we have a channel structure here, out.h and in.h denote the sequences of messages sent along channel out and in. $\mathcal{M}$_BUFF(∞) is a straightforward extension of the abstract version BUFF(∞), only the explicit specification of the FIFO discipline in lines (2) and (4) is new. Again $\mathcal{M}$_BUFF(∞) can be compactified:

$$\mathcal{M}\_BUFF(\infty) \equiv \langle \;\; \alpha.h \subseteq in!\mathcal{M} \cup out!\mathcal{M} \;\; \wedge \;\; out.h \leqslant in.h \;\; \rangle .$$

The construction of a process $\mathcal{M}$_P(∞) satisfying $\mathcal{M}$_BUFF(∞) follows the pattern used for P(∞) in the previous subsection. In fact, with the process

$$\mathcal{M}\_P(\infty) \equiv_{df} \mu\xi.in?x \rightarrow (\xi \gg out!x \rightarrow \mathcal{M}\_P(1))$$

we obtain

$$\mathcal{M}\_P(\infty) \Longrightarrow \mathcal{M}\_BUFF(\infty) \; .$$

Here in?x→Q(x) abbreviates $\underset{m \in \mathcal{M}}{\Box}$ in!m→Q(m) as explained in Section 2. Further on, $\mathcal{M}$_P(1) is the real 1-place buffer

$$\mathcal{M}\_P(1) \;\; \equiv \;\; \mu\xi.in?x \rightarrow out!x \rightarrow \xi \;\; ,$$

and the linking operator $\gg$ is defined as before, i.e. by

$$P \gg Q = (P[link/out] \;\|_{\{link\}}\; Q[link/in]) \setminus link \; ,$$

though "in", "link" and "out" are treated now as channels (cf. Section 2).

Counter

Close to BUFF(∞) is the specification of a counter. Informally, a counter holds a value $\geqslant 0$ and allows three operations to be performed: the operation "zero" tests whether the current value is 0, the operations "up" adds 1 to the current value, and the operation "down" subtracts 1 from the current value provided it is > 0 /BHR/. Formally, we specify:

$$\begin{aligned} COUNT =_{df} \langle \;\; & \alpha.h \subseteq \{zero, up, down\} \\ & \wedge \; down.h \leqslant up.h \\ & \wedge \; \underline{if} \; \underline{last}.h = zero \; \underline{then} \; down.h = up.h \;\rangle . \end{aligned}$$

Thus, except for the communication "zero", COUNT corresponds to BUFF(∞), with "up" and "down" corresponding to "in" and "out".

To construct a counter, we first apply the Initial Communication Theorem:

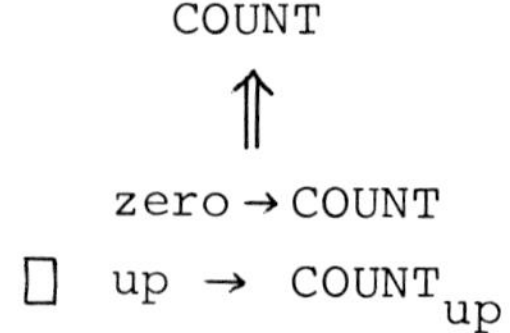

$$\begin{array}{c} \text{COUNT} \\ \Uparrow \\ \text{zero} \rightarrow \text{COUNT} \\ \Box\ \text{up} \rightarrow \text{COUNT}_{\text{up}} \end{array}$$

where $\text{COUNT}_{\text{up}} =_{\text{df}} \text{COUNT}[\text{up}\cdot\text{h/h}]$. Again COUNT_{up} is very close to $\text{BUFF}(\infty)_{\text{in}}$. However,

$$(\text{COUNT}[\text{link/down}] \parallel_{\{\text{link}\}} (\text{down} \rightarrow \text{P}(1)[\text{link,down/in,out}]) \setminus \text{link}$$

does not satisfy COUNT_{up} here since the additional communication "zero" in COUNT[link/down] is not treated properly. This deficiency can be solved by changing

$$\text{P}(1)[\text{link,down/in,out}] \equiv \mu\xi.\text{link} \rightarrow \text{down} \rightarrow \xi$$

into the process

$$\begin{array}{ll} \text{M} \equiv_{\text{df}} \mu\xi. & \text{zero} \rightarrow \xi \\ & \Box\ \text{link} \rightarrow \text{down} \rightarrow \xi \end{array}$$

and by changing the operator $\parallel_{\{\text{link}\}}$ into $\parallel_{\{\text{zero,link}\}}$. Then, using the theorems for Parallel Decomposition, Renaming, Hiding and Substitution, we can show:

$$\begin{array}{c} \text{COUNT}_{\text{up}} \\ \Uparrow \\ (\text{COUNT}[\text{link/down}] \parallel_{\{\text{zero,link}\}} \text{down} \rightarrow \text{M}) \setminus \text{link}\ . \end{array}$$

Now we have derived a recursive implication from COUNT. Finally, the Guarded Recursion Theorem yields:

$$\begin{array}{c} \text{COUNT} \\ \Uparrow \\ \begin{array}{ll} \mu\xi. & \text{zero} \rightarrow \xi \\ & \Box\ \text{up} \rightarrow (\xi[\text{link/down}] \parallel_{\{\text{zero,link}\}} \text{down} \rightarrow \text{M}) \setminus \text{link}\ . \end{array} \end{array}$$

Mutual Exclusion

Consider the following specification of a process for mutual exclusion:

$$\text{MUTEX} =_{df} \langle \quad \alpha.h \subseteq \{\text{free, wait, signal}\}$$
$$\wedge\ \text{signal.h} \leq \text{wait.h} \leq 1+\text{signal.h}$$
$$\wedge\ \underline{\text{if}}\ \underline{\text{last}}.\text{h} = \text{free}\ \underline{\text{then}}\ \text{signal.h} = \text{wait.h} \rangle .$$

Then

$$\text{M[free,wait,signal / zero,link,down]} \Longrightarrow \text{MUTEX}$$

holds.

4. Access Control: An Extended Application

The general structure of the problem is as follows: ρ readers $R_1,\ldots,R_\rho$ and ω writers $W_1,\ldots,W_\omega$ use a shared data structure with reading and writing access, respectively.

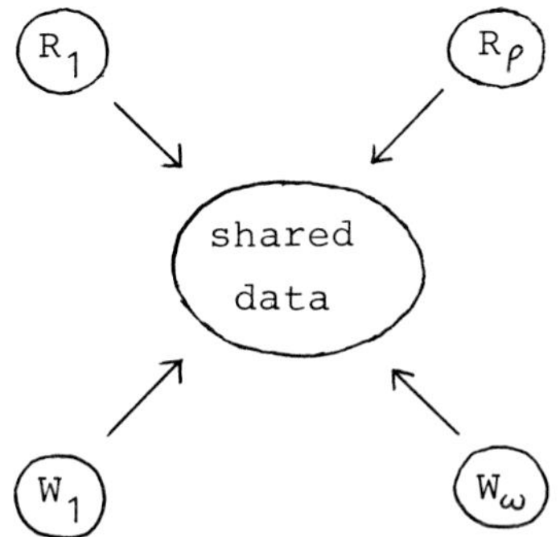

We wish to enforce certain user disciplines among the R_i and W_j. In /RV/ a general approach to this problem is outlined, consisting of two steps:

Step 1 Introduction of FIFO disciplines for readers and writers separately.

Step 2 Introduction of scheduling disciplines which define when the first reader or writer in the FIFO queue is allowed to access the shared data structure.

Robert and Verjus discuss Step 2 in some detail /RV/. We will present both steps within the rigorous framework of specification-oriented programming using the basic knowledge of the previous Section 3. We start with a preliminary Step 0 modelling the general structure of the problem.

Step 0

Readers and writers are special instances of a general concept of a user. As far as our synchronization problem is concerned, a user engages in the following three communications:

$$\left.\begin{array}{ll} r & \text{request} \\ a & \text{access} \\ t & \text{terminate} \end{array}\right\} \text{ the use of the shared data structure}$$

Whenever a user wants to access the shared data, it engages in the communications r, a and t in that order. All other activities of a user can be considered as unobservable. Thus we specify:

$$\begin{array}{llr} USER \equiv_{df} \langle & \alpha.h \subseteq \{r, a, t\} & (1) \\ & \wedge\ (r \geqslant a \geqslant t \wedge r \leqslant 1{+}t)\ \underline{in}\ h \rangle & (2) \end{array}$$

Recall that the notation "<u>in</u> h" in line (2) is used to abbreviate

$$r.h \geqslant a.h \geqslant t.h \wedge r.h \leqslant 1{+}t.h \qquad (2')$$

(cf. Section 2). The second conjunct of (2) resp. (2') says that a user can have at most one outstanding request.

To obtain the individual readers R_i and writers W_j we specialize the general pattern of a user by the following channel structure

rR!i, aR!i, tR!i,

rW!j, aW!j, tW!j

for the general communications r, a, t:

$$R_i \equiv_{df} USER[rR!i, aR!i, tR!i \ / \ r,a,t] \ ,$$

$$W_j \equiv_{df} USER[rW!j, aW!j, tW!j \ / \ r,a,t]$$

for $i=1,\ldots,\rho$ and $j=1,\ldots,\omega$.

The simplest way of grouping the readers into a system $READ_\rho$ is to run them all in parallel:

$$READ_\rho \equiv_{df} R_1 \parallel_\emptyset \cdots \parallel_\emptyset R_\rho \ .$$

Similarly for writers:

$$WRITE_\omega \equiv_{df} W_1 \parallel_\emptyset \cdots \parallel_\emptyset W_\omega \ .$$

By the Parallel Decomposition Theorem

$$\mathrm{READ}_\rho \Rightarrow \langle \quad \alpha.h \subseteq \{rR!i,\ aR!i,\ tR!i \mid i=1,\dots,\rho\} \wedge \bigwedge_i (rR!i \geq aR!i \geq tR!i \wedge rR!i \leq 1+tR!i)\ \underline{in}\ h \rangle$$

and analogously for WRITE_ω .

Step 1

We now specify separate FIFO disciplines for readers and writers. For readers we require:

$$\mathrm{Q\_READ}_\rho \equiv_{df} \langle \quad \alpha.h \subseteq \{rR!i,\ aR!i,\ tR!i \mid i=1,\dots,\rho\} \wedge \bigwedge_i (rR!i \geq aR!i \geq tR!i \wedge rR!i \leq 1+tR!i)\ \underline{in}\ h \wedge \quad rR.h \geq aR.h \quad \rangle$$

We can decompose $\mathrm{Q\_READ}_\rho$ as follows:

$$\mathrm{Q\_READ}_\rho \Leftarrow \mathrm{READ}_\rho \ \|_{\{rR!i,aR!i \mid i=1,\dots,\rho\}}\ \mathrm{QUEUE}_\rho$$

where

$$\mathrm{QUEUE}_\rho \equiv_{df} \langle \quad \alpha.h \subseteq \{rR!i,\ aR!i \mid i=1,\dots,\rho\} \wedge rR.h \geq aR.h \quad \rangle$$

Fortunately, we know QUEUE_ρ already:

$$\mathrm{QUEUE}_\rho \equiv \mathcal{M}\_\mathrm{BUFF}(\infty)[rR,aR \ / \ in,out]$$

with $\mathcal{M} = \{1,\dots,\rho\}$.

Analogously we define and deal with $\mathrm{Q\_WRITE}_\omega$. The combined readers-writers system with separate FIFO disciplines is now

$$\mathrm{Q\_RW}_{\rho\omega} \equiv_{df} \mathrm{Q\_READ}_\rho \ \|_\emptyset\ \mathrm{Q\_WRITE}_\omega \ .$$

Step 2 : Version 1

Here we specify the first of our scheduling disciplines. Informally, this discipline allows the first reader in the FIFO reader queue to access the shared data if no writer is active, and the first writer in the FIFO writer queue to access the shared data if no reader or writer is active. Thus arbitrarily many readers may access the shared data at a time, but only one writer.

Formally, we express the number of active readers and writers as follows:

$$active(R) = (\sum_i aR!i) - (\sum_i tR!i) ,$$

$$active(W) = (\sum_j aW!j) - (\sum_j tW!j) .$$

This leads to the following overall specification:

$$S1_{\rho\omega} \equiv_{df}$$

$$\begin{aligned}
\langle \quad & \alpha.h \subseteq \{rR!i,\ aR!i,\ tR!i \mid i=1,\dots,\rho\} \\
& \qquad \cup \{rW!j,\ aW!j,\ tW!j \mid j=1,\dots,\omega\} \\
\wedge\ \bigwedge_i\ & (rR!i \geqslant aR!i \geqslant tR!i \wedge rR!i \leqslant 1+tR!i)\ \underline{in}\ h \\
\wedge\ \bigwedge_j\ & (rW!j \geqslant aW!j \geqslant tW!j \wedge rW!j \leqslant 1+tW!j)\ \underline{in}\ h \\
\wedge\ & rR.h \geqslant aR.h \\
\wedge\ & rW.h \geqslant aW.h \\
\wedge\ & active(W) \leqslant 1 \\
\wedge\ \bigwedge_i\ & \underline{if}\ \underline{last}.h = aR!i\ \underline{then}\ active(W) = 0\ \underline{in}\ h \\
\wedge\ \bigwedge_j\ & \underline{if}\ \underline{last}.h = aW!j\ \underline{then}\ active(R) = 0\ \underline{in}\ h \quad \rangle
\end{aligned}$$

Using the previous readers-writers system $Q\_RW_{\rho\omega}$ we can decompose $S1_{\rho\omega}$ into

$$S1_{\rho\omega} \Leftarrow Q\_RW_{\rho\omega} \parallel_A SCH1_{\rho\omega}$$

where

$$A = \{aR!i,\ tR!i \mid i=1,\dots,\rho\} \cup \{aW!j,\ tW!j \mid j=1,\dots,\omega\}$$

and where

$$\begin{aligned}
SCH1_{\rho\omega} \equiv_{df}\ \langle\ & \alpha.h \subseteq A \\
\wedge\ & (active(R) \geqslant 0 \wedge 1 \geqslant active(W) \geqslant 0)\ \underline{in}\ h \\
\wedge\ \bigwedge_i\ & \underline{if}\ \underline{last}.h = aR!i\ \underline{then}\ active(W) = 0\ \underline{in}\ h \\
\wedge\ \bigwedge_j\ & \underline{if}\ \underline{last}.h = aW!j\ \underline{then}\ active(R) = 0\ \underline{in}\ h\ \rangle
\end{aligned}$$

specifies the scheduler to be constructed next.

This construction of $SCH1_{\rho\omega}$ is simplified somewhat by first using the <u>inverse image</u> operator. More specifically, let

$$\Phi_{\rho\omega} : \text{Comm} \rightarrow \text{Comm}$$

be the identity function on communications, except for

$$\Phi_{\rho\omega}(aR!i) = aR ,$$
$$\Phi_{\rho\omega}(tR!i) = tR ,$$
$$\Phi_{\rho\omega}(aW!j) = aW ,$$
$$\Phi_{\rho\omega}(tW!j) = tW$$

for $i=1,\dots,\rho$ and $j=1,\dots,\omega$ where

aR, tR, aW, tW

are new communications. Now let

$$\begin{aligned} SCH1 \equiv_{df} \langle\ & \alpha.h \subset \{aR,\ tR,\ aW,\ tW\} \\ & \wedge (activeR \geqslant 0 \wedge 1 \geqslant activeW \geqslant 0) \ \underline{in}\ h \\ & \wedge \underline{if}\ \underline{last}.h = aR\ \underline{then}\ activeW = 0\ \underline{in}\ h \\ & \wedge \underline{if}\ \underline{last}.h = aW\ \underline{then}\ activeR = 0\ \underline{in}\ h\ \rangle \end{aligned}$$

where

$$activeR = aR - tR \quad \text{and} \quad activeW = aW - tW .$$

Then

$$SCH1_{\rho\omega} \equiv \Phi_{\rho\omega}^{-1}\ (SCH1)$$

by the definition of the inverse image operator. Note that SCH1 works uniformly for all ρ and ω. Intuitively, the use of $\Phi_{\rho\omega}^{-1}$ means that in order to construct $SCH1_{\rho\omega}$, the actual names of the readers and writers trying to access the shared data are not needed.

SCH1 can be decomposed further. Let

$$\begin{aligned} A\_READ \equiv_{df} \langle\ & \alpha.h \subseteq \{aR,\ tR,\ aW\} \\ & \wedge\ activeR \geqslant 0\ \underline{in}\ h \\ & \wedge\ \underline{if}\ \underline{last}.h = aW\ \underline{then}\ activeR = 0\ \underline{in}\ h\ \rangle \end{aligned}$$

and

$$A\_WRITE \equiv_{df} \langle\ \alpha.h \subseteq \{aW,\ tW,\ aR\}$$
$$\wedge\ 1 \geq activeW \geq 0\ \underline{in}\ h$$
$$\wedge\ \underline{if}\ \underline{last}.h = aR\ \underline{then}\ activeW = 0\ \underline{in}\ h\ \rangle .$$

Then

$$SCH1 \Leftarrow A\_READ \parallel_{\{aR,aW\}} A\_WRITE .$$

Here A_READ specifies the constraints of the readers' access to the shared data and A_WRITE the ones of the writers' access. Looking more closely at A_READ and A_WRITE, we discover two well-known processes of Section 3:

$$A\_READ \equiv COUNT[aR,\ tR,\ aW\ /\ up,\ down,\ zero]\ ,$$

$$A\_WRITE \equiv MUTEX[aW,\ tW,\ aR\ /\ wait,\ signal,\ free]\ .$$

Clearly, COUNT reflects the idea that arbitrarily many readers can access the shared data, and MUTEX the idea that only one writer may do so at a time. Note, however, how the extra communications "zero" of COUNT and "free" of MUTEX are utilized to express the mutual dependencies of the access rights for readers and writers.

Summarizing, the whole system $S1_{\rho\omega}$ was constructed systematically from processes USER, $\mathcal{M}$_BUFF(∞), COUNT and MUTEX as basic components. The structures set up in the three steps were as follows:

(0) R_i = USER[...] , W_j = USER[...]

(1) $Q\_RW_{\rho\omega} \Leftarrow ((R_1 \parallel_{\emptyset} \cdots \parallel_{\emptyset} R_{\rho}) \parallel_{\{\ldots\}} \mathcal{M}\_BUFF(\infty)[\ldots])$
$\parallel_{\emptyset} ((W_1 \parallel_{\emptyset} \cdots \parallel_{\emptyset} W_{\omega}) \parallel_{\{\ldots\}} \mathcal{M}\_BUFF(\infty)[\ldots])$

(2) $S1_{\rho\omega} \Leftarrow Q\_RW_{\rho\omega} \parallel_{\{\ldots\}} \Phi_{\rho\omega}^{-1}(SCH1)$

$SCH1 \Leftarrow COUNT[\ldots] \parallel_{\{\ldots\}} MUTEX[\ldots]$

Operationally, the scheduler SCH1 can be described by the following infinite state transition diagram:

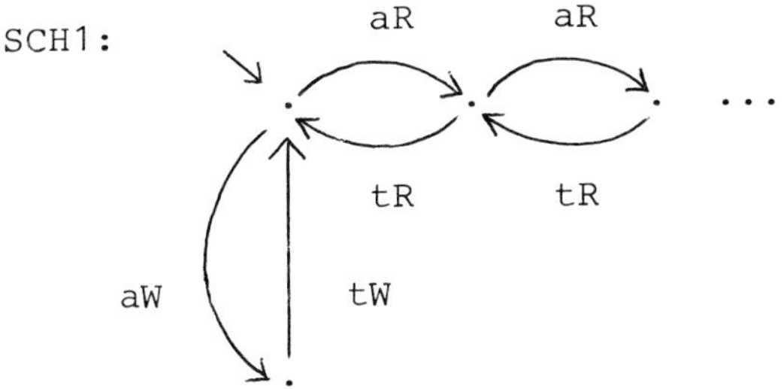

Step 2 : Version 2

Next, we refine the specification of the readers-writers system S1 $\rho\omega$ to a system S2 $\rho\omega$ where in case of waiting readers and writers priority is given to the readers. The general approach to specification and development of S2 $\rho\omega$ is analogous to S1 $\rho\omega$ except that the corresponding scheduler is now described by:

$$\begin{aligned} SCH2 \equiv_{df} \langle\ & \alpha.h \subseteq \{rR,\ aR,\ tR,\ aW,\ tW\} \\ & \wedge\ (requestR \geqslant 0\ \wedge\ activeR \geqslant 0\ \wedge\ 1 \geqslant activeW \geqslant 0)\ \underline{in}\ h \\ & \wedge\ \underline{if}\ \underline{last}.h = aR\ \underline{then}\ activeW = 0\ \underline{in}\ h \\ & \wedge\ \underline{if}\ \underline{last}.h = aW\ \underline{then}\ requestR = 0 \wedge activeR = 0\ \underline{in}\ h\ \rangle \end{aligned}$$

where activeR and activeW are as before, and where

$$requestR = rR - aR\ .$$

Again we can decompose SCH2:

$$SCH2 \Leftarrow R\_READ\ \|_{\{aR,aW\}}\ SCH1$$

where

$$\begin{aligned} R\_READ \equiv_{df} \langle\ & \alpha.h \subseteq \{rR,\ aR,\ aW\} \\ & \wedge\ requestR \geqslant 0\ \underline{in}\ h \\ & \wedge\ \underline{if}\ \underline{last}.h = aW\ \underline{then}\ requestR = 0\ \underline{in}\ h\ \rangle\ . \end{aligned}$$

Now it is obvious that

$$R\_READ \equiv COUNT[rR,\ aR,\ aW\ /\ up,\ down,\ zero]\ .$$

Thus the structure of SCH2 is

$$SCH2 \Leftarrow COUNT[...]\ \|_{\{...\}} (COUNT[...]\ \|_{\{...\}} MUTEX[...])\ .$$

Operationally, SCH2 is more complex than SCH1 as the following infinite state transition diagram shows:

SCH2:

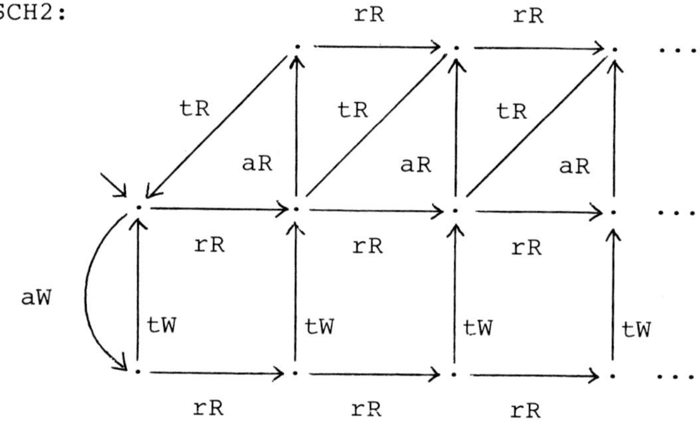

Step 2 : Version 3

Alternatively, we may wish to realize a readers-writers system $S3_{p\omega}$ where in case of waiting readers and writers priority is given to the writers. The corresponding scheduler SCH3 is specified by:

$$\text{SCH3} \equiv_{df} \langle\ \alpha.h \subseteq \{\text{aR}, \text{tR}, \text{rW}, \text{aW}, \text{tW}\}$$
$$\wedge\ (\text{activeR} \geqslant 0 \wedge \text{requestW} \geqslant 0 \wedge 1 \geqslant \text{activeW} \geqslant 0)\ \underline{\text{in}}\ h$$
$$\wedge\ \underline{\text{if}}\ \underline{\text{last}}.h = \text{aR}\ \underline{\text{then}}\ \text{requestW} = 0 \wedge \text{activeW} = 0\ \underline{\text{in}}\ h$$
$$\wedge\ \underline{\text{if}}\ \underline{\text{last}}.h = \text{aW}\ \underline{\text{then}}\ \text{activeR} = 0\ \underline{\text{in}}\ h\ \rangle$$

where

$$\text{requestW} = \text{rW} - \text{aW}\ .$$

SCH3 can be decomposed into

$$\text{SCH3} \Leftarrow \text{R\_WRITE}\ \|_{\{\text{aR},\text{aW}\}}\ \text{SCH1}$$

where

$$\text{R\_WRITE} \equiv_{df} \text{R\_READ}[\text{rW}, \text{aW}, \text{aR} / \text{rR}, \text{aR}, \text{aW}]\ .$$

Thus

$$\text{R\_WRITE} \equiv \text{COUNT}[\text{rW}, \text{aW}, \text{aR} / \text{up}, \text{down}, \text{zero}]\ .$$

The structure of SCH3 is again

$$\text{SCH3} \Leftarrow \text{COUNT}[\ldots]\ \|_{\{\ldots\}}\ (\text{COUNT}[\ldots]\ \|_{\{\ldots\}}\ \text{MUTEX}[\ldots])\ .$$

But the infinite state transition diagram for SCH3 differs considerably from that of SCH2.

SCH3:

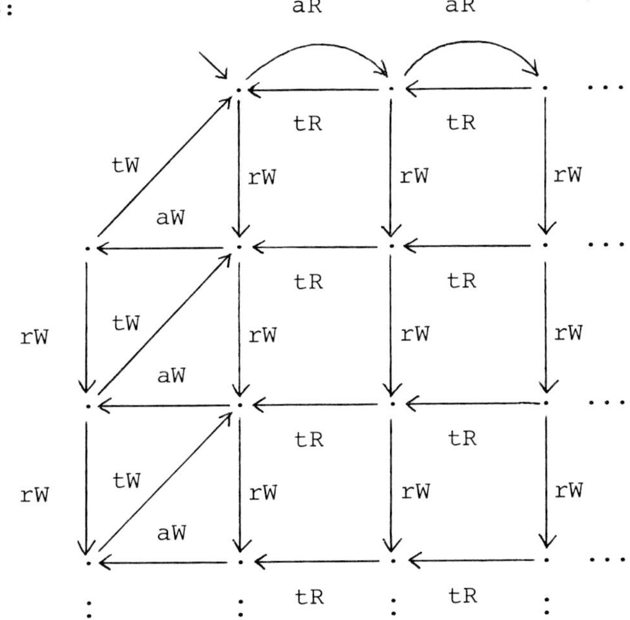

Remarks

Comparing the state transition diagrams for SCH1, SCH2 and SCH3, we realize an increasing degree of complexity. It is very interesting that these differences are not that visible at the level of specification. There, decomposing SCH2 or SCH3 just requires one step more than decomposing SCH1. In particular, dealing with SCH3 is not more difficult than dealing with SCH2.

Acknowledgements

The author is indepted to Tony Hoare for introducing him to the exciting world of concurrency, and to Ludwik Czaja for drawing his attention to the article of /RV/.

References

/Bac/ R.J.R. Back, Correctness preserving program refinements: proof theory and applications, Mathematical Centre Tracts 131 (Mathematical Centre, Amsterdam, 1980).

/Bau/ F.L. Bauer et al., The Munich project CIP, volume I: the wide spectrum language 84, Tech. Rep., Institut für Informatik, Tech. Univ. München, December 1983.

/BKT/ J.A. Bergstra, J.W. Klop, J.V. Tucker, Algebraic tools for system construction, in: E.M. Clarke, D. Kozen (Eds.), Logics of Programs, Lecture Notes in Computer Science 164 (Springer, Berlin, 1984).

/BHR/ S.D. Brookes, C.A.R. Hoare, A.W. Roscoe, A theory of communicating sequential processes, J. ACM 31 (1984) 560-599.

/BD/ R.M. Burstall, J. Darlington, A transformation system for developing recursive programs, J. ACM 24 (1977) 44-67.

/EC/ E.A. Emerson, E.M. Clarke, Using branching time temporal logic to synthesize synchronization skeletons, Science of Computer Programming 2 (1982, publ. 1983) 241-266.

/He/ E.C.R. Hehner, Predicative programming, part I and II, Comm. ACM 27 (1984) 134-151.

/Ho1/ C.A.R. Hoare, A calculus of total correctness for communicating processes, Science of Computer Programming 1 (1981) 49-72.

/Ho2/ C.A.R. Hoare, Specifications, programs and implementations, Tech. Monograph PRG-29, Oxford Univ. Progr. Research Group, 1982.

/KS/ R.B. Kieburtz, J. Schultis, Transformations of FP programs, in: Proc. ACM Conf. on Functional Progr. Languages and Comp. Architectures, Portsmouth, New Hampshire (1981) 41-57.

/La/ L. Lamport, What good is temporal logic? , in: R.E.A. Mason (Ed.), IFIP Information Processing 83 (North Holland, Amsterdam, 1983) 657-668.

/MWa/ Z. Manna, R. Waldinger, A deductive approach to program synthesis, ACM TOPLAS 2 (1980) 90-121.

/MWo/ Z. Manna, P. Wolper, Synthesis of communcating processes from temporal logic specifications, ACM TOPLAS 6 (1984) 68-93.

/Mi/ R. Milner, A calculus of communicating systems, Lecture notes in Computer Science 92 (Springer, Berlin, 1980).

/NH/ R. de Nicola, M. Hennessy, Testing equivalences for processes, Internal Report CSR-123-82, Dept. of Computer Science, Univ. of Edinburgh, 1982 (to appear in Theoret. Computer Science).

/OH/ E.-R. Olderog, C.A.R. Hoare, Specification-oriented semantics for communicating processes, Tech. Monograph PRG-37, Oxford Univ., Progr. Research Group, 1984 (a preliminary version appeared in: J. Diaz (Ed.), Proc. 10th Coll.

Automata, Languages and Programming, Lecture Notes in Computer Science 154 (Springer, Berlin, 1983) 561-572).

/RV/ P. Robert, J.-P. Verjus, Toward autonomous descriptions of synchronization modules, in: B Gilchrist (Ed.), IFIP Information Processing 77 (North Holland, Amsterdam 1977) 981-986.

/SSc/ W.S. Scherlis, D.S. Scott, First steps towards inferential programming, in: R.E.A. Mason (Ed.), IFIP Information Processing 83 (North Holland, Amsterdam 1983) 199-212.

/Wi/ G. Winskel, A new definition of morphism on Petri nets, in: M. Fontet, K. Mehlhorn (Eds.), 1st Symp. on Theoret. Aspects of Computer Science, Lecture Notes in Computer Science 166 (Springer, Berlin, 1984) 140-150.

/WY/ E. Wong, K. Youssefi, Decomposition - a strategy for query processing, ACM TODS 1 (1976) 223-241.

MISCELLANEOUS

THEORETICAL FOUNDATIONS FOR NON-MONOTONIC REASONING IN EXPERT SYSTEMS

D. M. Gabbay
Department of Computing,
Imperial College of Science and Technology,
180 Queen's Gate,
London SW7 2BZ

1 BACKGROUND AND STATEMENT OF THE PROBLEM

Suppose we are given some collection of confirmed data items (information). We can assume that the information is represented as a set $\underline{P}$ of propositions of predicate logic. We look at $\underline{P}$ and try to use some sort of inference mechanism to extract more information out of $\underline{P}$.

There are two main methods of getting (or deducing) more information out of (or on the basis of) $\underline{P}$.

These are the methods of monotonic deduction and the methods of non-monotonic deduction. The monotonic deductive systems are the familiar logical systems such as classical logic, intuitionistic logic, modal logics etc. They are called monotonic logics because the addition of information $\underline{P}'$ to $\underline{P}$ does not affect the validity of the deductive inference. Thus:

If $\underline{P} \vdash A$

then in a monotonic system for any $\underline{P}$, we also have that:

$\underline{P} \cup \underline{P}' \vdash A$

holds.

The non-monotonic deductive systems are built from rules which rely on $\underline{P}$ and when $\underline{P} \cup \underline{P}'$ is encountered the old deduction may fail. Thus Reiter's default systems, Clark's negation as failure in prolog, McCarthy's circumscription and other systems are all non-monotonic. We may have in these systems that:

$\underline{P} \mid\!\sim A$

NATO ASI Series, Vol. F13
Logics and Models of Concurrent Systems
Edited by K. R. Apt

but not:

$\underline{P} \cup \underline{P}' \mathrel{|\!\sim} A.$

[Where we write $\mathrel{|\!\sim}$ instead of $\vdash$ to hint that the system is non-monotonic.] Any combination of these two methods can comprise, in practice, the inference procedure of some specific expert system.

For example one may take classical logic as the deductive component and some default system as the non-monotonic component.

The logical foundations of monotonic deduction systems are well understood. Any $\vdash$ relation satisfying certain rules is the provability relation of a monotonic deductive system. These rules are given at the end of this section.

In this paper we attempt to provide foundations for non-monotonic reasoning. What do we mean by "foundations"? The rest of this section will try to state our problem precisely. For the time being, however, let us explain intuitively what we are looking for.

Suppose we are given an inference expert system in some specific area of application. Suppose knowledge in this area of application is represented by formulas of the form A, B, C etc. The question that we ask the expert system have the following form:

$A1, \ldots , An \mathrel{|\!\sim}^{?} B$

In words:

Does B follow from A1, ... , An?

Assume that something went wrong with the machine (coffee was spilt into the hardware). We can still get answers for our questions but what we are not sure of is whether the "logic" of the machine is still working properly. One way to check that, is to look at the meanings of the questions and see whether the answers make sense in the context of the area of application. Suppose further that the meaning of A is given via an interface which was itself damaged. All we have now is a meaningless list of questions and answers like:

A1, ... , An $\mid\!\sim$ A : yes

B1, ... , Bm $\mid\!\sim$ B : no

....

Is there any test which we can apply to check whether $\mid\!\sim$ represents any system of reasoning?

Of course we can ask whether A $\mid\!\sim$ B holds again and again and see whether we get the same answer each time. Suppose the machine is perfectly consistent in its answers. Is the machine "logical" or is it damaged?

It is quite possible that all the machine does when it is asked the question:

A1, ... , An $\mid\!\sim^?$ A

is to compute some binary representation numbers #A1, ... , #An, #A and check whether #A divides the product of #Ai. In this case not only will the machine be consistent in its answers but we will also get "logical" rules like:

A $\mid\!\sim$ A

and

A, B $\mid\!\sim$ A

our problem is therefore the following:

Given a relation $\mid\!\sim$ of the form mentioned above, are there (or what are) any formal properties of $\mid\!\sim$ which will characterise it as an inference relation of a non-monotonic expert system?

To get a better understanding of what we are looking for, let us ask how can we tell that a provability relation $\vdash$ is a provability relation of a monotonic deductive system? This question has been answered by Tarski and Scott. If $\vdash$ satisfies the three conditions below then $\vdash$ is a provability relation of some monotonic logical system.

In fact we can say that to be a deductive monotonic logical system is to be a relation $\vdash$ satisfying the three conditions below:

Reflexivity: A1, ... , An, B $\vdash$ B

Monotonicity:
$$\frac{A1, \ldots, An \vdash B}{A1, \ldots, An, X \vdash B}$$

Transitivity: (or Cut) $\dfrac{A1, \dots , An \vdash X; \; A1, \dots , An, X \vdash B}{A1, \dots , An \vdash B.}$

$\vdash$ characterises the logic. If an axiom system $\underline{L}1$ and a semantical system $\underline{L}2$ end up defining the same $\vdash$ (i.e. $\vdash_1$ equals $\vdash_2$), then they are regarded as the same logic, and the theorem proving that $\vdash_1 = \vdash_2$ is called a completeness theorem.

We are seeking a similar characterization of the non-monotonic logical systems via their relations $\mid\!\sim$.

If we are successful, we may be able to classify and compare the different non-monotonic logical systems which have been discussed in the literature. This is of course in addition to our success in answering the question:

What is a non-monotonic logic?

The appendix gives a classification of some monotonic logics through their relation $\vdash$. This will give us an idea of how the classification is done. In the remainder of this section we want to give an example of a system in detail, in order to help illustrate the logical mechanisms involved in expert system deduction.

Assume in this example that our knowledge representation is in the language of the propositional calculus.

Let the data $\underline{P}$ be:

(1) $A \wedge B \rightarrow C$

(2) $\neg D \rightarrow B$

(3) A

The above is actually a prolog programme. We regard it as a set of data of propositional logic, and our inference will be bottom up.

Let us use as our deductive component the classical truth functional logic. Of course the way we do our deductions depends on the rules chosen for the logic. For example we may use truth tables or a natural deduction system for classical logic or semantic tableaux or some specific resolution method etc. In this example let us take among other rules (for classical logic) the following deductive (monotonic) rules.

(R1) $\dfrac{X \wedge Y \to Z}{X \to (Y \to Z)}$

(R2) $\dfrac{X;\ X \to Y}{Y}$

(R3) $\dfrac{X \to Y;\ Y \to Z}{X \to Z}$

(R1) is an axiom schema in many systems. (R2) is modus ponens, and (R3) is the transitivity of ->. We write:

A1, ... , An => B

to mean that B is deduced (in the monotonic component) via an application of one rule. In our case via (R1) or (R3)). We can thus write the following deductions:

$\underline{P}$ => (A -> (B -> C)) (Use (R1))

$\underline{P}$ + (A -> (B -> C)) => (B -> C) (use (R2))

$\underline{P}$ + (A -> (B -> C)) + (B + C) => ¬D -> C (use (R3))

Thus we can conclude that $\underline{P} \vdash_{R1-R3} (\neg D \to C)$.

We cannot proceed to extract any more information out of $\underline{P}$ using the deductive system above. For example we cannot deduce C from $\underline{P}$.

Our system may have a non-monotonic component. For example, we can take a default rule (D1) stating that for any literal X not appearing in $\underline{P}$ as a head of a clause we can deduce by default that ¬X.

Default rules may operate under assumptions as well. Such rules were put forward by Reiter. For example a reasonable rule is

[¬ A -> B; A cannot be deduced] imply B.

In our case we take the default rule:

(D1) $\dfrac{\text{X literal and X not a head of a clause in } \underline{P}}{\neg X}$

If B is obtained from A1, ... , An by the application of one non-monotonic rule we write:

A1, ... , An > B.

Thus we get:

$\underline{P} > \neg D$ (by rule (D1))

$\underline{P} + \neg D \Rightarrow B$ (by (R2)).

combining the derivations above we get that C follows non-monotonically from $\underline{P}$ using the (expert) system S= {R1 - R3, D1}.

In symbols:

$\underline{P} \mid\!\sim_S C$

denotes the final non-monotonic deduction.

Here is a summary of the proof of $\underline{P} \mid\!\sim C$.

Step #:	Deduction	Rule
0	$\underline{P}$	
1	$\underline{P} > \neg D$	D1
2	$\underline{P} + \neg D \Rightarrow B$	R2
3	$\underline{P} + \neg D + B \Rightarrow (A \to (B \to C)$	R1
4	$\underline{P} + \neg D + B + (A \to (B \to C)) \Rightarrow (B \to C)$	R2
5	$\underline{P} + \neg D + B + (A \to (B \to C)) + (B \to C) \Rightarrow C$	R2
	$\underline{P} \mid\!\sim C$	

C was derived from $\underline{P}$ via a chain Y1, ... , Y5 = C. Such that Y(k+1) was derived from $\underline{P}$ + Y1 ... Yk, k = 0, ... , 4.

Thus any non-monotonic system is comprised of monotonic one step rules and non-monotonic one step rules. => is used to denote the monotonic rules and > is used to denote the non-monotonic rules. Since monotonic rules can be regarded as non-monotonic rules we write A $\mid\!\sim$ B to denote B follows from A using <u>any</u> rule. $\vdash$ is reserved for monotonic deductions.

The above presentation is proof theoretical and not goal directed. It is possible to present a system in a goal directed way but there may be complications especially related to failure. We shall discuss the goal directed presentation at a later section, after we have answered the question of this paper, namely "what is a non-monotonic system?"

Appendix to § 1:

Let $\vdash$ be a monotonic provability relation satisfying reflexivity, monotonicity and transitivity. Other properties of $\vdash$ may be true for some logics but may not be true for others. For example the deduction theorem for implication -> holds for many logics but not for e.g. Lukasiewiz many valued logics. Where

Deduction Theorem:

$$\frac{A1, \ldots, An, B \vdash C}{A1, \ldots, An \vdash B \to C}$$

The double line means: if and only if.

Thus to the question: What is a (monotonic) logical system?

We can answer:

A (monotonic) logical system is any consequence relation $\vdash$ satisfying the above three rules.

Different logics can be characterised via properties of their consequence relation $\vdash$. To give some examples, take a language with atomic propositions and a symbol for implication, e.g. —>. All formulas in this language are built up from atoms and —>.

The following characterise three well known logics of implication:

Intuitionistic Implication:

Let $\vdash$ be the smallest consequence relation $\vdash$ satisfying the deduction theorem. Then —> is intuitionistic implication.

Classical Implication

Classical Implication is obtained by also requiring $\vdash$ to satisfy Pierce-Law: $(A \to B) \to A \vdash A$

Relevant Implication

Let $\vdash$ be the smallest consequence relation $\vdash$ satisfying the deduction theorem restricted to relevant wffs. Where the notion of relevance is taken as the minimal closure of

(a) A is relevant to A

(b) If A -> B is asserted, then A is relevant to B.

2 THE NOTION P > B FOR CAUSAL EXPERT SYSTEMS:

We saw in the previous section that non-monotonic reasoning can be built up from basic single step rules of the form A1, ... , An > B.

Note first that since > is non-monotonic, any application of the rule must use the entire set P of data. So when we write Ai > B we tacitly assume that Ai are all the (at least relevant) data.

There are many non-monotonic systems. They can be divided into two main groups. One which we can loosely call "Causal", satisfy some consistency conditions which the other non-causal ones do not. We shall describe shortly what we mean by that, but first let us put forward some obvious properties which all systems satisfy.

(1a) Consistency of the new data with the old data:

If P is consistent and P > B holds in the system then P + B is also consistent.

(2) Compatibility of > with =>:

In a non-monotonic expert system with both monotonic => and non-monotonic >, > is compatible with =>:

In symbols:

P => B implies P > B

The two main groups of non-monotonic logics differ on propery (3):

(3) Compatibility of the > rules:

If A and B each can be derived from P in a single step use of > rule then P + A + B is consistent. In view of rule (1) above (3) can be written as:

P > A and P > B iff P > A $\wedge$ B.

Rule (3) is not so obvious. It is valid for default systems. It is also true for any system where P > B is asserted through causal considerations, based on e.g. agreed models of behavious, or on the guessing of some global strategy etc. Systems based on probabilistic considerations on the other hand fail to satisfy this rule.

The validity of rule (3) or its rejection distinguishes between the two main types of non-monotonic systems. The causal type satisfy rule (3) and the (probabilistic) non-causal type satisfy only one direction of it, namely:

$$\underline{P} > A \wedge B \rightarrow (\underline{P} > A) \wedge (\underline{P} > B).$$

Example of non-causal deductions

(a) $\underline{P} > A$ if the probability of having A given $\underline{P}$ is > 0.5.

(b) $\underline{P} > A$ if it cannot be shown that $\underline{P} \vdash \neg A$ (for e.g. $\vdash$ being classical logic).

The following are instances of causal non-monotonic deductions.

(c) John has an accident > John is taken to the nearest hospital.

(b) John is going into the bath and the time is 3 00 in the morning > John switches on the light.

This section assume rule (3) to hold.

Another reasonable condition is restricted monotonicity.

(4) Restricted monotonicity

$$\frac{\underline{P} > X,\ \underline{P} > B}{\underline{P} + X > B}$$

We know > is non-monotonic. But if we add an X which > tells us is deducible, it does not affect the deducibility of other deducible sentences B.

In the context of the default rule (D1) of the last section, this means that if A is negated by default and B is negated by default then B is still negated by default even if A is explicitly negated.

Another example - If we expect A to be true and we also expect B to be true all on the basis of the information $\underline{P}$, then if A is indeed confirmed, we still expect B!

Definition 6 (Weak deduction)

(a) A weak non-monotonic inference system for a language $\underline{L}$ is composed of a set of monotonic deductive rules of the form

A1, ... , An => B

and a set of non-monotonic rules of the form

A1, ... , An > B

such that the following holds:

(1) If Ai => B then Ai > B

(2) If {Ai} is consistent and Ai > B then {Ai, B} is consistent.

(3) (Ai > B) and (Ai > C) iff Ai > (B $\wedge$ C)

(4) If (Ai > X) and (Ai > B) then Ai, X > B.

Definition 7 Deduction chains:

We define the notion of $\underline{P} \mid\!\sim_m B$ by induction on m:

(a) $\underline{P} \mid\!\sim_1 B$ iff $\underline{P} > B$

(b) $\underline{P} \mid\!\sim_{m+1} B$ iff for some X1, ... , Xm we have:

$\underline{P} > X1$

$\underline{P} + X1 > X2$

$\underline{P} + X1 + \ldots + Xm > B$

(c) Define $\mid\!\sim$ by:

$\underline{P} \mid\!\sim B$ iff for some m $\underline{P} \mid\!\sim_m B$

$\mid\!\sim$ is our notion non-monotonic deduction. We now study its properties:

Lemma 8

If $\underline{P} \mid\!\sim B$ then $\underline{P} + B$ is consistent.

Proof: By induction on the chain

Theorem 9

If $A \mid\!\sim_n X$ and $A \mid\!\sim_m Y$ and $n \leq m$ then $A \mid\!\sim_m X \wedge Y$

To prove the theorems, we use some lemmas.

Lemma 10

If $A > X$ and $A \mid\!\sim_m B$ then $A \wedge X \mid\!\sim_m B$ and $A \mid\!\sim_m B \wedge X$

Proof

By induction on m the length of the chain leading from A to B.

$A \vdash_m B$ implies by definition that there is a chain Y1 = A,

Y1, ... , Ym, Y(m+1) = B

such that

$\bigwedge_{i=1}^{k} Yi > Y(k+1)$ holds for k = 1, ... , m.

we prove the lemma by induction on m.

Case m = 1:

We have A > B (i.e. Y1 > Y2) and A > X then certainly by available axioms

$A \wedge X > B$ and $A > B \wedge X$

Case m = m:

By the induction hypothesis

(a) $Y1 \wedge \ldots \wedge Y(m-1) \wedge X > Ym$

(b) $Y1 \wedge \ldots \wedge Y(m-1) > X \wedge Ym$

From (b) we get, using axioms:

(c) $Y1 \wedge \ldots \wedge Y(m-1) \wedge Ym > X$

and since we are also given initially that

$Y1 \wedge \ldots \wedge Ym > Y(m+1)$

we get again by axioms:

(d) $Y1 \wedge \ldots \quad Ym \wedge X > Y(m+1)$

(e) $Y1 \wedge \ldots \wedge Ym > X \wedge Y(m+1)$

This proves the induction step and lemma 10.

Lemma 11

Let there be two chains given:

X0, ... , X(m+1)

Y0, ... , Y(m+1)

such that X0 = Y0 = A

and for k = o, ... , m

$\bigwedge_{i=o}^{k} Xi > X(k+1)$

$$\bigwedge_{i=o}^{k} Yi > Y(k+1)$$

Then we have for each k = o , ... , m and j = o, ... , m

$$(\bigwedge_{i=o}^{j} Yi) \wedge (\bigwedge_{i=o}^{k} Xi) > X(k+1) \wedge Y(j+1)$$

especially for j = k we get

$$(\bigwedge_{i=o}^{k} Yi) \wedge (\bigwedge_{i=o}^{k} Xi) > X\ (k+1) \wedge Y(k+1).$$

Proof: By induction on j, and k

(a) for j = o and any k we have to show that

$$\bigwedge_{i=o}^{k} Xi > X(k+1) \wedge Y1$$

clearly since Y0 > Y1 and Y0 = X0 we can use the previous lemma.

(b) j = 1 and k = 1 we have to show

$$X0 \wedge X1 \wedge Y0 \wedge Y1 > X2 \wedge Y2$$

Since $Xo \wedge \ldots \wedge Xk \wedge Y0 > Y1 \wedge X(k+1)$

by the case j = 0 we get

$$X0 \wedge X1 \wedge Y0 \wedge Y1 > X2$$

we now want to show that

$$X0 \wedge X1 \wedge Y0 \wedge Y1 > Y2$$

but this follows by symmetry.

Thus we got

$$X0 \wedge X1 \wedge Y0 \wedge Y1 > X2 \wedge Y2$$

(c) Assume that the lemma holds for any j' < j, k' < k .

we want to show it for j, k.

We can assume

$$(X0 \wedge \ldots \wedge Xk') \wedge (Y0 \wedge \ldots \wedge Yj' > X(k'+1) \wedge Y(j'+1)$$

We show the same for k' = k and any j' < j.

By induction on j'.

For j' = 0 and any k we have shown in (a).

Assume for j' < j and any k.

Show for j' + 1 < j and k.

We have

(*) $X0 \wedge \ldots \wedge Xk \wedge Y0 \wedge \ldots \wedge Yj' > X(k+1) \wedge Y(j'+1)$

by the induction hypothesis for j' and k.

(**) $X0 \wedge \ldots \wedge X(k-1) \wedge Y0 \wedge \ldots \wedge Y(j'+1) > Xk \wedge Y(j'+2)$

by the induction hypothesis (c).

Hence from (*) and (**) resp.

$X0 \wedge \ldots \wedge Xk \wedge Y0 \wedge \ldots \wedge Yj \wedge Y(j'+1) > X(k+1)$

$X0 \wedge \ldots \wedge Xk \wedge Y0 \wedge \ldots \wedge Y(j'+1) > Y(j+2)$

and hence

$X0 \wedge \ldots \wedge Xk \wedge Y0 \wedge \ldots \wedge Y(j'+1) > X(k+1) \wedge Y(j'+2)$

We thus proved by induction (c) for any $j' < j$ and any $k' < k + 1$. By symmetry of proof we get the result for any $k' < k$ and any $j' < j' + 1$. The only case to check now is (j, k).

We have

(+) $X0 \wedge \ldots \wedge Xk \wedge Y0 \wedge \ldots \wedge Y(j-1) > X(k+1) \wedge Yj$

(++) $X0 \wedge \ldots \wedge X(k-1) \wedge Y0 \ldots \wedge Yj > Xk \wedge Y(j+1)$

The above holds because we proved the induction case for any $j' < j$ and $k' < k + 1$ and any $k' < k$ and $j' < j + 1$.

From (+) (++) we get respectively

$X0 \wedge \ldots Xk \wedge Y0 \wedge \ldots \wedge Yj > X(k+1)$

$X0 \wedge \ldots Xk \wedge Y0 \wedge \ldots \wedge Yj > Y(j+1)$

and hence we get

$X0 \wedge \ldots \wedge Xk \wedge Y0 \wedge \ldots \wedge Yj > X(k+1) \wedge Y(j+1)$

This proves the induction case for (c).

Thus we can conclude the induction for lemma 11 and lemma 11 is proved.

<u>Proof of theorem 9</u>

Assume that $A \mid\!\sim Y$ and $A \mid\!\sim X$. We can assume that there are chains of the form X0 = A, ... X(m+1) = X and Y0 = A, ... , Y(m+1) = Y such that the assumption of lemma 11 hold. We can assume both chains have the length m+1 because any chain Z0, ... , Zn can be made longer by taking Z0, ... , Zn,

Zn, Zn,... . Certainly $\bigwedge_{i=1}^{n} Zi > Zn$ because of the axiom $A \wedge B \Rightarrow B$, and rule 2. Now by lemma 11 for our two chains we get for $j = k < m + 1$.

$$(\bigwedge_{i=0}^{k} Xi) \wedge (\bigwedge_{i=0}^{k} Yi) > X(k+1) \wedge Y(k+1)$$

or in other words

$$\bigwedge_{i=o}^{k} (Xi \wedge Yi) > X(k+1) \wedge Y(k+1)$$

Let $Z0 = X0 \wedge Y0 = A$

$$Zi = Xi \wedge Yi, \; i = 1, \ldots, m$$

$$Z(m+1) = X(m+1) \wedge Y(m+1) = X \wedge Y$$

then we got that $Z0 = A, Z1, \ldots, Z(m+1) = X \wedge Y$ is a chain for $A \mathrel{|\!\sim}_m X \wedge Y$.

This proves theorem 9.

The previous theorem shows that if $\underline{P} \mathrel{|\!\sim} A$ and $\underline{P} \mathrel{|\!\sim} B$ then $\underline{P} \mathrel{|\!\sim} A \wedge B$ and hence $\underline{P} + A + B$ is consistent. This means that if we start with the core information $\underline{P}$ and apply our chain deductions, we enlarge the body of information more and more, to a bigger and bigger consistent sets $\underline{P}1$, $\underline{P}2$, $\underline{P}3$, etc. as we apply longer and longer chains.

Let $\underline{P}0 = \underline{P}$

$\underline{P}m+1 = \underline{P}m \cup \{A \mid \underline{P} \mathrel{|\!\sim}_{m+1} A\}$

$\underline{P}\infty = \cup^{n} \underline{P}n$

then we have

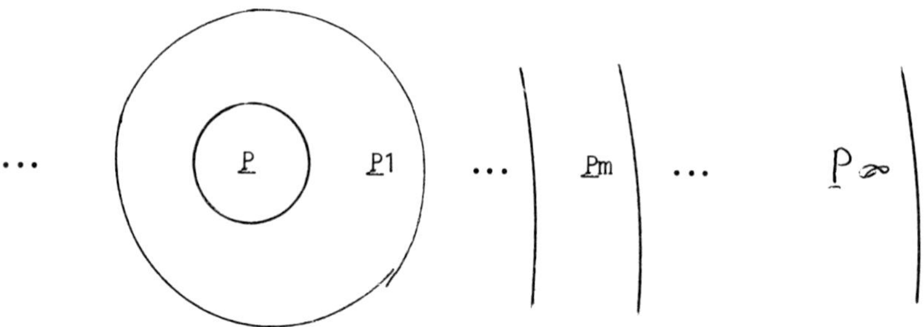

It stands to reason, according to our intuition that if $\underline{P} \mathrel{|\!\sim} X$ and X is confirmed, then the prediction chain remain unchanged. In symbols:

(rule 12) Restricted monotonicity:

$$\frac{(\underline{P} > A);\ \underline{P} \mid\!\sim_m X \text{ for some } m}{\underline{P} + X > A}$$

rule 12 generalises rule 4. It is possible to state rule 12 because we know now that $\underline{P}$ + A + X are consistent. The intuition behind this rule is the same as the intuition behind rule 4 and therefore rule 12 should be adopted. It is quite unreasonable to say first that X can be deduced from $\underline{P}$ through a chain of m steps and A is deduced immediately, and then when X is confirmed, to say that the situation has changed and we no longer expect A!

We now ask what if A is deduced not immediately but through a k-long chain, do we still have $\underline{P} + X \mid\!\sim_k A$?

The answer is yes:

Theorem 13

$$\underline{P} \mid\!\sim_k A \text{ and } \underline{P} \mid\!\sim_m X \text{ imply } \underline{P} + X \mid\!\sim_k A$$

Proof: By induction on k.

Case k = 1

This is rule 12.

Case k = n + 1

Let A1, ... , An be such

$\underline{P} > A1$

$\underline{P} + A1 > A2$

$\underline{P} + A1 \ \ldots + An > A$

Since $\underline{P} + A1 \mid\!\sim_n A$ and $\underline{P} \mid\!\sim_m X$, we have $\underline{P} + X + A1 \mid\!\sim_n A$ by the induction hypothesis.

We also have $\underline{P} > A1$ and $\underline{P} \mid\!\sim_m X$, hence by case 1, $\underline{P} + X > A1$. The two conclusions together mean $\underline{P} + X \mid\!\sim_{n+1} A$.

Definition 14

(a) A weak non-monotonic deduction system whose relation > satisfies rule 12 is called an (ordinary) non - monotonic deduction system.

(b) The consequence relation $\mid\!\sim$ arising from an orinary non monotonic deduction system is called an (ordinary) non-monotonic consequence relation.

Corollary 15

Let $\mid\!\sim$ any non-monotonic consequence relation (i.e. arising from a non monotonic deduction system) then for any $\underline{P}$, A, X.

$\underline{P} \mid\!\sim A$ and $\underline{P} \mid\!\sim X$ imply $\underline{P} + X \mid\!\sim A$.

Proof:

This is theorem 13

Theorem 16

Let $\mid\!\sim$ be any (ordinary) non monotonic consequence relation then for any $\underline{P}$, X, A.

$\underline{P} + X \mid\!\sim A$ and $\underline{P} \mid\!\sim X$ imply $\underline{P} \mid\!\sim A$

Proof

Assume that $\underline{P} + X \mid\!\sim_m A$ and $\underline{P} \mid\!\sim_k X$ we will show that $\underline{P} \mid\!\sim_{m+k} A$. We use induction on k.

Case k = 1

We have $\underline{P} > X$ and $\underline{P} + X \mid\!\sim_m A$. Clearly this implies by definition $\underline{P} \mid\!\sim_{m+1} A$.

Case k + 1

Assume that $\underline{P} + X \mid\!\sim_m A$ and $\underline{P} > X1$ and $\underline{P} + X1 \mid\!\sim_k X$.

By rule 12, since $\underline{P} > X1$, and $\underline{P} \mid\!\sim_{k+1} X$ we get $\underline{P} + X > X1$.

By lemma 10, since $\underline{P} + X \mid\!\sim_m A$ and $\underline{P} + X > X1$ we get $\underline{P} + X + X1 \mid\!\sim_m A$.

We also have $\underline{P} + X1 \mid\!\sim_k X$.

Hence by the induction hypothesis for k we get $\underline{P} + X1 \mid\!\sim_{m+k} A$. Since $\underline{P} > X1$, we finally conclude $\underline{P} \mid\!\sim_{m+k+1} A$, which completes the induction case of k + 1 and thus proves theorem 16.

Theorem 17

Let $\mid\!\sim$ be a relation such that

(a) $\underline{P} \mid\!\sim A$ for $A \in \underline{P}$

(b) $\underline{P} \mid\!\sim A \wedge B$ iff $\underline{P} \mid\!\sim A$ and $\underline{P} \mid\!\sim B$

(c) If $\underline{P}$ is consistent and $\underline{P} \mid\!\sim A$ then $\underline{P} + A$ is consistent.

(d) If $\underline{P} \mid\!\sim A$ and $\underline{P} \mid\!\sim B$ then $\underline{P} + A \mid\!\sim B$.

Let > be $\mid\!\sim$. Then > satisfies conditions (1) ... (4) and rule (12) and $\mid\!\sim^*$, the consequence relation arising from > equals the original $\mid\!\sim$.

Proof

Theorem 16 tells us that if for some X

$\underline{P} > X$

and $\underline{P} + X > A$

then $\underline{P} > X$.

This means that $\underline{P} \mid\!\sim^*_2 A$ implies $\underline{P} > A$. By induction one can show that $\underline{P} \mid\!\sim^*_m A$ implies $\underline{P} > A$ and hence deduce that $\mid\!\sim^*$ equals > which is identical with $\mid\!\sim$.

Definition 18 (What is a non-monotonic logic)

Let $\mid\!\sim$ be a relation among wffs of the form $A1, \ldots, An \mid\!\sim B$. We say that $\mid\!\sim$ is a non-monotonic consequence relation iff it satisfies the rules below:

(Reflexivity):

$$A1, \ldots, An, X \mid\!\sim X$$

(Restricted Monotonicity):

$$\frac{A1, \ldots, An \mid\!\sim X;\ A1, \ldots, An \mid\!\sim B}{A1, \ldots, An, X \mid\!\sim B}$$

(Transitivity) (Cut):

$$\frac{A1, \ldots, An \mid\!\sim X;\ A1, \ldots, An, X \mid\!\sim B}{A1, \ldots, An \mid\!\sim B}$$

Definition 18 is the correct definition, following the constructions of this section. We want to show that the rule of consistency, follows from the rules of definition 18, in order to use the previous theorem 18.

Remark 19:

We show the following is valid, for the $\mid\!\sim$ of definition 19:

$$\frac{A_i \mid\!\sim X; \; A_i \mid\!\sim Y}{A_i \mid\!\sim X \wedge Y}$$

Proof

Using restricted monotonicity twice we get:

$$A_i, Y \mid\!\sim X$$

Using reflexivity we get:

$$A_i, X, Y \mid\!\sim X \wedge Y$$

(We assume $\wedge$ is in the language and X, Y is equivalent to $X \wedge Y$).

Using Cut on the last two rules we get:

$$A_i, Y \mid\!\sim X \wedge Y$$

Since $A_i \mid\!\sim Y$

We use cut again and get

$$A_i \mid\!\sim X \wedge Y.$$

CONCLUSION FOR § 2

The answer to our original question, namely "When does a relation represent a non monotonic logic", is definition 18. The evidence that definition 18 is the correct one comes from two directions.

(a) If we start with basic principles of $A_i > B$ and $A_i \Rightarrow B$ rules and define deduction chains in the most straightforward manner we arrive at a relation $\mid\!\sim$ satisfying definition 18. This was done and proved in this section.

(b) If we follow another route, namely just drop the monotonicity condition and replace it by restricted monotonicity, we also end up with the same notion of what is a non monotonic logic. Thus (b) strengthens the case for (a).

TO BE CONTINUED

References

[1] D. M. Gabbay - Semantical Investigations in Heyting's Intuitionistic Logic. D. Reidel pub. comp. 1981.

[2] D. M. Gabbay - Intuitionistic Basis for non monotonic Logic, Proceedings of 6th conference of automated deduction, D. W. Loveland, editor, Lecture notes in computer science 138, Springer-Verlag, 1982, pp. 260-273.

[3] J. McCarthy - Circumscription, a form of non monotonic reasoning, in Artificial Intelligence 13, 1980, pp. 27-39.

[4] B. Moore - Semantical considerations on non monotonic logics, proc. 8th Int. joint conference on Artificial Intelligence, 1983, pp. 272-279.

[5] R. Reiter - A logic of default reasoning, in Artificial Intelligence 13, 1980, pp. 81-132.

[6] D. Scott - completeness and axiomatizability in many valued logics, proceedings of Tarski symposium, L. Henkin et all editors AMS 1974, pp. 411-435.

[7] R. Turner - Logics for Artificial Intelligence, Ellis Horwood 1984.

Towards a Theory of Knowledge and Ignorance: Preliminary Report

Joseph Y. Halpern
IBM Research, San Jose, CA 95193

Yoram Moses *
Computer Science Department,
Stanford University, Stanford, CA 94305
and
IBM Research, San Jose, CA 95193

Abstract: Communication in a distributed system changes the state of knowledge of the processors. But what is a state of knowledge? Here we attempt to characterize this notion. In the case where an agent's information is completely described by a formula, we give a number of equivalent ways to characterize the agent's state of knowledge, as well as an algorithm for computing the formulas that are true in this state. The relationship between this work and related works by Stark, Konolige, and Moore is discussed.

1. Introduction

This research was originally motivated by the question of how communication in a distributed system changes the state of knowledge of the processors in the system (cf. [HM1]). Answering such a question clearly first requires characterizing a processor's state of knowledge at a given point in time. But this can be quite subtle. To see some of the difficulties here, consider a processor that has only one bit of information, namely, that the propositional fact P is true. We assume that processors can do perfect propositional reasoning, so that our processor also knows all the logical consequences of P, but this is far from all it knows. Suppose Q is another propositional fact. By introspection it can discover that it doesn't know Q, and by further introspection it discovers that it *knows* that it doesn't know Q. (Note that we are assuming here that an ideal processor has perfect introspective knowledge about its knowledge and lack of knowledge.) But not knowing Q is *not* a logical consequence of knowing P.

The situation is further complicated by the presence of a second processor. Since the first processor does not know Q, it knows that the second processor cannot know that the first processor knows Q (we assume that only true facts can be known). And since the first processor also knows that the second processor can do perfect introspection, the first processor knows that the second processor knows that it does not know that the first processor knows Q. Thus a processor can make inferences about another processor's knowledge through its own ignorance! (See [FHV] for further discussion on this point.)

---

* This work supported in part by DARPA contract N00039-82-C-0250.

NATO ASI Series, Vol. F13
Logics and Models of Concurrent Systems
Edited by K. R. Apt

In order to focus in on these issues, we concentrate in this paper on the one-processor or single-agent case (we use words like "agent", "processor", or "knower" interchangeably throughout this paper). Many of the general problems are already present here. This discussion is not limited to the domain of distributed systems of processors. It applies just as well to intelligent robots functioning in the real world or to knowledge bases. Our assumptions that an agent can do perfect propositional reasoning and has complete introspection regarding its own knowledge and ignorance make our agents like the knowledge bases of Levesque [Le] and like Konolige's introspection machines [Ko1].

Intuitively, given a complete description of the information on which the knowledge is based, it seems that there should be a unique state of knowledge characterizing what the knowledge base knows. Every query of the form "Do you know q?" should have a unique answer. But, as the discussion above suggests, describing this state of knowledge is nontrivial. It is also easy to see that the state of knowledge changes non-monotonically as more information is acquired. If the knowledge base "knows only P", then it knows that it does not know Q. But if it later discovers Q, then of course it does know Q.

Further problems arise because some formulas do not uniquely characterize a knowledge state. For example, it cannot be the case that all a knowledge base knows is that it either knows P or it knows Q. (Note that this is quite different from knowing that one of P or Q holds.) If the only information the knowledge base has is that it knows P or it knows Q, then it doesn't know P (since all it knows is that it knows one of P and Q), and similarly, it doesn't know Q. But this state of affairs is inconsistent! A knowledge base cannot know one of P and Q without knowing either one of them.

In the next section, we introduce various approaches to the characterization of the state of an agent's knowledge corresponding to "knowing only α". In each of the approaches there are formulas that do not uniquely characterize an agent's state of knowledge. We call formulas that do uniquely characterize an agent's state of knowledge *honest*, while we call formulas that do not uniquely characterize a state of knowlege *dishonest.** Intuitively, an agent is being dishonest if it claims to "know only α" for a dishonest formula α. All of the approaches are shown to lead to the same notions of honesty, and for honest formulas, they are shown to specify the same state of knowledge. One of the approaches also gives an algorithm that, given an honest formula α and a formula p, decides whether an agent whose sole information is α knows p.

---

* Mike Fischer and Neil Immerman suggested the use of the word honest for this notion. Neil Immerman first convinced us of the existence of dishonest formulas.

As suggested in the discussion above, the multi-agent case is even harder to analyze than the single agent case, since nontrivial inferences about the knowledge and ignorance of other agents can now be made. In section 3, we briefly discuss how the results of section 2 can be extended to the multi-agent case.

Using the theory developed in sections 2 and 3, we can define a nonmonotonic provability relation $\vdash\!\sim_A$, where $\alpha \vdash\!\sim_A p$ exactly if agent A knows p, when his knowledge is based solely on α. This nonmonotonic provability relation is much in the spirit of Stark's nonmonotonic *model theorist's deduction rule* [St], but has wider applicability.

Two other works in a spirit similar to ours are those of Konolige [Ko2] and Moore [Mo2]. Konolige is also concerned with a situation where agents have only a limited amount of information, but in his formalism, agents cannot use introspection to acquire knowledge of their ignorance. Moore is concerned with describing what an ideally rational agent should *believe* (rather than know) given some information about the world. This leads to some interesting differences between our results and those of [Mo2]. The relationship between our work and that of Stark, Konolige, and Moore is discussed in section 4. We conclude with remarks about the relationship this work has with default rules in non-monotonic reasoning.

2. The knowledge theory

Let us first consider the case of a single knower or knowledge base. Imagine an ideal agent A with very powerful computing capabilities and perfect introspection. A knows precisely what facts he knows, and what facts he doesn't know. A lives in a propositional real world, and his conceptual world consists of formulas regarding the real world and his knowledge. The class $\mathcal{L}$ of formulas of the propositional logic of knowledge, within which A reasons, is defined as follows:

(L1) All primitive propositions P, Q, ... are formulas.

(L2) If p and q are formulas, then $\neg p$, $p \wedge q$, $p \vee q$, $p \supset q$ are formulas.

(L3) If p is a formula then $K_A p$ is a formula (denoting "A knows p").

(L4) The only formulas of $\mathcal{L}$ are those required by (L1)–(L3).

We call the set of formulas A knows at a given point in time A's *knowledge state* (cf. [MSHI]). Thus a formula p will be in A's knowledge state iff $K_A p$ is true. What properties should this set have? Let T be a knowledge state. Since we assume that A can do perfect propositional reasoning, we have:

(St1) All instances of propositional tautologies are in T.

A knows about modus ponens, therefore

(St2) If $p \in T$ and $p \supset q \in T$, then $q \in T$.

We also assume that A is capable of introspection with regards to his own knowledge, so:

(St3) $p \in T$ iff $K_A p \in T$.

(St4) $p \notin T$ iff $\neg K_A p \in T$.

Finally, we demand that a knowledge state be consistent

(St5) T is (propositionally) consistent.

Following Stalnaker [S], we call such a set a *stable* set of formulas. (Actually, Stalnaker does not require that a stable set satisfy (St5); we add this requirement for convenience. Note that the only set of formulas satisfying (St1)–(St4) and not satisfying (St5) is the inconsistent set $\mathcal{L}$ of all the formulas in the language. Property (St5) simply says that $\mathcal{L}$ is not an admissible state of knowledge.) Properties (St3) and (St4) imply that lower depth formulas in a stable set determine those of higher depth. In fact we have:

Proposition 1 ([Mo2]): A stable set is uniquely determined by the propositional formulas it contains.

This result is also proved in [Mo2]; we reprove it here for completeness. We first need to prove the following:

Lemma 1: Let S be a stable set. For any formulas $p, q \in \mathcal{L}$, (a) $K_A p \vee q \in S$ iff $p \in S$ or $q \in S$, and (b) $\neg K_A p \vee q \in S$ iff $p \notin S$ or $q \in S$.

Proof: The 'if' direction in both (a) and (b) is immediate from (St1)–(St4). We now prove the 'only if' direction. Assume $K_A p \vee q \in S$. If $p \in S$ then we are done. Otherwise, $p \notin S$ and by (St4), $\neg K_A p \in S$. But since S is closed under propositional reasoning by (St1) and (St2), $q \in S$ must hold. To show (b), assume that $\neg K_A p \vee q \in S$. If $p \in S$ then $K_A p \in S$, and again by propositional reasoning $q \in S$ must hold. Otherwise, $p \notin S$ and we are done. $\square$

Proof of Proposition 1: Assume that S and S' are two stable sets containing exactly the same propositional formulas. We will prove by induction on the depth of nesting of the K_A operators in a formula p that $p \in S$ iff $p \in S'$. For propositional formulas this is given. Assume that for all formulas of depth less than n the claim holds, and that p is a formula of depth n. By propositional reasoning, p is equivalent to a formula p' that is in "conjunctive normal form", i.e., p' is of the form $\bigwedge_i d_i$, where each d_i is a disjunction of the form $K_A q_1 \vee \cdots \vee K_A q_l \vee \neg K_A q_{l+1} \vee \cdots \vee \neg K_A q_m \vee g$, with the q_j's all formulas of degree less than n, and g a propositional formula. By (St1) and (St2), $p \in S$ iff $p' \in S$, and by propositional reasoning $(\bigwedge_i d_i) \in S$ iff $d_i \in S$ for all i. By Lemma 1, $d_i \in S$ iff either one of $g \in S$, $q_1 \in S, \ldots, q_l \in S, q_{l+1} \notin S, \ldots, q_m \notin S$ holds. An analogous property holds for S'. Since S and S' agree on all formulas of depth less than n we have $d_i \in S$ iff $d_i \in S'$. Therefore $p' \in S$ iff $p' \in S'$ and $p \in S$ iff $p \in S'$. □

Suppose α is a formula that describes all the facts that A has learned or observed. What is A's knowledge state when he "knows only α"? Clearly, this knowledge state should contain α, and since "only α" is known, it seems that it should be in some sense minimal among knowledge states containing α. However, the obvious notion of "minimal" – set inclusion – will not work. As the following proposition shows, no two knowledge states are comparable with respect to inclusion:

Proposition 2: No stable set properly includes another stable set.

Proof: Assume that a stable set S' properly includes a stable set S. There is some formula p such that $p \in S'$ and $p \notin S$. By properties (St3) and (St4) it follows that $K_A p \in S'$ and $\neg K_A p \in S$. Now since S' properly includes S, it must be the case that $\neg K_A p \in S'$, but then S' is inconsistent, a contradiction. □

By Proposition 1, a stable set is uniquely determined by the purely propositional formulas it contains. We denote by *Prop*(S) the subset of S consisting of its purely propositional formulas. A possible candidate for the "minimal" knowledge state containing α is the stable set containing α whose propositional subset is minimum (w.r.t. inclusion). Not all formulas α have such a minimal set. For example, consider the formula $\alpha = K_A P \vee K_A Q$. Any stable set containing α must contain either P or Q. Furthermore, there is a stable set S_P that contains α and P but does not contain Q, and a stable set S_Q containing α and Q and not containing P. However, the intersection of *Prop*(S_P) and *Prop*(S_Q) contains neither P nor Q. Thus, there is no stable set T containing α with *Prop*(T) $\subset$ *Prop*(S_P) and *Prop*(T) $\subset$ *Prop*(S_Q). This leads us to the following definition: A formula α is *honest*$_S$ iff there exists a stable set containing α

whose propositional subset is minimum. For an honest$_S$ formula, we denote this stable set by S^α.

Our intention is that S^α denote the stable set that describes A's state of knowledge if he "knows only α" (at least if α is an honest$_S$ formula). This definition may seem somewhat *ad hoc*, so we now consider a number of other ways of characterizing this state of knowledge.

Possible-world or *Kripke* semantics have been frequently used as a means of giving semantics to logics of knowledge (cf. [Hi,MSHI,Mo1]). Given our assumptions about an agent's power of introspection, the appropriate logic of knowledge is one that satisfies the axioms of the modal logic S5 (cf. [HC]), namely:

A1. All substitution instances of propositional tautologies.

A2. $K_A(p \supset q) \supset (K_A p \supset K_A q)$

A3. $K_A p \supset p$

A4. $K_A p \supset K_A K_A p$

A5. $\neg K_A p \supset K_A \neg K_A p$

A6. $K_A \psi$, if ψ is an instance of axiom A1 – A6.

The inference rule for S5 is *modus ponens*: from p and $p \supset q$ infer q.

In the case of one agent, the possible world semantics for S5 have a particularly simple structure: a (Kripke) model is just a nonempty set of *states*, where a state is an assignment of truth values to the primitive propositions of $\mathcal{L}$. We can think of these states as the worlds that the agent thinks are possible. Taken another way, they are the propositional assignments that do not contradict A's knowledge.

Given a model M, we now define what it means for $p \in \mathcal{L}$ to be true at a state $s \in M$, written $M, s \models p$, inductively as follows:

$M, s \models P$ iff $s(P) = \textbf{true}$ (i.e., s assigns P the value **true**).

$M, s \models p \wedge q$ iff $M, s \models p$ and $M, s \models q$.

$M, s \models \neg p$ iff $M, s \not\models p$.

$M, s \models K_A p$ iff $M, t \models p$ for all $t \in M$.

Thus $K_A p$ is true at a state in a Kripke model if p is true in all the worlds that A thinks are possible, and $K_A p$ is false exactly if there is a possible world where p is false.

This semantics precisely captures the intuition captured in the axioms above. In fact, as Kripke showed,

Theorem 1 ([Kr]): Axioms A1—A6, together with the inference rule *modus ponens*, form a sound and complete axiomatization for (S5) Kripke models.

We now relate Kripke models for knowledge and stable sets. Given a Kripke model M, we define $K(M)$, the set of facts that are known in M, to be the set $\{p : M, t \models p$ for all $t \in M\}$. Note that $p \in K(M)$ iff $M, t \models K_A p$ for all states $t \in M$ and $p \notin K(M)$ iff $M, t \models \neg K_A p$ for all states $t \in M$.

Lemma 2: If M is a Kripke model then $K(M)$ is a stable set.

Proof: Axiom A6 implies that $K(M)$ satisfies (St1) by A1, (St2) by A2, (St3) by A3 and A4, and (St4) by A5. By Theorem 1, $K(M)$ is consistent and therefore satisfies (St5). □

Proposition 3: Every stable set S determines a Kripke model M_S for which $S = K(M_S)$. Furthermore, if $\mathcal{L}$ has only a finite number of primitive propositions, then M_S is the unique Kripke model with this property.

Proof: Given S, let M_S consist of all the states consistent with S; i.e.,

$$M_S = \{s : s \text{ is a state that satisfies all the propositional formulas of } S\}.$$

By Lemma 2, $K(M_S)$ is a stable set. By the definition of M_S, the propositional formulas of $K(M_S)$ are exactly those of S. By Propostition 1, this implies that $S = K(M_S)$. Now assume that $\mathcal{L}$ has only finitely many primitive propositions, say $P_1, \ldots, P_N$. To show that the model M_S is the unique Kripke model such that $S = K(M_S)$, it suffices to show that if M and M' are two Kripke models and $M \neq M'$, then $K(M) \neq K(M')$.

So suppose $M \neq M'$. Without loss of generality, there is some state s such that $s \in M$ and $s \notin M'$. Let g be the propositional formula that completely describes the assignment s, namely $g = q_1 \wedge \ldots \wedge q_n$, where $q_i = P_i$ if $s(P_i) = \mathbf{true}$ and $q_i = \neg P_i$ if $s(P_i) = \mathbf{false}$. It is now easy to see that $\neg g \in K(M')$, since $s \notin M'$, but $\neg g \notin K(M)$ since $M, s \models g$. So $K(M) \neq K(M')$, and we are done. □

Lemma 2 and Proposition 3 were also observed independently by R. Moore, M. Fitting, and J. van Benthem. As a corollary to Proposition 3, we get:

Corollary 1: Stable sets are closed under S5 consequence. □

We remark that Corollary 1 shows that we could have replaced (St1) by (St1′):

(St1′) T contains all instances of S5 tautologies.

Which Kripke model is the one where A knows "only α"? Recall that a Kripke model consists of states which may be viewed as the worlds that A thinks are possible. Thus if $M \supset M'$, then the intuition is that A "knows less" in M than he does in M', since there are more worlds that he thinks the real world could be. Since the model in which A knows "only α" is intuitively the model in which he knows the least among all the models in which he knows α, this suggests that the appropriate model is one which is a superset of any other model in which A knows α. Denote by M_α the model that is the union of all models in which $K_A\alpha$ holds. By the above analysis, M_α should be the model that corresponds to A's state of knowledge when he "knows only α". However, it turns out that in some cases $\alpha \notin K(M_\alpha)$, meaning that $K_A\alpha$ does not hold in M_α. In those cases it seems that there is no good candidate for A's knowledge state when he knows only α. We call a formula α *honest*$_M$ if $\alpha \in K(M_\alpha)$.* An example of a formula that is not honest$_M$ is the familiar $\alpha = K_A P \vee K_A Q$. The models $M_P = \{s : s(P) = \mathbf{true}\}$ and $M_Q = \{s : s(Q) = \mathbf{true}\}$ both satisfy $K_A\alpha$. Let $M' = M_P \bigcup M_Q$. M' is a submodel of M_α, and therefore $K(M') \supseteq K(M_\alpha)$. But $\alpha \notin K(M')$ (check!) and therefore $\alpha \notin K(M_\alpha)$, and thus our chosen α is not honest$_M$.

As we show below, the notions of honest$_M$ and honest$_S$ coincide, as do $K(M_\alpha)$ and S^α for an honest formula α. But before we do this we present yet another approach to the problem, this one motivated by the intuition that given formulas p and α, there ought to be an algorithm for deciding if A knows p given that A knows only α. We now present such an algorithm. Our algorithm constructs a set D^α which is intended to consist of the facts that A knows, if A "knows only α".

What formulas belong in D^α? Since our perfect reasoner knows that his knowledge satisfies S5, any formula p for which $K_A\alpha \supset p$ is S5-valid should surely be in D^α. (We remark that S5 validity is decidable. Ladner [L] shows that, in the case of one knower, S5 validity is in Co-NP, which makes it no harder than the validity problem for propositional logic.) However, our previous remarks show that more than just the logical consequences of α should be in D^α. For example, if $\alpha = P$, then $\neg K_A Q$ is in D^α, as is $P \wedge \neg K_A Q$.

The algorithm is simply:

$p \in D^\alpha$ iff $[K_A\alpha \wedge \psi_\alpha(p)] \supset p$ is S5-valid,
where $\psi_\alpha(p)$ is the conjunction of $K_A q$ for all subformulas $K_A q$ of p for which $q \in D^\alpha$,

* M. Vardi first suggested this definition of honesty to us. H. Levesque suggested it independently.

and $\neg K_A q$ for all subformulas $K_A q$ of p for which $q \notin D^\alpha$ (where p is considered a subformula of itself).

It is easy to see that the above algorithm decides for any formula in the language whether or not it is a member of D^α. In order to decide if $p \in D^\alpha$, we must only invoke the algorithm on strict subformulas of p and then use the decision procedure for S5. Note that if a formula p is n characters long then it has no more than n subformulas, so that $\psi_\alpha(p)$ is finite and not much larger than p.

The intuition behind the algorithm is that a formula p is in D^α exactly if it is a logical consequence of knowing α and the K_A-subformulas of p that have already been decided. To understand what the algorithm does a bit better, the reader should note that a propositional formula g is in D^α exactly if $K_A\alpha \supset g$ is S5-valid. If $q \in D^\alpha$, then by definition $K_A q$ is one of the conjuncts of $\psi_\alpha(K_A q)$, so $K_A q \in D^\alpha$. Similarly, if $q \notin D^\alpha$, then $\neg K_A q$ is one of the conjuncts of $\psi_\alpha(\neg K_A q)$ and $\neg K_A q \in D^\alpha$.

This discussion suggests that D^α is a stable set, but this is not necessarily true. It turns out that there are formulas α for which D^α is not consistent. For example, consider $\alpha = P \wedge \neg K_A P$. Clearly α is consistent, but $K_A\alpha$ implies both $K_A P$ and $\neg K_A P$, and therefore is not consistent. Obviously, if $K_A\alpha$ is inconsistent then **false** $\in D^\alpha$, hence D^α is also inconsistent.

Even for formulas α for which $K_A\alpha$ is consistent, the set D^α generated by the algorithm might not be consistent. Consider again the formula $\alpha = K_A P \vee K_A Q$. The reader can easily verify that $\neg K_A P \in D^\alpha$, $\neg K_A Q \in D^\alpha$, and therefore $\neg K_A P \wedge \neg K_A Q \in D^\alpha$. But $\alpha = K_A P \vee K_A Q \in D^\alpha$. So, for this α, D^α is inconsistent. We call a formula α *honest*$_D$ if the set D^α is S5-consistent. At this point, the reader will not be surprised to learn that all the notions of honesty that we have defined coincide. We prove this in Theorem 2 below, but first we need:

Proposition 4: If α is honest$_D$ then D^α is a stable set.

Proof: Suppose α is honest$_D$. For any propositional tautology g, $K_A\alpha \supset g$ is S5-valid (by A1 and some straightforward propositional reasoning), so $g \in D^\alpha$ and (St1) is satisfied. By the discussion above, (St3) and (St4) are satisfied. By assumption, α is honest$_D$, so D^α is consistent and (St5) holds. Finally, for (St2), suppose that $p \supset q \in D^\alpha$, $p \in D^\alpha$, and $q \notin D^\alpha$. By (St3) and (St4), it follows that $K_A(p \supset q) \in D^\alpha$, $K_A p \in D^\alpha$, and $\neg K_A q \in D^\alpha$. Thus D^α is not S5-consistent, which contradicts the assumption that α is honest$_D$. $\square$

Our standard example of a "troublesome" formula is $K_A P \vee K_A Q$. As we have argued earlier, it is inconsistent for A to know this formula while knowing neither P nor Q. More generally, we say that a formula α is honest$_K$ if it satisfies the *propositional disjunction property*: whenever $K_A\alpha \supset K_A g_0 \vee K_A g_1 \vee \cdots \vee K_A g_m$ is an S5-valid formula, where $g_0, \ldots, g_m$ are propositional formulas, it is the case that $K_A\alpha \supset g_j$ is S5-valid, for some $0 \leq j \leq m$. A formula α that satisfies the propositional disjunction property also satisfies a slightly stronger property, namely: Whenever $K_A\alpha \supset g_0 \vee K_A g_1 \vee \cdots \vee K_A g_m$ is an S5-valid formula, where $g_0, \ldots, g_m$ are propositional formulas, it is the case that $K_A\alpha \supset g_j$ is S5-valid, for some $0 \leq j \leq m$. This follows because in S5 $K_A\alpha \supset K_A g_0 \vee K_A g_1 \vee \cdots \vee K_A g_m$ and $K_A\alpha \supset g_0 \vee K_A g_1 \vee \cdots \vee K_A g_m$ are equivalent.

We are finally ready to prove

Theorem 2:

(a) A formula α is honest$_M$ iff it is honest$_D$ iff it is honest$_S$ iff it is honest$_K$.

(b) For an honest α, $K(M_\alpha) = D^\alpha = S^\alpha$.

Proof: We will prove (a) by showing a cycle of implications involving the different notions of honesty. (b) will follow from the proof of (a).

honest$_M \Rightarrow$ honest$_D$: If α is honest$_M$ then M_α is the maximum model that satisfies $K_A\alpha$. We claim that $K(M_\alpha) = D^\alpha$, and show this by proving, by induction on the structure of p, that $p \in D^\alpha$ iff $p \in M_\alpha$. Thus assume that for any strict subformula q of p, we have $q \in D^\alpha$ iff $q \in K(M_\alpha)$. Suppose $p \in D^\alpha$. Thus we must have $\vdash_{S5} K_A\alpha \wedge \psi_\alpha(p) \supset p$. For every conjunct of the form $K_A q$ in $\psi_\alpha(p)$, we must have $q \in D^\alpha$, and thus by inductive hypothesis $q \in K(M_\alpha)$, so that $M_\alpha, t \models K_A q$ for every state $t \in M$. Similarly, for every conjunct of the form $\neg K_A q$ in $\psi_\alpha(p)$, we have $q \notin D^\alpha$, so $q \notin K(M_\alpha)$ and $M_\alpha, t \models \neg K_A q$ for all $t \in M_\alpha$. Thus $M_\alpha, t \models K_A\alpha \wedge \psi_\alpha(p)$ for all $t \in M_\alpha$. Since $\vdash_{S5} K_A\alpha \wedge \psi_\alpha(p) \supset p$, we must have $M_\alpha, t \models p$ for all $t \in M_\alpha$, and thus $p \in K(M_\alpha)$. For the converse, suppose $p \in K(M_\alpha)$, but $p \notin D^\alpha$. Thus it follows that $K_A\alpha \wedge \psi_\alpha(p) \wedge \neg p$ is S5-consistent, so there must be a model M' and a state $s' \in M'$, such that $M', s' \models K_A\alpha \wedge \psi_\alpha(p) \wedge \neg p$. Since $M' \subset M_\alpha$, we have $s' \in M_\alpha$. We claim that necessarily $M_\alpha, s' \models \neg p$. This contradicts the assumption that $p \in K(M_\alpha)$, so once we prove the claim we will be done. We prove the claim by showing, by induction on the structure of subformulas q of p, that if both $M_\alpha, s' \models \psi_\alpha(q)$ and $M', s' \models \psi_\alpha(q)$, then $M_\alpha, s' \models q$ iff $M', s' \models q$. The cases where q is a primitive proposition, a conjunction, or a negation are all straightforward and left to the reader. If q is of the form $K_A q'$, then $M_\alpha, s' \models K_A q'$ iff $K_A q'$ is one of the conjuncts of $\psi_\alpha(K_A q')$ (since $M_\alpha, s' \models \psi_\alpha(K_A q')$ by hypothesis, and one of $K_A q'$ and $\neg K_A q'$ must be a conjunct of $\psi_\alpha(K_A q'))$ iff $M', s' \models K_A q'$. Since $K(M_\alpha) = D^\alpha$, D^α must be consistent, so α is honest$_D$.

honest$_D \Rightarrow$ honest$_S$: By Proposition 4, if α is honest$_D$ then D^α is stable. By construction, $\alpha \in D^\alpha$, and for any propositional formula g, we have $g \in D^\alpha$ iff $K_A\alpha \supset g$ is S5-valid. Thus, D^α must be the stable set containing α with the smallest propositional subset. Therefore α is honest$_S$ and $D^\alpha = S^\alpha$.

honest$_S \Rightarrow$ honest$_K$: Since stable sets are closed under S5 consequence (Corollary 1), if $K_A\alpha \supset K_A g_0 \vee K_A g_1 \vee \cdots \vee K_A g_m$ is S5-valid, then every stable set containing α (and thus also $K_A\alpha$ by (St3)) must also contain $K_A g_0 \vee K_A g_1 \vee \cdots K_A g_n$. By repeated applications of Lemma 1, it follows that every stable set containing α must contain one of the g_i's. Given that α is honest$_S$, S^α is a stable set containing α. Let g_{i_0} be one of the g_i's such that $g_{i_0} \in S^\alpha$. g_{i_0} appears in all the stable sets that contain α. It follows that $K_A\alpha \supset g_{i_0}$ must be S5-valid. Otherwise, $K_A\alpha \wedge \neg g_{i_0}$ is S5-consistent, so for some model M and state $s \in M$, we have $M, s \models K_A\alpha \wedge \neg g_{i_0}$. Thus $K(M)$ is a stable set containing α but not containing g_{i_0}, a contradiction.

honest$_K \Rightarrow$ honest$_M$: Let $\mathcal{L}'$ be the sublanguage of $\mathcal{L}$ whose only primitive propositions are those that appear in α. It is straightforward to check that α has a maximum model with respect to $\mathcal{L}'$ (i.e. where the states only give truth assignments to the propositions in $\mathcal{L}'$) iff it has a maximum model with respect to $\mathcal{L}$. Thus without loss of generality we can assume that we are dealing with a language with only finitely many primitive propositions. Assume that α is honest$_K$ and not honest$_M$. Thus there are maximal models (w.r.t. inclusion) of $K_A\alpha$, but their union – M_α – is not a model of $K_A\alpha$. Since we have assumed that we are dealing with a language with only finitely many primitive propositions, there can only be finitely many maximal models of $K_A\alpha$, say $M_0, \ldots, M_{m-1}$. Each model M_i must have a state, say s_i which is not in $M_{i+1(mod\ m)}$. Let g_i be the formula that completely describes s_i, constructed just as in the proof of Proposition 3. The proof of Proposition 3 also shows that $\neg g_i \in K(M_{i+1(mod\ m)})$. It follows immediately from the Kripke semantics for S5 that $\neg g_i \in K(M')$ for any model $M' \subset M_{i+1(mod\ m)}$. Thus the formula $K_A\neg g_0 \vee \cdots \vee K_A\neg g_{m-1}$ is true at every state in every model of $K_A\alpha$. By Theorem 1, it follows that $K_A\alpha \supset K_A\neg g_0 \vee \cdots \vee K_A\neg g_{m-1}$ is an S5-valid formula. From (g), it follows that $K_A\alpha \supset \neg g_i$ must also be S5-valid for some i. But by construction, $M_i, s_i \models g_i \wedge K_A\alpha$, a contradiction. □

Theorem 2 indicates that the notion of what an agent knows if it "knows only α" is quite robust, as is the notion of honesty. Since we have proved that all our notions of honesty coincide, we will henceforth drop the subscript. The proof of the theorem also shows

Theorem 3: Honesty is decidable.

Proof: To check whether α is honest, it suffices to consider Kripke models for the subset of $\mathcal{L}$ containing only the primitive propositions that appear in α. There are only finitely many such Kripke models, and by enumerating them and checking in which ones α is known, it is simple to check whether $\alpha \in K(M_\alpha)$. $\square$

Of course, the decison procedure for honesty described above is computationally ineffecient, taking both exponential time and space. In the full paper we show that α is honest iff $\psi_\alpha(K_A\alpha)$ is S5-consistent. This gives us a method of deciding honesty which takes space linear in the size of α.

3. Extending to many knowers

In section 2, the agent A is the only knower. A can reason only about propositional facts in the world and about his own knowledge. In a situation where there are many agents (such as a distributed system), an agent can also reason about other agents' knowledge. As we mentioned in the introduction, such reasoning can become much more complex than that required for the one-knower case. We briefly discuss some of the issues here.

We extend the language $\mathcal{L}$ to allow formulas of the form $K_B p$, for all agents B. We can now define a notion of stable set that describes the properties of A's knowledge state in the many-knower case. Clearly properties (St1) – (St5) still hold, but (St1) is not quite strong enough. For example, A might know that B doesn't know P, i.e., $\neg K_B P \in T$. But since A knows that B can do perfect introspection, A also knows that B knows that B doesn't know P, so $K_B \neg K_B P \in T$. We could therefore expect $K_B \neg K_B P \in T$ whenever $\neg K_B P \in T$. Although $\neg K_B P \supset K_B \neg K_B P$ is a tautology of S5, it is not a propositional tautology. Thus we must strengthen (St1) to

(St1′) T contains all instances of S5 tautologies.

Recall that in the one-knower case, replacing (St1) by (St1′) yielded the same notion; this is not true in the many-knower case. We call a set satisfying (St1′), (St2) – (St5) *stable with respect to A*.

We remark that the validity problem for S5 with many knowers is complete for polynomial space (see [HM2] for a proof), while for a single knower it is in Co-NP. This increase in complexity supports our experience that the many-knower case is more complicated than the single knower case.

Characterizing honesty and the state of knowledge described by an honest α in the many-knower case is quite subtle. We outline some of the difficulties here, leaving details to the full paper.

For example, it is easy to see that the analogue of Proposition 1 no longer holds in the many-knower case, i.e., the propositional formulas no longer determine a stable set. Indeed, even all of the K_A-free formulas do not uniquely determine a set that is stable w.r.t. A. It is easy to construct two sets, both stable w.r.t. A, that agree on all K_A-free formulas, but differ on what agent B knows about what agent A knows. Thus the obvious approach to defining minimality for stable sets (in order to define the stable set S^α where A "knows only α") will not work. At this point, finding such a definition remains an open problem.*

Since propositional formulas no longer play the same essential role in the many-knower case, it should come as no surprise that honesty$_K$ (satisfying the propositional disjunction property) does not correspond to our intuitive notion of honesty in the many-knower case. For example, one can show that $K_A K_B P \vee K_A \neg K_B P$ is honest$_K$, although it should be considered dishonest for the same reasons $K_A P \vee K_A Q$ was dishonest in the single-knower case.

A more promising approach is via Kripke models. As is well-known, Kripke models for multi-agent S5 can be constructed (see, for example, [MSHI,Mo1,HM2]), and given a Kripke model M, it is straightforward to define a stable set $K(M)$ in a manner completely analogous to the one-knower case, and show that every stable set is of the form $K(M)$ for some Kripke model. We can also define a notion of a *canonical* Kripke model, for which a notion of a maximum model M_α makes sense, and thus define a notion of honest$_M$. The algorithm of the previous section can also be extended to the many-knower case, leading to a definition of honest$_D$ that is provably equivalent to honest$_M$. We leave further details of the multi-agent case to the full paper.

4. Comparison to related work

As we remarked in the introduction, our work is closely related to [St], [Ko2] and [Mo2]. We discuss the relationship in this section.

---

* A stable set w.r.t. A *is* uniquely determined by its non-K_A formulas (i.e., those in which no K_A operator appears at top level). However, no formula α has a stable set with a minimum non-K_A subset. To see this, pick your favorite α. Let Q be a primitive proposition that does not appear in α, and is therefore independent of $K_A\alpha$. Any stable set that contains α but does not contain Q contains $\neg K_A Q$ and $\neg K_B K_A Q$. But there is a stable set containing α and Q that does not contain $\neg K_B K_A Q$. Therefore, there is no stable set containing α with a minimum non-K_A subset.

Suppose we define a nonmonotonic provability relation $\mid\!\sim_A$ via

$$\alpha \mid\!\sim_A p \text{ iff } p \in D^\alpha.$$

Of course, if α is dishonest, then $\mid\!\sim_A$ "proves" inconsistent statements, so we restrict our attention to honest α's.

In [St], Stark introduces a nonmonotonic logic MK, where a nonmonotonic inference rule, the *model theorist's deduction rule* (m.t.d.r.), that allows individuals to reason about their ignorance, is added to the S5 axioms. The rule is:

$$\text{From } T \not\vdash_{\text{S5}} K_A p \text{ deduce } T \vdash_{\text{MK}} \neg K_A p.$$

The intuition behind this rule is that if T characterizes A's knowledge, and from T it is not possible to conclude (using S5) that A knows p, then indeed A does not know p.

As Stark observes, we quickly run into inconsistencies if we allow unrestricted use of this rule. For example, if $T = \{\textbf{true}\}$, the empty theory, we get $T \not\vdash_{\text{S5}} K_A p$ and $T \not\vdash_{\text{S5}} K_A \neg K_A p$, so by the m.t.d.r. we get $T \vdash_{\text{MK}} \neg K_A p$ and $T \vdash_{\text{MK}} \neg K_A \neg K_A p$. But $\vdash_{\text{S5}} \neg K_A \neg K_A p \equiv K_A p$, which gives us an inconsistency.*

Stark's solution to this problems is to restrict the p in the conclusion of the m.t.d.r. to be K_A-free. However, this restriction limits the usefulness of the rule. In a multi-agent scenario, A might certainly want to reason about what B knows about A's knowledge. This restriction also has the effect that the m.t.d.r. cannot be used repeatedly, since the result of an application of m.t.d.r. is a K_A formula.

Our $\mid\!\sim_A$ relation satisfies a cleaner version of the m.t.d.r. rule, namely:

$$\text{If } \alpha \not\mid\!\sim_A K_A p \text{ then } \alpha \mid\!\sim_A \neg K_A p.$$

In this rule the application of the model theorist's deduction is done within the theory. Furthermore, for honest α's its usage is unrestricted. Thus $\mid\!\sim_A$ captures the intuitive intent of the m.t.d.r. without imposing any unnatural restrictions. (See also [Pa] for a treatment of this issue.)

In [Ko2], Konolige develops a theory of "Circumscriptive Ignorance". He treats knowledge for which he assumes the axioms of S4; i.e., S5 without the axiom $\neg K_A p \supset$

---

* Stark also notices that if T is a dishonest formula, such as $K_A P \vee K_A Q$, we again get an inconsistency (since $T \vdash_{\text{MK}} \neg K_A P$ and $T \vdash_{\text{MK}} \neg K_A Q$). He shows that no problems arise if T is *natural* in that whenever $T \vdash_{\text{S5}} K_{A_{i_1}} q_1 \vee \ldots \vee K_{A_{i_m}} q_m$, then $T \vdash_{\text{S5}} K_{A_{i_j}} q_j$ for some $1 \leq j \leq m$. Compare this with our notion of honest$_K$ and Theorem 2.

$K_A \neg K_A p$. In his formalism, $[K_A p]q$ denotes that A knows q if all he knows is p. Roughly speaking, $[K_A p]q$ if $\models_{S4} K_A p \supset q$. This roughly corresponds to $p \mid\!\sim_A q$. Indeed, $[K_A p]q$ implies $[K_A p]K_A q$, just as $p \mid\!\sim_A q$ implies $p \mid\!\sim_A K_A q$. However, while $p \not\mid\!\sim_A q$ implies $p \mid\!\sim_A \neg K_A q$, it is *not* the case that $\neg[K_A p]q$ implies $[K_A p] \neg K_A q$. (The fact that q is not an S4 consequence of $K_A p$ does not imply that $\neg K_A q$ is an S4 consequence of $K_A p$.) Thus, in Konolige's formalism, although given α you can deduce your ignorance, there is no way to incorporate this information into the set of things you know.

In [Mo2], Moore presents a non-monotonic logic of belief, where he assumes that belief satisfies the axioms of K5 (S5 without the axiom $Kp \supset p$). Moore defines a stable set T to be "grounded in a set of premises α" if, roughly speaking, a rational agent is justified in believing T given that the agent knows only α. More formally, Moore denotes belief by L, and defines T to be a *stable expansion of* α if T is equal to the set of *propositional* consequences of

$$\{\alpha\} \bigcup \{Lp : p \in T\} \bigcup \{\neg Lp : p \notin T\}.$$

Not surprisingly, it turns out that for many formulas α, T is a stable expansion of α exactly if $T = S^{\alpha}$. In fact, it can be shown that if an honest formula has a stable expansion, then that set is unique and equals S^{α}.

However, it turns out that there are formulas, both honest and dishonest, that have no stable expansion, and dishonest formulas that have a stable expansion. The reason hinges on the difference between knowledge and belief. For example, the formula $\alpha = LP$ has no stable expansion. Technically, this happens because any stable set containing LP must contain P, but P is not a propositional consequence of any set of L and $\neg L$ formulas. More informally, this is true because believing P does not give any grounds for concluding that P is true in the world. On the other hand, $K_A P$ is honest because an ideally rational agent that claims to know only $K_A P$ is completely describing its state of knowledge (and incidentally also saying that P is true in the world). Conversely, $\neg K_A P \supset Q$ (or equivalently $K_A P \vee Q$) is dishonest, while $\neg LP \supset Q$ has a unique stable expansion. We return to this point in the next section.

Roughly speaking then, if we consider knowledge rather than belief, an ideally rational agent knowing α also knows all the facts about the world that are S5 consequences of $K_A \alpha$. This suggests the following alternative definition:

A set R is *rooted in* α if R equals the set of propositional consequences of

$$\{\text{propositional } g : K_A \alpha \supset g \text{ is S5} - \text{valid}\} \bigcup \{K_A p : p \in R\} \bigcup \{\neg K_A p : p \notin R\}.$$

This notion is clearly closely related to the Moore's notion of a stable expansion. The following theorem relates it to our other notions.

Theorem 4:

(a) For all α, there is a unique set R^α rooted in α.

(b) If $K_A\alpha$ is consistent then R^α is stable; otherwise, R^α is the inconsistent set $\mathcal{L}$ of all formulas.

(c) α is honest iff R^α is consistent and $\alpha \in R^\alpha$.

(d) For an honest α, $R^\alpha = S^\alpha = D^\alpha = K(M_\alpha)$.

Proof: Let R be a set that is rooted in α. If $K_A\alpha$ is inconsistent, then **false** $\in R$, and because R contains all the propositional tautologies and is propositionally closed, $R = \mathcal{L}$. Otherwise it is easy to check that R must be the stable set S such that $Prop(S) = \{\text{propositional } g : K_A\alpha \supset g \text{ is S5} - \text{valid}\}$. The theorem follows from these observations; we leave details to the reader. □

5. Conclusions

We have investigated the state of knowledge of an agent whose information is completely described by a formula α. This arises, for example, if α is the formula that completely describes the agent's database of known facts. We made a number of attempts at characterising this state of knowledge, motivated by semantic considerations and heuristic guidelines. For a certain class of formulas α that we call "honest", the state of knowledge corresponding to knowing "only α" turned out to be the same in all our approaches. For α's that are not honest, none of the approaches specifies a state of knowledge corresponding to knowing "only α". This suggests that the notions involved are in some precise sense robust, and do not depend in an essential way on the specific definition of what "knowing only α" means.

We have suggested here how our results can be extended to the many-knower case, but more work needs to be done in this regard. In particular, we have not considered what happens when certain properties of the system or group are common knowledge; e.g., it may be commonly known that databases are secure, so if a processor does not reveal that it knows a certain fact P, then it will know that no other processor can know that it knows P. Further work is also required on the first-order case. Note that once we can completely describe the state of knowledge a processor is in when it "knows only α", we can answer the original question that motivated this paper: we simply take

α to describe the communication that has taken place thus far (we are assuming here, of course, that the language is powerful enough to permit us to do this).

Let us briefly consider how this work relates to default rules in non-monotonic reasoning (cf. [Re]). Roughly speaking, a standard default rule has the form $\neg K_A p \supset q$, meaning that q (the default) is true unless p is known to be true. If p and q are propositional formulas, then the formula $\neg K_A p \supset q$ by itself is dishonest. In fact, for an honest α, this formula is a consequence of "knowing only α" exactly if one of p or q is. It follows that formulas of the form $\neg K_A p \supset q$ do not behave as default rules in our formalism. It might seem that we must now make a grave decision: either give up on default rules, viewing the results of this paper as sound technical testimony to the inexistence of consistent non-monotonic default rules, or give up on the modal logic S5 as an appropriate way to model our knowledge, and resort either to a logic that exludes one or both of the introspective axioms, or to a logic of belief such as K5. In a sense, Moore [Mo2] chooses to go to belief.

For certain applications, especially those involving distributed computation, the axioms of S5 are indeed a useful way of modelling an agent's knowledge (cf. [HM1]). Nevertheless, it is often still desirable to have and use default rules in order to compensate for an agent's lack of complete information. It seems that we can have our cake and eat it too if we extend our language to talk about knowledge *and* belief. A default rule is in some sense a "rule of conjecture", because for the propositional p and q above it is not our knowledge or ignorance of p that makes q true, but it is our information regarding our knowledge-gathering capabilities that leads us to believe q in the absence of our knowledge of p. It follows that in many cases of interest, the default rules can be taken to be "rules of conjecture", and therefore may be believed rather than known. A default rule may therefore be written as

$$B_A(\neg K_A p \supset q),$$

where B_A stands for A's belief. We may assume that the belief operator is fully introspective and in fact satisfies the axioms of K5 (cf. [Le]), and the axiom linking knowledge to belief is

$$K_A p \supset B_A K_A p.$$

We conjecture that such an approach can be successfully carried out, and that it may turn out combine knowledge and belief in a framework that retains the best of both worlds.

Acknowledgements: We would like to thank Ron Fagin, Mike Fischer, Neil Immerman, Danny Lehmann, Hector Levesque, Bob Moore, Johan van Benthem, and Moshe Vardi for many stimulating discussions on knowledge which helped decrease our ignorance. We also thank Bob Moore for pointing out an error in an early version of Theorem 4.

References

[FHV] R. Fagin, J. Y. Halpern, and M. Y. Vardi, A model-theoretic analysis of knowledge: preliminary report, *Proceedings of the 25th IEEE Symposium on Foundations of Computer Science*, 1984, pp. 268-278; also appears as IBM RJ 4373.

[HM1] J. Y. Halpern and Y. Moses, Knowledge and common knowledge in a distributed environment, *Proceedings of the 3rd ACM Symposium on Principles of Distributed Computing*, 1984, pp. 50–61; a revised version appears as IBM RJ 4421.

[HM2] J. Y. Halpern and Y. Moses, A guide to modal logics of knowledge, to appear as an IBM RJ, 1985.

[Hi] J. Hintikka, *Knowledge and Belief*, Cornell University Press, 1962.

[HC] G. E. Hughes and M. J. Cresswell, *An Introduction to Modal Logic,* Methuen, London, 1968.

[Kr] S. Kripke, Semantical considerations of modal logic, *Zeitschrift fur Mathematische Logik und Grundlagen der Mathematik* **9**, pp. 67–96, 1963.

[Ko1] K. Konolige, A deduction model of belief, unpublished manuscript, 1984.

[Ko2] K. Konolige, Circumscriptive ignorance, *Conference Proceedings of AAAI–82*, pp. 202–204.

[La] R. E. Ladner, The computational complexity of provability in systems of modal propositional logic, *Siam J. Computing*, **6**:3, 1977, pp. 467–480.

[Le] H. J. Levesque, A formal treatment of incomplete knowledge bases, Fairchild Technical Report No. 614, FLAIR Technical Report No. 3, 1982.

[Mc] J. McCarthy, Circumscription – a form of non-monotonic reasoning, *Artificial Intelligence* **13**, 1980, pp. 27–39.

[MSHI] J. McCarthy, M. Sato, T. Hayashi, S. Igarashi, On the model theory of knowledge, *Computer Science Technical Report* STAN-CS-78-657, Stanford University, April 1978.

[Mo1] R. C. Moore, Reasoning about knowledge and action, *Artificial Intelligence Center Technical Note* 191, SRI International, 1980.

[Mo2] R. C. Moore, Semantical considerations on nonmonotonic logic, *SRI International Technical Note 284*, 1983.

[Pa] R. Parikh, Monotonic and non-monotonic logics of knowledge, unpublished manuscript, 1984.

[Re] R. Reiter, A logic for default reasoning, *Artificial Intelligence* **13**, 1980, pp. 81–132.

[S] R. Stalnaker, A note on non-monotonic modal logic, unpublished manuscript, Department of Philosophy, Cornell University.

[St] W. R. Stark, A logic of knowledge, *Zeitschrift fur Mathematische Logik und Grundlagen der Mathematik* **27**, pp. 371 – 374, 1981.

On the Development of Reactive Systems*

D. Harel and A. Pnueli

Department of Applied Mathematics
The Weizmann Institute of Science
Rehovot 76100, Israel

January, 1985

Abstract

Some observations are made concerning the process of developing complex systems. A broad class of systems, termed ***reactive***, is singled out as being particularly problematic when it comes to finding satisfactory methods for behavioral description. In this paper we recommend the recently proposed statechart method for this purpose. Moreover, it is observed that most reactive systems cannot be developed in a linear stepwise fashion, but, rather, give rise to a two-dimensional development process, featuring behavioral aspects in the one dimension and implementational ones in the other. Concurrency may occur in both dimensions, as ***orthogonality*** of states in the one and as ***parallelism*** of subsystems in the other. A preliminary approach to working one's way through this "magic square" of system development is then presented. The ideas described herein seem to be relevant to a wide variety of application areas.

Why Another Paper on System Development?

The literature on software engineering, programming languages, and system and hardware design, is brimming with papers describing methods for specifying and designing large and complex systems. Why then are we

* This research was supported in part by grants from AD CAD Inc. and the Israel Aircraft Industries.

NATO ASI Series, Vol. F13
Logics and Models of Concurrent Systems
Edited by K. R. Apt

writing yet another one?

In many kinds of computation-oriented or data-processing systems, sometimes characterized as sequential or functional systems, there is, for the most part, consensus as to the basic philosophy for design. For more complex systems, involving many concurrently executing components, which at times integrate software and hardware, there is much less of an agreement. As we argue below, this is due to an essential difference between two kinds of systems that makes the process of developing the more complicated of the two inherently more difficult. Indeed, we would like to think of the present paper as primarily containing an attempt to clarify some of the underlying notions which seem to us to be fundamental. In passing, we shall attempt to address such issues as the kinds of systems that require new ideas, and the gaps such ideas ought to fill.

Which Systems are Problematic?

We would like to state from the start that by "systems" we do not wish to restrict ourselves to ones which are software-based, hardware-based or so-called computer-embedded. The terminology we shall be using is general enough for these and others, and so we shall not be specific about the final form the implementation of the system takes.

In many circles it is common to try to identify the features characterizing "difficult" systems; that is, the ones for which special methods and approaches are needed. Resulting from these efforts are various dichotomies distinguishing the easily-dealt-with systems from the problematic ones. Some people (e.g. in the programming language semantics community) have put forward the deterministic/nondeterministic dichotomy: systems for which the next action is uniquely defined can be easily defined, while nondeterminism requires special treatment. Others (such as certain verification researchers) have suggested that the problems lie in perpetual systems, whereas terminating ones are easy. Additional dichotomies that have been suggested are the synchronous/asynchronous, "lazy" / real-time, and off-line/on-line ones, and what is perhaps the most popular one: the sequential/concurrent dichotomy. Indeed, concurrency gives rise to problems that are quite different from the ones sequential systems present, and there are entire schools of thought devoted to solving the problems raised by the presence of concurrently operating elements.

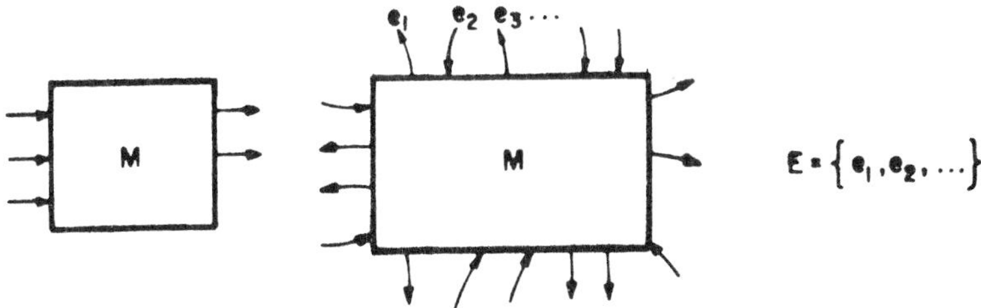

Fig. 1: A transformational system as a black box **Fig. 2**: A reactive system as a "black cactus"

As it turns out, all the dichotomies mentioned are real and the problems the more difficult members of each pair present are indeed crucial. We wish, however, to point to another dichotomy, one which we think is the most fundamental of all and the one that seems to us to best distinguish systems that are relatively easy to develop from those that are not. We feel that once the problematic part of this pair is satisfactorily solved, most of the others will yield less painfully too. Our proposed distinction is between what we call *transformational* and *reactive* systems. A transformational system accepts inputs, performs transformations on them and produces outputs; see Fig. 1. Actually, we include in the definition of a transformational system also ones which may ask for additional inputs and/or produce some of their outputs as they go along. The point, however, is that, globally speaking, these systems perform input/output operations, perhaps prompting a user from time to time to provide extra information. Reactive systems, on the other hand, are repeatedly prompted by the outside world and their role is to continuously respond to external inputs; see Fig. 2. A reactive system, in general, does not compute or perform a function, but is supposed to maintain a certain ongoing relationship, so to speak, with its environment.

At this point, the reader should observe that reactive systems are everywhere. From microwave ovens and digital watches, through man/machine based software systems, silicon chips, robots and communication networks, all the way to computer operating systems, complex industrial plants, avionics systems and the like. Common to all of these is the notion of the system responding or reacting to external stimuli, whether normal user-generated or environment-generated ones (such as a lever pulled or the temperature rising), or abnormal ones (such as a power failure). Such systems do not lend themselves naturally to description in terms of functions and transformations. Of course, mathematically speaking, it is always possible to take time itself as an additional input (and output) and turn any reactive system into a transformational one; needless to say, this idea is unrealistic and we shall not adopt it here.

The transformational/reactive dichotomy cuts across all the aforementioned ones: both types of systems can be deterministic or not, terminating or not, on-line or not, and contain concurrently executing components or not. Also, reactive systems can be required to respond in real-time or not, and the cooperation of their components can be required to be synchronous or not. What then is so important about the distinction we are making, and why are we claiming that it is the reactive nature of systems that is problematic?

What is the Problem?

The answer to these questions seems to us to be rooted in the notion of the ***behavior*** of a system. While the design of the system and then its construction are no doubt of paramount importance (they are in fact the only things that ultimately count) they cannot be carried out without a clear understanding of the system's intended behavior. This assertion is not one which can easily be contested, and anyone who has ever had anything to do with a complex system has felt its seriousness. A natural, comprehensive, and understandable description of the behavioral aspects of a system is a must in all stages of the system's development cycle, and, for that matter, after it is completed too.

Taking a very broad and abstract view, we may describe a typical top-down development process as a sequence of transformations:

$$(\mathbf{M}^{(0)}, \mathbf{S}^{(0)}) \rightarrow (\mathbf{M}^{(1)}, \mathbf{S}^{(1)}) \rightarrow \cdots \rightarrow (\mathbf{M}^{(f)}, \mathbf{S}^{(f)})$$

The structure studied at each level is a pair $(\mathbf{M}^{(i)}, \mathbf{S}^{(i)})$ comprising a ***specified system*** at the i'th level of detail; $\mathbf{M}^{(i)}$ is the i'th level physical, or implementational, description, and $\mathbf{S}^{(i)}$ is the behavioral specification. At the top level $\mathbf{M}^{(0)}$ might be highly underspecified, with $\mathbf{S}^{(0)}$ using such vague terms as "a data-base system responding to conjunctive queries", "a plane for interception", etc. Each level, even the 0'th one, needs some description of the interface of the system with its environment. This can be done by including a list $\mathbf{E}^{(i)}$ in each of the $\mathbf{M}^{(i)}$, containing descriptions of those input and output channels, signals, requests and responses, that constitute the system's interaction with the "outside world". The level of detail in the interface lists can also vary with i, from highly abstract items such as "request communication" or "display target", all the way down to concrete lists of buttons, levers, displays and alarms. The corresponding behavioral specification $\mathbf{S}^{(i)}$ should characterize the desired behavior of the system, in as complete a manner as possible, using the elements of $\mathbf{E}^{(i)}$.

Any development step progressing from level i to level $i+1$ must include a verification of the consistency of $S^{(i+1)}$ with $S^{(i)}$. This is true regardless of whether it was the refinement of $M^{(i)}$ or of $S^{(i)}$ that prescribed the progress made. At times one can provide a rigid set of possible refinement rules for producing $S^{(i+1)}$ from $S^{(i)}$. In these cases the rules are internally, or locally, consistent, so that a development process that uses them is automatically guaranteed to be globally consistent. A good example of this is in pure software systems where one may use various established program transformations which also prescribe the corresponding transformations on the specification.

To be slightly more specific, one can think of a reactive system $\mathbf{M}$ as a "black cactus" of sorts (in contrast with a black box). The "thorns" of this cactus are simply the interface elements comprising the set $\mathbf{E}$; see Fig. 2. A behavioral description $\mathbf{S}$ of the system should give rise to a set consisting of the legal sequences of these external input and output events and conditions. Thus, describing the behavior should boil down to defining a subset of the set of finite and infinite words over $\mathbf{E}$. Of course, if timing is important, this simplistic definition has to be extended, for example by attaching a time stamp to each element in the sequence, or by specifying the timing constraints separately, but for now specifying the sequences will suffice. This relationship between $\mathbf{M}$, $\mathbf{E}$ and $\mathbf{S}$, holds for the level-dependent versions $\mathbf{M}^{(i)}$, $\mathbf{E}^{(i)}$ and $\mathbf{S}^{(i)}$ too.

Now, there have been numerous suggestions for methods, languages and formalisms to be used in the development of complex systems. Many of these are extremely helpful, and in general adopt a stepwise approach such as the one just outlined. They are, for the most part, well-structured and modular, and recommend a gradual step by step development in a top-down, bottom-up or mixed fashion; many of them are visual in nature, or at least have a visual counterpart and are thus easy to grasp; a number of them are based on firm and precise mathematical models which admit certain kinds of formal reasoning.

However, as it turns out, the methods existing for stepwise, well-structured and coherent development of systems are predominantly ***transformational*** in nature. In transformational systems it is possible, actually highly desirable, to decompose the system in a way reflecting the natural "structure of the problem", as it is sometimes referred to. In other words, a high-level description of the problem, in the form of the transformation, or function, that the system is supposed to carry out, is decomposed in these methods into several smaller problems of the same species, in the form of lower level transformations, with the appropriate identifications made among incoming and outgoing items. Each lower level transformation is then considered in its own right, and further decomposed. This is but another way of saying that each $\mathbf{S}^{(i+1)}$ consists of a set of transformations, each of which was obtained from a transformation in $\mathbf{S}^{(i)}$ by transformational, or functional, decomposition. The system description $\mathbf{M}^{(i+1)}$ is then taken to match the transformations described in $\mathbf{S}^{(i+1)}$ as closely as possible.

This is admittedly a very crude and sketchy account of such methods, but the point we wish to make is that the procedure it illustrates works nicely for transformational systems because transformations decompose naturally into other transformations, and implementations of transformations decompose into implementations of other transformations. It is therefore a small thing for one to observe that the two decompositions can (and then even recommend that they should) be essentially the same, or at least that they be related via a simple mapping. This is particularly attractive due to the fact that transformational decomposition provides not only static information but also the dynamics necessary for a good behavioral description. For example, a conventional structure diagram or a function tree, two of the kinds of descriptions recurring in the literature, can be given clear operational meanings when considered for transformational systems: inputs (data and/or control) flow into boxes, modules or functions, which proceed to perform their designated transformations, yielding outputs which in turn flow into others, etc. This is a wholly satisfactory behavioral description of a transformational system.

It is for these reasons that in most software engineering views of the life cycle of a system the specification stage is more or less followed by the design one: decompose the problem (=specify), and then use its parts and their interconnections as the basis for planning the implementation (=design). This idea is also one of the implicit mottos of structured programming: let the structure of the program reflect the structure of the problem, or, as one might say, let chunks of implementation (e.g. procedures, blocks, tasks, etc.) be made to correspond to chunks of behavior.

Our main argument here is that this cheerful situation does not apply to reactive systems at all. In a reactive system, even a pure software one, it is not clear if or how complex behavior can at all be decomposed beneficially into chunks, let alone for that decomposition to become the basis for system design. This observation notwithstanding, it is ironical that a breakup of the behavior is precisely what will eventually have to be found, whether one likes it or not: the final system will, if completed, consist of various increasingly more complex actual components (software, hardware or mixed), each of which will, by its very existence, have to have some kind of associated behavior. Moreover, these components will most probably be reactive themselves. And so, developing the system will ultimately have to involve some kind of physical decomposition, which, one way or another, will have to be matched by a behavioral decomposition too.

Let us for now, however, postpone the problem of connecting behavioral descriptions of reactive systems with their implementational ones. Our first concern is with specifying the reactive behavior itself. How does reactive behavior decompose? What can be done to encourage stepwise refinement of the behavioral aspects of a system? How can one cope with the intricacy that the behavior of a complex reactive system presents??

Before attempting to answer these questions, let us state the following requisites, which we feel ought to be required from any satisfactory method for behavioral description:

(i) It should provide descriptions that are well-structured, concise, unambiguous, readable, and easy to understand.

(ii) It should be solely descriptive, eliminating, or at least minimizing, dependence on any implementational issues.

Requirement (i) implies that the method must have a simple but rigourous semantics, and (ii) implies that the structuring of a behavioral description should reflect the natural decomposition of the problem rather than that of the implementation.

A Method for Behavioral Description

The ***statecharts*** method was introduced recently[1] as a visual formalism for specifying the behavior of complex reactive systems. The process of preparing statecharts for a system is called the system's ***statification***, and

---

[1] See D. Harel, "Statecharts: A Visual Approach to Complex Systems", CS84-05, The Weizmann Institute of Science, February 1984 (revised December 1984).

it consists of describing the system's behavior in terms of states, events and conditions, with combinations of the latter two causing transitions between the former. Both states and transitions can be associated in various ways with output events, called ***activities***, which can be triggered either by executing a transition or by entering, exiting, or simply being in a state. The system's inputs are thus the (external) events and its outputs are the (external) activities; their union comprises the interface set **E**.

This, as the reader can no doubt see, is a standard and well-known idea, and is actually a simple combination of the Moore and Mealy definitions of finite state automata. The allowed sequences over **E** correspond to the language accepted by the automaton. Moreover, such automata come complete with a standard visual renderation, the transition diagram. This classical state transition method, however, has been all but abandoned as a way of specifying the behavior of complex systems since it provides no modularity or hierarchical structure, and suffers acutely from the exponential blowup in the number of states that need be considered, and hence also in the number of transitions. Indeed, a state/event description seems to have to consider all possible combinations of states in all the components of the system; hence the exponential growth.

The statechart method is rooted in an attempt to revive this old and natural way of thinking about a system's behavior, by extending it in several fundamental ways aimed at overcoming the aforementioned difficulties. The extensions apply to the underlying nongraphical formalism too, but personal preference towards visual descriptions has led us to present the ideas in terms of the graphical version. Some of the extensions are now briefly described, but the reader is strongly advised to consult the original paper for the others, as well as for a detailed example and further discussions.

States in a statechart can be repeatedly combined into higher-level states (or, alternatively, high-level states can be refined into lower-level ones) using AND and OR modes of clustering. Fig. 3 shows a state B whose meaning is "to be in B the system must be in precisely one of D, E or F," and Fig. 4 shows a state A whose meaning is "to be in A the system must be both in B and in C." Notice, however, that in Fig. 4, B and C are themselves OR states, thus the actual possibilities are the state configurations (D,G), (D,H), (E,G), (E,H), (F,G), and (F,H). We say that D, E and F are ***exclusive*** and B and C are ***orthogonal***.

Transitions in a statechart are not level-restricted and can lead from

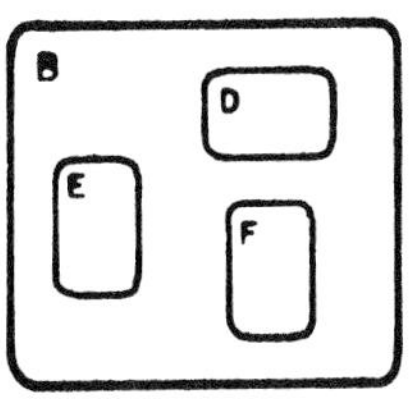

Fig. 3: OR-ing states

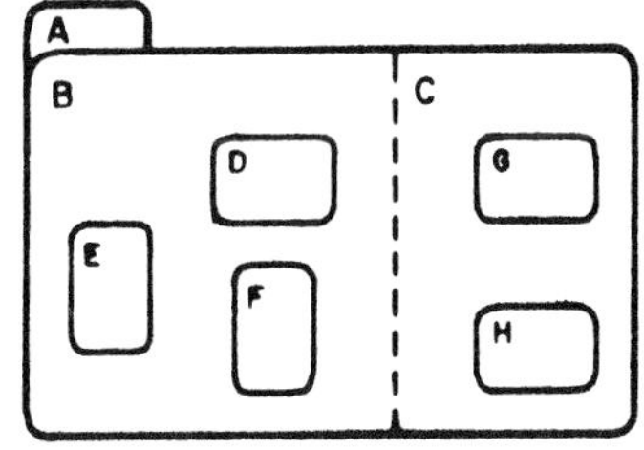

Fig. 4: AND-ing states

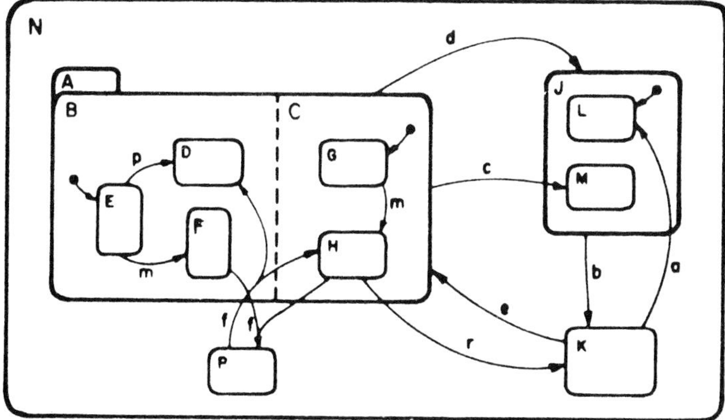

Fig. 5: An output-free statechart

a state on any level of clustering to any other. A significant decision here is to take a transition whose source state is a "superstate" to mean "the system leaves this state no matter which is the present configuration within it." In this way, while event a in Fig. 5 causes a simple transition from state K to L, the event b exemplifies a concise way of causing the system to leave L or M, i.e. any possibility of being in J, and to enter K. Likewise, c causes the system to exit any one of the A-configurations listed above and enter M. If the target of a transition is a superstate, as in the case of events d or e in this example, a default arrow must be present indicating which of the lower-level states is actually to be entered (L or the combination (E, G) in this example).

Actually, transitions are in general from configurations to configurations, owing to the possibility of orthogonal components in the source and target states. Thus, in Fig. 5 if event f takes place in configuration (F, H) the system enters P and if the same happens in P the system enters (D, H). Concurrency and independence are both made possible by orthogonality: on the one hand event m causes simultaneous transitions in B and C if the configuration is (E, G), and on the other p causes E to be replaced by D regardless of, and with no change to, the present state in C. It is noteworthy that orthogonality (and hence the possibilities it raises) is allowed and encouraged on any level of detail, as the statifier sees fit. Accordingly, a configuration can be layered too, containing orthogonal state components on many levels.

Outputs can be associated with transitions as in Mealy automata by writing a/b along an arrow; the transition will be triggered by a and will in turn cause b to occur. Similarly, b can be associated with (entering, exiting, or simply being in) a state, in line with Moore automata. In either case b can be an external event or an internal one, in the latter case triggering perhaps other transitions elsewhere in some orthogonal state.

The statification method is purely behavioral and requires of its user to think in terms of the system's conceptual states and their interconnections. It caters for modular "chunking" of behavior in several ways, most notably by using exclusivity and orthogonality of states, and provides the mechanisms needed for manipulating these modules as separate entities. Statecharts are strongly oriented towards "deep" structured descriptions that are organized into many levels of detail, and permit "zooming" easily in and out of these levels. One can construct them in a disciplined hierarchical way, statifying a system level by level, or use interlevel transitions and vary the depth as deemed appropriate. Statification can proceed by top-down refinement, bottom-up clustering, or a mixture of both. Note that the exponential blowup in states does not arise here at all, as the option of using orthogonality on any level eliminates the need for explicit consideration of all state combinations.

As a truely simple example of the way statechart levels refine reactive behavior, consider the system whose interface set **E** is as in Fig. 6. Its behavioral specification is given on two succesive levels in Figs. 7 and 8. The allowed sequences in Fig. 7 can be described by the regular expression

$$B_1^* \cdot (a \cdot B_2^* \cdot a \cdot B_1^*)^\omega \cup B_1^* \cdot (a \cdot B_2^* \cdot a \cdot B_1^*)^* \cdot (B_1^\omega \cup a \cdot B_2^\omega)$$

where $B_1 = (b \cup c \cup d)$ and $B_2 = (b \cup c \cup e)$. The version in Fig. 8, on the other hand, refines the allowed behavior to the sequences given by the same expression, but with $B_1 = (b \cup bcd)$, and $B_2 = (b \cup bce)$.

This, then, is the formalism we wish to recommend for specifying reactive behavior. It is important to observe that the description can be made to reflect the statifier's personal and natural view of the system's

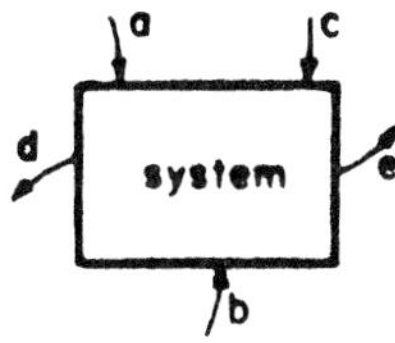

Fig. 6: A reactive system with its interface set

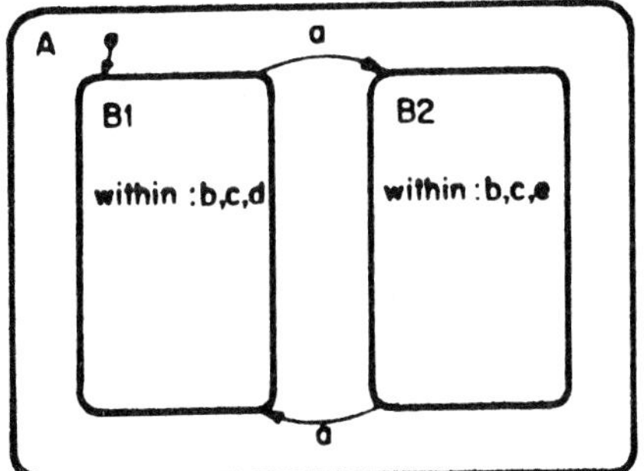

Fig. 7: A statechart

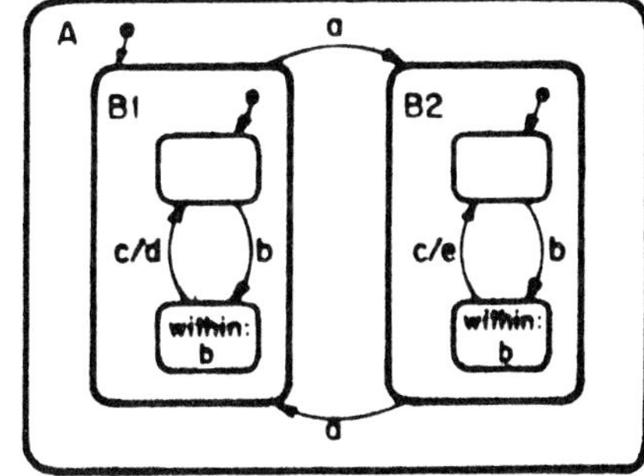

Fig. 8: A refined statechart

behavior, free, if so desired, from implementational details. If lifting a receiver conceptually causes a communication system to enter conversation mode, and this mode entails certain actions, one can say just that, disregarding such questions as which component is responsible for sensing the lifting of the receiver and how the sensed fact is communicated to the others. Of course, the crucial problem here is bringing this conceptual description down to earth; meaning, how does one combine it with the natural implementational process of breaking the system down into its physical parts and their interconnections.

The Magic Square of System Development

Now that we know how to decompose reactive behavior, we can attempt to apply the "problem structure matches system structure" principle. Indeed, if there are no limitations on the implementation at all one can do just that; refine the behavioral specification by adding statechart levels as illustrated above, and then perform the implemenatational refinement to match. While this might sound overly naive, in a pure software system with a sufficiently high-level programming language, the statecharts can be directly encoded into software, with multi-level orthogonality being translated into nested concurrency. This applies to other possible methods for reactive behavior specification, such as Petri nets or languages like CCS.

It is clear, however, that the vast majority of interesting reactive systems feature various preconceived, unavoidable limitations on the structure, distribution, capabilities and interconnections of their implemenational components. Examples include geographical distribution of portions of an airline reservation system, standard components of an avionics system, physical limits on hardware components and their interaction, etc. Even concurrent programs are, in general, not all that pure, as one typically is constrained by a limit on the maximal number of concurrently executing processors. In this way, if the implemenational restricions are to be honored, being overly liberal in the use of orthogonality, for example, can easily cause severe problems in a naive attempt to model the implemenational refinement according to the behavioral one.

What this means is obvious: our recommendation for a method that enables natural behavioral decomposition notwithstanding, the implemantational description has a nasty habit of prescribing, at least in part, its own decomposition, which need not, in general, match our conceived behavioral one.

These observations prepare the ground for a very simple idea: by and large, the development of a reactive system is not a one-dimensional process in which specification and design are two temporally related stages, but rather it is a two dimensional "magic square" in which they play the role of the dimensions themselves. One might label the two dimensions simply "specification" and "design", but we prefer to use those terms as verbs, and so we label the dimensions "behavior" and "implementation". One thus specifies the system's behavior but one designs its implementation. See Fig. 9.

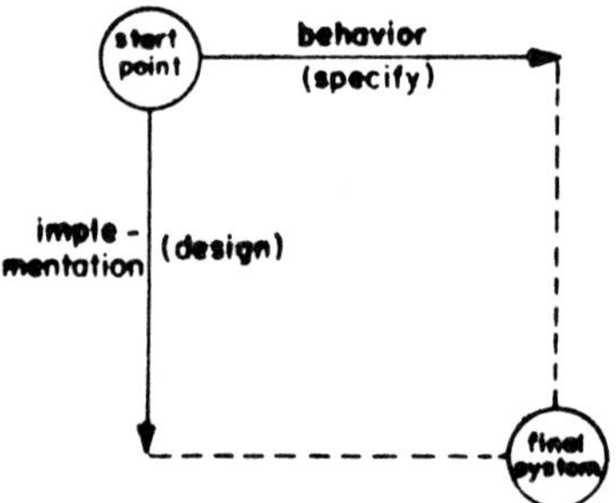

Fig. 9: The magic square

Along both dimensions making progress amounts to supplying more detail, but the two axes involve fundamentally different kinds of detail. Proceeding vertically (downwards), one is bringing the system closer to its final form by supplying more information about its implementation, and proceeding horizontally (rightwards), one is fine-tuning the system's performance by providing more information about its behavior. In either case, and this explains in part our use of the term "magic square", every line or column amounts to a full, stratified, description of the system along one axis, but at a fixed level of detail along the other.

Ideally, the development process starts at the upper leftmost point, with nothing known about the system's intended behavior or its desired implementation, and ends at the lower rightmost point, with everything known about both. The more subtle side of the term "magic square" is rooted in the many possible ways of traversing the square from its initial point to its final one; following any of these correctly should result in the system being fully specified and fully designed.

It seems almost an accident that for the easier systems in our dichotomy, i.e. transformational ones, or reactive ones with no implementational constraints, this process can actually be linearized by, in essence, mapping one dimension onto the other relatively easily as discussed earlier. In our opinion this accident is the heart of many misconceptions and difficulties encountered in the development of complex systems, and to some extent also in pure concurrent programming.

We are aware of the fact that even with concrete formalisms in mind any discussion of such a general model for system development is bound to seem naively idealistic when considered for real-world applications. Nevertheless, we are determined to describe our model in the simplest possible terms, and for that purpose, besides adopting simple statecharts, free of global constraints, for the behavioral axis, we adopt a very simple decomposition method for the vertical, implementational axis.

At level 0 of the vertical axis the system resides as an unspecified entity $\mathbf{M}^{(0)}$, together with its interface set $\mathbf{E}^{(0)}$. Progressing down the vertical axis is characterized by a step of implementational decomposition. For a typical descent from level i to level $i+1$, a subsytem M on level i, with interface set E, might be decomposed into its constituent components $M_1, \ldots, M_n$, with their interface sets $E_1, \ldots, E_n$; see Fig. 10. For this decomposition to be acceptable certain obvious properties must be satisfied. For exampie, each element of E, the interface set of M, must appear in at least one set E_j, or at least be refined into more concrete elements, each of which appears in at least one E_j.

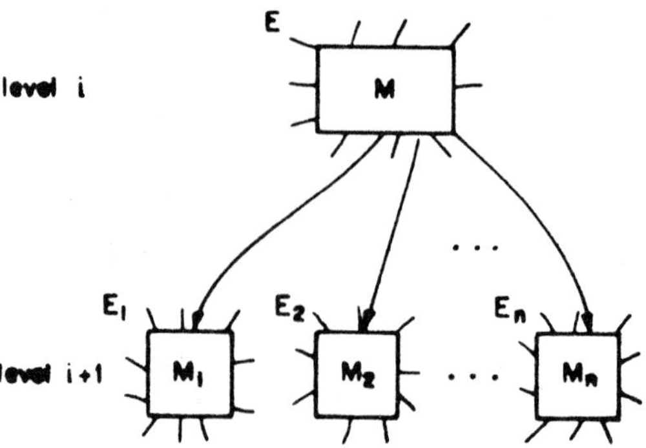

Fig. 10: Implementational decomposition

In addition to interface elements that are external to the whole system, the interface set E_j of M_j may contain additional elements which are external to M_j but internal to M. These elements provide the components with the ability to communicate, synchronize, and influence one another. Thus, each element in $E_j - E$ must be tagged with some indication as to its source or target subsystem(s) from among the others. We shall not go into more detail here so as not to detract attention from the underlying issues. Besides, our presentation of this decomposition method is highly simplified anyway, and many standard methods can be readily adopted for a satisfactory treatment of the implementational axis.

In contrast to making progress down the vertical axis by refining the implementational design of the system, progressing along the horizontal axis refines and structures its behavior, and as discussed above can be thought of as adding levels to the appropriate statecharts. Having reached some fixed vertical level i, one has essentially decided upon a set of implementational modules, say $M_1, \ldots, M_k$, and now proceeding horizontally at this vertical level amounts to statifying each of these. The outcome, of course, is a set $S_1, \ldots, S_k$ of statecharts whose interface sets are simply those of $M_1, \ldots, M_k$.

As a side remark, note that the magic square is not a square at all. First, there is no reason whatsoever for the levels of implementational detail to be equal in number to those of behavioral detail, so that at the very best the development model should be called a magic rectangle. Secondly, and more significantly, the implementational decomposition, even using the simple model above, forms a tree, and one whose branches are not necessarily of equal length, so that the outcome is more like a tree with

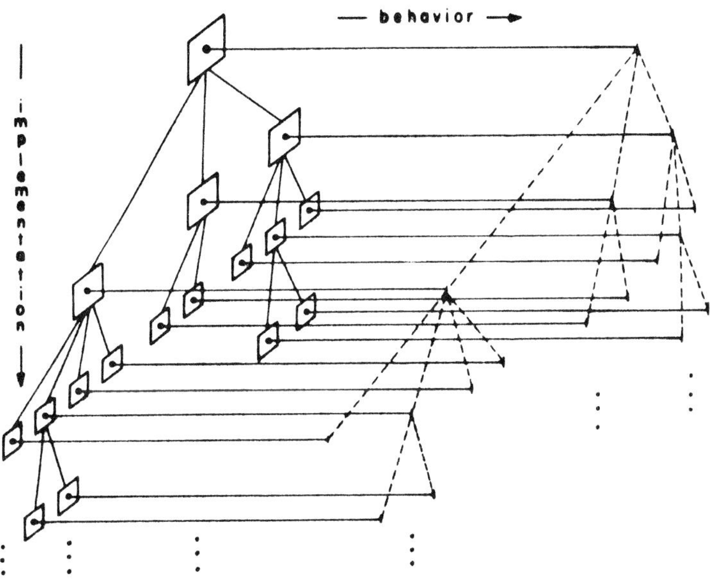

Fig. 11: The magic square as a spiky tree

long spikes; see Fig. 11. Thirdly, and most significantly, for any given node in the implementation tree (=system component) the behavioral description itself, even using simple statecharts on their own, is actually a tree or worse, again with no uniform depth existing either amongst or within each other. For a fixed system, therefore, the actual development creature is far more complicated, rather like a multidimensional tangled tree (and the reader must forgive us for not supplying a picture of one here). Nevertheless, we stick to the term "square", emphasizing its two dominating dimensions.

An observation worth emphasizing is the presence, indeed highly desirable presence, of concurrency along both dimensions of the square. In the implemenational axis concurrency appears as the obvious coexistence of physical entities, usually termed the ***parallelism*** of system components, and in the behavioral axis concurrency appears as the coexistence of modes of behavior, which in statechart terminology is simply the ***orthogonality*** of states. Both, either directly or indirectly, can cause simultaneity of activities in the final system. In fact, orthogonality seems to us to be a more natural manifestation of concurrency in the specification than certain suggestions in the literature, such as specifying concurrency by Boolean conjunction.

With the story we have told so far, two obvious ways of traversing the magic square come immediately to mind: the *L*-shaped all-the-way-down then all-the-way-to-the-right traversal, and its dual. The first corresponds to a practice common in certain kinds of concurrent programs: obtain information as to the number, type and interconnections of available processors, and then specify the behavior of each, which is tantamount to programming them. Whether the programming, which can itself proceed in a stepwise disciplined manner, is regarded here as specification or design is irrelevant; the main point is that one is programming per processor. Actually, one usually has some high level description of the intended behavior in mind even when one proceeds in this *L*-shaped way, but rather than being used in a rigorous way in the development process it is more often simply referred to at the end for the purpose of verifying the final product against it.

The dual traversal calls for a complete behavioral specification prior to any implementational decomposition, and was hinted at earlier. Neither of these traversals of the magic square can be particularly recommended for complex systems. Actually, neither of them makes essential use of the available two-dimensionality at all, and as a consequence neither requires that behavioral descriptions be projected in a nontrivial way from one vertical level to the next. This kind of behavioral projection, however, is one of the most crucial aspects of our magic square, as we now set out to show.

A Consistency Criterion for The Magic Square

In general, we wish to argue, a healthy development process prescribes some horizontal progress prior to each significant progress made on the vertical level. That is, at vertical level i system component M is given a behavioral specification S of certain depth, that is, extending to some horizontal point. One then decomposes M (or is provided with a decomposition of M) into its subcomponents $M_1, \ldots, M_n$ and somehow specifies the behavior of each, to the *same* horizontal depth, yielding the preliminary $S'_1, \ldots, S'_n$. The S'_j are then refined as discussed above, yielding the final behavioral descriptions $S_1, \ldots, S_n$ of vertical level $i+1$. Of course, this set of behavioral descriptions of the M_j has to be consistent with

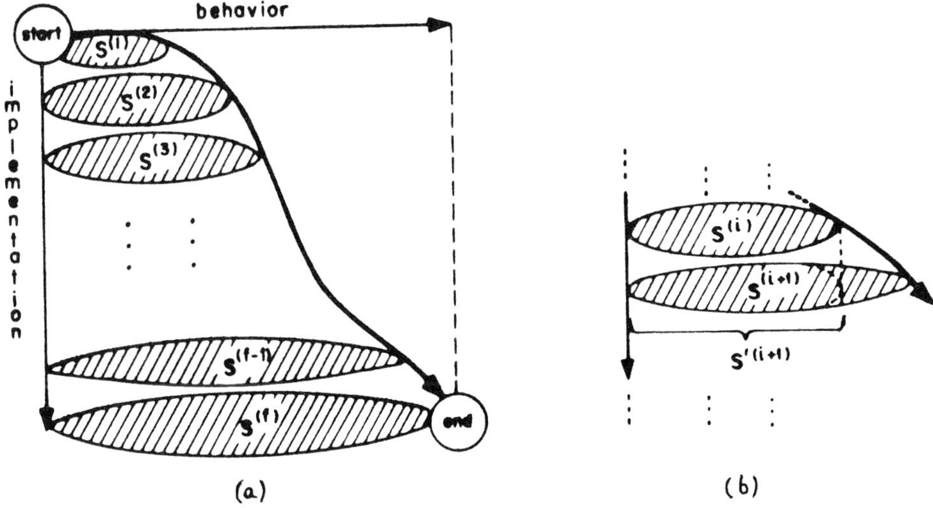

Fig. 12: Traversing the magic square

the behavioral description S of the higher-level system M, and we define the nature of this consistency below. The general progress can thus be schematically described as in Fig. 12, with the progress arrow aiming and hitting the final point corresponding to the fully-specified, fully-designed system. Each shaded area $\mathbf{S}^{(i)}$ in Fig. 12 thus represents the collection of behavioral descriptions of all subsystems relevant to level i of the implementation.

At the expense of sounding repetitious we remind the reader of Fig. 11 and its more realistic, hence far more complicated version of our simple "square", meaning that the S of each M on any level is given at the depth of behavioral detail appropriate to it and its "neighbor" subsystems. However, as mentioned earlier, for our purposes the issues can be discussed under the pretensions implicit in Fig. 12.

Three questions come immediately to mind:

(1) What is, or should be, the precise consistency criterion relating $\mathbf{S}^{(i)}$ to $\mathbf{S}^{(i+1)}$?

(2) Given a satisfactory answer to (1), can one recommend a recipe for obtaining $\mathbf{S}^{(i+1)}$ from the decompositions carried out when progressing downwards from level i to level $i+1$, together with $\mathbf{S}^{(i)}$?

(3) Whatever the answers to questions (1) and (2) are, can one recommend a "good curve" for traversing the square?

Question (1) is purely technical, and without answering it satisfactorily the whole magic square model collapses. There must be a firm and precisely defined connection between the specified behavior of a portion of the system and that of its constituent components, one which then transcends to become a global connection between the initial and final stages of the entire development process.

The answer to question (1) can be stated informally as follows:

> The external behavior implicit in $\mathbf{S}^{(i)}$ must be equivalent to that implicit in $\mathbf{S}'^{(i+1)}$, the preliminary behavioral description on level $i+1$ which is of the same horizontal detail as $\mathbf{S}^{(i)}$.

This simple answer contains some subtlety, since apart from the haziness of "external", "implicit" and "equivalent", $\mathbf{S}^{(i)}$, in our chosen framework of formalisms, is but a collection of statecharts, one for each component on level i, and $\mathbf{S}'^{(i+1)}$ is a different collection, associated with a different level and different components. Nevertheless, the answer can be made precise quite naturally, as illustrated in Fig. 13.

Take a typical level i component M and its subsystems $M_1, \ldots, M_n$ on level $i+1$. In $\mathbf{S}^{(i)}$ there will be a statechart S for M and in $\mathbf{S}'^{(i+1)}$ statecharts $S'_1, \ldots, S'_n$ for the M_j. As discussed earlier, each pair (M_j, S'_j)

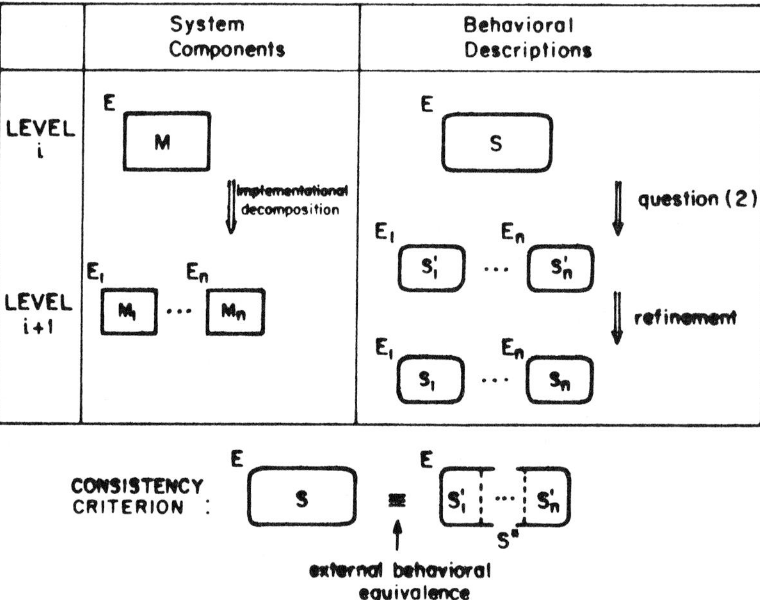

Fig. 13: The consistency criterion for the magic square

has an interface set E_j, only part of which is external to $\{M_1, \ldots, M_n\}$ by corresponding directly to the interface set E of (M, S). For the sake of simplicity let us assume that the elements in E have not been themselves refined in the transition to the E_j, but, as discussed above, each E_j consists of elements in E and possibly some new elements, internal to the set $\{M_1, \ldots, M_n\}$. Now form a new statechart S^* by simply placing $S'_1, \ldots, S'_n$ side by side as orthogonal components. Their interconnections via the internal interface sets $E_j - E$ will be taken care of by the statechart formalism itself. In this way, S^* will be a single statechart whose interface set consists of all interface elements which are not internal to the set $\{M_1, \ldots, M_n\}$, that is, to the union over j of $E_j - (E_j - E)$, which is simply E itself. We now require S and S^*, compatible by virtue of their common interface set E, to be actually ***equivalent***, i.e., to define the same set of sequences over E.

If this equivalence holds when applied to each and every implementational component on level i, we say that $\mathbf{S}^{(i)}$ and $\mathbf{S}'^{(i+1)}$ are equivalent, and, more importantly, that $\mathbf{S}^{(i)}$ and $\mathbf{S}^{(i+1)}$ are ***consistent***. The latter term is justified by the former, together with the fact that $\mathbf{S}^{(i+1)}$, the final behavioral description on implementational level $i+1$, is obtained from $\mathbf{S}'^{(i+1)}$ by adding levels of detail to the statecharts therein, thereby refining the behaviors they define.

In the case where E is indeed refined in making the vertical transition, the notion of equivalence, and accordingly the notion of consistence, has to be appropriately modified to account for the matching of interface elements. Also, if the statecharts are accompanied by a set of additional global constraints $\mathbf{G}$, a possibility mentioned earlier, the refinement of $\mathbf{S}'^{(i+1)}$ to $\mathbf{S}^{(i+1)}$ must adhere to those, and hence might require a separate, specially tailored, consistency criterion, stating, roughly, that $\mathbf{S}'^{(i+1)} \cap \mathbf{G}$ is equivalent to $\mathbf{S}^{(i)} \cap \mathbf{G}$. Furthermore, one might be interested in the possibility of refining, and hence making more concrete, the global constraints too in the process of making vertical progress. This progress will then relativize to the interface sets of each level, just as the statecharts do, resulting in a $\mathbf{G}^{(i)}$ for level i, and, again, the notions of equivalence and consistency will have to change too. These, and numerous other possible complications might surface in specific attempts to use the magic square, but they can be dealt with by extending the basic model in a natural way, and with the underlying principles being the same.

The main consequence of the definition of local consistency between vertical levels is in its transitivity. By this we mean that consistency is propagated down (or up) the vertical axis, resulting in the following fact:

> If a complete development process is carried out in the magic square model, using any desired traversal, while checking local consistency, the final behavioral description of the system, $\mathbf{S}^{(f)}$, is consistent with the initial one, $\mathbf{S}^{(0)}$. In other words, if one constructs the entire system using the "atomic" implementational components prescribed by the final vertical decomposition level f and connects them as prescribed by the interface sets on that level, and if one then convinces oneself that each of these low-level components behaves as prescribed by its behavioral description in $\mathbf{S}^{(f)}$, then the entire system is ***correct*** with respect to its initial specification $\mathbf{S}^{(0)}$.

This, by the way, should remind the reader of classical methods for program verification, where global correctness follows from the correctness of the consituent modules.

Precisely how one convinces oneself of the behavioral correctness of the atomic components is of no concern here. It might follow from a manufacturer's documentation, a programmer's verification, or be regulated to mere belief. Just as in any typical verification process, the soundness of one's use of the magic square in this fashion is a doubly-relative concept; it relies on an accepted initial specification, against which one verifies what one has constructed (in this case this is the initial behavioral specification $\mathbf{S}^{(0)}$), and it relies on an "axiomatic" acceptance of the fact that the atomic elements, which constitute the building blocks with which one has carried out that construction, are correctly specified (in this case this amounts to accepting the final vertical level $\mathbf{M}^{(f)}$, $\mathbf{S}^{(f)}$, as is).

At this point, one might be tempted to ask the following question: if the S and S^* appearing at a certain stage in the process (see Fig. 13) are required to be two equivalent descriptions of the same part of the final system, given in the same formalism, and over the same interface set E, why then is S^* not constructed directly? Why was S^* not given as the level i behavioral description of component M, especially since it is already conveniently decomposed in accordance with the decomposition $M_1, \ldots, M_n$ of M? It goes without saying that this would eliminate any necessity for checking the equivalence of behavioral descriptions. The answer, of course, embodies the main issue here: S^* is not necessarily a natural behavioral description of M ***because*** it is composed according to $M_1, \ldots, M_n$. A good behavioral description of an airline reservation system which uses ten geographically distributed computers and a thousand terminals might be one which decomposes in ways that cut across this physical decomposition, just as a good behavioral description of a VLSI chip need not be given in terms which even mention its breakup into design-related blocks. Whatever the case, the "unnatural" S^*, which consists of the preliminary behavioral descriptions $S'_1, \ldots, S'_n$ of the components $M_1, \ldots, M_n$, has to be prepared somehow; but how? This is precisely question (2) above.

How to Traverse the Magic Square?

We are in no position to present detailed answers to questions (2) and (3), and even less so to claim that we know of answers that can or should be used universally. Quite to the contrary, different kinds of systems present different kinds of problems in behavioral specification, and the entire development process can be regarded as an art, with many facets and many possibilities.

Moreover, more often than not, a complex development effort does not start at the initial point of a totally blank magic square. It usually starts with various portions of the square already filled in. That is, certain system components, and even certain chunks of behavior, are already prescribed to the developer in advance, and the development process must accomodate them as it proceeds. Therefore, as far as question (3) is concerned, we can only say that, when viewed as a function that plots horizontal progress against vertical progress, the development curve should be monotonically increasing (see Fig. 12); it makes very little sense to provide a subcomponent with less behavioral detail than its parent component. However, other than that, and other than observing that the curve should probably be nontrivial (i.e., not L-shaped or its dual), developers should be free to define their own preferred curves for traversing the square.

As to question (2), there is one general point to be made here. Let M be a component on vertical level i, decomposed on level $i+1$ into $M_1, \ldots, M_n$, and let S be the behavioral specification of M. If E and $E_1, \ldots, E_n$ are the interface sets of the components (no refinement in the E's; as above), then one can proceed as follows: for each $1 \leq j \leq n$, start with S itself as a first approximation to S_j, the behavioral specification of M_j on level $i+1$.

Now, clearly S is not a legal statification of S_j in general, since it refers to elements from $E - E_j$. However, this can be fixed as follows. Output elements in $E - E_j$ are simply eliminated, and for each input element e therein one finds a k with $e \in E_k$, and modifies the two copies of S, that of E_k and that of E_j, so that the former, whenever e is sensed, outputs a new item e' to M_j, in whose copy of S each e is replaced by e'. In this way M_j can sense the input event e even though it can be directly sensed only by M_k. The resulting statecharts, call them $S_1'', \ldots, S_n''$, are now legel behavioral specifications of the M_j, in the sense that their orthogonal product is equivalent to S. Moreover, the S_j'' are on the same horizontal level of detail as S. These S_j'', therefore, conform to the definition of the preliminary description of $\mathbf{S}'^{(i+1)}$, see Fig. 12, and hence, in principle, we have answered question (2). However, we clearly do not recommend that one stop here; the result will be an exponentially growing behavioral specification, not to mention its complete detachment from any naturalness involved in the implementation refinement of M into the M_j. Rather, one should work on the S_j'', simplifying and changing them to reflect the intended behavior of the M_j. In this sense, the only useful role S_j'' can play, is that of a starting point leading to the desired S_j, the final behavioral specification of M_j.

Actually, we feel that it is worthwhile to search for good transformations for weeding out portions of S_j'' not really relevant to M_j, using the difference between E and E_j, and S itself as directives. Such transformations, certain simple examples of which come immediately to mind, should be required to preserve equivalence of the behavior, modulu the transition from E to E_j.

The equivalence problem for reactive behavioral specifications, and in particular equivalence-preserving transformations of statecharts, seems to be an important area for future research. Satisfactory and useful results in this direction can help turn the magic square from a *model* of system development, which is the way we have tried to portray it here, into a detailed *methodology*, or prescription, a line we have not yet tried to pursue.

Acknowledgement

The contents of this paper owe much to many colleagues and authors. In particular, we have been influenced by several ideas found in the work of M. Alford, L. Lamport and D. Parnas.

NATO ASI Series F

Vol. 1: Issues in Acoustic Signal – Image Processing and Recognition. Edited by C. H. Chen. VIII, 333 pages. 1983.

Vol. 2: Image Sequence Processing and Dynamic Scene Analyisi. Edited by T. S. Huang. IX, 749 pages. 1983.

Vol. 3: Electronic Systems Effectiveness and Life Cycle Costing. Edited by J. K. Skwirzynski. XVII, 732 pages. 1983.

Vol. 4: Pictorial Data Analysis. Edited by R. M. Haralick. VIII, 468 pages. 1983.

Vol. 5: International Calibration Study of Traffic Conflict Techniques. Edited by E. Asmussen VII, 229 pages. 1984.

Vol. 6: Information Technology and the Computer Network. Edited by K. G. Beauchamp. VIII, 271 pages. 1984.

Vol. 7: High-Speed Computation. Edited by J. S. Kowalik. IX, 441 pages. 1984.

Vol. 8: Program Transformation and Programming Environments. Report on an Workshop directed by F. L. Bauer and H. Remus. Edited by P. Pepper. XIV, 378 pages. 1984.

Vol. 9: Computer Aided Analysis and Optimization of Mechanical System Dynamics. Edited by E. J. Haug. XXII, 700 pages. 1984.

Vol. 10: Simulation and Model-Based Methodologies: An Integrative View. Edited by T. I. Ören, B. P. Zeigler, M. S. Elzas. XIII, 651 pages. 1984.

Vol. 11: Robotics and Artificial Intelligence. Edited by M. Brady, L. A. Gerhardt, H. F. Davidson. XVII, 693 pages. 1984.

Vol. 12: Combinatorial Algorithms on Words. Edited by A. Apostolico, Z. Galil. VIII, 361 pages. 1985.

Vol. 13: Logics and Models of Concurrent Systems. Edited by K. R. Apt. VIII, 498 pages. 1985.